First published in 1991 by:
Stanley Thornes (Publishers) Ltd
Ellenborough House
Wellington Street
CHELTENHAM GL50 1YD
England

Second edition 1994

A catalogue record for this book is available from the British Library.

ISBN 0-7487-1699-8

The cover photographs are reproduced by courtesy of: Nissan (*top*); Grace Dearborn Limited (*second and fourth from top*); Mars UK Limited (*third from top*).

Typeset by Northern Phototypesetting Co Ltd, Bolton, Lancs
Printed and bound in Great Britain by The Bath Press, Avon

Quality Improvement Through Standards

Second Edition

Barrie G Dale and John S Oakland
UMIST
and
University of Bradford Management Centre

Stanley Thornes (Publishers) Ltd

Contents

Preface to the second edition

The authors were invited by the British Standards Institution (BSI) and Stanley Thornes (Publishers) Ltd. to prepare a book based on those British Standards which are related to quality. This resulted in the first edition of *Quality Improvement through Standards* which was published in 1991.

The second edition of the book is the result of their latest efforts and represents the current work on quality contained within the Standards, together with some of their own thoughts on how to apply the concepts and methods.

A British Standard (BS) is prepared by a capable technical committee which, typically, comprises industrialists, consultants, academics and government and BSI representatives. Each BS is a significant piece of work in its own right. Unfortunately, because of their purpose as National, European and International Standards they do not always make for easy reading, particularly, for chief executives, senior and middle managers and those people seeking knowledge related to the topic to which a particular BS is devoted.

The second edition of this book, like the first, has been put together by first culling material from the relevant British Standards and from various available documents on National, European and International Standards and their uses. In order to illustrate the points made in the text and to cover aspects of quality management which are not adequately dealt with by the Standards, the material has been supplemented with information and experiences from the UMIST and Bradford TQM University research teams. A deliberate attempt has been made not to depart too far from the material contained within the Standards, but where current best practice differs from the Standards, for example in the case of statistical process control (SPC), the alternative approaches have been presented for comparison. A number of the Standards which are quality-related tend to be oriented to mechanical engineering situations and attempts have been made, wherever possible, to make the text more applicable to non-engineering manufacturing, and to commerce and service-type operations. In a number of chapters this has been difficult, but we hope we have been successful. One objective in preparing this book is to make the text more reader-friendly than the typical BS and to facilitate ready accessibility of the material contained within the standards. The reader will judge whether or not this has been achieved.

This book is aimed at those managers and specialists who are responsible for designing, developing, setting up and maintaining systems, procedures, methods and operating instructions for the management of quality and reliability and putting into place a process of continuous improvement.

It is unlikely that the chief executive and members of an organisation's senior management team will read this book from cover to cover. They will, however, benefit from using the text as a reference to obtain detailed knowledge on particular aspects of quality management and/or to clarify particular points.

The book has undergone substantial revision, to reflect the launch of new Standards which are related to quality management since publication of the first edition. These standards include: BS 7850 *Total quality management*, BS 5750: Part 8 *Guide to quality management and quality system elements for services* and Part 13 *Guide to the application of BS 5750: Part 1 to the development, supply and maintenance of software*, BS 4778: Part 2 *Quality concepts and related definitions*, BS 5760: Part 5 *Guide to failure modes effects and criticality analysis* and Part 7 *Guide to fault tree analysis* and BS 7750 *Specification for environmental management systems*. There have also been a number of revisions to a number of Standards and Published Documents, including: PD 3542 *The role of standards in company quality management*, BS 5781 *Measurement and calibration systems* and BS 6001: Part 1 *Specification for sampling plans indexed by acceptable quality level (AQL) for lot by lot inspection*. The second edition of the book also reflects the recent picture in terms of European and International Standardisation. Another addition to the edition is the referencing, where available, of equivalent European and International Standards to the British Standards. A new chapter on *Service procedures and concepts* has also been introduced and the chapter on *Quality circles* has been replaced with one on quality improvement teams generally.

An individual seeking detailed knowledge of a

particular aspect of quality which is contained within a BS, must buy or get sight of the relevant Standard. If this is repeated on a number of occasions it can prove time-consuming and costly to the user. This book covers much of the material in the British Standards which is quality-related and provides convenient and relatively inexpensive access. If, after studying the book, more detailed information on particular topics is required, the reader will be aware of the content of the relevant British Standards and will know where to obtain further information. In this way the book should make more readily available the quality-related knowledge contained within the British Standards, and provide an understanding of what BSI can do for industry and commerce.

Undergraduates, postgraduates and those studying for professional examinations or undergoing continuing education which involve considerations of quality should also find the book of interest, as will the growing number of academics in Universities, Business Schools and Colleges of Higher and Further Education with a teaching or research interest in quality management.

The authors are leaders of research teams at The European Centre for Total Quality Management, University of Bradford and at The University of Manchester Institute of Science and Technology (UMIST). They both have national and international track records in quality management. They have taken time out of hectic research and teaching schedules to prepare the revisions to the book and this can be taken as an indication of their belief in the need for the book. The authors believe that the second edition, in the spirit of continuous improvement, is better than the first and hope the readers agree. They have also enjoyed collaborating in the preparation of the book and hope the reader will find the fruits of their efforts valuable.

Dr B G Dale,
Reader and Director,
Quality Management Centre,
Manchester School of Management, UMIST,
Manchester, UK

Professor J S Oakland
Exxon Chemical Professor of Total Quality Management,
The European Centre for TQM,
The Management Centre,
University of Bradford
Bradford, UK

Foreword

BSI, the British Standards Institution, is an independent national body established by Royal Charter. It is responsible for the publication of technical standards and for the licensing of marks of quality.

Since BSI's origins in 1901 British Standards have helped industry and commerce to become more efficient and to improve their quality. Today more than 10,000 British Standards cover an enormous range of products and processes. They set down technical criteria which help to:

- rationalize and simplify manufacture reducing needless variety and promoting economy of effort and resources, so helping to reduce costs.
- ensure that goods and services are fit for their purpose and will meet consumers' quality needs.
- provide a means of communication which can be used in applications such as contract specifications.
- ensure safety and good health.

In the last decade, one British Standard has attracted overwhelming attention. BS 5750 was the world's first published national standard dealing with a complete approach to company quality management. It has been adopted widely in all sectors of industry. BS 5750 forms a cornerstone of the Government Enterprise Initiative and the reference for the Department of Trade & Industry's Register of Quality Assessed United Kingdom Companies.

Internationally, BS 5750 is the basis of the ISO 9000

series and EN 29000 series. Since 1987, BS 5750 has been identical with these world and European standards. BSI has assessed thousands of companies worldwide to BS 5750. Our Registered Firm and Registered Stockist symbols are acquiring the same kind of general recognition as the Kitemark symbol of product quality assurance.

BS 5750 covers all aspects of a company's management system which have an effect on quality. It sets down definitive requirements which can be used in contract specification and systems development. Other standards such as BS 7229 *Guide to quality systems auditing* or BS 5729 *Guide to stock control* deal with specific techniques or details of quality systems.

This publication provides a thorough and readable guide to the whole range of British Standards that relate to quality management. It has been written in an easy-to-use and comprehensible style. It shows the relationship between Standards and provides a guide to their application making it simpler for the practising professional and student alike to get a complete picture of Standards support for the achievement of quality.

A further major virtue of this book is the careful integration of terminology and techniques from the wider field of quality management. Because of the proliferation of terms in this area it may be difficult for many students (and existing professionals) to keep pace. This volume is both authoritative in its broad coverage and reassuring in its explanation of identical, similar and overlapping concepts.

Although the standards discussed in this book cover a wide range of important quality topics new standards in this area continue to be published. It is important for the quality professional to keep up-to-date with developments. BSI also runs a range of membership services including regular information on new standards, discounts on standards and private list updating. For further information contact:

- Membership Services
  Tel: (0908) 220022

Further information on published standards:

- Customer Information
  Tel: (0908) 221166

For information on BSI's Quality Assurance Systems including the Registered Firm Scheme, the Registered Stockist Scheme and the Kitemark Licensing Scheme please contact:

- Business Development
  Tel: (0908) 220908

Derek Prior,
Head of Communication,
British Standards Institution

Acknowledgements

Barrie Dale is indebted to the late James Plunkett for allowing some of his research findings to be used in Chapter 4.

The authors wish to thank the following companies for allowing some of their material to be used in the text: Ford Motor Company, Garrett Automotive (Turbocharge Division), Grace Dearborn Ltd., Widnes, Hydro Polymers (Vinyls Division), Nissan Motor Manufacturing (UK) and Tetra Pak Systems.

The cover photographs are reproduced by courtesy of: Nissan (top); Grace Dearborn Limited (second and fourth from top); Mars UK Limited (third from top).

CHAPTER 1

Quality management: an overview

1.1 Quality concepts

In any book on the management of quality, it is first necessary to define what is meant by *quality* and its related concepts. In 1951 Juran, one of the pioneers of quality management, summarised a basic rule which is applicable here:

'Any widespread discipline must identify and clarify the universal concepts which underlie its very existence as a discipline. In addition it must evolve and standardise the key words and phrases through which practitioners of the discipline can communicate with each other.'

Quality is not a property which has an absolute meaning. The word 'quality' is often used for several distinct purposes. It is sometimes used to signify 'excellence' of a product, service, person, action etc. People talk about 'Rolls Royce quality', 'top quality', 'quality service', 'quality of communication', 'right quality', etc. In some engineering companies, the word may be used to indicate that a piece of metal conforms to certain physical characteristics often set down in the form of a particularly 'tight' specification. If we are to define quality in a way which is useful in its management then we must recognise the need to include in the assessment of quality, the true needs and requirements of the 'customer'.

Quality then is simply about meeting the customer requirements and current and future expectations. This has been expressed in many ways by others, for example:

> fitness for purpose or use,
>
> (Juran, 1988)

> the totality of features and characteristics of a product or service that bear on its ability to satisfy stated or implied needs,
>
> (BS 4778: Part 1, 1987)

> the total composite product and service characteristics of marketing, engineering, manufacture, and maintenance through which the product and service in use will meet the expectation by the customer,
>
> (Feigenbaum, 1983)

It is interesting to note that the world-class organisations are now talking about 'delighting the customers' and 'winning customers'.

Clearly, part of the acceptability of a product or service will depend on its ability to function satisfactorily over a period of time, and it is this aspect of performance which is labelled *reliability*. Reliability is the ability of the product or service to continue to meet the customer requirements for a defined period of time. In qualitative terms, reliability relates to success or failure of performance and unreliability seriously undermines the value or usefulness of a product or service. Reliability is itself an essential performance characteristic. Reliability ranks with quality in importance, since it is a key factor in many purchasing decisions where alternatives are being considered, for example, in the purchase of a car. Many of the general management issues related to achieving product or service quality are also applicable to reliability. Because of the difficulty of achieving reliability, it is usually necessary to reinforce the normal disciplines of quality management and design engineering by applying specialist techniques in the form of an integrated reliability programme. A satisfactory reliable product or service is one which combines the required level of intrinsic reliability in its design with the freedom from faults achieved through the audits of its manufacture/delivery.

For any organisation in industry, the public sector, commerce or service, the ability of its products or services 'to satisfy stated or implied needs' is of prime importance to their corporate well-being. The concept of quality and its requirements will obviously require some attention at the detailed planning stage, but initially the quality of an article or service has meaning only when related to its use. The characteristics which benefit the customer and ultimate user, not the producer, determine the fitness for purpose.

Juran and Gryna (1980) have described *fitness for purpose* as the sum of certain concepts – quality of design, quality of conformance, 'the abilities' and field service. This is an all encompassing view which includes within the quality framework such things as usability, reliability, safety, durability, maintainability and after sales service. It must also be said that product or service quality is influenced by many stages of interactive activities, such as design, production or service operations and maintenance.

Quality of design

This is best considered in three parts or stages:

- The identification of that which constitutes fitness for purpose to the user;
- The choice of a product or service concept which will correspond to the identified needs of the user;
- The translation of the chosen product or service concept into a detailed set of specifications which, if faithfully executed, will then meet the user's needs.

Quality of conformance

The *quality of conformance* can be expressed simply as the extent to which the product or service, once it has been made or generated, conforms to the design, specification or requirements. This is very easy to state, but much effort is required to ensure that products and services do conform to their intended design, and this is the area of most concern to the quality assurance function.

It should be noted that some people often confuse quality of design and quality of conformance. A well-designed product with high levels of technical sophistication may be manufactured in such a way that it is at a low level of quality of conformance.

'The abilities'

Juran (1988) has identified three parameters which are fundamental to meeting the customer's requirements:

- Availability (of the product or service): the concept of availability and the complementary concept of unavailability emanate from the alternating transitions between the two states. These states are those in which the item is either capable or incapable of performing the intended functional requirements in the intended environment and other conditions of use. In such black and white situations, these two states can be translated into the intended function being available or unavailable. These are usually expressed as fractions of the total time considered and are a measure of the extent to which the user can secure the required product or service when he or she wants it.
- Reliability: the probability of a product or service performing, without failure, a

specified function under given conditions for a specified period of time. The importance of reliability as a fundamental performance is now widely recognised by most industries. It is also an important consideration with consumers since there is an increasing demand for products and services that consistently provide trouble-free operation. The consequences of unreliability are manifest in two principal ways. The immediate and obvious effect is that the product and service no longer functions as required with consequences that may vary from major disaster to minor inconvenience depending on the failure and the timing of the failure. The secondary effect is that the failed equipment has either to be replaced or repaired with consequent economic implications.

- Maintainability: this is the ease with which products or services can be maintained to achieve long service life and reliability. The maintainability of an item relates not only to the inherent attributes of the design and the use of the item in isolation, but also to the surrounding items and the environment in which they are situated. Maintainability can also be influenced by the provision of the appropriate staff and facilities necessary for controlling and carrying out the work. In any specific situation the optimum form of maintainability will depend on the maintenance policy adopted and the tasks performed within this, the repair methods and the choices between preventive or corrective maintenance, scheduled or unscheduled maintenance.

Field service

An important element in the quality equation comes after the product or service has been sold to the customer. It is important to consider:

- provision of clear service contracts;
- establishment of adequate repair equipment capacity and supply of spare parts;
- recruitment and training of a service force competent to diagnose and remedy;
- conductance of all field service affairs with courtesy and integrity;
- customer care in general;
- feedback and feed-forward of information gathered in the field;
- speedy and effective response to customer queries.

1.2 The quality function

It is possible in any organisation to identify a quality function. The achievement of fitness for purpose or meeting the requirements involves the performance of a number of separate deeds or activities in a logical progression.

The activities needed to achieve this are divided among many persons in the organisation, some of whom are in specified departments. These activities must be co-ordinated into a unified effort if satisfying customer expectations with the product and/or service is to be achieved in an efficient and effective manner.

Inspection

Inspection in a variety of forms is an activity of the quality function. This inspection can be in-process inspection, which is carried out at various stages during processing, patrol inspection, carried out during routine or random visits, acceptance inspection, to determine whether an item or lot delivered or offered for delivery is acceptable, or final inspection, which is the last of several inspections at successive stages during processing. Accredited and independent inspection may be required for specified products or services.

It is now well accepted that the philosophy of prevention is preferred to the philosophy of detection by inspection. In order of preference:

a) upstream prevention is better than upstream control;
b) in-process control is better than inspecting the outcome;
c) inspecting the outcome is better than rejection by the customer.

The degree of inspection actually practised will depend on the type of quality management system applied and the nature of the product, process or service. When practised, the following three key aspects need consideration:

- inspection is most effective when it provides information which is fed back and used to ensure fault prevention;
- even with inspection of every item of product or service (100% inspection) some faults may evade detection. Inspection efficiency is frequently lowest on subjective inspection tasks. Here special attention needs to be paid to aspects such as establishing reference standards and development of detection skills and decision judgements;
- inspection does not run counter to prevention provided that it is progressively transferred to inspection of the transformation process/system itself rather than the subsequent product.

Quality control

To produce and monitor quality, some sort of control activity is necessary. Quality control is the regularity process through which product and service quality performance is measured. Comparisons with standards enable decisions to be made with regard to corrective action and preventive measures. Reference is made to this in the British Standards Institution's (BSI's) definition of quality control as:

> the operational techniques and activities that are used to fulfil requirements for quality
> (BS 4778: Part 1, 1987).

The term may be applied to the system of control, or to the product or service being controlled.

For an organisation to produce a product or service of the quality required by a customer, a number of procedures may be undertaken to cover all stages from initial design and development, through procuring materials and components, to manufacturing, final inspection, delivery and installation where appropriate. These procedures can consist of a series of steps applied at intervals during the above stage. These steps are as follows:

a) identifying the characteristics of the stage to be controlled;
b) establishing criteria by which these characteristics can be measured;
c) setting a standard value with appropriate tolerances for each characteristic to meet the requirements for quality at that stage;
d) measuring each characteristic and recording the result;
e) comparing these results with the required standards;
f) deciding whether these comparisons indicate that the required quality has been achieved;
g) identifying and undertaking appropriate corrective actions.

These steps in the procedures of quality control are aspects of the totality of quality assurance and quality management.

Quality assurance

A term which has grown into management thinking and literature during the recent decades is *quality assurance*. This is essentially the activity of providing, to all concerned, the evidence required to establish confidence that the quality function is being performed adequately.

In BS 4778: Part 1, 1987 a definition of quality assurance is given:

> All those planned and systematic actions necessary to provide adequate confidence that a product or service will satisfy given requirements for quality.

Unless the given requirements fully reflect the needs of the user, quality assurance will not be complete.

The term quality assurance can be applied by those seeking assurance or by other organisations, who may be potential or existing suppliers of product or service, or the organisation or part of the organisation that is under their control. The systems and procedures that are required for quality assurance are those necessary to satisfy an internal or external customer. The systems and procedures may contain many elements in addition to the minimum needed for quality assurance. Within an organisation, quality assurance serves as a management tool. In contractual situations, it also serves to provide confidence in the supplier.

For effectiveness, quality assurance usually requires continuing evaluation of factors that affect the adequacy of the design or specification for intended applications as well as verifications and audits of production, installation and inspection operations. Providing confidence may involve providing evidence.

There are many views of quality and how far it should extend into the after sales performance of the product or service. As early as 1951 Feigenbaum coined the term, 'total quality control' and in 1969 Ishikawa used the phrase 'company-wide quality control'. These concepts will provide the framework for the approach described in subsequent chapters of this book.

Quality management

To be successful any company or organisation needs to have defined policies and objectives together with the necessary operational system to effect these aims in the provision of their product or service. For this operation to run efficiently and effectively requires there to be appropriate levels of management and control in the technical, administrative and personnel areas. A primary concern has to be the quality of the products or services supplied, which should be a key aspect of the organisation's policy. The determination and implementation of the quality policy will itself require management since it forms one element of the corporate policy and is authorised by senior management. The attainment of the desired quality involves all members of the organisation operating in a system for quality, embracing strategic planning, resourcing and operations, including quality measurement and evaluation, from market research through to product or service delivery.

1.3 The evolution of inspection and quality control

Before the concepts and ideas described above were formalised, much work took place during the 20th century to reach this stage. In 1915, Frederick W Taylor is given credit for having established the basic management principles known as 'scientific management'. Taylor served his apprenticeship in several trades. He was rapidly promoted, until at the age of 31 he was appointed Chief Engineer of the Mid-Vale Steel Works in the USA. It was during this time that his attention became focused on some fundamental industrial questions such as, 'Which is the best way to do a job?' and 'What should constitute a day's work?'. He began to develop his studies further and eventually explained their objectives, one of which is the following:

> The division of work into almost equal shares between management and workers, each department taking over the work for which it is best fitted.
>
> (Currie, 1959)

This was instead of the former condition in which almost all of the work and the greater part of the responsibility was thrown on the workforce.

During the early days of manufacturing, before the industrial revolution, firms existed as small units employing perhaps a dozen or more operatives. Presiding over these people was the 'master' of the firm who had overall responsibility for the commercial and production functions. This included the job of inspecting an operative's work and making the decision to either accept or reject it.

As firms expanded the master's job grew more complex and time consuming. Consequently, he had to delegate some of his responsibilities, one of which was the job of inspection. This initially fell on the shoulders of the production foreman, whose work, in turn, was soon to outgrow him. This created, then, a need for full-time inspection posts. Owing to the fact that the production foreman originally inspected operatives' work, the newly appointed inspectors reported to him.

Accompanying the creation of the inspection function were numerous changes:

> More technical problems arose which required specialised skills, often not possessed by the production supervisors;
>
> More attention was given to the shop floor

> operatives by the production supervisor instead of the inspectors, and the latter lacked training;
>
> The production supervisor often ordered the inspectors to accept defective goods, in the interests of output.
>
> (Juran and Gryna, 1980)

In the early 20th century, these changes led to the birth of the separate inspection department and the position of chief inspector was created. Usually, the chief inspector was responsible to the person in charge of manufacturing. In the case of a multiplant or multidivisional company, he or she usually reported directly to the works manager. With the creation of the new department came new services, for example, standards, training, recording of data and the accuracy of measuring instruments. Evidently, it became clear that the responsibilities of the chief inspector were more than product acceptance. Therefore, an addition to product inspection was required and the quality control department evolved with the quality control manager in charge. He or she typically presided over the chief inspector, the inspection services and quality control engineering.

The UK quality effort in the industrial context began because of a military need in World War I to ensure the safety and interchangeability of products and spare parts. It concentrated, however, on the inspection of goods against specification and drawing. Later, it was realised that this only separated conforming from non-conforming components and that it would make more sense to prevent non-conforming components being produced, but it was some years after World War II before this became a reality.

1.4 Control and breakthrough

For years, the writings and teachings of Juran have represented the frontiers of the literature on the management of quality. Juran has also made significant contributions outside the quality area, in particular, his book *Managerial Breakthrough* (Juran, 1964) in which the ideas derive from Juran's experience in the management of quality and its application in Japan. These ideas have been recognised in the management of quality. His central management thesis is the distinction between control and breakthrough. *Control* means maintaining the status quo and preventing adverse change. *Breakthrough* refers to the change to a new and more desirable situation.

A second feature of Juran's ideas relates to the nature and extent of management responsibilities. This derives from Juran's empirical observations in quality control. In the first edition of the *Quality Control Handbook* he stated:

> There is widespread feeling . . . that the principal cause of defects is operator carelessness or indifference. This is dead wrong. Over 80 per cent of failures to meet specifications are, in the author's experience, for reasons not related to the operators at all.
>
> (Juran, 1951)

In relation to Juran's observation, control and responsibility must be explicit. Operatives can be said to be responsible if three criteria are met:

- They have the means of knowing what they are supposed to do;
- They have the means of knowing what they are actually doing;
- They have available to them the means of regulating their performance.

When all of these criteria are met, operatives can be said to be in a state of self-control, and can, therefore, be held responsible for the quality of their output. If any of these three criteria are not met, then no state of self-control exists.

A third idea outlined by Juran, is that the control of quality can only be exercised at the point of production or operation. This is a recurring theme in the recent literature on total quality management. It is often expressed in terms of slogans such as 'Quality cannot be inspected into a product' and 'Get it right first time', although this form of cheerleading is insufficient by itself to produce the desired effect.

Nearly every aspect of quality control had its parallel in Taylorism. Both concepts were concerned with careful measurement; quality control involved measurement of products, whereas scientific management usually involved the measurement of operator performance.

The idea of operator self-control contradicts one of the main characteristics of Taylorism, which was based upon a division of responsibility between operators and management. Management devised the best working procedures and the workers then carried out management's wishes. The idea that operators are supposed to know what to do, what they are doing, and be able to regulate their performance, gives them a degree of responsibility which is not necessarily consistent with the ideas of scientific management.

Control then is about management activity, or inactivity, related to the maintenance of existing practices and standards. Breakthrough is about improvement and establishing new practices and standards. Control and breakthrough require contrasting sequences of management activities. Control is concerned with the measurement of an object, then comparing that measurement with a standard. It can then be decided if action is going to be taken on the basis of the comparison. However, there are some assumptions which have to be made: there is an object to be measured; units have been chosen for the measurements; the standard has been established; and the appropriate measuring equipment and methods have been chosen and are available.

In most organisations it is unlikely that these control characteristics develop directly as a result of conscious management thinking. They are more likely to have evolved gradually. Either way, seven activities need to be identified for control:

- choosing objectives for control;
- selecting the measures;
- deciding on standards of performance;
- designing sensors or measuring instruments;
- measuring performance;
- comparing performance with standard;
- acting on the difference.

The corresponding sequence for breakthrough requires adherence to quite a different set of activities. These can be expressed in eight stages:

- choosing objectives for breakthrough;
- convincing others that a breakthrough is needed;
- identifying the vital few projects (Pareto Analysis);
- organising for breakthrough in knowledge;
- creation of a steering arm;
- diagnosis;
- breakthrough in cultural pattern;
- transition to a new level.

Juran has developed a 10-step approach to total quality management (TQM) (see Table 1.1).

Table 1.1 *The Juran method*

1	Build awareness of the need and opportunity for improvement
2	Set goals for improvement
3	Organise to reach the goals
4	Provide training
5	Carry out projects to solve problems
6	Report progress
7	Give recognition
8	Communicate results
9	Keep score
10	Maintain momentum by making annual improvement part of the regular system and processes of the company

The crucial difference between the two sets of sequences is motivation. The first thought that should come to management's mind when breakthrough is being sought is motivation. In contrast, the first task management take for control is measurement; motivation is already assumed.

Quality control can claim to be more scientific than classical scientific management. Taylorism involves little more in the way of measurement than observation, however sophisticated this measurement became with later developments in work study.

In the 1920s statistical theory began to be applied effectively to quality control. The first to apply the new statistical methods was Walter

A Shewhart of the Bell Telephone Laboratories. In 1924, Shewhart made the first sketch of a modern control chart and in 1931 he published a book entitled *Economic Control of Quality of Manufactured Product* (Shewhart, 1931). This, the first book on *statistical quality control (SQC)*, set the pattern for subsequent applications of statistical methods of process control. At the same time Dudding, a British statistician, was experimenting with similar ideas applied to the manufacture of filament light bulbs. Two other Bell System men, H F Dodge and H E Romig, took the leadership in developing the application of statistical theory to sampling inspection, the culmination of their work being the well-known Dodge–Romig *Sampling Inspection Tables*. The early work of Shewhart, Dodge and Romig constitutes much of what today comprises the theory of SQC and *statistical process control (SPC)*.

1.5 Total quality control and company-wide quality control

Juran's original ideas on the management of quality seemed to be focused on production personnel. Further developments occurred from Juran's ideas. Three distinct product quality trends were identified by Feigenbaum (1951, 1983).

- Customers (industrial, consumer and military) had increased their quality requirements sharply;
- As a result of this increased customer demand for 'higher' quality products, the in-company quality practices were soon to be outdated;
- Quality costs had become very high. For many companies probably much too high.

  Feigenbaum outlined what was necessary to overcome these problems:
- Considerable improvement in the quality of many products and quality practices was required;
- At the same time, substantial reductions in the overall cost of maintaining quality were needed.

From these necessities evolved the concept of *total quality control (TQC)* which can be defined as an effective system for integrating the quality, maintenance and quality improvement efforts of the various groups in an organisation, so as to enable production and operation at the most economical levels which allow for full customer satisfaction (Feigenbaum, 1951, 1983).

The underlying principle of Feigenbaum's ideas and the basic difference between total quality control and the other ideas was the provision of genuine effectiveness. Control must start with the design of the product or service and end only when the product or service has been placed in the hands of the customer, who remains satisfied. The reason for this breadth of scope is that the quality of any product or service is affected at many stages of the production cycle. Feigenbaum itemised eight sections of the production cycle and their relationship to the quality of a product (see Figure 1.1). Total quality control is thought of as an aid, not a substitute, for good engineering designs, good manufacturing methods and

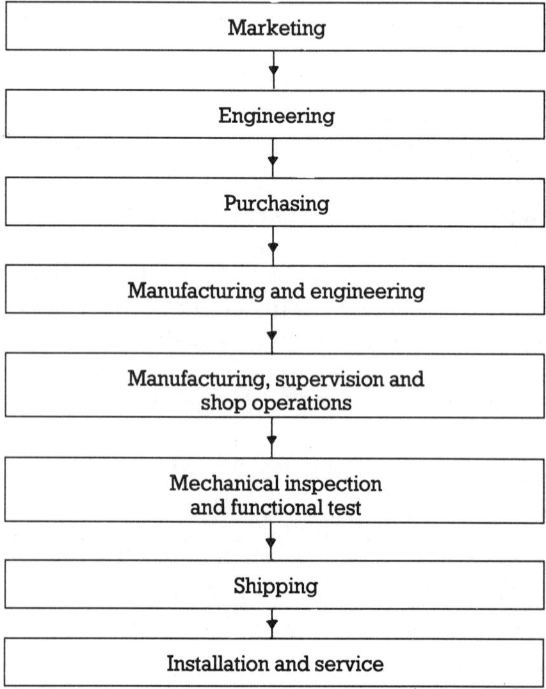

Figure 1.1 Feigenbaum's eight stages of the industrial cycle

conscientious inspection activity that have always been required for the production of defect-free articles.

The main benefits which are claimed for total quality control are: improvement in product and service quality; reductions in operating costs and losses; improvement in employee morale; and reduction of production line bottlenecks. Side benefits, include improved inspection methods, sounder setting of time standards for labour, definite schedules for planned maintenance, the availability of reliable data for use in company advertising, and the furnishing of a factual basis for cost accounting standards for scrap, rework and inspection.

After World War II, Japan's industrial system was virtually destroyed. In addition, Japan in general had a reputation for cheap imitation products. The Japanese recognised their problems and set about solving them. The first assistance they received in the area of quality improvement was from the Civil Communications Section of the occupation forces in the form of three American engineers – Frank Polkinghorn, Charles Protznan and Homer Sarashon (see Hooper, 1982). They then had the good fortune to gain the services not only of Joseph Juran, but also another stalwart in the field of quality management, Dr W Edwards Deming.

In the early 1950s Deming recognised the lack of awareness of product quality at all levels of Japanese management and began promoting the introduction of quality control procedures in particular and an improved quality awareness in general (Deming, 1986). From 1951 to 1954, quality control developed rapidly in leading Japanese plants and had become a major theme in Japanese management philosophy. By 1960, quality control had become a national preoccupation.

In 1969, the Japanese Union of Scientists and Engineers in co-operation with the American Society for Quality Control and the European Organisation for Quality Control, sponsored the first international conference on quality control held in Tokyo. In the first session of this conference, which covered company-wide quality control, Feigenbaum gave a paper entitled *Total Quality Control* which, consistent with his book, urged that managers should 'work intimately with . . . quality control professionals' (Feigenbaum, 1969). Another paper in the same session entitled *Company-Wide Quality Control Activities in Japan* (Ishikawa, 1969) explained that the term total quality control is used as a synonym for company-wide quality control.

The total quality control which took place in Japanese companies had a considerably wider application and included the collection of quality information by the business department, checks on purchase data and acceptance of parts in the purchasing department, teaching and training of quality control in the personnel department, and overall vendor/vendee relations such as increasing output, cost cutting and securing the data of delivering the products to the consumers, besides quality assurance activities for products.

The difference was also made explicit in the paper given by Karou Ishikawa, in which he explained how total quality control in Japan was different from that defined by Feigenbaum. He pointed out that in Japan when a company wished to apply company-wide quality control, all the employees from top management to the foreman and workers must study SQC and participate in quality control (Ishikawa, 1969). In the authors' view this is playing with semantics. From recent total quality management (TQM) study missions to Japanese manufacturing companies, it is clear that they use TQC to describe their total quality efforts (Dale and Asher, 1989).

1.6 Recent developments

Crosby

In 1979, Philip Crosby of ITT in the USA produced *Quality is Free* (Crosby, 1979). One of the things Crosby did was to set up a method for measuring the status of a company's quality improvement process and to show what positive steps should be taken to evaluate and improve it. The means of evaluation was the quality management maturity grid (see Figure 1.2). There are five levels or stages of maturity

QUALITY MANAGEMENT MATURITY GRID

Rater ______________________ Unit ______________________

Measurement categories	*Stage I: uncertainty*	*Stage II: awakening*	*Stage III: enlightenment*	*Stage IV: wisdom*	*Stage V: certainty*
Management understanding and attitude	No comprehension of quality as a management tool. Tend to blame quality department for quality problems.	Recognising that quality management may be of value but not willing to provide money or time to make it all happen.	While going through quality improvement programme learn more about quality management; becoming supportive and helpful.	Participating. Understand absolutes of quality management. Recognise their personal role in continuing emphasis.	Consider quality management an essential part of company system.
Quality organisation status	Quality is hidden in manufacturing or engineering departments. Inspection probably not part of organization. Emphasis on appraisal and sorting.	A stronger quality leader is appointed but main emphasis is still on appraisal and moving the product. Still part of manufacturing or other.	Quality department reports to top management, all appraisal is incorporated and manager has role in management of company.	Quality manager is an officer of company; effective status reporting and preventive action. Involved with consumer affairs and special assignments.	Quality manager on board of directors. Prevention is main concern. Quality is a thought leader.
Problem handling	Problems are fought as they occur; no resolution; inadequate definition; lots of yelling and accusations.	Teams are set up to attack major problems. Long-range solutions are not solicited.	Corrective action communication established. Problems are faced openly and resolved in an orderly way.	Problems are identified early in their development. All functions are open to suggestion and improvement.	Except in the most unusual cases, problems are prevented.
Cost of quality as % of sales	Reported: unknown. Actual: 20%	Reported: 3%. Actual: 18%.	Reported: 8%. Actual: 12%.	Reported: 6.5%. Actual: 8%.	Reported: 2.5%. Actual: 2.5%.
Quality improvement actions	No organised activities. No understanding of such activities.	Trying obvious 'motivational' short-range efforts.	Implementation of the 14-step programme with thorough understanding and establishment of each step.	Continuing the 14-step programme and starting Make Certain (a check that the programme is in place).	Quality improvement is a normal and continued activity.
Summation of company quality posture	'We don't know why we have problems with quality.'	'Is it absolutely necessary to always have problems with quality?'	'Through management commitment and quality improvement we are identifying and resolving our problems.'	Defect prevention is a routine part of our operation.'	'We know why we do not have problems with quality.'

Figure 1.2 Crosby's quality management maturity grid

and six management activities which serve as the basis of assessment. By considering the findings summarised in each block it is possible to analyse a company's situation and then to set about improving the management accordingly.

Table 1.2 Crosby's 14-step quality improvement programme

1	Management commitment
2	Quality improvement team
3	Quality measurement
4	Cost of quality evaluation
5	Quality awareness
6	Corrective action
7	Establish an ad hoc committee for the zero defect programme
8	Supervisor training
9	Zero defects day
10	Goal setting
11	Error cause removal
12	Recognition
13	Quality councils
14	Do it over again

Crosby also set down the four absolutes of quality and 14 points for their implementation (see Table 1.2). The four absolutes of quality are as follows:

- quality means conformance, not elegance;
- it is always cheaper to do the job right first time;
- the only performance indicator is the cost of quality;
- the only performance standard is zero defects.

The Ford Motor Company and SPC

The Ford Motor Company in North America in the late 1970s and in Europe in the early 1980s placed the emphasis, throughout the company, on SPC. The core of the Ford Motor Company drive towards improving quality was the ideas and philosophy of Deming. Deming itemised 14 management obligations to improve quality (see Table 1.3 on p. 12). One of the main ideas was that the traditional method of detection – inspecting the finished product for defects – had to be replaced by a strategy of prevention. Corrective action eliminates a problem which has occurred. Preventive action eliminates or minimises the causes of the problem and hence any future occurrence. Thus, preventive action improves the processes of an organisation and is essential for continuous quality improvement. For this to be effective, the necessary tools had to be used, i.e. the techniques of SPC. A typical prevention system is shown in Figure 1.3 (Ford Motor Company, 1985).

In a system based on prevention the emphasis is placed on product and process design and process control and, by concentrating on source activities, it stops non-conforming products being produced and non-conforming services being delivered. The end result is

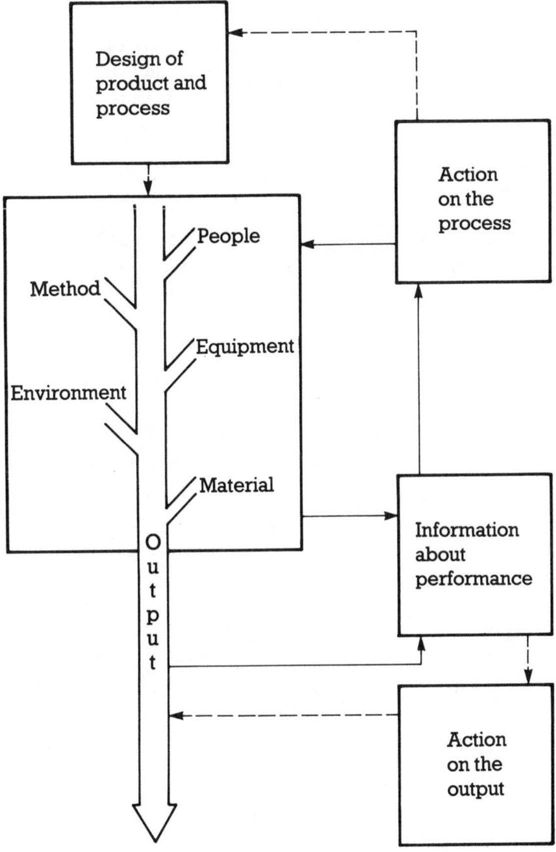

Source: Ford Motor Company, 1985

Figure 1.3 A prevention-based quality system

Table 1.3 Deming's 14 points for management

1 Create constancy of purpose towards improvement of product and service, with the aim to become competitive, stay in business, and to provide jobs.

2 Adopt the new philosophy – we are in a new economic age. Western management must awaken to the challenge, learn their responsibilities and take on leadership for future change.

3 Cease dependence on inspection to achieve quality. Eliminate the need for inspection on a mass basis by building quality into the product in the first place.

4 End the practice of awarding business on the basis of price tag. Instead, minimise total cost. Move toward a single supplier for any one item on a long-term relationship of loyalty and trust.

5 Improve constantly and forever the system of production and service, to improve quality and productivity, and thus constantly decrease costs.

6 Institute training on the job.

7 Institute leadership: the aim of supervision should be to help people, machines and gadgets to do a better job. Supervision of management, as well as supervision of production workers, is in need of overhaul.

8 Drive out fear, so that everyone may work effectively for the company.

9 Break down barriers between departments. People in research, design, sales and production must work as a team, to foresee problems of production and problems in use that may be encountered with the product or service.

10 Eliminate slogans, exhortations and targets for the workforce that ask for zero defects and new levels of productivity. Such exhortations only create adversarial relationships, as the bulk of the causes of low quality and low productivity belong to the system and thus lie beyond the power of the workforce.

11a) Eliminate work standards (quotas) on the factory floor; substitute leadership instead.

11b) Eliminate management by objectives, by numbers and by numerical goals; substitute leadership instead.

12a) Remove barriers that rob the hourly worker of his or her right to pride of workmanship. The responsibility of supervisors must be changed from sheer numbers to quality.

12b) Remove barriers that rob people in management and in engineering of their right to pride of workmanship. This means, inter alia, abolishment of the annual or merit rating, and of management by objectives.

13 Institute a vigorous programme of education and self-improvement.

14 Put everybody in the company to work to accomplish the transformation. The transformation is everybody's job.

improved product and service quality and increased productivity. This is clearly a more creative approach than a system based on detection, and with it there is a change of emphasis from downstream to upstream processes. The prevention approach to quality recognises the importance of the process.

The Ford Motor Company did not restrict the use of these ideas to their own manufacturing plants. They made it a contractual requirement that their suppliers use SPC as a fundamental element of their quality system. In the chemical, rubber, packaging and textile industries, firms have seen the knock-on effect of this and the requirements to use SPC have literally exploded throughout industry in the USA and Europe.

The British national quality initiatives

In a UK government white paper it was stated that the UK's world trade share was declining (Department of Trade and Industry, 1982). This was having a dramatic effect on the standard of living in this country, amply demonstrated by rising unemployment and bankruptcies. Demand for British goods had to be rekindled, it was no longer automatic. There was intense global competition, and it was obvious that any country's economic performance and its reputation for quality was made up of the reputations and performances of its individual companies, products and services.

The British Standard BS 5750 Series for quality systems had been published three years earlier in 1979. A campaign to bring to the attention of industry the importance of product and service quality in order to remain competitive and survive in the world marketplace was needed. Hence, the government launched the National Quality Campaign in 1983 and used the BS 5750 Series as its core.

The BS 5750 Series, now revised and equivalent to the International Organisation for Standardisation 9000 Series (ISO 9000: 1987) and the EN 29000 Series (EN 29000: 1987), is the UK's national Standard for quality systems. The Series is a set of Standards, giving the requirements for quality assurance and providing guidance on how to manage and achieve quality (see Chapter 7). It is a practical Standard for quality systems which can be used by all of UK industry, including the public sector, commerce and service, and it lays emphasis on the prevention philosophy. It also provides for continuous improvement through audit and review procedures.

The Standards provided a very broad set of requirements, and were seen as a very positive step towards improving the UK's reputation for quality. By issuing a *Register of Quality Assessed United Kingdom Companies* and requiring that, wherever possible, all government purchasing should be from companies on the Register, the government was able to persuade many companies to follow the Standard's recommendations. The quality assessment carried out is essentially an independent third-party quality audit. One of the authorities/accredited organisations for carrying out this quality assessment and providing the subsequent certification in the UK is the BSI Quality Assurance which assesses companies' compliance with the requirements set out in BS 5750 Parts 1, 2 and 3 (1987).

The campaign in the UK matured through the 1980s to promote a company-wide commitment to quality, involving everyone from the chief executive officer and the senior management team to the newest recruit. The aim is to make every individual aware of the importance of their own particular role and where it fits into the drive for total quality. This was clearly an ambitious objective, but by no means an impossible one. A growing number of UK companies have fought determinedly for dramatic improvements in their design, technology, production/operations and marketing.

In 1989, through the Enterprise Initiative, the Department of Trade and Industry (DTI) launched the Managing into the '90s programme, aimed at promoting a strategic approach to the four key areas of design, quality, purchasing and supply, and manufacturing management.

A complete programme was put together to help companies to improve performance and competitiveness through the total quality approach. There were booklets, management briefings, seminars, workshops, videos, mobile demonstrations and visits. The government also encouraged training, the use of professional consultants and other organisations offering help and communications with other firms.

The DTI's Enterprise Initiative provided counsellors, experienced business people, to review with firms their business needs, and offered to find the right consultants to meet the requirements. They met at least half the costs for five to 15 consultant days, for UK firms with fewer than 500 employees. Links with the Employment Department, and higher education were encouraged through schemes such as Teaching Company and Integrated Graduate Development.

Lascelles and Dale (1989) reporting on a study carried out to assess the impact of the Campaign on industry said that 'The campaign material had been relatively successful in reaching its prime target of senior management, the majority of respondents have found the material to be useful and believe that the campaign has benefited their organisations in terms of increased awareness of the importance of total quality management'.

While the UK quality campaign has changed its name, it has always been concerned with changing attitudes and trying to ensure that the importance of industry is understood and appreciated by all. It has clearly assisted many UK companies to move towards the kind of strategy which is at the heart of some of the world's most successful organisations.

1.7 Total quality management

Total quality management (TQM) is the management philosophy and company practices that aim to harness the human and material resources of an organisation in the most effective way to achieve the objectives of the organisation. These objectives may include customer satisfaction, business objectives such as growth, profit or market position, or the provision of services to the community. They must always be compatible with the requirements of society, whether legislated or as perceived by the organisation. Of course, any organisation operates within the community and may directly service it; this may require a broad interpretation of the term 'customer'.

The ability to meet customer requirements is vital, not only between two separate organisations, but within the same organisation. In every department, office, even household, there are a number of processes with a series of suppliers and customers. The word-processor operator is a supplier to the boss. Is the operator meeting the specified requirements? Does the boss receive error-free work set out as he or she wants it and on time? If so, then we have a 'quality' word-processing service. Does the waiter or waitress receive from the supplier in the restaurant the correct food trays in the right quantity? Equally important in the internal customer–supplier relationship is the requirement that customers specify and communicate their requirements to the suppliers in an accurate and clear manner.

Throughout and beyond all organisations, whether they be manufacturing concerns, banks, retail stores, universities, or hotels, there is a series of quality chains, which may be broken at any point by one person or one piece of equipment not meeting the requirements of the customer, internal or external. The interesting point is that this failure usually finds its way to the interface between the organisation and its outside customers, and the people who operate at that interface – like the waiter or waitress – usually experience the ramifications. If every person is satisfying their own impending customers' needs then there is a much greater chance that the final product and/or service will meet the external customers' expectations.

Quality has to be managed – it will not just happen. Clearly, it must involve everyone in the process and be applied throughout an organisation. Failure to meet the requirements in any part of a quality chain has a way of multiplying and failure in one part of the system creates problems elsewhere, leading to a cycle of yet more failure and more problems. The price of quality is the continual examination of the requirements and our ability to meet them. This will lead to a continuing improvement philosophy.

TQM is a way of managing to improve the effectiveness, efficiency, flexibility and competitiveness of a business as a whole. Quality management, quality assurance and quality control are all embodied in TQM, together with all other management activities. TQM involves whole companies getting organised, in every department, in every activity, with every single person, at every level. This involves putting in place processes and systems which will ensure that every aspect of its activity is aligned to satisfying customer needs and the organisation's objectives without waste of effort by releasing the full potential of every person in the organisation. For an organisation to be truly effective, every single part of it must work properly together, because every person and every activity affects and in turn is affected by others. It is in this way that Japanese companies have become so competitive and successful (Oakland, 1993).

When introducing and developing the concept of TQM the executives of an organisation should ensure that the system will facilitate and promote continuous quality improvement. The constant goal of management of all functions and at all levels of an organisation is to strive for quality and its improvement in a balanced way. Quality improvement is achieved by improving the processes of an organisation. This should be a continuous activity, aiming for ever higher levels of process effectiveness and efficiency; efforts should be directed towards constantly seeking opportunities for improvements, rather than only waiting for a problem to reveal an opportunity.

The motivation for quality improvement comes from conscious awareness shared by all members of an organisation that every process can be done more effectively, giving increased value and satisfaction to customers, and more efficiently, with less waste and resource consumption. These increases in effectiveness and efficiency benefit customers, the organisation and its members, and society in general. Continuous quality improvement fundamentally affects the ability of an organisation to compete and the ability of its members to contribute, grow and excel.

If product and service are to meet customer requirements then this has wide implications. The requirements may include availability, delivery, reliability, durability, maintainability and cost effectiveness, among many other features. The first item on the list of things to do is find out what the requirements are. If we are dealing with a supplier-customer relationship crossing two organisations, then the supplier must establish a marketing activity charged with this task. The marketing personnel must, of course, understand not only the needs of the customer, but also the ability of their own organisation to meet the demands.

Total quality management must apply to, and interact with, all activities pertinent to the quality of a product or service. It involves all phases from initial identification to final satisfaction of requirements and customer expectations. These phases are discussed in some detail in Chapter 7.

The use of this approach goes under other names, some of which are: total quality, total business management, total quality performance, company wide quality management, cost effective quality management, continuous quality improvement.

1.8 Commitment to quality

Investment in material things is an accepted and well-developed management practice but the application of TQM primarily involves investment in time and people:

- time to train people;
- time to implement new concepts;
- time for people to recognise the benefits; and
- time for people to move forward into new and different company cultures.

Every organisation has to give these commitments if total quality management is to succeed.

To be successful in promoting business efficiency and effectiveness, TQM must be truly company-wide and it must start at the top with the chief executive (or equivalent), the most senior directors and management, who must all demonstrate that they are serious about quality. They have to become good rôle models and TQM champions. The middle management have a particularly important role to play, they must not only grasp the principles of TQM, they must go on to explain them to the people for whom they are responsible, and ensure that their own commitment is not only communicated, but practised. Only then will TQM spread effectively throughout the organisation. This level of management must also ensure that the efforts and achievements of their subordinates obtain the resources, recognition, attention and reward that they deserve.

TQM should be promoted in all activities and at all levels and is fundamental to success. The accomplishment of quality is achieved by individual involvement and accountability devoted to continuous improvement with measurable levels of performance. It involves every department, function and process and the active commitment of all employees to meeting the customer's needs. In this regard all employees should be aware of their individual customers and suppliers whether internal or external to the organisation.

Continuous identification and resolution of existing and potential problems is essential and the means of improvement – to people and process performance – should be continually sought and monitored. This means, of course, that the total strengths and abilities of all members of an organisation should be fully and effectively utilized, and they should be recognised as the links in the quality chain. This, in turn, requires recognition and acceptance of individual responsibility and authority, together with the continual removal of any prejudices and restrictive approval that inhibit organisational effectiveness. Process measurement should be applied to all organisational activities and there should be continuous appraisal, training and development of individuals at all levels.

If the chief executive of an organisation accepts the responsibility for, and commitment to, a quality policy, this action alone will offer a broad approach extending well beyond the accepted formalities of the disciplines required in the quality function. It creates in turn, through a process of quality policy deployment, responsibilities for interaction between the marketing, design, producing, purchasing, distribution and service functions, along with improvement objectives. Within each and every department of the company at all levels, starting at the top, basic changes of behaviour and attitudes will be required to introduce and develop TQM. If the owners or directors of the organisation do not recognise and accept their responsibilities for the initiation and operation of TQM, then these necessary changes will not happen. Systems, techniques and procedures are important in TQM, but they are not the primary requirement. It is more an attitude of mind, based on pride in the job, and requiring total commitment from the management which must then be extended to all employees at all levels and in all departments.

Management's commitment must be obsessional, not lip service. It is possible to detect real commitment, it shows on the shop floor, in the offices and indeed at any point of operation. Going into organisations sporting posters and slogans campaigning for quality instead of belief in quality, one is quickly able to detect the falseness. Personnel are told not to worry if quality problems arise, 'just do the best you can', 'the customer may never notice'. This contrasts with a company where total quality means something and can be seen, heard and felt. Things happen at this operating interface as a result of real commitment. Material problems are corrected with suppliers, equipment difficulties are put right by improved maintenance programmes based on total productive maintenance, and/or replacement, people are trained and change takes place.

TQM is user-driven, it cannot be imposed from outside the organisation, as perhaps a quality system standard or statistical process control. This means that the ideas for improvement must come from those with knowledge and experience of the methods and techniques, and this has massive implications for training and follow-up. TQM is not a cost-cutting or productivity improvement device and it must not be used as such. Although the effects of a continuous process of improvement will certainly produce these benefits, TQM is concerned chiefly with changing behaviour, attitudes and skills so that the culture of the organisation becomes one of preventing failure and the norm is operating correctly first time.

In many organisations there will need to be a change of attitude and a positive move towards this wider dynamic approach of management for continuous improvement. Management should recognise that this is an evolutionary process.

The remaining chapters of this book should assist managers to focus on the systems and techniques necessary to achieve the never-ending improvements now required in all types of organisations.

1.9 Definitions and terminology

The following are some useful definitions and terms used in this chapter.

Acceptance inspection: inspection to determine whether an item, or lot, delivered or offered for delivery is acceptable.

Availability: the ability of an item to be in a state to perform a required function under given conditions at a given instant of time or over a given time interval, assuming that the required external resources are provided.

Controlled maintenance: a method to sustain a desired quality of service by the systematic application of analysis techniques using centralised supervisory facilities and/or sampling to minimise preventive maintenance and to reduce corrective maintenance.

Corrective action: action taken to eliminate the causes of an existing non-conformity, or other undesirable situation, to prevent recurrence.

Corrective maintenance: the maintenance carried out after fault recognition and intended to put an item into a state in which it can perform a required function.

Customer: any person(s) internal or external to the organisation, who receive(s) the output of the process.

Durability: the ability of an item to perform a required function under given conditions of use and maintenance, until a limiting state is reached.

Final inspection: the last of several inspections at successive stages during processing.

In-process inspection: inspection carried out at various stages during processing.

Inspection: activities such as measuring, examining, testing and gauging, one or more characteristics of a product or service and comparing these with specified requirements to determine conformity.

Maintainability: the ability of an item under given conditions of use, to be retained in, or restored to, a state in which it can perform a required function, when maintenance is performed under given conditions and using stated procedures and resources.

Maintenance: the combination of all technical and administrative functions, including supervisory actions, intended to retain an item in, or restore it to, a state in which it can perform a required function.

Mission statement: broad statement of the main aims of an organisation.

100% inspection: inspection of every item of product or service.

Organisation: a managed group of persons and resources formed to carry out a function.

Patrol inspection: inspection carried out during routine or random visits to several production stages.

Preventive action: action taken to eliminate the causes of a potential non-conformity, or other undesirable situation, in order to prevent occurrence.

Preventive maintenance: the maintenance carried out at predetermined intervals or according to prescribed criteria and intended to reduce the probability of failure or the degradation of the functioning of an item.

Process: any activity that accepts inputs, adds values to these inputs for customers, and produces outputs for these customers. The customers may be internal or external to the organisation.

Process owner: the owner has full responsibility for, and authority over, the process.

Quality: the totality of features and characteristics of a product or service that bear on its ability to satisfy stated or implied needs.

Quality assurance: all those planned and systematic actions necessary to provide adequate confidence that a product or service will satisfy given requirements for quality.

Quality control: the operational techniques and activities that are used to fulfil requirements for quality.

Quality improvement: actions taken throughout the organisation to increase the effectiveness and efficiency of activities and processes to provide added benefits to both the organisation and its customers.

Quality losses: losses caused by failure to utilize most effectively and efficiently the potential of human, financial and material resources in a process.

Quality management: that aspect of the overall management function that determines and implements the quality policy.

Quality of service: the collective effect of service performance which determines the degree of satisfaction of a user of the service.

Quality policy: the overall quality intentions and direction of an organisation as regards quality, as formally expressed by top management.

Quality system: the organisational structure,

responsibilities, procedures, processes and resources for implementing quality management.

Reliability: the ability of an item to perform a required function under stated conditions for a stated period of time.

Safety: the freedom from unacceptable risks of personal harm.

Scheduled maintenance: the preventive maintenance carried out in accordance with an established time schedule.

Service: a set of functions offered to a user by an organisation.

Supplier: any person(s) internal or external to the organisation, who supplies (supply) an input to the process.

Total quality management: a management philosophy embracing all activities through which the needs and expectations of the customer and the community, and the objectives of the organisation, are satisfied in the most efficient and cost-effective way by maximising the potential of all employees in a continuing drive for improvement.

British standards

BS 4778: *Quality vocabulary*: Part 1: 1987 *International terms*; (ISO 8402: 1986, EN 28402: 1991); Part 2: 1991 *Quality concepts and related definitions*; Part 3: 1991 *Availability, reliability and maintainability terms* (IEC 5O(191): 1990).

BS 5750: 1987 *Quality systems* (ISO 9000: 1981; EN 29000: 1987).

BS 7850 *Total quality management*: Part 1: 1992 *Guide to management principles*; Part 2: 1992 *Guide to quality improvement methods*.

References

Crosby P B. *Quality is Free*. McGraw-Hill, NY, USA, 1979.

Currie, R M. *Work Study*. Pitman, London, UK, 1959.

Dale B G and Asher J M. 'Total Quality Control: Lessons European Executives can learn from Japanese Companies.' *European Management Journal*, 7(4), pp 493–503, 1989.

Deming W E. *Out of the Crisis*. MIT Centre for Advanced Engineering Study, Massachusetts, USA, 1986.

Department of Trade and Industry. Standards *Quality and International Competitiveness*. Cmnd 8621, HMSO, 1982.

Department of Trade and Industry. *The Case for Quality*. DTI, London, 1983, 1988.

Department of Trade and Industry. *Register of Quality Assessed United Kingdom Manufacturers*. HMSO, updated regularly.

Dotchin J A and Oakland J S. 'Theories and Concepts in TQM'. *Total Quality Management*, 3(2), pp 133–45, 1992.

Feigenbaum A V. *Total Quality Control*. McGraw-Hill, New York, USA, 1st edition, 1951.

Feigenbaum A V. *Total Quality Control*, Proceedings of International Conference on QC in Tokyo, Prentice Hall, NJ, USA, 1969.

Feigenbaum A V. *Total Quality Control*. McGraw-Hill, NY, USA, 3rd edition, 1983.

Ford Motor Company. *Three Day Statistical Process Control Course Notes*. Essex, UK, 1985.

Hopper K. 'Creating Japan's New Industrial Management: The Americans As Teachers'. *Human Resource Management*, 21 (2 and 3), pp 13–34, 1982.

Ishikawa K. *Company-wide Quality Control Activities in Japan*, Proceedings of International Conference on QC in Tokyo. Prentice Hall, NJ, USA, 1969.

Ishikawa K. *What is Total Quality Control – the Japanese Way*. Prentice Hall, NJ, USA, 1985.

Juran J M (Editor). *Quality Control Handbook*. McGraw-Hill, NY, USA, 1st edition 1951.

Juran J M. *Managerial Breakthrough*. McGraw-Hill, NY, USA, 1964.

Juran J M (Editor). *Quality Control Handbook*, McGraw-Hill, NY, USA, 4th edition, 1988.

Juran J M and Gryna H M. *Quality Planning and Analysis*. McGraw-Hill, NY, USA, 2nd edition, 1980.

Lascelles D M and Dale BG. *The National Quality Campaign: A Study of its Impact on Industry*. Proceedings of the Institution of Mechanical Engineers, 203(B4), pp 201–9, 1989.

Oakland J S. 'The Two Pronged Approach to Quality'. *Professional Engineering*, May 1989.

Oakland J S. 'Right First Time Through TQM'.

Journal of the Oil and Colour Chemists Association, 73(2), pp 60–65, 1990.

Oakland J S. *Total Quality Management*; 2nd edition, Butterworth–Heinemann, Oxford, UK, 1993.

Shewhart W A. *Economic Control of Quality of Manufactured Product*. Van Nostrand, NY, USA, 1931.

Taylor F W. 'The Principles of Scientific Management', (1911). *Scientific Management*, Harper & Row, London, UK, 1964.

CHAPTER 2

Standards, certification and accreditation, and the role of national, European and international standards bodies

2.1 Origin and objectives of the BSI

The British Standards Institution (BSI) is the recognised body in the UK for the preparation and dissemination of national standards in all fields. It was the first national standards body in the world. There are now more than 90 similar organisations which belong to the International Organisation for Standardisation (ISO) (founded in 1947) and her sister organisation the International Electrotechnical Commission (IEC) (founded in 1906). An agreement reached in 1976 ensures that the IEC covers the field of electrical and electronic engineering, all other subjects being attributed to ISO. When necessary, attribution of responsibility for work programmes to the ISO or IEC is made by mutual agreement. In the past, ISO and IEC have pursued separate and distinct paths with separate procedures and formats for documents. Recently, moves have been made to bring the operations of the two bodies more into line and for there to be closer co-operation between them. These moves have been given added impact in areas where there is an overlap of interest between the general and the electrotechnical fields. Joint committees have been set up to avoid duplication of work and common drafting rules now apply. BSI represents the views of British industry on these and other bodies which work towards harmonising world standards. Through the joint European Standards Institution, European Committee for Standardisation (CEN)/European Committee for Electrotechnical Standardisation (CENELEC), BSI presents the British view in discussions on the European Standards which will be used in the single European market. It is an independent, non profit-making body; its organisation and activities are fully described in BS0: Part 2 (1991) together with the committee procedures involved in the preparation of British Standards. BSI's independence and impartiality are reflected in its sources of revenue. It has four distinct accounts – one for standards, the second for quality, the third for testing and the fourth for technical help to exporters. The British government contributes to the standards account by means of a grant.

BSI began in 1901 as the Engineering Standards Committee, set up by the professional engineering bodies, and in 1918 became the British Engineering Standards Association. A Royal Charter was granted in 1929 and a Supplemental Charter in 1931 when the present name was adopted. The objectives of BSI were restated in the 1981 consolidated Royal Charter as follows:

> to co-ordinate the efforts of producers and users for the improvement, standardisation and simplification of engineering and industrial materials so as to simplify production and distribution, and to eliminate the national waste of time and material involved in the production of an unnecessary variety of patterns and sizes of articles for one and the same purpose;
>
> to set up standards of quality and dimensions, and prepare and promote the general adoption of British Standards specifications and schedules in connection therewith and from time to time to revise, alter and amend such specifications and schedules as experience and circumstances may require;
>
> to register, in the name of the Institution, marks of all descriptions, and to prove and affix or license the affixing of such marks or other proof, letter, name, description or device;
>
> to take such action as may appear desirable or necessary to protect the objectives or interest of the Institution.

Briefly, BSI's main function is to draw up voluntary standards by agreement among all the interests concerned and to promote their adoption. Under the Royal Charter, the by-laws prescribe requirements for the establishment and constitution of councils and committees, and for the general conduct of the Institution's work.

The July 1982 white paper 'Standards, Quality and International Competitiveness' stressed the need for closer co-operation between BSI and the government in order to produce standards that are of the required quality, relevant to the needs of the market, and, therefore, internationally respected and suitable for public purchasing and regulatory purposes. In November 1982, the white paper led to the signing of a 'memorandum of understanding' between the government and BSI, which set out ways of achieving a stronger standards system in the UK. The work of BSI was given added national recognition by the event. The memorandum recognised BSI as the national standards authority, operating under a consolidated Royal Charter and by-laws granted in 1981, and confirmed the status of British Standards as agreed national technical criteria developed and used to serve the public interest. The full text of the memorandum is given in BS 0: Part 2 (1991).

Standards projects related to international and European work now account for most of BSI's Standards activity. Wherever practicable, the detailed committee structure is aligned with that of the corresponding international or European Standards organisation, so that the committee responsible for national work has equal responsibility for relevant international and European work.

2.2 An outline of BSI activities

The activities of BSI can be categorised as follows:

- the production of standards,
- product certification and capability assessment,
- as a test house and inspectorate,
- to provide technical help to exporters, publications,
- information services,
- education,
- the British Standards Society,
- participation in international and European standards work.

Production of standards

British Standards are documents which spell out the essential technical requirements for a product, material or process to be fit for its purpose. They are produced by technical committees representing all interested parties in response to the needs of the consumer, industry and government.

Demand for standards arose initially in the heavy engineering industries (Woodward, 1972). For example, steel girders, nuts and bolts, and sheet steel were among the first subjects for standards. Today, standards cover every industry, from toy manufacture to petrochemicals, from building and construction to leisurewear and requests for standards include the new technology industries, for management systems, for the environment and for safety specifications. They influence every aspect of the industrial process: materials, dimensions, performance requirements, codes of practice, test methods and technology. In many cases the production of a standard also clarifies basic safety requirements which are then incorporated into specifications. Standards are sometimes called up in legislation, either in contractual use or in trade descriptions, and the status of standards has been enhanced by their greater use in this way (for example, health and safety, building regulations, and the 1987 Consumer Protection Act). A considerable number of British Standards are referred to in government regulations with even more listed as significant to health and safety at work. They are required for product certification. The requirements for quality assurance, set out in the BS 5750 Series, tell suppliers and manufacturers what is required for the assurance of quality and/or services. This Standard is being used increasingly as a basic requirement by many purchasing organisations, particularly in the public sector. Standards are, of course, used as a marketing tool.

There are over 10 000 British Standards and each year more than 700 new or revised Standards are issued to keep the technical content up-to-date and to encompass new materials, processes and technologies. They are dealt with by six Standards Councils or Sector Boards – automation and information technologies, chemical and health, building and civil engineering, electrotechnical, engineering and multitechnics. There are currently about 8000 Standards, all of which are for voluntary application.

Product certification and capability assessment

There are a number of different certification schemes but there are two basic types, product certification and capability assessment.

Product certification

Product certification requires testing resources and relies on standard test methods that will be accepted, often coupled with factory inspection and market surveillance regimes.

BSI operates two product certification marking systems, the Kitemark, BSI's certification trade mark, first used in 1903, and the Safety Mark, introduced in 1974 to provide manufacturers with an alternative means of demonstrating compliance with a British Standard specifically related to safety. These product conformity marking schemes take random samples from a production line and subject the product to tests of conformance. These marks are shown in Figure 2.1.

Figure 2.1 BSI Safety Mark and BSI Kitemark symbols

A licence to use the Kitemark or Safety Mark on, or in relation to, a product will be granted to any manufacturer or producer who demonstrates that they can and will consistently be able to make that product to the requirements specified in the particular British Standard product specification. The manufacturer's capability for doing this is established initially by assessing their production processes, quality system and test facilities against the required part of the BS 5750 Series, and by testing the product against all the criteria of the relevant product Standard. The licensee is required to document for BSI the quality plans setting out the specific quality practices, resources and activities relevant to achieving compliance with the product standard. BSI carries out unannounced inspection visits to the manufacturer's premises and audit testing of the product, and may withdraw the licence for any failure of the manufacturer to comply with the relevant Standard. The presence of the mark on, or in relation to, a product is an assurance that the goods have been produced under an independently assessed quality system and have been subject to testing and the periodical inspection of the manufacturer's premises in accordance with the certification trade mark regulations of BSI.

In a society where most standards are applied on a voluntary basis and in a market environment where brand name reputation is preeminent, independent product certification has traditionally been little supported by manufacturing industry in the UK. It is government policy not to make standards mandatory, unless there are exceptional grounds for doing so in the interest of health or safety, and only one example exists of certification marking to a standard as a mandatory requirement through regulations: the Kitemark on the helmets sold for motor cyclists.

In summary, the main advantages of buying such certified products are:

- independent assurance that they comply with the standard in question and have been manufactured under a strict system of quality control,
- reduction of goods inward inspection,
- easier selection for fitness-for-purpose.

Capability assessment

Capability assessment is a different kind of certification, confidence in a firm's ability consistently to met customer's requirements being promoted through its registration on the basis of assessment to the appropriate part of the BS 5750/ISO 9000 Series.

BSI began the registration of firms as a service to those parts of industry for which the Kitemark was not available. The aim was to produce for the non-defence sectors of industry an equivalent to the Ministry of Defence's contractors list.

An organisation supplying products or services can be registered by BSI as a 'Registered Firm of assessed capability'. The company must have a documented quality system in accordance with the relevant part of the BS 5750 Series, and BSI check that this system is implemented on site. The assessment indicates the manufacturer's ability to control the systems of production, irrespective of the product, whereas product certification examines the manufacturer's ability to make a particular category of product in accordance with the recognised British Standard. Where unqualified or qualified registration is granted, a Certificate of Registration is issued to which is attached an appendix stating the scope of the firm's registration. The initial assessment is followed by regular unannounced surveillance visits, normally at a rate of four times per annum, but at the discretion of BSI, to ensure that standards are maintained. BSI registers the firm which is then entitled to use the Registered Firm symbol on publicity material and company documentation (see Figure 2.2).

Figure 2.2 BSI Registered Firm symbol

Several thousand firms have been registered as having been assessed by BSI and met the requirements of the BS 5750 Series. There are several other organisations which are also qualified to carry out independent third-party registration of companies in this way.

To meet the particular quality needs of individual sectors of industry or the requirements of a technological discipline, BSI designs and operates special systems which have their own rules and scope of application. An example of this is the BS 9000 Series, which is designed to meet the needs of the electronic components industry and has its own image, certification and capability assessment and covers manufacturers, distributors and test houses. Its special mark is shown in Figure 2.3.

The DTI publishes a *Register of Quality Assessed United Kingdom Companies* containing many thousands of entries which have been assessed to BS 5750: Parts 1, 2 and 3 (1981). This information is also contained in the BSI *Buyer's Guide* which is published annually.

In its certification activities, BSI does not have nor does it seek a monopoly position; it responds to community needs and aims to provide a service which can be used by industry. Through its Quality Assurance Council, BSI cooperates with other organisations concerned with the certification of compliance with standards.

Figure 2.3 BS 9000 for the electronic components industry

BSI also provides certification and testing services to other bodies and in other countries. For example, there is a Memorandum of Understanding (MOU) between BSI and the Singapore Institute of Standards and Industrial Research (SISIR) and the Standards and Industrial Research Institute of Malaysia (SIRIM) on the assessment of the quality systems of companies in Singapore and Malaysia and Europe which are seeking registration for compliance to the ISO 9000 Series of standards on quality systems. Such MOUs provide for recognition of audit work by one certification body in a country for certification by another body in another country. For example, BSI carried out the testing needed for the export of electrical equipment to Canada, administers the certification procedures for insulated electric cables and flexible cords on behalf of the British Approval Service for Electric Cables (BASEC), and even more specifically carried out a third-party assessment of the quality system at Exxon Chemicals Antwerp polymers plant in Belgium.

Inspectorate

BSI Inspectorate carries out much of the assessment and routine surveillance for BSI certification schemes, but can also cater for individual company needs. It operates not only in the UK but throughout the world and, in addition, acts as agent for British and overseas purchasers and certification organisations.

BSI testing

The BSI test facility which has been in operation for more than 25 years and now has 23 laboratories, is the largest of its kind in Europe and can test a wide range of products against a variety of national, foreign and international standards, government regulations, and trade associations' and companies' specifications. The major proportion of such testing is for clients other than BSI. The test facilities are financially self-supporting and are organised into the four distinct groups of mechanical, physical, electrical and electronic tests.

BSI Testing has approval from the British Calibration Service and is accredited by the National Measurement Accreditation Service (NAMAS). NAMAS brings together the former National Laboratories Accreditation scheme (NATLAS) and the British Calibration Service (BCS) under the one accreditation scheme. The testing services are used by manufacturers and users who wish to know if a product meets a particular standard or that it functions as intended. Local authorities, consumer organisations and trading standards officers submit, for a variety of reasons, items which require testing. Kitemark and Safety Mark products are also tested on a regular basis to ensure that they conform to requirements.

Technical Help to Exporters (THE)

The Technical Help to Exporters (THE) service was set up in 1966 to provide technical information and assistance to all sectors of industry engaged in exporting. These services cover the identification and sale of foreign specifications and regulations and provide assistance in meeting their requirements. The range of publications covering various matters of interest to exporters is being expanded continually. Detailed information on regulations and approval systems is disseminated through enquiry, advisory and consultancy services, and special projects are undertaken to meet the individual needs of industry.

THE can also help manufacturers with the translation of specifications and regulations, and can assist in the actual export of products to particular markets, for example by obtaining test certificates and by arranging for testing and factory investigation in the UK, if this is acceptable to the overseas organisation concerned.

Membership of THE is operated on a company basis and is open to any British manufacturer. This is completely separate from subscribing membership of BSI but it offers an exporting company distinct advantages.

Publications

The *BSI Standards Catalogue* lists all (over 10 000) published British Standards and other special series with short abstracts. The *BSI Yearbook* published at the beginning of each year is a complete guide to BSI literature. Cumulative sales bulletins, issued to subscribing members every two months, provide an updating service for the catalogue. *BSI News*, issued monthly to members, gives details of new and revised British Standards, amendments to British Standards, withdrawals, British Standards declared obsolescent, drafts circulated for public comment, new work started (both national and international), and newly published international standards. It also includes general information and articles on matters relating to standards.

The Annual Report gives a broad review of the preceding year's work and shows the constitutions of the board and the councils. Manufacturers and products covered by BSI certification and assessment schemes are listed annually in the *Buyer's Guide* and THE publishes a quarterly bulletin.

The other main publications, in addition to British Standards specifications, include:

- Drafts for developments (DD) which are intended to be precursors of standards;
- Published documents (PD) which are informative or advisory publications but without the status of standards;
- Promotional publications (PP) which are prepared by BSI Education Section as guidance on how to use British Standards in particular fields and are intended for students;
- Handbooks which comprise texts taken (without any technical changes to their content) from a number of separate Standards publications relating to a particular field. For example, *Handbook 22 – Quality Assurance*.

Information services

One of the main aims of BSI is to promote the use of British Standards to national and local government, industry, commerce and the consumer. To achieve this it is necessary that accurate information on standards is readily available. The enquiry section of BSI is the first point of contact. Enquiry officers have access to information about all aspects of BSI's work, and can answer or refer questions on almost any standards-related subject.

The BSI library contains a full set of current, withdrawn and obsolescent British Standards, international standards publications and the standards issued by the national standards bodies of other countries, together with their catalogues and journals, and other material about the theory and practice of standards. The collection contains over 500 000 technical documents and is the largest of its type in the world. The library runs the 'World Wide Standards Information Service' which provides a listing of all standards and technical regulations acquired from all over the world.

The provision of information is not confined to hard copy or by telephone. BSI STANDARDLINE is a bibliographic online database designed to cover the complete collection of British Standards, and keep the information up-to-date. This facility eases the task of information retrieval. Direct searching is available on aspects such as BS numbers, corresponding international standards, subjects, designation codes and committee references.

Education

The education section of BSI provides information for lecturers, teachers and students, promotes the principles and use of standardisation and produces teaching materials and manuals of British Standards specifically for use by students and their teachers. It also publishes materials for home economists and the general public. Services and publications include illustrated lectures, information sheets and posters.

Sets of British Standards are available for consultation in libraries around the UK and throughout the world.

The British Standards Society

The principal aims of the British Standards Society are:

- to promote the benefits and techniques of standardisation at company, national and international level;
- to encourage closer co-operation between BSI and standards users and to provide feedback to BSI on the practical application of British Standards;
- to provide training and exchanges of information on matters relating to standards through regular conferences, courses, and regional meetings at different centres in the UK.

The Society represents the UK in the International Federation for the Application of Standards (IFAN). (This is an association representative of the national organisations concerned with the application of Standards, for details see PD 6515:1986.) Membership is open to any individual concerned with standards work, whether working in the UK or overseas, on payment of a small annual subscription. Many members serve on BSI technical committees, in some cases as representatives of the Society.

Participation in international standards work

As one of the world's leading standards organisations, BSI is very active in the production and dissemination of international standards. This work is carried out through the International Organisation for Standardisation, and the International Electrotechnical Commission. The mission of the international standardisation system composed of these two bodies is to promote international co-operation on all issues of standardisation and related matters such as testing and certification, and hence to further understanding and co-operation amongst nations and people. BSI also co-ordinates UK participation in the standards of three further international organisations: European Committee for Standardisation (CEN), European Committee for Electrotechnical Standardisation (CENELEC), and European Coal and Steel Community (ECSC).

CEN, like ISO, is a private association and is primarily a service which is helping to facilitate European regional harmonization. Both CEN and CENELEC originated in the 1960s and draw their membership from the respective national bodies within the IECC and EFTA counties. Appendix A lists the national standards organisations of CEN. CEN and CENELEC have the facility to administer, or formally to associate with, such other organisations as may exist on a sufficiently authoritative and participative basis for the purpose of preparing standards in particular sectors. The IEC and CENELEC enjoy a close working relationship with 80% of CENELEC's documents being based on IEC Standards. Historically, CEN has not benefited from such close working relationships with ISO, however, the 'Vienna Agreement' will help to facilitate closer technical co-operation. This agreement specifies the modes of co-operation between CEN and ISO.

The aim of the agreement is to avoid duplication of work and allow joint development of Standards, and if possible, future European standards should reflect agreement at the international level. 'Special fast track' procedures are used in CEN to facilitate the adoption of ISO standards as European standards in most cases without significant changes. The numbering principle followed in CEN is that when an International standard is taken over in identical form 20 000 is added to the ISO number. This code allows people to recognise the relationship between the ISO and CEN numbers. The main types of CEN and CENELEC publications are European standards (designated EN), harmonization documents (HD) and European pre-standards (ENV). A short guide to these and other international organisations concerned with standards is included as an appendix in BS0: Part 1 (1991).

The work of preparing international standards is normally carried out through ISO Technical Committees. Each member body interested in a subject for which a Technical Committee has been established has the right to be represented on that Committee. In reaching agreement on international standards, draft standards are circulated to national bodies for voting. Publication as an international standard requires approval by at least 75% of the national bodies casting a vote.

Whenever possible, international standards are adopted as British Standards and given dual ISO/BS or IEC/BS numbers. BSI counterparts in the major countries of the world also endeavour to use international standards at the national level whenever it is practicable to do so.

Where an international standard has been adopted as an identical British Standard the latter is dual numbered and can be used in lieu. British Standards which are identified as 'technical equivalent' to international standards can also be used in lieu but care should be taken. More recently, BSI has decided to dispense with dual numbering on the grounds that the standards will be best known by their international identity.

When a standard issued by ISO or IEC is published without alteration as a British Standard, the British Standard carries the number and date of the international standard immediately below the BS number. Also published nowadays are British Standards Implementations, simply comprising the international text with a standard front and back cover and an indication of the BSI committee responsible. Such a British Standard can be made available approximately six weeks after international publications.

When a European Standard is published as a British Standard, the identifier of the European Standard is used, prefixed by 'BS' (e.g. BS EN.000) where '000' represents the number of the EN.

A major difference exists between standards from ISO and CEN. ISO which is a non-governmental organisation, imposes no formal obligations on its members. Individual countries can adopt ISO standards in total. Although, this policy was followed by the UK, it was not universal and resulted in many national standards being prepared which differed in varying degrees.

CEN has a constitution which comprises the 12 member standard bodies of the EC countries and those of EFTA. It works through the Member Standard Bodies (MSB) but is ultimately responsible for seeing that the standards proposed for harmonisation are harmonised. In CEN, the obligations on members are much more strict and apply even when a member has voted negatively. If agreed by the voting criteria:

a) each member must implement an EN, normally within 6 months. This means publishing a national standard identical except for the language in which it is written. (European standards are ratified in the three official languages of CEN – English, French and German.)
b) conflicting national standards must be withdrawn (i.e. a national standard on the same subject and with requirements such that what complies with the national standard does not comply with the EN, or vice versa).

The production of harmonised technical standards in agreed key areas is an essential part of the Single European Market development. BSI is Britain's representative in this process and attempts to ensure that the standards produced are acceptable to both industry and consumers. European work takes priority in the BSI Standards programme.

The use of standards is always the result of voluntary action by trade, industry and social and economic partners. However, standards are sometimes related to European technical legislation (Directives) and conformity to such standards may then constitute a presumption of conformity to the Directives, and as such allow the use of the CE mark (see Figure 2.4). Such marking may be self-certified and might be sufficient for a frontier official, but is not a quality mark. Voluntary schemes for certification of conformity to ENs are also available from CEN (using the CEN mark) and/or its National Members.

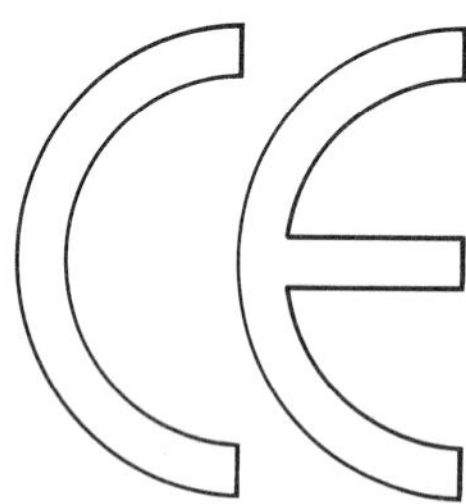

Figure 2.4 European Certification mark

UK participation in the work of international standards organisations and the nature and presentation of the UK view is decided through the BSI committees dealing with the relevant subject matter and this participation is explained in BS0: Part 2 (1991). PD 6515 (1986) provides guidance to companies to help them make the best use of international standardisation and also use the international aspects of quality assurance as related to standardisation.

2.3 Standards in general

What is a standard?

Standards influence everyone's lives daily and every organisation, public or private, large or small, and whatever its activity, needs to know about them. They are essential tools for industry and commerce and provide the basic ingredients for competitive and cost-effective production. A *standard* is a technical or management specification or other document. It is a precise and authoritative statement of the criteria necessary to ensure that a material, product or procedure is fit for the purpose for which it is intended. They embrace product and performance specifications, codes of practice, management systems, methods of testing, measurement, analysis and sampling, guides and glossaries. Standards are drawn up with the co-operation and consensus, or general approval, of interested parties. They are based on the consolidated results of science, technology and experience, aimed at the promotion of optimum community benefits and approved by a body recognised on a national, regional or international level. Standards are made publicly available mainly by the National Standards bodies, which collaborate in the European and global standards organisations. These bodies cannot, however, compel the use of the standards they adopt. Use of standards may be enforced by law only through their incorporation and in contracts, in trade descriptions or in legislation. Standards:

- facilitate design and manufacture;
- rationalise processes and operations;
- promote quality with economy;
- simplify communication and trade;
- inspire confidence in both manufacturer and user.

What is standardisation?

Standardisation is an activity to improve efficiency by bringing consistency to the products, services or processes. It also helps to make things operate as they should, so that there are no unexpected or dangerous surprises. The activity generally consists of the processes of formulating, issuing and implementing standards. The main principles involved in standardisation are that:

- Standards should be wanted. The production of standards relies upon the willingness of all parties concerned to reach voluntary agreement among themselves for one or more stated purposes.

- Standards should be used. Application of standards relies upon the voluntary commitment required in their preparation being extended to their use. The publication of a standard is of little value if it is not applied. The intended application of a standard should be clearly understood at the start and borne in mind throughout its preparation.
- Standards should be planned. The social and/or economic benefits of a standard should be compared with the total cost of preparing, publishing and maintaining it. In areas of rapid development, the balance should be struck between the risk of inhibiting innovation by premature standardisation and the danger of allowing the spread of divergent and mutually incompatible solutions to the same problem. If the latter occurs, the cost of subsequent standardisation is likely to be much greater.
- Standards express what has been established or is about to be established. The process of writing standards is essentially one of selection. A standard can contain only what the interested parties are prepared to agree on at the time it is written. Thus, decisions are needed regarding when and how it is appropriate to standardise in a rapidly developing industry or to satisfy new community needs relating to safety or the environment.
- Standards should be reviewed at regular intervals and appropriate action taken. A standard that does not evolve in keeping with changing circumstances or technological advance may become irrelevant or inhibit progress.
- Standards should not be duplicated. Standardisation can be pursued at different levels: by individuals, firms, associations, countries, regions such as Europe, and world-wide. For economy of total effort, a standard should logically be prepared at the broadest level consistent with meeting the needs of all interested parties within an acceptable timescale. The simultaneous preparation, at different levels, of standards on identical subjects should be avoided as far as practicable.

The scope and opportunities for standardisation are extensive and Figure 2.5 provides an indication of the scope for company standards. The ultimate success of standardisation in an organisation will be realised when every person has the initiative and the will to apply standards in his/her own sphere of influence.

Standardisation is particularly beneficial, indeed essential, to the success of the following:

- Company amalgamations and mergers. These present special opportunities to achieve significant results in, for example, management control, variety reduction and specification writing;
- Production rationalisation;
- Suggestion schemes based on standardisation;
- Health and safety legislation such as COSHH or product liability;
- New managerial appointments, when new heads of department will be anxious to know the standard practices of their departments;
- Environmental protection, waste control, energy conservation;
- Quality system registration to the ISO 9000 quality system series.

Tiers of standardisation

It is a well-known concept that there are three basic tiers of standardization: company, national and international (see Figure 2.6). Each tier has its particular uses and it is a fallacy to believe that there will ever be no need for all three to go on co-existing, but each tier should make the maximum use of standards issued by the appropriate organisation in the next tier above. Because of the company-based constitution of the national standards committees and the national basis of the international standards making committees this is a two-way process and each tier will have contributed to

Application	Method	Purpose	Benefits
Management control	Directives, procedures, codes of practice	To communicate rules from management; Company and product rationalization	Efficient and effective control, better industrial relations
Environment	Codes of practice	Health and safety standards that relate to the environment	Health and safety
Plant and equipment	Catalogue, specifications, standards, codes of practice	Identity and control plant, its maintenance and use of spares	Process control; Plant management and efficiency; Environmental control
Design	Specify materials, components, processes, codes of practice	Meet market requirements; Maintain optimum design possibilities, product liability, manufacturing efficiency	Product quality and reliability, environmental protection, health and safety
Drawing office	Use of design and manufacturing standard, classification and coding	Information retrieval, design codes of practice, variety control	Better product design, design control
Material control	Catalogue, identification coding, handling, codes of practice	Stock control, quality assurance, health and safety	Availability of parts, reduced stock investment, COSHH controls
Purchasing	Purchase and material specifications, coding	Purchase specification supplier approval, quality control	Quality and availability of components and materials at the right price
Manufacture	Specifications, codes of practice, coding, health and safety	Production control, education and training, quality control, testing	Productivity, quality, health and safety of employees
Packaging	Codes of practice, coding	Protection in transit, cost-effectiveness	Customer satisfaction
Sales	Codes of practice, instruction manuals	Communication with customer, quality assurance	Delivery, better customer relationships
Accounting	Catalogue, procedures	Control of capital and depreciation	Financial control
All	All	Quality management	To employees, customers and company

Source: PD 3542: 1991

Figure 2.5 The use of company standards

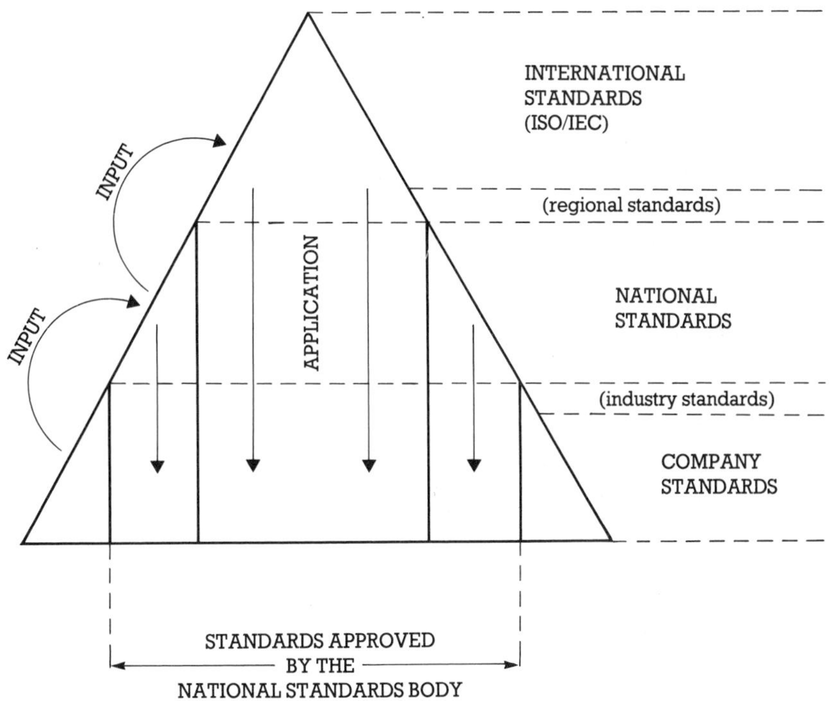

Figure 2.6 Tiers of standardization

the one above and will benefit from it. As part of the closed loop (see Figure 2.7) the people responsible for preparing standards must be involved with national and international standards.

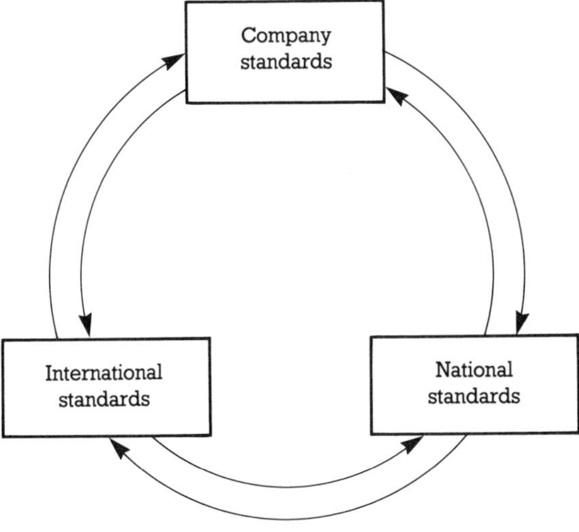

Figure 2.7 The closed loop

The first and most important level is the company. The word 'company' may be taken here to mean anything from a large government department to a small private firm, or from a multi-national corporation to a local firm. The company is the unit of enterprise which makes things or gives a service to people.

Any company may set up its own standards and use them; simply stated this is good management practice. The sensible way to write a company standard is to see what is available from the next tier up, i.e. national standards and to make maximum use of them. National standards however will never be sufficient by themselves. Companies will often need to amplify or qualify standards to meet their own particular requirements. They will also need to develop their own standards for their own production procedures and for that element of their product which is original and unique and without which they could not sell it competitively.

A major element of national standardization

is the banding together of companies in their own interest and in a disciplined way to simplify production and distribution, where it is to their mutual advantage, and to eliminate the waste of time and material involved in the production of unnecessary variety and in the individual research and design of common items. This banding together is, by custom, organised by the National Standards Body (NSB) which, while it may not be an arm of government, must have its activities recognised by government. Influences on national standardization are more diverse than in the company, but a national standard can often be used as the basis for a company standard, which may for example restrict more precisely a multiplicity of variants which has already been restricted in the national standard.

International standardization is the banding together of the NSBs, in the interest of the companies they serve, to achieve the same objective all over the world. In some areas regional standardization is important. That too is operated through the NSBs and the main objective of regional standards bodies such as CEN and CENELEC is to make the maximum use of the International Standards of ISO and IEC.

In urging the use of International Standards it must not be forgotten that, in their location at the top of the pyramid (Figure 2.6), international standards are influenced by many more factors than are national standards, just as national standards are subject to more influences than company standards. An international standard may be adopted nationally but it is useless if it is not directly relevant to the company.

Quality and standards

Standards have three main roles in quality assurance:

- To provide design specifications. Quality assurance starts with good design;
- To provide text which forms the basis of quality control and, if requested, product certification;
- To provide information on the management techniques of quality assurance itself and criteria against which a company's quality management can be assessed.

Types of British standards

Types of British standards fall mainly into four categories:

- glossaries, symbols and classifications,
- methods of all kinds,
- specifications,
- codes of practice, guides and recommendations.

Glossaries

Definition of terms, often with associated conventions, units and symbols, is a necessary first stage in standardisation. British standard glossaries bring together agreed sets of terms and definitions. For example, BS 4778: Parts 1 (1987) and 2 (1992)is a glossary of terms used in quality assurance.

Methods

British standard methods comprise a variety of standards describing formalised ways of doing things. In drafting such methods, the aim of these standards is to state clearly and completely the way in which the activity is performed and how conclusions are drawn from it by calculation or otherwise.

The following examples indicate the range of different kinds of methods:

- methods of measurement (for example, BS 5694: 1979);
- methods of determination (for example BS 5381: 1986);
- methods of verifying compliance with a specific requirement using a 'go, no-go' basis for finding the result (for example, BS 5777: 1979);
- methods for sampling and analyses (for example, BS 1743: 1991);
- methods for specifying (for example, BS 5328: 1989);
- methods of presentation, declaration, classification, etc. (for example, BS 5727: 1979);

- methods of evaluating (performance) (for example, BS 5558: 1989).

Specifications
A specification is a detailed statement of a set of requirements to be satisfied by a product, a material or a process, indicating the procedures for checking compliance with these requirements. The requirements should fall completely within the scope of the specification. Therefore, the characteristics covered by the requirements depend upon the scope and the following questions need to be considered:
What is to be standardised?
Who will be the parties involved in the use of the standard?
What are the requirements to be specified?
What methods are necessary to judge compliance?

Codes of practice
The main function of codes of practice is to recommend good accepted practice as followed by competent practitioners. Codes bring together the results of practical experience and scientific investigation in a form that enables those concerned to make immediate use of proven developments and practices in particular branches of industry.

2.4 Standards relating specifically to quality

It might be claimed that all standards are quality-related since they provide for quality of goods and services by defining those features and characteristics that govern their ability to satisfy given needs. However, there are a wide range of British Standards which relate to specific aspects of product and/or service quality. For example, quality assurance terminology is explained in BS 4778: Parts 1 and 2 (1987 and 1991) and reliability terminology in BS 4778: Part 3 (1991); metrology is explained in BS 5233 (1986); BS 5750: Parts 1, 2 and 3 (1987) specifies quality systems applicable to all industries and there are a number of British Standards on process control chart techniques including BS 2564 (1955), BS 5700 (1984), BS 5701 (1980) and BS 5703 (1980). BS 6143: Parts 1 and 2 (1992 and 1990) deals with the economics of quality. Sampling methods and procedures for acceptance inspection are detailed in BS 6000 (1972), BS 6001: Parts 1 (1991), 2 (1993) and 3 (1993) and BS 6002. Reliability is dealt with in BS 5760: Parts 0–10 and BS 5781 (1988) details the requirements for measurement and calibration systems. In addition, methods for the selection of samples from various types of bulk commodity are dealt with in BS 5309 (1976) and statistical interpretation of data is detailed in BS 2846: Parts 1 to 7, BS 2987 (1958), BS 3518: Part 5 (1984), BS 5324 (1976), BS 5497: Part 1 (1987) and BS 5532: Parts 1 to 3.

While British Standards on quality management are referenced individually and may be obtained individually, some have been classified in *Handbook 22 Quality Assurance* which brings them together under a hard cover and forms a convenient and economical way of obtaining and holding them. The handbook includes standards which can be grouped under three headings:

a) Terminology standards which set down agreed terms and definitions in current quality assurance practice:
   BS 4778 *Quality vocabulary* (in three parts).
   BS 5233 *Glossary of terms used in metrology*.
b) Basic or generic standards which are written in the form of guides (not involving contractual requirements):
   BS 4891 *Guide to quality assurance*. (Now withdrawn.)
   BS 5760 *Reliability of constructed or manufactured products, systems, equipment and components* (in ten parts).
   BS 6143 *Guide to the economics of quality* (in two parts).
   BS 7000 *Guide to managing product design*.
   BS 7229 *Guide to quality systems auditing* (in three parts).
c) Definitive system specifications (with guides) for use in contractual situations:
   BS 5750 *Quality systems* (in eight parts).
   BS 5781 *Measurement and calibration systems*.

BS 4778 and BS 5233 define terms used directly in the other standards listed in b) and c) above. Wherever possible, terms and definitions from EOQ, ISO and IEC publications have been adopted. An appendix in BS 4778: Part 2 makes reference to other British Standards and ISO glossaries that contain additional terms relating to quality assurance.

BS 5750 is currently in eight parts. Part 0 is a guide to selection and use and to quality management and quality system elements; Part 1 is a quality system specification for design/development, production, installation and servicing; Part 2 is a quality system specification for production and installation; Part 3 is a quality system specification for final inspection and testing; Part 4 is a guide to the use of Parts 1, 2 and 3; Part 8 is a guide to quality management and quality system elements for services, Part 13 is a guide to the application of BS 5750: Part 1 the development, supply and maintenance of software and Part 14 is a guide to dependability programme management.

BS 5760 is currently in ten parts. Part 0 is an introductory guide to the principles of reliability; Part 1 discusses the essential features of a comprehensive reliability and maintainability programme and is concerned mainly with what has to be done and why, when and how. Part 2 recommends general procedures for the assessment of reliability; Part 3 contains authentic practical examples; Part 4 gives guidance on specification clauses concerned with the achievement of reliability. Part 5 describes and gives guidance on the use of failure modes and effects analysis; Part 6 describes procedures to expose and remove weaknesses in hardware and software items in order to achieve reliability in a product; Part 7 outlines the concept and application of fault tree analysis; Part 9 describes the use of the block diagram technique for modelling and evaluating the reliability of both elementary and more complex systems and Part 10 is a guide to reliability testing. BS 6143 gives advice on determination of costs associated with defect prevention and appraisal activities, failures, and the operation of quality-related cost systems. BS 7000 gives guidance on the management of product design based on five pre-requisites:

- commitment to good product design at all levels of management;
- motivation of staff involved;
- clear objectives;
- adequate resources;
- organizational systems.

Part 1 of BS 7229 gives guidance on auditing quality systems which can be applied to:

- a quality systems audit carried out by a company on its own;
- an audit by one organization on another;
- third party audits by independent agencies.

Part 2 of BS 7229 outlines the qualification criteria for auditors and Part 3 gives guidance on managing an audit programme.

2.5 Standards and the law

Implications of the law

The Health and Safety at Work Act 1974 and similar legislation are a part of the criminal law as are the many supporting regulations and orders. In some cases compliance with designated British Standards is specifically required by legislation – the British Standard becomes 'mandatory' – and the failure of a product or service to comply with the standard would be an offence. However, in other cases products or services supplied or offered for supply and described or marked as complying with any standard could, if falsely described, infringe the general provisions of the Trade Description Act 1968. This wide-ranging legislation creates offences for false and misleading statements applied to all types of products and services. Civil action may also be possible by one company against another for misrepresentation or similar failure to comply with a specific description or implied quality of a product or service.

Codes of practice are increasingly being used to complement statute law such as the Health and Safety at Work Act 1974. They underpin the law and provide further guidance on implications and procedures. Failure to comply with a statutory code of practice may be cited in criminal proceedings against a company or an individual.

The European Community is providing an even wider framework of law and, given the range and scope of the new approach directives linked to completion of the single market, it is clear that standards are taking on an even greater significance as means of compliance with the law.

The Health and Safety at Work Act 1974

The scope of the 1974 Act was:

> 'to make further provision for securing the health, safety and welfare of persons at work, for protecting others against risks to health or safety in connection with the activities of persons at work, for controlling the keeping and use and preventing the unlawful acquisition, possession and use of dangerous substances, and for controlling certain emissions into the atmosphere; to make further provision with respect to the employment medical advisory service; to amend the law relating to building regulations'.

The Act is an enabling measure superimposed over existing health and safety legislation. The existing duties under, for example, the Factories, Offices, Shops and Railway Premises Act and the Mines and Quarries Act remain in force, the main provisions of which, for the time being, continue. This provides a comprehensive and integrated system of law to deal with health and safety at work, and the protection of the public affected by the activities of people at work.

The provisions for enforcement of the earlier Acts have been replaced by the Health and Safety at Work Act 1974. This includes powers to issue improvement and prohibition notices and to prosecute. The general duties of employers to their employees are set down in Section 2 of the Act.

Section 2 (1) Establishes 'the duty of every employer to ensure, so far as is reasonably practicable, the health, safety and welfare at work of all his/her employees'.

Section 2 (2) (a) Requires the provision and maintenance of plant, which the Act defines as including machinery, equipment and appliances used at work. It does not supersede the more detailed and specific provisions covering certain equipment contained in existing legislation, but it applies to all plant used in any work activity, whether or not subject to existing safety legislation.

Section 2 (2) (b) Requires 'arrangements for ensuring, so far as it reasonably practicable, safety and absence of risks to health in connection with the use, handling, storage and transport of articles and substances'.

This subsection is concerned with materials and substances whether in solid or liquid form or a gas or vapour, and covers everything used at work and all work activities.

Section 2 (2) (c) Requires of an employer 'the provision of such information, instruction, training and supervision as is necessary to ensure, so far as is reasonably practicable, the health and safety at work of his/her employees'.

Section 2 (2) (d) Requires 'so far as is reasonably practicable as regards any place of work under the employer's control, the maintenance of it in a condition that is safe and without risks to health and the provision and maintenance of means of access to and egress from it that are safe and without such risks'.

Section 6 Places specific duties on those who can ensure that articles and substances are as safe and without risks to health as it is reasonably practicable to make them. Articles must also be properly erected and installed. The section was amended with effect from 1st March, 1988 by the Consumer Protection Act 1987. It covers:

a) new and second-hand articles designed for use at work, whether for sale or hire, and their component parts;
b) items which though capable of domestic use are designed to be used also at work;
c) new and second-hand items of fairground equipment;
d) all substances, including micro-organisms, which are supplied to workplaces or to certain other non-domestic premises.

The safety of goods originally intended for domestic use is subject to other legislation, particularly the Consumer Protection Act 1987 and Regulations relating to consumer goods.

In addition to placing duties of a general character on employers, manufacturers employees, and the self-employed and others, the Act provides a wide regulation-making power. Part 1 provides for securing the health, safety and welfare of people at work; protecting other people against risks to health or safety arising from the activity of people at work; controlling the keeping and use of dangerous substances and preventing unlawful acquisition, possession and use; and controlling the emission into the atmosphere of noxious or offensive substances from prescribed premises.

Control of substances hazardous to health (COSHH)

The Control of Substances Hazardous to Health Regulations 1988 came into force on 1st October, 1989. These regulations enable Directive 80/1107/EEC concerned with workers' health to be implemented and impose duties on employers to protect employees and other persons who may be exposed to substances hazardous to health and also impose certain duties on employees.

The regulations introduce a new legal framework for the control of substances hazardous to health in all types of business including factories, farms, quarries, leisure and service activities, offices and shops. Hazardous substances include any dusts, liquids, pastes, gases, powders, oils, sprays, aerosols or microorganisms that can cause long-term harm to workers.

The regulations do not cover asbestos, substances below ground in mines, materials producing ionizing radiations and lead, which are all regulated by separate legislation. Employers must:

- assess the risk to health arising from work and what precautions are needed;
- introduce appropriate measures to prevent or control the risk;
- ensure that control measures are used and that equipment is properly maintained and procedures observed;
- where necessary, monitor the exposure of the workers and carry out an appropriate form of surveillance of their health;
- inform, instruct and train employees about the risks and the precautions to be taken.

The Consumer Protection Act 1987

The Consumer Protection Act 1987 covers responsibilities to the consumer, rather than the employee, and encompasses product liability (Part 1) and consumer safety (Part 2). The Act became law in March 1988.

Product liability

Responsibility is now imposed on the manufacturer/producer to prove he is not liable for damage caused by a defective product. Standard systems and procedures must be designed to identify and control components, materials and methods to ensure a safe and reliable product. Standards are not directly mentioned in Part 1 of the Act, but they can be used by either party as a means of defining the expected level.

Consumer safety

Part 2 of the Act makes it a criminal offence to 'supply, offer for supply, expose or possess for supply any consumer goods which fail to comply with the general safety requirement'. The general safety requirement makes specific reference to standards and safety regulations.

The Environmental Protection Act 1990

There is concern to improve the environment in cities, towns and places of work as well as the surrounding countryside; of growing concern today is waste disposal. Most of the Act is relevant to industry and can be briefly summarized as follows:

Part 1 (a) Integrated pollution control (IPC)
This applies to some of the potentially worst polluting industries and will be administered by Her Majesty's Inspectorate of Pollution. Industries scheduled for IPC will have to employ Best Available Techniques Not Entailing Excessive Cost (BATNEEC) and the controls will apply to all discharges whether to land, air or water.

Part 1 (b) Air pollution control
This is for those industries slightly less polluting than those scheduled for IPC and will

cover a wide range of uses from glass works to coating processes. Again BATNEEC will apply and industries will have to apply to their local authority Environmental Health Officers for prior authorization. In the case of existing premises some will benefit from temporary relaxations in the early years but must have been authorized in one of three phases between 1st April, 1991 and 1st April, 1993.

Part 2 Waste on land
Responsibility for waste will come under much stricter control and this will extend 'from the cradle to the grave'. This will involve carriers as well as disposal site operators and responsibility for licensed disposal facilities will continue until the waste regulation authority issues a certificate of completion. In many cases this will be several years after disposal has ceased. Fresh and far-reaching controls will also be provided in relation to gaseous and liquid emissions from closed sites.

Part 3 Statutory nuisance
These provisions are already in force and re-enact the nuisance provisions of the Public Health Act and the noise nuisance provisions of the Control of Pollution Act.

Part 5 Amendments to the Radioactive Substances Act 1960
These remove exemptions from the UK atomic authority and crown premises and introduce enforcement and prohibition procedures.

Part 8 Miscellaneous
This part brings in wide-ranging controls over the importation and export of wastes, including powers to obtain information. It introduces the concept of public registers for potentially contaminated land and extends the controls over disposal of substances and articles at sea first introduced under the Food and Environment Protection Act 1985.

Environmental audit

Environmental audits will involve checking against existing legislative and in-house standards to ensure protection of the environment. Quality assurance techniques can be employed to ensure compliance with the standards. BS 7750 (1992) is designed to enable any organisation to establish an effective management system, as a foundation for both sound environmental performance and participation in 'environmental auditing' schemes.

It is expected that the new European legislation which began to be implemented in 1993 will set new, higher standards for the UK. The design stage could incorporate factors such as energy conservation, waste reduction and recycling of materials. This would mean a review of the materials used, the waste produced or the energy consumed and could mean altering processes, for example, painting or spraying to use less or no solvents.

2.6 Benefits and use of standards

Aims of standardisation

Standards are of importance to companies as a means of communication in trade, of achieving economies in production, of regularising procedures, of specifying performance and product and service quality, and of preventing the reoccurrence of abnormalities in processes. They are written to be easily understood, worked to and applied, and they should prevent problems being tackled which others have already solved. Their use should give confidence to manufacturers and customers alike. Buyers can often write a complete technical specification by quoting BS numbers and Standards are frequently quoted within tenders and contracts (see Chapter 9). Hence, in every organisation there is a need to establish standards that will harmonise with, and make use of, relevant national and international standards, and which will improve productivity through better design, reduced variety, improved quality and lower unit cost.

The broad aims of standardisation can be summarised as follows:

- to promote the quality of products, processes and services by defining those features and characteristics that govern their ability to satisfy given needs (i.e. fitness for purpose);

- to promote improvement in the quality of life, safety, health and protection of the environment;
- to promote the economic use of materials, energy and human resources in the production and exchange of goods;
- to promote clear and unambiguous communication between all interested parties, in a form suitable for reference or quotation in legally binding documents;
- to promote international trade by the removal of barriers caused by differences in national practices;
- to promote efficiency through variety control.

Table 2.1 Advantages and disadvantages of standardisation

Advantages	Disadvantages
Reduced: • overhead costs • labour costs • material costs • stock investment • stores space • spares and maintenance costs • equipment costs.	Marginal increase in costs in some cases. Cost of standardisation exercise. Cost of changing. Restriction of freedom of choice.
Improved: • design for economic production • communication within the organisation • Specification of bought-out parts • availability of parts • management control • quality and reliability	Practical obstacles to implementation and enforcement. Cost of maintenance.
Increased: • customer satisfaction • manufacturing efficiency • communications.	
Compliance with legislation.	

Table 2.1 lists, in general terms, the advantages and disadvantages of standardisation. PD3542 (1991) discusses, in considerable detail, the benefits of standardisation in various organisational functions and PD6495 (1986) outlines methods for determining the advantages of company standardisation projects.

2.7 Certification

Certification is the act of certifying, by means of a certificate or mark, that a product, service or system conforms with a standard or specification. The purpose of certification is to assure a customer that they have received what was specified. It is the act of documenting compliance with requirements. The requirements can relate to personnel, processes, products, organisations and services. There are three main types of certification: first-party, second-party and third-party, certification.

First-party certification

This form of certification means that the manufacturer declares to the customer that products or services are to the specification. It is self-certification by the supplier and is sometimes known as the producer's declaration. The producer may prepare and sign a release certificate, release note or a certificate of conformance or conformity, affirming that the product or service at the time of assessment met the stated specification. However, one of the problems of self-certification is the opportunity it gives the supplier for falsification of compliance to standards or requirements.

The unreliability of first-party certification is highlighted by Cardew in describing a situation at Cross International (UK) Ltd (who are now trading as Giddings and Lewis) (Cardew, 1986). In a three-month period, 1575 details were received by Cross covered by 329 vendor inspection reports, certifying to the quality of the parts. Of these details, 225 were rejected by Cross.

Second-party certification

Here the purchaser carries out their own assessment of whether or not the producer's product, systems or services are to specification and would meet their own requirements. This process is commonly called a *purchaser audit* or *supplier quality assurance (SQA)*. During the last two decades or so, the practice by large purchasers of carrying out their own assessments has become well established. Lascelles and Dale (1988) in a study of automotive suppliers report 'that major customers in the automotive industry are not willing to accept third-party certification, they wish to carry out their own assessment and surveillance'. This situation is beginning to change. We are aware of motor vehicle manufacturers becoming registered to the ISO 9000 Series and, in turn, encouraging the same of their suppliers.

In these circumstances, with each major customer carrying out their own assessments and audits, this can lead to extra costs for both customer and supplier. It was just such a situation which caused the Process Plant EDC to fund a study among process plant fabricators, with a particular emphasis on the cost implications of second-party audits and inspection. The main findings of this work by Dale and Plunkett in 1984 include:

- The general feeling in the industry was that once a quality assurance system had been established, to the satisfaction of a reputable and competent auditor, there should be no further need for auditing by clients;
- Clients were usually not willing to accept each other's accreditations through audit;
- In general, fabricators were subjected to about six separate audits per year, plus a number of mini-audits or checks;
- Many fabricators found they had to submit to audits from major clients, just to get on bid-lists.

Third-party certification

The impact of second-party audits made suppliers adapt their internal procedures to reflect what they believed major clients or potential customers wanted to see. This led to a proliferation of procedures, systems, manuals, in particular, for specific project assessment criteria, etc. This multiple assessment is costly for both customer and supplier. One of the aims of third-party certification is to reduce such cost. Third-party certification is independent of supplier and purchaser, it is sometimes termed *independent certification*. The producer demonstrates to an impartial expert/independent agency (the third party) that their systems, products, or services conform to an agreed specification and the third party then issues a certificate to verify compliance. The certification body assesses registers (for office and DTI purposes) and certifies the supplier organisation after it has satisfied itself that the supplier's quality system meets the ISO 900 Series. It also inspects and tests products to ascertain if they conform to standards or meet specified requirements. Some bodies also assess personnel. The use of third-party certification schemes allows organisations to demonstrate publicly their commitment to quality assurance.

Third-party certification is of particular value where there is no two-party relationship in place, for example, where the product is manufactured for general sale and the producer has no knowledge of exactly who the final purchaser will be.

Confidence in third-party schemes is progressively reducing the continuing need for second-party (purchaser) supplier assessment arrangements. In practice, purchaser organisations often audit portions of the quality systems of their suppliers, but because of supplier quality system certification, the purchaser does not have to duplicate the, say, 80 per cent that has already been audited by the third-party auditor.

Certification bodies

There are impartial bodies possessing the necessary competence and reliability to operate a certification system and in which the interests of all parties concerned with the functioning of the system are represented.

BSI Quality Assurance Services is part of BSI and is one of the 30 or so bodies currently accredited by the Secretary of State for Trade and Industry, offering independent certification, assessment and inspection facilities to industry. There are many more (around 20) unaccredited certification bodies. In all these areas, BSI Quality Assurance Services acts as an independent third party, able to assess or inspect a wide range of products, services and processes to a variety of specifications. The BSI Certification and Assessment Service administers all the third-party schemes of BSI Quality Assurance Service. All of these are based upon BS 5750: Parts 1, 2 or 3 (1987), or a quality assessment schedule, which defines the special system requirements relating to a contract, category of products or processes. It should be noted that quality assessment schedules, which are now going out of use, are not standards. They are only special requirements for industry sectors. In some circumstances, guidance notes are prepared to assist in the implementation of the BS 5750/ISO 9000 series.

Accreditation

The 1982 white paper 'Standards, Quality and International Competitiveness' emphasised the importance of certification in increasing the confidence of the customer in the capability of suppliers. It identified the encouragement of certification schemes as a principal way in which government action could enhance the level of quality performance and hence the efficiency and competitiveness of British firms. In recent times, the number of bodies offering a third-party certification service has increased. In such situations, it is vital that the customer has confidence that people awarding certification are capable of assessing the supplier. On 30 May 1984, BSI and the DTI signed a Memorandum of Understanding setting up the National Accreditation Council for Certification Bodies (NACCB). The Council was established under the Royal Charter of the BSI to advise the Secretary of State for Trade and Industry on the National Association of certification bodies. NACCB was subsequently launched in June 1985 and provides for the impartial assessment of applicant certification bodies in terms of independence, integrity and technical competence on behalf of the Secretary of State for Trade and Industry. They only accredit certification bodies within the UK.

Creation of the NACCB has resulted in the formation of the Association of Certification Bodies (ACB), providing for the first time collective representation of certifiers in national forums, in particular the Council itself. The NACCB are an independent Council under BSI with a chairman appointed under the rules agreed in the MOU. The Council is widely representative of those involved in certification including major purchasers, suppliers (industrial and domestic consumers) and the certification bodies themselves. To be eligible for accreditation, third-party certification bodies are required to meet criteria derived from the relevant ISO/IEC Guides, mostly now implemented in Europe in the form of the EN 45000 series of standards. The criteria for accreditation follow three standards.

- BS 7511 (1989) (EN 45011) for certification bodies issuing certificates for product conformity;
- BS 7512 (1989) (EN 45012) for certification bodies certificating that suppliers' quality systems comply with appropriate standards, normally BS 5750: Part 1 and 2;
- BS 7513 (1989) (EN 45013) for certification bodies certificating the competence of personnel.

This set of standards has been drawn up with the objective of promoting confidence as to the way in which product and quality system certification activities are performed, as well as promoting confidence in those accreditation systems and bodies which conform to them. They will assist with the harmonization of testing and certification and can create the environment for reciprocal recognition and facilitate co-operation between countries.

The series of standards specifies general criteria that a certification body operating product certification, quality system certification and certification of personnel shall follow if it is to be recognised at a national or European level as competent and reliable in the operation of a product and quality certification system and a system of certification of personnel, irrespective of the sectors involved. These standards cover the structure, operation and management of a certification body. They require that it should be impartial, staffed by competent people and with a governing body responsible for certification and representative of the principal interests involved. It also checks the effectiveness of their quality management systems. The frequency of surveillance visits is normally at intervals of around 12 months with reassessment every 4 years.

The common procedures and criteria would provide the basis for:

- recognition of the competence of certification bodies;
- agreements between certification bodies;
- agreements between national bodies responsible for recognising certification bodies;

Figure 2.8 National accreditation mark for certification bodies

- the nomination of certification bodies for regulatory purposes by member governments.

Members of the Council represent all the interests involved, including industry, government, local authorities, trade unions, retailers and consumers. If successful, the certification body receives an accreditation certificate for the scheme assessed and the right to display the national accreditation mark – the gold tick and crown (see Figure 2.8) alongside their own certification mark. The gold crown signifies government and the tick signifies approval. NACCB publish a Directory which lists the certification bodies accredited by the Secretary of State for Trade and Industry and provides details of their accredited scope, as set out in the accreditation certificates. The Directory lists the following categories of certification which are eligible for accreditation:

- supplier quality management systems;
- product conformity;
- personnel.

Certification bodies are invited to apply for accreditation for the category or categories of certification they offer and will be assessed against the relevant criteria. From the accreditation granted it will be clear whether the body is accredited for quality system assessment only, and in what fields, or whether it has the additional qualification of being accredited to certificate conformity of products, each to its own specification. This strengthening of certification arrangements is a further development of the government policy to support greater use of standards and quality systems in the UK.

The aims of accreditation are:

- to enhance the status and authority both nationally and internationally, of UK certification bodies;
- to strengthen the international competitiveness of UK industry;
- to develop quality assessment procedures which encourage the achievement of excellence;
- to support the promotion of independent

certification in the UK;

- to harmonize accreditation practices in Europe and throughout the world as a basis for reciprocal recognition of accredited certificates;
- to foster the growth of internationally recognised accredited certification sales;
- to offer advice to the government on certification.

The accreditation system is based on internationally recognised procedures. Thus the status of accredited bodies will be recognised around the world, helping to eliminate many of the technical barriers which face British producers overseas and widening the opportunities for overseas trade.

It is an objective of NACCB to foster the growth of world-wide arrangements for reciprocal arrangements of accredited certification bodies and to this end they work through the body European Accreditation of Certification (EAC). The ISO Committee on Conformity Assessment (CASCO) has provided guidelines on the structure and operation of testing and certification bodies and this is assisting with mutual recognition agreements. NACCB chair the EAC and are striving to agree mutual recognition of accreditation bodies in the 15 countries which have signed a MOU. A considerable number of bilateral MOUs are in existence and there is a real need for international recognition of national accreditation bodies to ensure that resources are used to best advantage.

Supporting arrangements for the national accreditation of testing laboratories had been established in 1980. NACCB assesses, accredits and monitors calibration and testing laboratories in accordance with EN 45000 criteria. NAMAS accreditation is voluntary and open to an UK laboratory including independent commercial laboratories or those which form part of a larger organisation such as a manufacturing company, educational establishment or government department.

In late 1989, with the support of CEN/CENELEC (the joint European Standards Institution), the European Committee for Quality System Assessment and Certification (EQS) was established in Brussels. Representations of all Western European countries signed a memorandum of understanding of the establishment on the committee. The objective of EQS is to promote acceptance throughout Europe, and to outside countries, of third-party assessments and certification of companies' quality systems.

The ISO 9000 Series of international standards provides the basis for such assessments. These standards have been adopted by CEN/CENELEC as the EN 29000 Series. This movement imposes mandatory adoption of the EN 29000 Series into national standards by the 18 countries of the EC and EFTA. EQS is to develop agreed procedures for the assessment and certification to EN 29000 (EN being the European Norm). This will provide the basis for the confidence of purchasers that assessments and certifications carried out by different certification bodies within Europe, but in accordance with EQS procedures, are equivalent.

2.8 European standardisation

The elimination of technical barriers to trade has been recognised at the highest political level of the Community as a priority task in the programme for the completion of the Single European Market. European standardisation is being perceived as a tool by which to obtain the full economic benefits of this market. As well as being a means of eliminating technical barriers to trade, European standards are becoming an economic objective in their own right. One of the aims of CEN is 'the implementation of standardisation throughout Europe to facilitate the development of the exchange of goods and services, by the elimination of the barriers set by provisions of a technical nature'. Several thousand standards will be needed to fulfil the needs of the single market. There is little doubt that the rate of production of European standards by CEN is accelerating at a fast rate in response to this demand. As already mentioned in this chapter CEN is the European organisation responsible for the planning, drafting and adoption of these standards (with the exception of those pertaining to the two sectors of electrotechnology and telecommunications) through procedures which guarantee respect for the following principles:

- openness and transparency: all interested concerns take part in the work programme;
- consensus: standards are developed on the basis of voluntary agreement between the interested parties;
- National commitment: formal adoption of European Standards is decided by a majority vote of CEN National Members binding on all of them;
- Technical coherence at the European and national level: standards form a collection, which ensures its own continuity for the benefit of users.

The Commission and the European Standards Bodies, CEN, CENELEC and European Telecommunications Standards Institute (ETSI) have met and discussed the challenge and have agreed the following:

- the necessity of harmonizing national standards to facilitate the single market;
- the need to speed up the output of harmonized standards;
- the need for European industry to recognise the challenge and to contribute towards the standardisation effort required.

This has resulted in the EC Commission submitting a proposal in the form of a Green Paper on European Standardisation (1990), on the development of European Standardisation. The objectives of the Green paper are:

- to underline the strategic importance of European standardisation;
- to propose methods of accelerating the delivery of European standards;
- to stimulate debate on the most appropriate structure for European standardisation.

The proposals of the Green Paper are in three main areas covering industry, standardisation bodies and Member State authorities. The major areas of proposal are in relation to existing European and national standardisation bodies and they are reproduced below.

Industry

Industry must give the standardisation process a higher priority in its own strategic planning and resource allocation with specific reference to:

a) funding the infrastructure;
b) prioritisation of standards work;
c) provision of technical experts

Existing European and National Standardisation Bodies

There are seven major areas of proposal as follows:

a) improved efficiency measures in standards preparation including:

- initial external drafting;
- shorter public discussion periods;
- greater use of majority voting on drafts;
- allowing European standards to exist in their own right rather than needing to be adopted as national standards.

b) co-ordination and structure:

- a new European standardisation system is envisaged under the direction of a new European Standardisation Council;
- the composition of this Council would be drawn mainly from European industry;
- under the Council would be a European Standardisation Board which would manage and co-ordinate the system;
- the Board would be composed of representatives of European standardisation bodies (e.g. CEN, CENELEC);
- the European standardisation bodies would be recognised by the Council as being exclusive in their areas of defined competence subject to compliance with common rules;
- the possible creation of new European sectoral standardisation bodies with autonomy in standards activity;
- national standardisation bodies (e.g. BSI) would be recognised as being exclusively competent at national level.

c) membership and international co-operation:

- no new members should be accepted by CEN and CENELEC for the present;
- technical co-operation with non-member countries should be co-ordinated at a European level;
- greater emphasis should be given to the production of international standards for European use.

d) openness and visibility
European standardisation should be open to all interested parties to:

- participate directly in technical work;
- observe processes;
- be represented on management boards.

National standards work should be open to other appropriate European nationals.

e) finance
The new structures would be funded by the following main means:

- membership subscriptions;
- a proportion of revenue from the sale of European standards;
- contributions directly from European industry;
- EC funding for at least the first five years.

f) information:

- improved information flow is required;
- a new European standardisation database should be developed.

g) status of European standards:

- the visibility of European standards should be improved by the exclusive use of European reference numbers;
- a common mark of conformity with European standards is urged to replace national marks.

h) testing and certification:

- European standardisation bodies (e.g. CEN) should define their relationship to the European Organisation for Testing and Certification (EOTC) and transfer their certification agreements to it (details of the EOTC are given in Chapter 12).

Member state authorities

The new European standardisation system should be recognised in Community law and provision for Community funding established.

There is no doubt that adoption throughout Europe of the EN 29000 and EN 45000 Series of standards should facilitate bilateral and multilateral arrangements for mutual recognition of certification activities in different countries in order to reduce barriers to trade within the loose framework of the EOTC. Coherent sector arrangements are expected to take shape on the basis of agreements reached amongst testing and certification bodies in response to the needs of the market place, subject to minimal central control. The goal is to enable industry to secure the form of testing and certification needed for the European markets from one source, knowing that this will provide a passport to the whole of the EC/EFTA economic area. Moreover, since the criteria assisting mutual recognition – EN 29000 and EN 45000 – are based on international agreement, they should, in the longer term, facilitate the removal of barriers to trade worldwide.

In practice, it will still be most important to provide the means of assurance that the customer requires. Different customer attitudes and preferences, built up over generations, are likely to persist and customers in different countries will continue to look for the certificates and marks (e.g. IMQ, DIN, VDN, AFNOR) with which they are familiar.

2.9 Definitions and terminology

The following are some useful definitions and terms used in this chapter.

Accreditation: the formal recognition – against published criteria – of the competence and impartiality of a certification body.

Applicant (for certification): person or body that seeks to obtain a licence from a certification body.

Capability approval: the status given to a supplier for a range of items or services for which it has been shown that his declared design rules, manufacturing processes and quality systems are capable of producing items or services, the quality of which meets the specified requirements.

Certificate of conformance/conformity: a document signed by a qualified party affirming that, at the time of assessment, the product or service met the stated requirements.

Certification: the authoritative act of documenting compliance with requirements.

Certification body: an impartial body, governmental or non-governmental, possessing the necessary competence and integrity to operate a certification system, and on which the interests of parties concerned with the functioning of the system are represented.

Certification system: a system having its own rules of procedure and management for carrying out certification.

Mark of conformity (for certification): protected mark, applied or issued under the rules of a certification system, indicating that adequate confidence is provided that the reliant product, process or service is in conformity with a specific standard or other normative document.

Memorandum of understanding (MOU): mutual recognition between two parties of their respective accreditations.

National standards body: standards body recognised at the national level that is eligible to be the national member of the corresponding international and regional standards organisations.

Product approval: declaration by a body vested with the necessary authority by means of certificate or mark of conformity, that a product is in conformity with a set of published criteria.

Product conformity certification: the act of certifying by means of a certificate or mark of conformity that a product is in conformity with specific standards or technical specifications.

Quality management certification: the act of certifying by means of a certificate or mark of conformity that a supplier's quality management system is in conformity with specific quality requirements.

Quality system: the organisational structure, responsibilities, procedures, processes and resources for implementing quality management.

Specification: the document that prescribes the requirements with which the product or service has to conform.

Standard: the document established by consensus and approved by a recognised body, that provides, for common and repeated use, rules, guidelines or characteristics for activities or their results, aimed at the achievement of the optimum degree of order in a given context.

Standardisation: activity of establishing, with regard to actual or potential problems, provisions for common and repeated use, aimed at the achievement of the optimising degree of order in a given context.

Supplier: the party that is responsible for the product, process or service and is able to ensure that quality assurance is exercised. The definition may apply to manufacturers, distributors, importers, assemblers, service organisations, etc.

British Standards and other BSI and European standardisation material

Accreditation – what's in it for you? BSI Publication PP.2399/8610/SK/AB.

BS 0: 1991 *A standard for standards: Part 1: 1991 Guide to general principles for standardisation*; Part 2; 1991 *BSI committee procedures*; Part 3; 1991 *A standard for standards: Guide to Drafting and presentation of British Standards.*

BS 1743: 1968 (1991) *Methods for the analysis of dried milk and dried milk products* (ISO 1736: 1991).

BS 2564: 1955 *Control chart techniques when manufacturing to a specification, with special reference to articles machined to dimensional tolerances.*

BS 2846: *Guide to statistical interpretation of data* Part 1: 1991 *Routine analysis of quantitative data*; Part 2: 1981 (1985) *Estimation of the mean: confidence level* (ISO 2602: 1985); Part 3: 1975 (1985) *Determination of a statistical tolerance interval* (ISO 3207: 1985); Part 4: 1976 (1985)

Techniques of estimation and tests relating to means and variances (ISO 2854: 1985); Part 5: 1977 (1985) *Power of tests relating to means and variances* (ISO 3494: 1985); Part 6: 1976 (1983) *Comparison of two means in the case of paired observations* (ISO 3301: 1985), Part 7: 1984 *Tests for departure from normality* (ISO/DIS.5479: 1985).

BS 2987: 1958 *Notes on the application of statistics to paper testing.*

BS 3518: *Methods of fatigue testing* Part 5 1966 (1984) *Guide to the application of statistics.*

BS 4778: *Quality vocabulary* Part 1: 1987 *International terms* (ISO 8402: 1986) (EN 28402: 1991); Part 2: 1991 *Quality concepts and related definitions;* Part 3: 1991 *Availability, reliability and maintainability terms.*

BS 4891: 1972 *A guide to quality assurance.* (Now withdrawn)

BS 5233: 1986 *Glossary of terms used in metrology.*

BS 5309 *Methods for sampling chemical products* Part 1: 1976 *Introduction and general principles* (ISO 3165: 1976); Part 2: 1976 *Sampling of gases* (ISO 4257: 1976); Part 3: 1976 *Sampling of liquids;* Part 4: 1976 *Sampling of solids* (ISO 8213: 1976).

BS 5324: 1976 *Guide to the application of statistics to rubber testing.*

BS 5328: 1989 *Concrete* Part 1: 1991 *Guide to specifying concrete.*

BS 5381: 1986 *Methods for determination of physical properties to tobacco and tobacco products.*

BS 5497 Precision of test methods Part 1: 1987 *Guide to the determination of repeatability and reproducibility for a standard test method by interlaboratory test* (ISO 5725: 1987).

BS 5532 *Statistical terminology* Part 1: 1978 *Glossary of terms relating to probability and general terms relating to statistics* (ISO 3534: 1978); Part 3: 1986 *Glossary of terms relating to the design of experiments* (ISO 3534/3: 1986).

BS 5558: 1989 *Controllers with analogue signals for use in industrial process control.* Part 1: (1989) *Methods for evaluating performance* (IEC 546–1: 1989); Part 2: 1989 *Guide to inspection and routine testing.* (IEC 546–2: 1989).

BS 5694: 1979 *Method for measurement of non-linearity in resistors.* (IEC 440: 1979)

BS 5700: 1984 *Guide to process control using quality control chart methods and cusum techniques.*

BS 5701: 1980 *Guide to number defective charts for quality control.*

BS 5703: *Guide to data analysis and quality control using cusum techniques* Part 1: 1980 *Introduction to cusum charting.*

BS 5727: 1979 *Method for describing aircraft noise heard on the ground.* (ISO 3891: 1979).

BS 5750: 1987 *Quality systems;* Part 0: Section 0.1: 1987 *Principle concepts and applications – Guide to selection and use* (ISO 9000: 1987, EN 29000: 1987); Part 0: Section 0.2: 1987 *Principle con cepts and applications – Guide to quality management and quality system elements* (ISO 9004: 1987, EN 29004: 1987). Part 1: 1987 *Specification for design/development, production, installation and servicing* (ISO 9001: 1987, EN 29001: 1987); Part 2, 1987 *Specification for production and installation* (ISO 9002: 1987, EN 29002: 1987); Part 3: 1987 *Specification for final inspection and test* (ISO 9003: 1987, EN 29003: 1987); Part 4: 1990 *Guide to the use of BS 5750: Part 1 Specification for design/development, production, installation and servicing; Part 2 Specification for production and installation, Part 3 Specification for final inspection and test, Part 8: 1991 Guide to quality management and quality system elements to service (ISO 9004–2: 1991), Part 13: 1991 Guide to the application of BS.5750: Part 1 Guide to the development, supply and maintenance of software (ISO 9000–3: 1991), Part 14: 1993 Guide to dependability programme management (ISO 9000–4: 1993. IEC 3001: 1993).*

BS 5760: Reliability of systems, equipment, and components. Part 0: 1986 *Introductory guide to reliability;* Part 1: 1985 *Guide to reliability and maintainability programme management;* Part 2: 1981 *Guide to the assessment of reliability;* Part 3: 1982 *Guide to reliability practices: examples;* Part 4: 1986 *Guide to specification clauses relating to the achievement and development of reliability in new and existing items;* Part 5: 1991 *Guide to failure modes, effects and crticiality analysis (FMEA and FMECA);* Part 6: 1991 *Guide to programmes for reliability growth* (IEC 1014: 1989); Part 7: 1991 *Guide to fault tree analysis;* Part 9: 1992 *Guide to the block diagram technique* (IEC 1078: 1991); Part 10: 1993 *Guide to reliability testing,* Section 10.1 *General requirements* (IEC 605–1: 1978) and Section 10.3

Compliance test procedures for steady state availability (IEC 1970: 1991).

BS 5777: 1979 *Methods of test for verification of stability of pallet stackers and high lift platform trucks.* (ISO5766: 1979)

BS 5781: *Quality assurance requirements for measuring equipment.* Part 1: 1992 *Metrological confirmation system for measuring equipment* (ISO 10012–1: 1992).

BS 6000: 1972 *Guide to the use of BS 6001* (ISO 2859: 1972/Addendum 1).

BS 6001: *Sampling procedures for inspection by attributes.* Part 1: 1991 *Specification for sampling plans indexed by acceptable quality level (AQL) for lot-by-lot inspection* (ISO 2859–1: 1989); Part 2: 1993 *Specification for sampling plans indexed by limiting quality (LQ) for isolated lot inspection* (ISO 2859–2: 1985); Part 3: 1993 *Specification for skip-lot procedures.* (ISO/DIS2859–3: 1986).

BS 6002: 1979 *Sampling procedures and charts for inspection by variables* (ISO 3951: 1979).

BS 6143 *Guide to the economics of quality* Part 1: 1992 *Process cost model;* Part 2: 1990 *Prevention, appraisal and failure model.*

BS 7511: 1989 *General criteria for certification bodies operating product certification* (ISO/IEC guides 28 and 40) (EN 45011: 1989).

BS 7512: 1989 *General criteria for certification bodies operating quality system certification* (ISO/IEC guides 40 and 48) (EN 45012: 1989).

BS 7513: 1989 *General criteria for certification bodies operating certification of personnel* (ISO/IEC Guide 40) (EN 45013: 1989)

BS 7750: 1992 *Specification for environmental management systems*

BS 7850: 1992 *Total quality management* Part 1: *Guide to management principles;* Part 2 *Guide to quality improvement methods.*

BS 9000: *General requirements for a system for electronic components of assessed quality.* Part 1: 1989 (CECC 00111: 1989) *Specification for general procedures;* Part 2: 1983 *Specification for national implementation of CECC basic rules and rules of procedure* (CECC 00107: 1983); Part 3: 1987 *Specification for national implementation of IECQ basic rules and rules of procedure* (QC 101001, QC 001002: 1987); Part 4: 1989 *Specification of procedures for the approval and conformance testing procedures* (CEEC 00107: Part 1: 1989); Part 5: 1989 *Specification of qualification approval and conformance testing procedures* (CECC 00107: Part 1: 1989); Part 6: 1989 *Specification of capability approval procedures* (CECC 00107: Part III: 1989) Part 7: 1989 *Specification of lot formation, release procedures and certified test records* (CECC 00109: 1989); Part 8: 1989 *Drafting requirements.*

BSI Handbook 22, Part 1: 1992 *Quality Assurance;* Part 2: 1992 *Reliability and Maintainability.*

BSI *Annual Reports.*

BSI *Introduction and Response to the Green Paper on European Standardisation* (Com(90) 456 Final), October 1990.

BSI *News.*

BSI *Sales Bulletins.*

BSI *Standards Catalogue.*

BSI *Standards – Working with Industry.*

BSI *Today.*

PD 3542: 1991 *The role of standards in company quality management.*

PD 6489: 1987 *Guide to the preparation of a company standards manual.*

PD 6495: 1986, IFAN-Guide 1, *Method for Determining the Advantages of (Company) Standardisation Projects.*

PD 6515: 1986 IFAN – Guide 2, *Company use of international standards.*

PD 6538: 1993 *Vision 2000 A strategy for international standards' implementation in the quality arena during the 1990s*

Systems for the registration of firms of assessed capability – assessment and registration, PAD 900044, Issue 5, May 1985.

The way to capture new markets: a guide to BSI quality assurance services.

Why are standards important? BSI STANDARDLINE.

CEN, Annual Report 1991, European Committee for standardisation, Brussels.

CEN: Setting Europe's New Standards, 1991, European Committee for standardisation.

National Accreditation for Certification Bodies, 1992. *Briefing Pack – Criteria of Competence, prospectus, rules of procedure, etc., NACCB, London.*

References

Cardew T. 'Putting quality into FMS.' *Quality Today,* October, pp 20–1, 1986.

Dale B G and Plunkett J J. *A study of audits, inspection and quality costs in the pressure vessel fabrication sector of the process plant industry*, Proceedings of the Institution of Mechanical Engineers. 198 (B2), pp 45–54, 1984.

Department of Trade and Industry. *Standards, quality and international competitiveness*. Cmnd 8621, HMSO, 1982.

Department of Trade and Industry. *Register of Quality Assessed United Kingdom Companies*, HMSO (updated regularly).

Lascelles D M and Dale B G. 'A study of the quality management methods employed by UK automotive suppliers', *Quality and Reliability Engineering International*. 4(4) pp 301–9, 1988.

Woodward C D. *BSI: the story of standards*. Gaylard and Son Ltd, London, UK, 1972.

CHAPTER 3

Organising for quality

3.1 Introduction

The general pattern of events from conception of a product or service to fulfilment of a customer's need is similar for most organisations. Any differences which occur are usually due to size, complexity, the particular nature of the business, audits, processes and the degree of assurance in the satisfactory completion of one activity prior to initiating the next. In general:

- The need has to be recognised and stated, and all relevant features, parameters and characteristics and their criteria specified, defined and communicated to those concerned, or otherwise published;
- In a contractual environment the needs are specified, whereas in other environments implied needs should be identified and defined. In many instances, needs can change with time; this implies periodic revision of specifications;
- The means by which the need is satisfied by the service or the product, together with all relevant features, parameters and characteristics and their criteria have to be devised, proposed and their feasibility demonstrated. Needs may include aspects of usability, safety, availability, reliability, maintainability, economics and environment;
- The arrangement or the contract for the supply of the service or the product, and any associated requirements, have to be devised, established and communicated;
- The ways and means by which a service is to be given, or a product is to be manufactured and supplied, and by which quality is to be ensured and verified, have to be devised, established, communicated, provided, maintained and applied;
- The methods by which the service or product are to be used and maintained for the continuance and verification of quality, have to be devised, established and communicated.

The success of any activity depends on:

- having the defined aims or needs;
- having, at the right time and place, defined and adequate resources (for example, capital, information, methods, materials, personnel, tools, handling and measuring equipment and the environment) to enable the activity to be carried out and its effectiveness to be verified;
- having adequate and defined facilities (for example, management, organisation, programming and analysis) to enable the activities to be carried out smoothly and efficiently;
- the defined use of all such resources and facilities.

The success of any organisation directed to the fulfilment of a need, depends on the collective and individual success of its several activities and functions, and the way in which these are organised. All these activities, and the functions and personnel engaged in them are directly or indirectly concerned with the attainment of meeting the customers' quality requirements. Therefore, in order to be successful, an organisation must offer products and services that:

- meet a well-defined need, use or purpose;
- satisfy and, if possible, exceed customers' expectations;
- comply with appropriate standards and specifications;
- comply with statutory legislation and other requirements of society;
- are made available – at competitive prices;
- are provided at a cost which will yield a profit.

In order to meet its objectives and be successful, a company needs to organise itself in such a way that the technical, administrative and human factors affecting the quality of its products and services will be under control. This control should be orientated towards the reduction, elimination and, most importantly, prevention of quality deficiencies.

This chapter explores the main issues in organising for quality. Some of these issues will be developed and discussed in more detail in subsequent chapters.

3.2 Objectives and strategy

As an organisation grows in size and divides it becomes possible for different departments to pursue their own objectives, which may not necessarily aid the overall objectives of the organisation in satisfying the quality requirements of its external customers. To prevent this from happening, it is necessary for an organisation's senior management team to have a long-range management vision and mission for product and service quality (see Table 3.1), and to define a set of corporate objectives and guiding principles. The objectives of an organisation may include customer satisfaction, business objectives such as growth, profit or market position, or the provision of services to the community, but they should always be compatible with the requirements of society whether legislated or as perceived by the organisation. The precise definition of these objectives must be closely linked with the market where the need has to be satisfied. Thus, a knowledge of the market with regard to quality, quantity, time, costs and competition is required before taking essential basic decisions. With respect to the mission statement for a total organisation it is usually concise and is communicated to every employee. Parts of an organisation may also declare their aims but these will be more detailed and specific while still supporting the overall objective.

Table 3.1 Mission Statement and Quality Policy

OUR MISSION STATEMENT

Our mission is to maintain our leadership in liquid food technology by providing the most economic packaging and processing systems with the least environmental impact for the safe and convenient distribution of liquid foods.

By these means we will maximise the volume of liquid food products processed and packed using Tetra Pak systems.

OUR QUALITY POLICY

Through our Total Quality concept, we are committed to quality in everything we do and everything we supply.

We have to give our Customers full satisfaction and the best products and services.

We recognise that we must continuously improve to maintain our Company's leading position and to assure the future of our staff, their families and the Company.

Source: Tetra Pak Systems

Management should ensure that the corporate objectives are brought to the attention of all personnel concerned for their implementation. This may be done in the form of a quality policy (see Table 3.1). Once the overall objectives of an organisation have been formulated, it is necessary to develop a corporate strategy in order to achieve the set objectives.

For the corporate quality policy, management should define objectives pertaining to the key elements of quality, such as fitness for use, grade of service to be provided, performance, safety and reliability. The calculation and evaluation of costs associated with all quality elements and objectives should always be an important consideration, with the objective of minimising quality losses. The quality policy, which must be authorised by the senior management team, forms one element of the corporate policy. This statement should be communicated and published throughout the organisation and be seen to be supported by management. All employees should be trained so that they understand the corporate and quality objectives and the commitment required to achieve these objectives. Management should also take the necessary steps to ensure that new employees are trained and that customers and suppliers are made aware of this policy.

Using overall corporate objectives as the starting point, each functional area (for example, production, personnel, quality, finance, purchasing) should then be in a position to articulate its departmental objectives and strategy to ensure that corporate objectives are met and that the objectives of individual departments are not in conflict. In doing this, appropriate levels of management and their staff, should define specialised quality improvement objectives and targets consistent with corporate quality policy, as well as with other corporate objectives. The ideal situation is that each person in the organisation is involved in the deployment of corporate policy from which they have clearly defined improvement objectives and targets. Quality policy deployment is a key element in the quality improvement process and all organisations should ensure that it is practised in an efficient manner.

As mentioned above the realisation of a quality policy requires the identification of primary goals for establishing quality objectives. For example, primary goals in a service situation should include:

- customer satisfaction consistent with professional standards and ethics;
- continuous improvement of the service;
- giving consideration to the requirements of society and the environment;
- efficiency in providing the service.

Management should translate these primary goals into a set of quality objectives and activities. Examples of these are:

- clear definition of customer needs with appropriate quality measures;
- preventive action and controls to avoid customer dissatisfaction;
- optimizing quality-related costs for the required performance and grade of service;
- creation of a collective commitment to quality within the service organisation;
- continuous review of service requirements and achievements to identify opportunities for service quality improvement;
- prevention of adverse effects by the service organisation on society and the environment.

An organisation should seek to accomplish the following three objectives with regard to quality:

- achieve and sustain the quality of the product or service produced so as to meet continually the purchaser's stated or implied needs;
- provide confidence to its own management that the intended quality is being achieved and sustained;
- provide confidence to the purchaser that the intended quality is being, or will be, achieved in the delivered product or service provided. When contractually required, this provision of confidence may involve agreed demonstrated requirements.

Management should provide sufficient and appropriate resources essential to the implementation of quality policies and the achievement of quality objectives. These resources may include:

- human resources and specialized skills;
- design and development equipment;
- manufacturing or operations equipment;
- inspection, test and measurement equipment;
- instrumentation and computer software.

They should also determine the level of

competence, experience and training necessary to ensure the capability of personnel. In order to allocate company resources on a planned and timely basis, quality factors affecting market position and objectives relative to new products, processes or services (including new technologies) must be identified. This activity should include benchmarking in one of its forms – internal, generic or competitive. Programmes and schedules covering these resources and skills should be consistent with the company's overall objectives.

3.3 Organisational aspects relating to the management of quality

Quality management involves the ongoing, incremental improvement of an organisation's processes. This invariably creates a need to continually review the appropriateness of the business organisational structures and change them where necessary. Changes in the following areas may be necessary:

- management processes, such as reward, payment, recognition and strategic planning;
- methods of resource allocation;
- administrative processes, such as secretarial, clerical and purchasing;
- building an environment of mutual trust and collaboration for continuous improvement;
- planned training for all;
- work processes and procedures.

The quality system should be organised in such a way that adequate and continuous control is exercised over all activities affecting quality. The organisational structure pertaining to the quality system should be clearly established within the overall management of a company, with lines of authority and communication clearly defined. The following are typical organisational aspects which need to be considered in allocating quality responsibility and authority.

- All the activities contributing to quality, whether directly or indirectly, should be identified and their rôle documented.
- General and specific quality responsibilities should be defined.
- Responsibility and authority delegated to each activity contributing to product and service quality should be clearly established.
- A management representative, preferably independent of other functions, should be appointed with authority to resolve matters pertaining to quality. This should not be construed as meaning that a quality assurance manager and the quality department are responsible for an organisation achieving its quality objectives. One department alone cannot satisfy the overall quality requirements and objectives, and many other departments in an organisation contribute to its quality efforts. 'Quality is the responsibility of each and every individual in an organisation' is useful in stressing this point.
- Interface control and co-ordination measures between different activities should be defined.
- Emphasis should be placed on the identification of actual or potential quality problems and the initiation of remedial or preventive measures.

The importance of various aspects of organisational structure to the effectiveness of quality is indicated by many contributors to the literature. Analysis of such literature reveals that there are many schools of thought concerning the basic types of organisational hierarchy necessary to achieve a company's desired quality objectives. Although case studies of similar organisations can provide useful information, it is dangerous to imagine that success stories are universally applicable, as organisational culture operating conditions, environments, people, history, company folklore, products and processes are rarely exactly comparable. In making use of these types of comparisons, management needs to appreciate fully the critical nature of some of the differing factors involved and to decide what reliance can be placed upon assumptions made and specialised techniques used.

There are dangers in making superficial comparisons between organisation charts and lines of responsibility because there are often inconsistencies between companies, the types of staff included in various quality groups, definitions of quality assurance systems and quality functions, terms used to describe quality control, quality and quality management, and understanding of the concept of TQM and continuous incremental quality improvement.

Dale and Plunkett (1984) reporting on studies which they carried out in 12 fabrication companies found that there were many variations in the way in which companies organise themselves for quality assurance and quality control. It was pointed out that the differences they found were so great that no useful conclusion could be drawn from an analysis of the various aspects of an organisation's structure to the effectiveness of quality assurance, other than that there are many routes to the same objectives. They did, however, find the following features which were common to most organisations:

- Quality control managers usually report to a director or senior manager responsible for production operations, but have direct access to higher authority;
- Where quality assurance and quality control are within the same department, it is common for quality control staff to report administratively to the production or operations function;
- Quality assurance managers and departments usually respond to a director or senior manager not directly responsible for production/operations;
- In some cases it is only inspectors who report administratively to the production or operations manager; non-destructive testing and other similar services report to technical or engineering managers.

In any discussion on the subject of organising for quality it should always be remembered that the responsibility for producing goods to specification rests primarily with the production/operations department. Quality cannot be inspected into a product, it must first be designed and then be manufactured into it. In some organisations, the inspection activity is the responsibility of the production/operations function, with only audit inspectors reporting to the quality assurance department, as is the case in a number of Japanese organisations. In other organisations, the complete inspection function is the responsibility of the quality assurance department. In operating to certain contracts it is sometimes a stipulation that the contractor's inspection department shall not be under the control of the production/manufacturing executive. It should also be noted that it is not the inspector's function to apply his or her own standards but to work to unambiguous specifications and company standards. Should such specifications be available and proper systems evolved this can lead to increased operator control, with the inspection and or quality assurance department being concerned mainly with monitoring checks, carrying out audits and providing advice. Whatever the approach adopted, the main aim should be one of integration, with the involvement, wherever possible, of the inspection and the quality assurance department activities with production or operations.

The concept of TQM involves everyone in an organisation being devoted to satisfying their customer needs and continuously improving their part of the process. Therefore, individual department managers need to take the lead and become responsible for the execution of matters pertaining to quality improvement in their particular chain of command. However, a quality assurance manager should advise and assist on all quality tasks, and monitor and co-ordinate them throughout an organisation wherever possible. The following activities are likely to be facilitated and/or co-ordinated by the quality assurance manager:

- developing the quality system;
- developing and applying quality assurance and quality control techniques;
- promoting quality improvement activities;
- co-ordinating quality improvement activities;
- planning for quality;
- developing the quality manual;

- metrology and test equipment calibration;
- applying metrology and statistical methods, to the analysis of quality parameters for both control and improvement purposes;
- developing and analysis of testing, inspection and sampling procedures;
- defect/error/failure analysis;
- auditing of the quality system to permit identification and correction of deficiencies;
- quality cost measurement and its analysis;
- advising on matters pertaining to the process of quality improvement and TQM.

In addition, a quality assurance manager might be required to carry out the training of staff throughout the company in matters relating to quality improvement and TQM, or to co-ordinate such training schemes.

It is the task of the senior management team to persuade personnel to have the correct attitudes towards quality, to behave in a manner which is not always the easiest in the short-term, and to remember that prevention is less costly than detection and cure. It is often claimed by management that their people have not got the time to get it right the first time, but the organisation commits considerable resources and effort to rectification, retesting and reinspecting the second, and even the third, time. The overall responsibility for TQM and quality improvement rests with the chief executive and it is vital that they are good role models.

3.4 Organising for quality improvement

An effective organisation for quality improvement identifies opportunities for improvement both vertically within the organisational hierarchy and horizontally in the processes that flow across organisation boundaries. Some of the points touched upon in relation to improvement in the previous discussion are now developed.

Within the organisational hierarchy responsibilities for quality improvement include the following:

- management processes of the organisation such as defining the mission of the organisation, clarifying roles and responsibilities, acquiring and assigning resources, providing education and training, strategic planning and recognition;
- work processes of the organisation;
- measurement and tracking of reduction of quality costs;
- administrative support processes such as secretarial, budgeting and purchasing;
- building and maintenance of an environment that empowers, enables and charges all members of the organisation to continuously improve quality.

Within the processes that flow across organisational boundaries, responsibilities for quality improvement include the following:

- defining and agreeing the purpose of each process and its relationship with the objectives of the organisation;
- establishing and maintaining communication among departments;
- identifying both internal and external customers of the process and determining their needs and expectations;
- identifying suppliers to the process and customers communicating to them their needs and expectations;
- searching for process improvement opportunities, allocating resources for improvement and overseeing implementation of these improvements.

An organisation for quality improvement should address the following methods:

- providing policy, strategy, major quality improvement goals, overall guidance, support and broad co-ordination of the organisation's quality improvement activities;
- establishing plans for improvement of product, service or process quality, safety, environmental impact dependability and customer satisfaction at all levels;
- identifying cross-functional quality improvement needs and goals and assigning resources to pursue them;

- identifying measures of performance of individuals or teams involved in each process related, where possible, to internal or external customer satisfaction;
- pursuit of quality improvement goals by team projects within their areas of direct responsibilities and authorities;
- encouraging every member of the organisation to pursue quality improvement activities related to their work and co-ordinating these activities;
- ensuring that all the plans, targets and measures throughout the organisation complement each other and reflect the overall objectives of the individual process targets and overall objectives of the mission statement;
- reviewing the results of improvement plans to obtain a measure of their effectiveness.

3.5 Quality-related decision making

The senior management team are ultimately responsible for making balanced judgements on issues relating to TQM and continuous improvement, assessing the significance of variations in relation to this, and making decisions. In arriving at such decisions the calibre and personal integrity of staff are of fundamental importance and management should ensure that each person in the organisation understands that quality is important to their future and that of the company, knows how they can assist in the achievement of product and service quality, and is stimulated and encouraged to do so.

In most manufacturing companies, quality-related decision making is a complicated affair and is dependent on a number of factors including: company size, the number of decisions made (as more decisions are made the scope or area of flexibility decreases and, consequently, the number of mistakes which may be remedied also decreases), strategy and objectives, and on the allocation of quality responsibility and authority within the organisation structure.

There is no shortage of written material on the subject of decision making, however, there is a dearth of information relating this to the area of quality. Among the best material is the research of Duncalf (1986) who carried out a number of studies to investigate the ways in which quality-related decisions are made. The main findings of this piece of work have been reported and include the following:

> The majority of senior managers had a limited appreciation of their rôle in formulating and communicating a corporate policy on quality management. Many of them did not recognise the influence of their leadership style on the attitude of middle and supervisory staff in accepting that the management of quality is a critical activity in their managerial rôle. To achieve successful implementation of their quality policy, senior managers should examine the following factors:
>
> - the attitudes and motivations of management, supervision and operatives;
> - the availability of adequate quality education and training programmes for all employees;
> - the design and operation of the quality structure;
> - the authorities and decision making on all quality-related activities;
> - the methods used to communicate policy;
> - the existing quality management information system.
>
> The rôle of quality staff in the range of quality-related decision making activities varied from company to company. In the more enlightened companies, quality staff played a more positive role in providing information and expertise. Senior managers should ensure that the role of the individual responsible for quality is clearly identified to people in other functional areas, this is particularly important in small companies. The findings also showed the complexity and multi-faceted nature of the quality-related decision making process. In most companies studied, the decision process and decision making unit were not formally organised and the participants were difficult to identify. Few companies exhibited the ability to effectively co-ordinate the many functions, levels and stages of decision making on quality management activities. This is demonstrated by the failure of companies to provide clear interrelated activities which provide for key decisions on quality to be made with quality improvement as the central focus. Despite the fact that quality problems are often inter-departmental, companies do not always identify specific quality-related activities, and this has

> resulted in none or limited participation of some functional managers in decision processes aimed at improving the quality of the product. Few of the companies studied had formal quality information systems which ensured that processes, procedures and decision making were carried out with the best, up-to-date information available. Feedback from the marketplace and/or via the customer was often processed in an informal and inadequate manner. In many decisions it was impossible to identify the precise route of this information in its circulation within an organisation.
>
> (Duncalf and Dale, 1988)

3.6 Planning for quality

Management should establish and maintain a continuous process for quality improvement which is planned and developed in conjunction with other functions such as research and development, marketing and production engineering, and which is capable of being effectively and progressively reviewed. Planning and establishing the processes form the link between the functional necessities of market demand and the technical and economic possibilities of supply are the means by which quality is built into the design and production processes and are fundamental to meeting customer requirements. Processes should define the system of management necessary for quality and indicate the intended proceedings for conceptual design through to post-delivery services, including education, training, motivation and costing procedures. The need for quality to be defined effectively, in order to give adequate confidence of achievement, either in terms that are agreed contractually with an individual purchaser or as judged to be required by the general market, is of paramount importance.

Quality planning is often carried out by an organisation in conjunction with its customer. The planning can help to form a basis for the subsequent development of:

- functional specifications;
- product specifications and/or designs;
- manufacturing/operational specifications/instructions;
- quality manuals and plans;
- review and evaluation procedures.

Nissan use the term 'pre-production quality assurance' (PPQA) to describe the action to promote effective planning and development. They describe it as:

> Pre-Production Quality Assurance is a project management activity designed to take a proactive approach to product and process development and based on the principle of defect prevention as opposed to defect detection.
>
> The activities to which PPQA is directed include:
>
> - newly-designed parts and materials for new vehicles;
> - newly ordered parts and materials for localisation programme;
> - parts and materials specifically designated by Nissan Quality Assurance Department.
>
> PPQA is a Total Quality activity in which ALL departments have an input.
>
> The PPQA system has been developed to coordinate the seven main activities of:
>
> - definition of project timing and responsibilities;
> - preparatory analysis (FMEA);
> - establishment of gauging requirements;
> - design validation and process confirmation testing;
> - establishment of part assurance method;
> - establishment of process assurance method;
> - process capability analysis.
>
> (Nissan Motor Manufacturing (UK) Ltd. 1991).

One of the main objectives of planning is to identify any special or unusual contingencies or requirements. If such requirements are found there is often a need for feasibility studies and planning to be undertaken to ensure the provision of appropriate resources. In such cases, planning should precede the initiation of the appropriate operations and provide for reviews to assure compatibility between the programme requirements and affected manufacturing operations, processes and techniques. Quality planning encourages the building of quality into the design and manufacturing or operations processes. It is important that mistake proofing is considered in the design and production preparation phases (see Shingo, 1986, for details of mistake proofing).

Management should conduct, during the earliest practicable phase of the design/ specification development, a sufficiently extensive review of target specification requirements to ensure:

- the timely identification and acquisition of any controls, processes, inspection and testing equipment, fixtures, tooling and skills of personnel that may be needed to ensure product and service quality;
- the updating of inspection and testing techniques, including the development of new instrumentation and calibration of existing equipment;
- the compatibility of manufacturing and inspection procedures and applicable documentation, before any production or operation is commenced;
- the deployment of appropriate resources for the design and production of the product or service;
- that feedback of data is adequate to optimise results and minimise costs.

It is often a requirement of major customers that suppliers use quality planning techniques in order to pursue an approach of prevention to quality management. For example, Section 2 of the Ford Motor Company's *Worldwide Quality System Standard Q-101* outlines their quality system evidence requirements of producers in planning for quality and is reproduced in Table 3.2. Ford make the point that 'quality planning is the cornerstone of defect prevention and continuous improvement', and outline their requirements as follows:

> Quality planning is required in the following situations:
>
> - during the development of new processes and products;
> - prior to changes in processes and products;
> - when reacting to processes or products with quality concerns;
> - before tooling is transferred to new producers or new plants;
> - prior to process or product changes affecting vehicle safety or compliance with regulations.
>
> Ford requires producers to have evidence of the use of the following defect prevention techniques prior to production launch. Producers should implement defect prevention methods at the earliest practical occasion in the new product development cycle.
>
> Producers should convene internal cross-functional teams for launches of new/changed products. These teams will use the quality planning techniques and will be active throughout the development and launch phases. The teams should typically include: the design, manufacturing and quality engineers; production; purchasing; other personnel; and for outside suppliers may include Ford purchasing, quality and product engineering personnel.
>
> (Ford Motor Company, 1990)

Ford have produced a detailed guide on planning for quality (Ford Motor Company, 1990) to assist producers. The quality planning process is shown in the flow chart in Figure 3.1.

Table 3.2 Planning for quality

1	Flow charts of production processes.
2	Feasibility assessments for proposed new products, changes in processes and products, and major volume changes.
3	FMEAs for processes and for design when the producer is responsible for the design.
4	Control plans.
5	Quality planning for gauging, measuring and testing equipment.
6	Preliminary process capability studies.
7	Written process monitoring and control instructions.
8	Appropriate packaging to protect the product.
9	Initial sample evaluation, documentation and certification.
10	Use data from prototype fabrication in quality planning.
11	A system to monitor and control sub-supplier quality.
12	Plans for maintaining on-going quality.

Source: *Worldwide Quality Systems Standard Q–101,* Ford Motor Company.

3.7 Quality plans

For projects relating to new products, services or processes, written *quality plans* (sometimes called *control plans*) consistent with all other requirements of a company's quality system should be prepared as appropriate. They are a pre-production or pre-operation requirement and are intended to summarise the quality

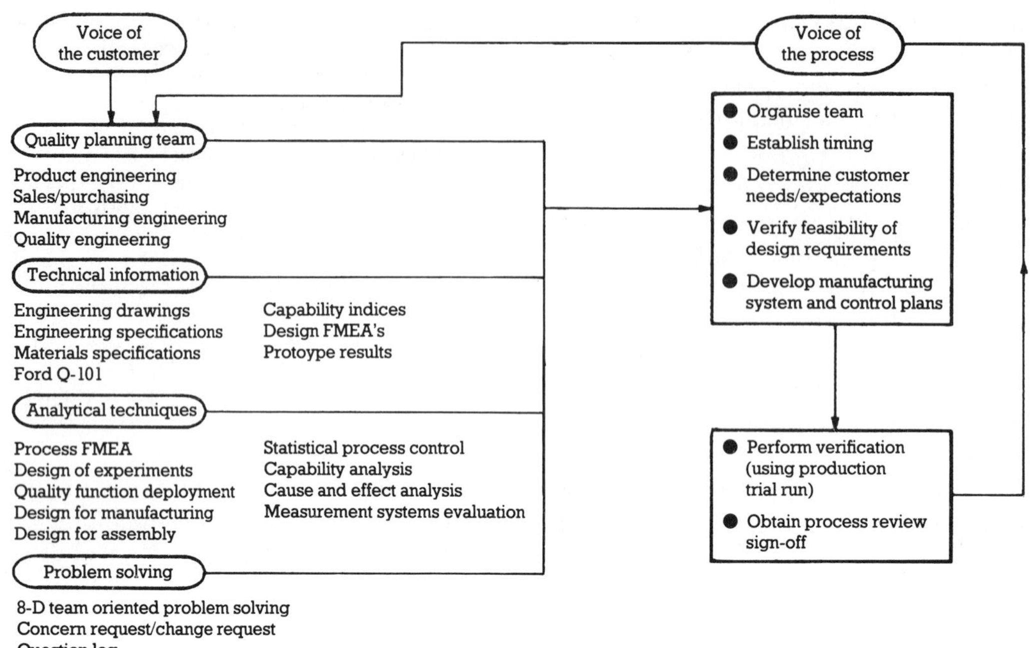

Figure 3.1 Ford Motor Company quality planning process

Source: *Planning for Quality*, Ford Motor Company, 1990.

planning for the ongoing quality assurance for a specific service, part or group of parts. The plan identifies those key elements in the product or service necessary to provide fitness for purpose and the means by which they are to be measured and provided. Quality plans should define:

- the quality objectives to be attained, expressed in measurable terms whenever possible;
- the specific allocation of responsibility and authority during the different phases of the project, including reviews and tests, configuration management and change control and defect control and corrective action;
- defined input and output criteria for each development phase;
- the specific procedure, methods, sequence of activities and work instructions to be applied;
- suitable testing, inspection, verification, examination and validation and audit programmes at appropriate stages (for example, design, development);
- a method for changes and modifications in a quality plan as projects proceed;
- other measures necessary to meet objectives.

An example of a quality or control plan is shown in Appendix B.

Suppliers are often required to submit control plans to their customers. For example, most automotive suppliers are required to prepare a control plan to summarise the quality planning for control item parts (parts which can affect either compliance with government regulations or safe vehicle operation) and they are strongly recommended for all other parts. The plans are required to include references to the statistical studies that will be conducted prior to the start-up of volume production and for control of ongoing production. The major motor companies now require that suppliers forward their control plans to their purchasing departments in advance of the initial sample review to permit review by their supplier quality assurance activities.

3.8 Principles of control

All control requires the establishment of a standard for the means of comparison, the assessment of conformity with the standard and the application of suitable corrective action where necessary. The general pattern of events is similar in all applications of quality assurance and any differences are due to the size and nature of the business. They include:

- an assessment of measurement of the quality of a product or service, carried out by comparison with established criteria or standards;
- the acceptance of the product or service, if deemed satisfactory;
- the rejection of the product or service, if considered to be unsatisfactory;
- a review of rejected products or services to determine the causes of failure and sources of error, and to recommend suitable corrective action and the implementation of countermeasures to: the product or the service, the resources, the facilities, the processes and the design which led to the unsatisfactory product or service;
- action, as necessary and as deemed suitable, to bring the quality of the product or service up to that required;
- verification that the recommended and applied action has fulfilled its aim.

The success of quality assurance depends on having an adequate system, organised and managed to ensure that all proper information, resources and facilities are provided and are properly used, and that all activities are carried out in an economic, efficient and effective manner.

3.9 Preparation of specifications

The purpose of a specification is to convey information; the ease with which this is achieved will be influenced by the style of presentation. Specifications are used for a variety of purposes (e.g. technical, commercial and legal). They must be used to describe the required attributes, so that product/service design can be initiated, the materials, dimensions and procedures used during the manufacturing process or the activities necessary to maintain, inspect, test, accept, install, use and dispose of a product or service.

Specifications can be written on a variety of subjects and with a variety of objectives (see Table 3.3). The content of a specification depends on the objectives to be achieved and these may be to give guidance, to list requirements, to educate, to inform or to instruct. Establishing the objectives should be the first task in the preparation of a specification.

Table 3.3 Some specification definitions

Target specification: the document that describes the primary purpose of an item and gives the essential guidance concerning such matters as its style, grade, performance, appearance, conditions of use (including health and safety considerations), characteristics, packaging, conformity, reliability and maintenance.

Functional specifications: the document that describes in detail the characteristics of the product with regard to its intended capability.

Material specification: the document that describes in detail the materials, components, or supplies used in manufacturing the item.

Product specification: the document that describes, for manufacturing purposes, the item concerned.

Acceptance specification: the document that describes in detail the criteria for acceptance of the product.

Inspection specification: the document that describes in detail the methods of inspection including, if necessary, the basis for consequent action.

(*cont.*)

Table 3.3 Some specification definitions (*cont.*)

Process specification
(a) *for discrete items*: the document that describes in detail the methods of assembling or producing the item.

(b) *for bulk commodities*: the document that describes in detail the procedures and operations to be carried out on the materials used.

(c) *for plant*: the document that describes the control of facilities used in a treatment or sequence of treatments of the item or commodity.

Test specification: the document that describes in detail the methods of conducting tests including, if necessary, the criteria for assessing the result.

Handling and packaging specifications: the document that describes in detail those requirements necessary to ensure that the product can be transported during and after manufacture with adequate protection from the environment.

Installation specification: the document that describes in detail the procedure for installing the product including, if necessary, the procedure for unpacking and preparation prior to installation.

Operational specification: the document that describes in detail the method of bringing into use, operating, controlling and adjusting the product.

Maintenance specification: the document that describes in detail the requirements of corrective and preventive procedures to maintain the product during its useful life. It may specify materials to be used and the periodic timing of activities.

Disposal specification: the document that describes in detail the method and precautions to be observed in discarding or otherwise disposing of the product when it has failed or is no longer required for any reason.

Source: BS 7373: 1991

There are numerous types of specifications and each serves a different purpose. The content of each may be different. However, the manner in which the information is ordered and described should, where possible, follow a similar pattern. For this reason it is recommended that planning takes place before work starts on the preparation of the specification, including the following:

- establish the operations of the specification and identify prospective users;
- establish whether specifications exist that contain the same information;
- set out a format for the specification, which should include the structure of all clauses.

In general, specifications fall into one of two categories: descriptive or requirement. A descriptive specification is a statement of attributes of a product, process or service that describes the subject so that prospective users can establish its fitness for their use. A requirement specification is a statement of attributes of a product, process or service in a form that provides for objective determination of conformity.

The content of a specification can be classified into three groups: performance, location and operation, as shown in Table 3.4. Table 3.5 shows the basic specification types. BS 7372 (1991) gives useful guidance on the layout and preparation of specifications and describes systems for their management.

3.10 Documentation

All the elements, requirements and provisions adopted by a company for the management of quality should be documented in a systematic and orderly manner in the form of written policies and procedures. It is management's responsibility to establish and maintain control of all appropriate documentation (including drawings, procedures for the control of quality, specifications, manufacturing procedures, process control methods, engineering change control, concessions and deviation procedures, and traceability) essential to the accomplishment of work at the design, production, inspection, delivery and post-delivery phase. Work instructions should also be developed

Table 3.4 Specification: breakdown of some elements

Performance		
Function	Material	Availability
Strength Speed Capacity Shape Size Scope Range	Hardness Texture Colour Appearance Weight Impurities (other physical properties)	Reliability Maintainability
Location		
Environment	Ergonomics	Interface
Temperature Humidity Vibration Shock Radiation Pressure Corrosion	Size Noise Weight Shock Illumination	Compatibility Size Shape Interchangeability
Operation		
Training	Safety	Timing
Skills Staff Selection Language Education	Health Equipment Custom Culture	Sequence Range Scope

Source: BS 7373: 1991

and maintained to prescribe the performance of all work. The written instructions should not only be created and brought to a satisfactory state and put into use, but should also be subject to continuing evaluation for effectiveness and adjusted as necessary. They provide a basis for control, evaluation and review, and without them differences in policy and procedures can arise and variations in practice may occur, which would undoubtedly result in confusion and uncertainty. Moreover, they provide the means for training in the work to be done, and for delegating authority and responsibility.

Adequate records also need to be kept and retained in order to demonstrate the effective operation of the quality system employed and to provide objective evidence of product or service quality. For example, the Ford Motor Company in their Q-101 Quality System Standard (1990) require their suppliers to retain the quality records for certain periods as shown in Table 3.6.

All changes to documentation need to be in writing and processed in a manner which would ensure prompt action at the specified effective point, indicating whether the modifications are retrospective, immediate or to be carried out at some later date. A record should be kept of changes as they are made. Provision should be made for the prompt

Table 3.5 Elements to be considered when writing some types of specification

Elements	Type of specification								
	Product	Manufacturing	Build	Test	Installation	Maintenance	Despatch	Disposal	General services
Performance									
Function	•			•					•
Material	•	•	•		•	•		•	
Availability	•					•	•	•	•
Location									
Ergonomics	•	•	•	•	•	•	•		•
Environment	•	•	•	•	•	•	•		
Interface	•		•		•	•	•		•
Operation									
Training		•	•	•	•	•		•	•
Safety		•	•	•	•	•	•	•	•
Timing		•	•	•	•	•	•	•	•

Source: BS 7373: 1991

removal of obsolete documents from all points of issue and use.

Table 3.6 Quality system evidence requirements

Quality system and performance records
The producer must keep adequate quality systems records, including FMEAs, control plans, process control guidelines, laboratory test instructions, gauge and test equipment verifications and calibrations, and engineering specifications test methods. Quality system records must be retained for one full calendar year after the year in which they were superseded or otherwise became inactive.
The producer must also keep quality performance records including control charts, test results, and routine part evaluation results. Quality performance records must be retained for one calendar year after the year in which they were created. Initial sample reports should be retained for one calendar year after the year in which production of the part is discontinued.
These records must be available for review.

Source: *Worldwide Quality Systems Standard Q-101*, Ford Motor Company

3.11 Quality manuals

A *quality manual* sets out the general quality policy and practices, it is the rule book by which the organisation for quality functions is carried out. Its primary purpose is to provide an adequate description of the quality system while serving as a permanent reference in the implementation and maintenance of that system. Such a manual is useful for a number of reasons:

- as an aid for training, it helps to complement work instructions;
- it gives an indication of the responsibilities and interrelated activities of personnel and functional groups. It is useful as a vehicle for auditing, reviewing and evaluating the quality system;
- it provides information from which the purchaser may derive confidence in the supplier's organisation – that the systems exist, they are operating and they are designed for their purpose;
- it is useful for supplier/vendor appraisal.

In larger companies, the documentation relating to the quality system may take various forms, including the following:

- a corporate quality manual;
- divisional quality manuals;
- specialised quality manuals (for example, design, procurement, project or work instructions).

A quality manual should be designed so that provision is made for continual updating. This is facilitated if the document is a concise statement of the basic quality assurance procedures without being too involved in more detailed aspects (for example, general work instructions are normally included as examples only). Dependent on the type of functions involved, this may necessitate:

- a part containing details of more permanent general policy, practices and organisation, this is usually given wide circulation;
- a part giving a more detailed account of normal procedures for quality assurance, possibly containing specific examples and details of resource allocation (including personnel); this is sometimes given a restricted circulation;
- a part containing particular quality plans setting out specific quality practices and activities relevant to a particular contract or project; this is usually given a restricted circulation.

Each quality manual format is unique to the company just as the quality system development is unique. Irrespective of the type of basic structure, a quality manual should include:

- a section describing the whole range of communications, responsibilities and controls, with which every department must conform to achieve the quality objectives. This section should state in general terms the quality assurance functions and relevant responsibilities allocated to various managers and departmental heads. It is usual to illustrate these interrelationships with organisation and/or functional charts;
- sections describing briefly the quality assurance procedures during design and development, with illustrations of how

liaison with design and research/development is maintained, including feedback of information of any corrective action which may be needed;

- sections describing briefly the quality assurance procedures during production or operations together with a brief description of inspection procedures and statistical methods used (where applicable);
- a section dealing with customer liaison (where appropriate);
- sections describing the organisation and procedures for suppliers' quality assurance and vendor assessment;
- sections describing review and evaluation procedures;
- sections describing training and education.

3.12 Review and evaluation procedures

Review and evaluation procedures take many forms and, during the development of any project, product, service, system or organisation, they are, by their very nature, continually being carried out. Of particular importance is the need for established systems of control to be periodically and systematically reviewed and evaluated to ensure their continuing effectiveness. Such reviews must be methodical and depending on the nature of the organisation, they may include management audits, systems audits, project or product audits, or process audits, carried out at particular times.

To carry out an audit adequately, it is essential that procedures be prepared which define:

- the conduct of the audit;
- objectives, responsibilities and rôles;
- what will be examined;
- where and when the audit will be done;
- to whom the results of the audit will be reported;
- how any necessary corrective actions will be instituted.

Audits should be conducted at intervals depending upon operating patterns and system requirements. Some elements of any system will undoubtedly require more frequent auditing than others and a schedule for audits should be established. This schedule needs to be adjusted on the basis of previous results.

Quality systems auditing

The growing use of British Standards, and now European and International Standards, giving minimum requirements for quality assurance (for example, the BS 5750/ISO 9000 Series) emphasises the importance of quality auditing as a management tool for achieving the objectives set out in a company's quality policy. Quality auditing is a non-executive function (as distinct from operations, such as inspection and surveillance which are performed for the sole purpose of product acceptance or process control) and involves making decisions for action, although it can involve the review of such functions. It can relate to the quality of a product, service, process or system. Quality auditing involves the independent and systematic examination of actions that influence product and service quality. Audits can be conducted for internal or external purposes. The quality audit typically applies to, but is not limited to, a quality system or elements thereof, to processes, to products, or to services. Such audits are often called 'quality system audits', 'process quality audits', 'product quality audits' or 'service quality audits'. Detailed guidance on auditing quality systems is provided in BS 7229: Part 1 (1991), in relation to:

- audit objectives rôle and responsibilities;
- initiating the audit;
- preparing the audit;
- executing the audit;
- audit documents;
- audit completion;
- corrective action follow-up.

Audits are normally designed for one or more of the following purposes:

- to determine the conformity or non-conformity of the quality system elements with specified requirements;

- to determine the effectiveness of the implemented quality system in meeting specified quality objectives;
- to provide the auditee with an opportunity to improve the quality system;
- to meet regulatory requirements;
- to permit the listing of the audited organisation's quality system in a register.

The results of these audits can be used by management for improving the performance of the organisation. However, an audit should not be confused with 'surveillance' or 'inspection' activities performed for the sole purpose of process control or product acceptance.

Audits are generally initiated for one or more of the following reasons:

- within a contractual framework:
  - i) to evaluate a supplier as part of a vendor appraisal operation, where there is a desire to establish a contractual relationship. A vendor rating is sometimes given partly as a result of such an audit;
  - ii) to verify that the supplier's quality system continues to meet requirements, and is being implemented effectively;
  - iii) to follow up corrective action from a previous audit;

  As indicated above a quality audit or quality assessment may be initiated as a requirement by a client, it is carried out by the auditor and the organisation being audited is known as the auditee. The client may be the representative of an organisation intending to purchase from the auditee or may be the management of an organisation seeking assurance that the quality system prevailing is adequate. The auditor or assessor may be a representative of the organisation that is purchasing, a member of the auditee organisation (but with no direct responsibility for the function audited), or a third party.

- for the purpose of an internal organisation audit:
  - i) as a routine examination of the organisation's quality system to verify that it continues to meet requirements:
  - ii) as a consequence of particular circumstances such as variation in the product quality, organisational modifications or to follow up corrective actions from a previous audit;
  - iii) for evaluation of the organisation's quality system against quality systems standards.

These audits may be routine, or may be prompted by significant changes in the organisation's quality system, process, product or service quality, or by a need to follow up on corrective action.

In auditing the quality system, objective evaluations of its elements should include the following activities or areas:

- organisational structures,
- administrative and operational procedures;
- personnel, equipment and material resources;
- work areas, operations and processes;
- service or items being produced (to establish degree of conformance to standards and specifications);
- documentation, reports, record-keeping, etc.

Roles and responsibilities

Whether an audit is carried out by a team or an individual, a lead auditor should be placed in overall charge. Depending upon the circumstances, the audit team may include experts with specialized background, auditor trainees or observers who are acceptable to the client, auditee and lead auditor.

Auditors are responsible for:

- complying with the applicable audit requirements;
- communicating and clarifying audit requirements;
- planning and carrying out assigned responsibilities effectively and efficiently;
- documenting the observations;
- reporting the audit results;
- verifying the effectiveness of corrective

actions taken as a result of the audit (if requested by the client);

- retaining and safeguarding documents pertaining to the audit, including submitting such documents as required, ensuring such documents remain confidential and treating privileged information with discretion;
- co-operating with and supporting the lead auditor.

The lead auditor is ultimately responsible for all phases of the audit. The lead auditor should have management capabilities and experience and should be given authority to make final decisions regarding the conduct of the audit and any audit observations. The lead auditor's responsibilities also cover:

- assisting with the selection of other audit team members;
- preparation of the audit plan;
- representing the audit team with the auditee's management;
- submitting the audit report.

Auditors should be free from bias and influences which could affect objectivity. All persons and organisations involved with an audit should respect and support the independence and integrity of the auditors. BS 7229: Part 2 (1991) gives guidance on the qualification criteria for auditors.

Managing an audit programme

Any organisation which has an ongoing need to carry out audits of quality systems should establish a capability to provide overall management of the entire process. This function should be independent of direct responsibility for implementing the quality system being audited. BS 7729: Part 3 gives basic guidelines for managing quality systems audit programmes under the following broad headings:

- Organisation;
- Standards;
- Qualification of staff;
- Suitability of team members;
- Monitoring and maintenance of auditor performance;
- Operational factors;
- Joint auditors;
- Audit programme improvement;
- Code of ethics.

Types of audits

Management audits usually afford the opportunity of carrying out simplification exercises on operational procedures. Such exercises can prove rewarding in reducing to a minimum, excessive paperwork which can build up during the development of any system. Constant vigilance is usually required in this respect to ensure that the amount of paperwork does not increase to an unacceptable extent.

In Japanese companies, the president carries out an annual audit of the quality improvement activities of the operational units under his or her control. In this way it is possible to see at first-hand the activities taking place, to develop a knowledge of TQM and to communicate quality policies, objectives and concerns direct to employees during the audit.

The first-party, or internal, audits can be carried out by the organisation's own staff, provided that they are independent of the systems being audited, or by an outside agency.

In addition to the internal audits carried out, customers will also wish to conduct audits of supplier systems and products. Such audits tend to focus on whether or not the supplier is operating to the requirements outlined in the customers' quality system standards. For example, Exxon Chemicals carry out audits at suppliers' premises to assess the policies, systems and procedures.

Third-party audits can be carried out by independent agencies that may be accredited, using a national or international standard such as the BS 5750/ISO 9000 Series to provide assurance on the effectiveness of the quality systems. In the case of a third-party audit the purpose of the audit would be to obtain confirmation of compliance with the standard which could be used to provide assurance to existing and prospective customers for the product or service.

In addition to internal and external audits, reviews will have to be carried out periodically and systematically. These are conducted to ensure that the policies, systems and procedures achieve the desired effect, while audits are done to make sure that the actual methods are adhering to the documented procedures. The reviews should use the findings of the audits, for failure to operate according to plans often signifies difficulties in doing so.

3.13 Design of the work system

Technological, economic, organisational and human factors affect the work behaviour and well-being of people as part of the work system. Consequently, these issues should be considered wherever possible by companies as part of organising for quality. The design of the work system should always satisfy human requirements by applying ergonomic knowledge in the light of practical experience (full details are given in DD 202: 1991).

There are a number of general guiding principles:

a) Design of work space and of work equipment – this should take into account constraints imposed by body dimensions, with due regard to the work process. The design of the work should be such as to avoid unnecessary or excessive strain in muscles, joints, ligaments and in the respiratory and circulatory system. Controls should be selected, designed and laid out in such a way as to be compatible with the characteristics of that part of the body by which they are operated.

b) Design of the work environment – this should be designed and maintained so that physical, chemical and biological conditions have no noxious effect on people but serve to ensure their health, as well as their capacity and readiness to work.

c) Design of the work process – this should safeguard the workers' health and safety, promote their well-being, and facilitate task performance, in particular avoiding overloading and underloading.

Attention should be directed to implementation of one or more of the following methods of improving the quality of the work process:

- having one operator perform several successive operations belonging to the same work function, instead of several operators (job enlargement);
- having one operator perform successive operations belonging to different work functions, instead of several operators. For example, assembly operations followed by quality checks performed by the operator who also removes defects (job enrichment).
- change of activity as, for example, voluntary job rotation among workers on an assembly line or in a team working with an autonomous group.

In implementing the above measures, particular attention should be paid to the following:

- variations in vigilance and work capacity over day and night shifts;
- difference in work capacity among operators, and changes with age;
- individual development.

3.14 Definitions and terminology

The following are some useful definitions and terms used in this chapter.

Audit programme management: organisation, or function within an organisation, given the responsibility to plan and carry out a programmed series of quality system audits.

Auditee: an organisation to be aduited.

Auditor: a person who has the qualification and is authorised to perform all or any portion of an audit.

Client: a person or organisation requesting the audit.

Defect: the non-fulfilment of intended usage requirements.

Instruction: the written and/or spoken direction given with regard to what is to be done, including the information given in training.

Mission statement: broad statement of the main aims of an organisation.

Non-conformity: the non-fulfilment of specified requirements.

Organisation: a managed group of persons and resources formed to carry out a function.

Product quality audit: the independent examination of product quality to provide information.

Quality audit: a systematic and independent examination to determine whether quality activities and related results comply with planned arrangements and whether these arrangements are implemented effectively and are suitable to achieve objectives.

Quality manual: a document stating the quality policy, quality system and quality practices of an organisation.

Quality plan: A document setting out the specific quality practices, resources and sequence of activities relevant to a particular product, service, contract or project.

Quality policy: the overall quality intentions and direction of an organisation as regards quality, as formally expressed by top management.

Quality programme: a documented set of activities, resources and charts serving to implement the quality system of an organisation.

Quality system: the organisation structure, responsibilities, procedures, processes and resources for implementing quality management.

Quality system audit: the independent examination of an organisation's quality system carried out by an auditing team belonging to the organisation.

Specification: a statement of the attributes of a product, process or service.

British Standards

BS 4778: *Quality vocabulary*: Part 1: 1987 *International terms; (ISO 8402: 1986) (EN 28402: 1991); Part 2: 1991 Quality concepts and related definitions.*

BS 5750: 1987 *Quality Systems* (ISO 9000: 1987) (EN 29000: 1987).

BS 5750: *Quality systems* Part 8: 1991 *Guide to quality management and quality system elements for service* (ISO 9004–2: 1991).; Part 13: 1991 *Guide to the application of BS 5750: Part 1 to the development, supply and maintenance of software* (ISO 9000–3: 1991).

BS 7229: *Quality systems auditing* Part 1: 1991 *Auditing* (ISO 10011–1: 1990); Part 2: 1991 *Qualification criteria for auditors* (ISO 10011–2: 1991), Part 3: 1991 *Managing an audit programme* (ISO 10011–3: 1991).

BS 7373: 1991 *Guide to the preparation of specifications.*

BS 7850: *Total Quality Management* Part 1: 1992 *Guide to management principles.*

References

Dale B G and Plunkett J J. *A study of audits, inspection and quality costs in the pressure vessel fabrication sector of the process plant industry.* Proceedings of the Institution of Mechanical Engineers, 198 (B2), pp 45–54, 1984.

Duncalf A J. *Quality assurance: an examination of the way that British manufacturing companies manage their product quality.* PhD Thesis, Manchester School of Management UMIST, 1986.

Duncalf A J and Dale B G. *The management of product quality: a study.* Proceedings of the Institution of Mechanical Engineers, 202 (B3), pp 135–41, 1988.

Ford Motor Company. *Worldwide Quality System Standard* Q–101. Ford Motor Company, Michigan, USA, 1990.

Ford Motor Company. *Planning for Quality.* Ford Motor Company, Michigan, USA, 1990.

Nissan Motor Manufacturing (UK). *Nissan quality standard for suppliers.* Nissan Motor Iberica SA and Nissan Motor Manufacturing (UK), Washington, UK, 1991.

Shingo S. *Zero Quality Control: Source Inspection and the Poka-Yoke System.* Productivity Press, Massachusetts, USA, 1986.

CHAPTER 4

Quality costing

4.1 Introduction

Traditionally quality performance has been reported to management in terms of rejection, defective material and waste reports. This vital information is often difficult to analyse and interpret in terms of costs and as a result, cost saving may be overlooked. Successful business requires sound financial planning and control and it is advisable that quality failures be presented in financial terms.

Initially the following two important facts should be appreciated:

- failures, however caused, reduce profits;
- preventive quality control type activities ad the appraisal of quality standards cost money to operate.

These costs can be regarded as quality-related costs and in simple terms can be classified as:

- prevention costs;
- appraisal costs;
- internal failure costs;
- external failure costs.

Quality losses are caused by failure to utilize most effectively and efficiently the potential of human, financial and material resources in a process. Some examples are:

- loss of customer satisfaction;
- loss of opportunity to add value – to the customer, organisation or society;
- loss due to waste or resource misuse, including people's health, property damage and process interruption.

Additional resources are usually allocated for quality related activities if it can be demonstrated that by so doing profitability will be increased. Effective quality management can provide a contribution to profit, and evidence shows that resources deployed to identify, reduce and control failure costs give a benefit in terms of improved quality, increased profitability, improved customer satisfaction and enhanced competitiveness.

This chapter defines quality costs and explains why they are important to management. It also explains how to determine, report and use quality-related costs. Some of the material used in this chapter is based on '*Quality Costing*' Dale and Plunkett (1991).

What are quality-related costs?

Quality-related costs are those incurred in the design, implementation, operation and maintenance of an organisation's quality system, the cost of organisational resources committed to the process of continuous quality improvement, plus those costs incurred owing to failures of the systems, products and services.

Quality systems may range from simple inspection to systems surpassing the requirements of the BS 5750 (ISO 9000) Series or other similar quality system standards. System failures can result in obsolescent stocks, production or operation delays, scrap, rectification work, late deliveries, poor service and non-conforming products. Product or service failures can result in warranty, guarantee and product liability charges, complaint administration and investigation, product recall and, generally the loss of customer goodwill. So, quality-related costs are not simply the costs of quality control and assurance, inspection, test and scrap materials, components and products.

Quality-related costs arise from a wide range of activities, (for example, sales and marketing, design, research and development, purchasing, storage and handling, production or operations planning and control, delivery and/or installation, and service) all of which may impinge on the quality of the product or service. Nor are they wholly determined or controlled from within the manufacturing, commercial or service organisation. Suppliers, sub-contractors, stockists, agents, dealers and consumers can all influence the incidence and level of quality-related costs.

Why are quality-related costs important?

First, because they are very large. The National Economic Development Office (NEDO) report (1985), of the Task Force on Quality and Standards chaired by Sir Frederick Warner estimated them to be between 10 and 20 per cent of total sales value. The figure of 10 per cent corresponds to an annual cost of some £6 billion in manufacturing industry in the UK alone. Reports from all types of industries indicate that quality-related costs commonly range from 5 to 25 per cent of company annual sales turnover. The costs depend on the type of industry, business situation or service, the view taken by the organisation of what is or is not a quality-related cost, the approach to TQM and the extent to which continuous quality improvement is practised by all departments and people in the organisation.

Secondly, 95 per cent of this cost is usually expended on appraisal and failure. These expenditures add little to the value of the product or service, and the failure costs, at least, may be regarded as avoidable. Reducing failure costs by eliminating causes of failure can also lead to substantial reductions in appraisal costs. The University of Manchester Institute of Science and Technology (UMIST) research evidence suggests that quality-related costs may be reduced to one-third of their present level, within a period of three years, by a commitment to a process of continuous and company-wide improvement. Some example of specific quality cost reductions are given by Dale and Plunkett (1992) in the DTI quality costing publication *'The Case for Costing Quality'*.

Thirdly, unnecessary and avoidable costs make goods and services more expensive. This in turn affects competitiveness.

Fourthly, despite the fact that the costs are large, and that a substantial proportion of them is avoidable, it is apparent that the costs and economics of many quality-related activities, including investment in prevention and appraisal activities, are not known. From the UMIST research work it is estimated that fewer than 40 per cent of companies know the extent of their quality costs. Such a state of affairs is surely indefensible in any well-run business. However, it is encouraging that an increasing number of organisations are now attempting to determine their quality-related costs.

Why measure quality-related costs?

The measurement of costs allows quality-related activities to be expressed in the language of management, i.e. money. This, in turn, allows quality to be treated as a business parameter as in marketing, research and development, and production/operations. Drawing quality costs into the business arena helps to emphasise the importance of product and service quality to corporate health and will influence behaviour and attitudes towards TQM at all levels in the organisation. They can be used as a measure of the effectiveness of the quality systems being used and also to assess and measure the effectiveness of improvements in performance against the costs incurred.

Quality cost measurement focuses attention on areas of high expenditure and potential cost-reduction opportunities. It allows measurement of performance and provides a basis for comparison between products, services, processes, departments and divisions. Measurement of quality-related costs also reveals quirks and anomalies in cost allocation and standards which may remain undetected by the more commonly used production/operation and labour-based analyses. It has been known to uncover fraudulent activities taking place within an organisation. Measurement can also obviate the dumping of embarrassing after-sales costs under quality-related headings.

Finally, and perhaps most importantly, measurement is the first step towards control.

How can quality-related costs be used?

Quality costs display the importance of quality-related activities to management in meaningful terms and often help to galvanise people into action. They are also helpful in educating staff in the concepts and principles of TQM and explaining why the organisation is setting out on the TQM journey.

Knowledge of quality-related costs enables business decisions about quality to be made in an objective manner. It permits the use of sensitivity analysis, discounted cash flow and other accounting techniques, for the evaluation of expenditure projects as in any other area of the business. In this way such knowledge helps companies to decide how, when and where to invest in prevention activities or equipment.

Costs may be used to monitor quality improvement performance, to identify products, services, processes and departments for investigation, to set cost-reduction targets, to measure progress towards targets and the cost effectiveness of the investment. They may be used to evaluate the worth of individual quality activities, for example, quality system accreditation, SPC, supplier development, or to compare performances between departments, works or divisions. Quality costs are tools for initiating improvement projects, and levers for uncovering quality problems.

Costs are the bases for budgeting and eventual cost control. They also enable valid comparisons to be made with other costs via the usual measurement bases (for example, sales turnover, units of saleable product and standard hours).

Quality costs help to provide information for quotations for products/services or contracts having difficult quality conditions.

Lastly, by featuring quality-related costs in the regular management accounts, quality aspects of the product or service can be kept under the spotlight. Abed and Dale (1987) have noted that appreciation of the use of quality costs correlates with the state of organisational development of TQM.

4.2 BSI publications featuring aspects of quality-related costs

Two Standards and a published document contain material relating directly to the definition, collection, analysis and use of quality-related costs. These are:

BS 4778: Part 1, 1987 *Quality vocabulary – International terms;*

BS 4778: Part 2: 1991 *Quality concepts and related definitions;*

PD6470: 1981 *Management of design for economic production;*

BS 6143: *Guide to the economics of quality;* Part 1: 1992 *Process cost model;* Part 2: 1990 *Prevention, appraisal and failure model.* (This is a revision of the former British Standard BS 6143: 1981 *Guide to the use of quality-related costs).*

4.3 Definitions

The importance of definitions cannot be overstressed. Without clear definitions there can be no common understanding or meaningful communication on the topic of quality costing. By their very nature costing exercises require rigorous definitions, and those concerned with quality-related costs are no exception. The definition of what constitutes quality costs is by no means straightforward and there are many grey areas where good production/operations practices overlap with quality-related activities. Unfortunately, there is no general agreement on a single broad definition of quality costs.

Considerations of quality in other contexts (for example, training, supplier development, SPC and quality function deployment) do not require such sharp distinctions to be made between what is quality-related and what is not.

Quality-related costs and other principal terms relating to the subject are defined in BS 4778: Parts 1 (1987) and 2 (1991) and BS 6143: Parts 1 (1992) and 2 (1990). In general, those outlined below have been taken from BS 6143.

Appraisal costs: the cost of evaluating the achievement of quality requirements, including the cost of verification and control performed at any stage of the quality loop.

Cost(s): the expenditure (actual or notional) incurred on, or attributable to, a given thing.

Cost function: an expression of the way cost varies with a given parameter.

Cost of conformance: the intrinsic cost of providing products or services to declared standards by a given, specified process in a fully effective manner.

Cost of non-conformance: the cost of wasted time, materials and capacity associated with a process in the receipt, production, despatch and correction of unsatisfactory goods and services.

Economic quality: the level of quality at which the cost of securing higher quality would exceed the benefits of the improved quality.

External failure costs: the costs arising after delivery to a customer/user due to non-conformities or defects which may include the cost of claims against warranty, replacement and consequential losses, and evaluation of penalties incurred.

Internal failure costs: the costs arising within an organisation due to non-conformities or defects at any stage of the quality loop and which may include costs of scrap, rework, retest, re-inspection and redesign.

Memorandum account: a financial statement, subsidiary to and not part of the actual accounts of an organisation, relating to a particular activity or for a purpose not available in the actual acccounts.

Payroll costs: the costs to an organisation, of employing a person, including, for example, gross pay, social security costs and company pension costs.

Process costs: the total cost of conformance and cost of non-conformance for a particular process.

Prevention costs: the cost of any action taken to investigate, prevent or reduce the risk of non-conformity.

Quality cost: the expenditure incurred by the producer, by the user and by the community, associated with product or service quality.

Quality-related cost: the expenditure incurred in defect prevention and appraisal activities, plus the losses due to internal and external failure.

BS 6143: Part 2 also contains an appendix of 35 cost elements which is sufficiently detailed and includes enough guidance notes for them to be regarded as definitions. This is reproduced as Appendix C.

Despite the need for rigorousness, the definitions of quality-related costs given in BS 4778: Parts 1 (1987) and 2 (1991) are different to those in BS 6143: Part 2, which is somewhat a puzzle to the would-be cost collector. The fact that there are not yet agreed definitions of the fundamental terms of quality costing should warn cost collectors of the uncertainties and difficulties which may be met when attempting to measure and report quality costs.

4.4 British Standards approach to quality costing

In their consideration of quality costing the BSI Technical Committees responsible for the preparation of BS 4891 (now withdrawn) and BS 6143 (the 1981 version of the Standard and now withdrawn) adopted two of the most solidly entrenched philosophies on the topic.

The first is the categorisation of quality-related costs into prevention, appraisal and failure, as proposed first by Feigenbaum (1956) in his seminal paper over 30 years ago. Feigenbaum's categorisation is accepted universally and almost all published quality-related cost reports adopt it in some form. It was acknowledged, during the review of the former standard (BS 6143: 1981) that this only addressed those organisations which manufactured or constructed a product and that the prevention-appraisal-failure (PAF) approach is too restrictive. To provide guidance to those organisations or parts of organisations providing services and those manufacturing organisations wishing to adopt an alternative approach, a process cost model is now included.

BS 6143 is now published in two parts:

- **Part 1: Process cost model (1992)** This sets out a method for applying quality costing to any process or service. It recognises the importance of process measurement and process ownership. The categories of quality costs have been rationalised to the cost of conformance and the cost of non-conformance, this serves to simplify classification. The method depends on the use of process modelling.
- **Part 2: Prevention, appraisal and failure (PAF) model (1990)** This is a revised version of the traditional method of product quality costing in manufacturing industries. It should be noted that this approach does not preclude the simultaneous development of the process cost model.

The approach taken and choice of model is dependent upon the objectives of the exercise and the audience for the resulting data.

The second is the notion that in each manufacturing situation there should be an optimum quality level corresponding to a minimum manufacturing/operations (or quality-related) cost. The notion of an optimum level of quality is, however, questioned by many quality management specialists (see Plunkett and Dale, 1988). It is encouraging that in BS 6143: Part 2 (1990), there is no reference to an optimum quality in the notional quality costs model outlined in the Standard. However, a number of production and operations management, and quality management texts still mention optimum quality level and it is worth briefly tracing its inclusion into British Standards and summarising the arguments against it.

BS 4891: the notion of an optimum level of quality first appears in a BSI publication in 1972 as Appendix A of BS 4891. Under the heading 'Economics of quality assurance' it is reasoned that:

> Figure 2 [see Figure 4.1] illustrates the economics of quality assurance assuming a constant basic manufacturing cost. To the left of the optimum, opportunities to effect better quality have been missed such that the losses due to defectives, etc. are higher than the cost of the solution and in this region 'better' quality assurance costs less.
>
> To the right of the optimum the costs are uneconomical due to 'perfectionism' and in this region the cure is perhaps worse than the disease so that 'better' quality assurance costs more.
>
> (BS 4891: 1972)

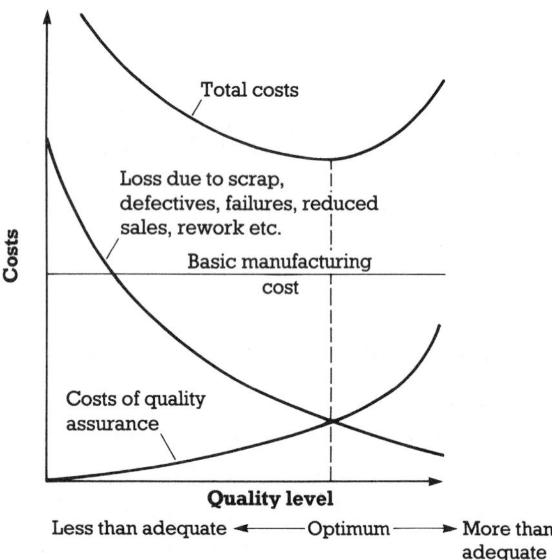

Source: BS 4891: 1972

Figure 4.1 Economics of quality assurance

At about the time BS 4891 was being prepared, rapid and fundamental changes were taking place in approaches to the attainment of standards of quality in manufactured products. The traditional inspection-oriented approaches were being ousted in favour of more rigorous quality assurance methods. Those opposed to the changes and concerned about the power and influence of the new quality assurance specialists were quick to warn of extra costs incurred and perhaps with some justification.

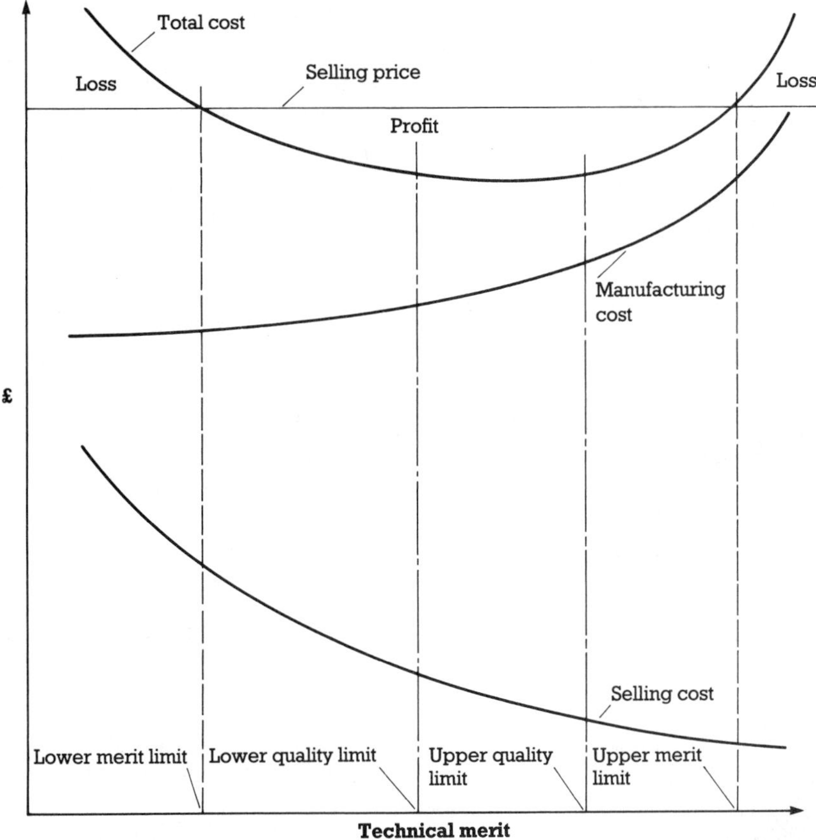

Figure 4.2 Graph illustrating total product cost **Source:** PD 6470: 1981

There is no doubt that, in many instances, there was an unnecessary proliferation of new systems and paperwork. This standard was withdrawn in 1993.

PD 6470: the notion of an economic level of quality was sustained in PD 6470 (published in 1973 with revisions in 1975 and 1981).

> Total product cost is the addition of manufacturing cost and selling cost and is shown graphically in Figure 1 [See Figure 4.2].
>
> Total production cost is not constant but varies in direct relationship with technical merit (quality), and any shift in product quality is reflected in total product cost.
>
> (PD 6470: 1981)

Figure 4.2, in common with Figure 1 from BS 4891, indicates clearly the notion of optimum quality level, though there are several incompatibilities in other respects.

BS 6143: when BS 6143, was first issued in 1981 the idea of an optimum quality level was still being advanced, as shown by the quality cost model and the accompanying text.

> The Figure 1 [See Figure 4.3], which is a notional quality costs model, shows how, by increasing expenditure on prevention costs, the costs of failure may be expected to fall. However, there is a point at which total costs will be at their lowest.
>
> Considerations such as prestige, safety, and goodwill may make it desirable to carry increased preventive costs at the expense of an economic balance.
>
> (BS 6143: 1981)

The latter point is enlarged upon by Cox (1979) and in this qualifying context, the uncompromising line taken in BS 4891 has softened somewhat in the intervening years in the face of increasingly intense international competition for trade. PD 6470, while pressing optimum quality levels concedes, when

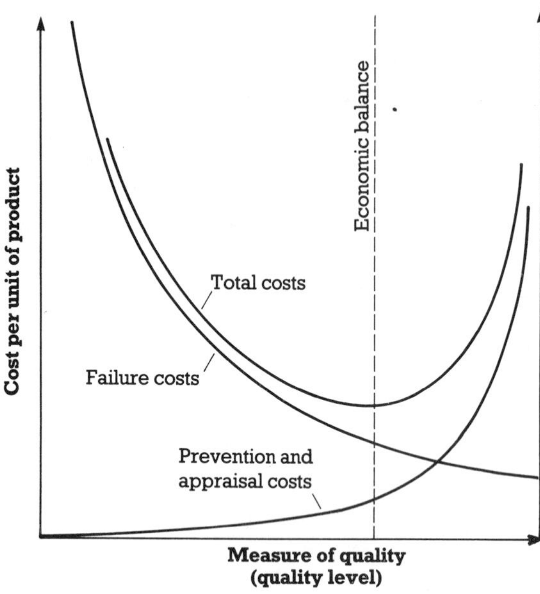

Figure 4.3 Quality costs model

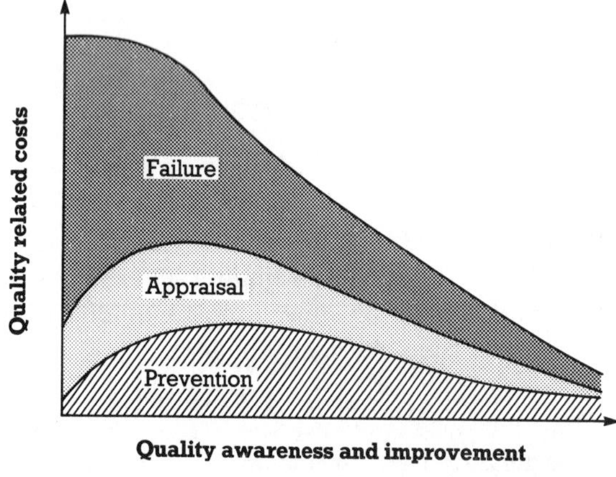

Figure 4.4 Increasing quality awareness and improvement activities

discussing design, that 'acceptable levels for (quality) are necessary at minimum cost' and BS 6143 describes PD 6470 as giving 'guidance on designing for minimum cost at a specified quality' – surely the correct approach. The notion of an optimum quality level is not confined to British Standards; it is fairly widespread. However, Plunkett and Dale (1988) reflect the opinions of many quality management specialists when they point out that:

- the idea conflicts with the widely accepted zero defects philosophy of TQM;
- if there is an optimum, it lies very close to perfection;
- the notion of an optimum quality level may inhibit the process of continuous incremental quality improvement;
- the cost curves of prevention, appraisal and failure portrayed in quality cost models suggest a small investment in prevention and/or appraisal results in a major reduction in failure cost. In practice this is not the case and could mislead the unwary to having too high expectations.

BS 6143: Part 2 (1990) does not recognise any ultimately acceptable level of defect or error.

> Figure 1 [See Figure 4.4] which is a notional quality costs model, shows how, by increasing awareness of prevention costs, the cost of failure and appraisal, may be expected to fall.
>
> The pattern of quality cost varies from company to company and the relationships shown in Figure 1 [See Figure 4.4] are schematic representations of the trends to be expected on quality costs as awareness of quality and improvement activities increased.
>
> Figure 1 [See Figure 4.4] illustrates how an increased awareness of the cost to the organisation of quality failure leads first to an increase in appraisal of product quality. Then, as appraisal together with investigation points to features/elements where improvement can be made to product design/process and systems, more is spent on prevention. Finally as preventive action takes effect the prevention, appraisal and failure proportions of the costs realign and all costs reduce.
>
> (BS 6143: 1990)

4.5 Identification, determination and reporting using the PAF approach

The stated scope of BS 6143: Part 2 (1990) is to provide guidance on the determination of costs associated with defect prevention and appraisal activities, internal and external failures and on the operation of quality-related costs systems for effective business management.

The strategy recommended is to start with a pilot study from a small department or a single product/service line to determine the scope of the work, and to gain management approval and commitment to a total quality costing system, before attempting to establish one across the whole company. The pilot study should also define the quality-related cost categories and the cost elements to be used.

Identification of costs

Quality-related costs appropriate to the organisation should be identified and monitored. The accompanying checklists of cost elements (Appendix C), categorised under prevention, appraisal and failure can be used to identify quality-related costs. The NEDO Report (1985) suggests that other checklists appropriate to specific industries should be drawn up. In our experience quality costs can arise in all parts of a company and elements for the calculation of quality costs may differ from company to company and industry to industry. It will be for management to decide which costs will be attributed to day-to-day operational control and set against production/operations costs, and which will be identified as being solely for the purpose of quality assurance.

In the authors' view the checklist given in the Standard does not reflect properly the usual distribution of quality-related costs between prevention, appraisal and failure found in industry, commerce and the service sector. For example, the data shown in Table 4.1 are given in the Standard as a typical quality-costs element comparison. But more than half of the detailed checklist and accompanying notes are devoted to prevention costs and to appraisal costs. These fractions are clearly disproportionate to the percentages of actual quality costs. It is also the case, especially in small companies, that prevention costs are the most difficult to identify. When cost elements, specific to an organisation, are identified department by department and process by process using a brainstorming-type approach or by process modelling, it is not unusual to find that the majority of cost elements identified are related to failure. Indeed, some organisations only collect the cost of failures.

Table 4.1 A typical quality costs element comparison

Category	Element	Percentage of total quality cost
Failure	Scrap	35
	Rework	11
	Reinspection	9
	Additional operations	8
	Warranty	5
	Downgrading	2
	Others	2
	Total failure costs	72
Appraisal	Inspection and test	26
Prevention	Control of preventive activities	2
	Grand total	100

Source: BS 6143: Part 2, 1990

It is recommended that the key words *prevention, appraisal, internal failure and external failure* be used to help to identify which costs are quality-related. The detailed checklists should be used if they are helpful, but there is no substitute for knowledge and experience of the business. In our view, the main use of the list of elements is to act as thought promoters and mind openers and to demonstrate to senior managers the type of quality costs their organisations are likely to be incurring. However, slavish adherence to the checklist may result in a great deal of effort being expended pursuing insignificant costs and may also act as blinkers to the identification of some key quality costs.

Guidance on the identification of costs given in BS 6143: Part 2 (1990) is as follows:

> When the list of costs elements has been identified using the checklist, the collection of costs data can begin. More analysis may be needed in a company that does not already have a departmental costing system than in one that has. The guidance that follows, however, gives all companies enough information to see what depth of analysis will be needed.
>
> The analysis may require all or most of the following five steps to identify the quality costs.

Step 1 is to calculate those costs that are directly attributable to the 'quality function'. These will normally include:

1) payroll costs of people specifically controlled by the quality function or department;
2) a proportion of building occupation costs related to the quality function, for example rents, rates, insurance, heating, lighting and security;
3) a proportion of canteen costs, office services and other administration costs;
4) the costs of depreciation of specialised quality control and assessment equipment;
5) the costs of quality training;
6) the costs of smaller items that the company does not capitalise.

Step 2 is to identify costs that are not directly the responsibility of the 'quality' function but which should be counted as part of the total quality-related costs of the organisation. These costs will usually be incurred by other departments. It is not necessary to make a formal accounting transfer to the 'quality' function costs centre, but they should be included in a memorandum account. A number of departments may incur these costs, for example purchasing, stores and planning. Costs in this category should be apportioned to quality on an equitable basis.

The costs so far identified in steps one and two will be mainly concerned with prevention and appraisal and those in steps three to five with failure costs.

Step 3 is to identify and enter in the memorandum account the internal costs of 'budgeting failures'. For example it may be normal practice to make a product in batches of 100. To be certain of completing 100 it may be a matter of routine to plan 110 starts. Only experience will eventually tell whether it is worth calculating the cost of the additional 10, but the costs should be calculated, at least for a trial period.

Step 4 is to identify the internal costs of failures not allowed for in Step 3. Related costs may include materials that have been scrapped or the cost of reworking to put the defective item right, or even of completely remaking. The costs will usually lie either in the accounts of the department causing the failure or in the department doing the rectification. Wherever they lie, the costs should be noted in the memorandum account.

Step 5 is to identify the cost of failures after change of ownership. Costs will include the time spent by the quality department in investigations (these need to be offset against the costs in Step 1 to avoid a double count) and those costs of other departments such as marketing, customer servicing and accounts. These costs are rarely identified in existing systems. An initial estimate should be made and the results entered in the memorandum account. Where the customer is eventually charged for the investigation and any costs of rectification, the income should be noted in the memorandum account.

(BS 6143: Part 2, 1990)

In our view a good working knowledge of the manufacturing and/or operational processes and experience of the company's management accounting systems are an essential prerequisite to a quality-cost collection exercise, because the expenditures cut across conventional accounting boundaries in most companies. It is also important to get the purpose of the exercise clear at the start, as this will help to avoid difficulties later and may influence the strategy of the exercise. If, for example, the main purpose of the exercise is to identify high-cost problem areas, approximate costs in known problem areas will suffice. If, on the other hand, the purpose is to set a percentage cost-reduction target on the company's total quality-related costs, it may be necessary to identify and measure all the contributing cost elements in order to be sure that costs are reduced and not simply transferred elsewhere.

Further guidance on the identification of costs may be found in Plunkett and Dale (1985, 1988 and 1988), Feigenbaum (1983), Campanella (1990), Blank and Solorzarno (1978).

Determination of costs

Before attempting to ascribe costs to the elements identified, it is essential to confer with the management accountants to review the list of elements and data sources. It will be found that a good percentage of the desired information is available in one form or another, though at first this might not appear to be the case.

Although there are no established rules for searching out data, the following are recommended as valuable source documents:

- payroll analyses;
- production/operations expense reports;
- scrap or waste reports (including time);

- rework or rectification authorisations/reports;
- travel expense claims;
- product or service cost information;
- field repair, replacement and warranty costs reports;
- inspection and test records;
- material review records;
- non-conformance reports;
- engineering/design charge and concession data.

Dale and Plunkett (1992) outline a wide variety of quality cost sources in case studies described in the DTI publication *The Case for Costing Quality*.

Data extracted from source documents should be transposed by appropriate collection work sheets and coded for easy tabulation. The aim is to have all cost data reported by code. The use of coding permits consistency of collection regardless of the source or size of the costs.

Each department should report its costs. Data from all sources should then be accumulated by code. Where actual costs cannot be directly associated with specific elements, it may be necessary to make an expense allocation by arbitration. If these costs are significant, it is recommended that the necessary records be established in order to record the data in a factual manner.

Quality cost collection should be a joint exercise. Quality costs should be collated and reported based on data collected by the accounts department. The separate roles most likely to be established for operation of the system are that the accounting department will collect quality costs data, allocate quality costs to agreed activities, provide comparative bases for quality cost assessment, and produce an operating report for the accountancy period. The quality management department, assisted by engineering and technical staff as appropriate, will analyse quality costs and take appropriate controlling action by investigating causes and making recommendations for improvement, co-ordinate inter-departmental activity to achieve quality-related cost objectives, pursue a continuing policy for quality cost reduction and control, and arbitrate on the allocation of responsibility for quality failure costs. It is also important that individual departments take ownership for reducing their quality costs. It is strongly recommended that the system used to collect quality costs should be made as automatic as possible without significantly increasing paperwork or the burden on accountants.

Important aspects of the determination of costs, not covered by the Standard, are the valuation of scrapped products and allocation of overhead costs. Should scrapped products be costed as materials plus added value to the point in the process at which they are scrapped or should they be valued at the cost when completed? If the latter method is adopted, should the production cost or the selling price be used and should overhead costs be included in the valuation? It is important to get agreement on such matters early in the costing exercise. For example, at a company forming, assembling and testing its products in small to medium batch production, it has been found to be satisfactory to value scrapped products at the materials cost to the point of scrapping, plus half the direct labour costs (including overhead) which would have been incurred if the product had been processed to completion (Dale and Plunkett, 1991).

It will also be necessary to decide how to deal with overheads, since many quality-related costs are normally included as part of the overhead, while others are treated as direct costs and attract a proportion of overheads. Failure to clarify this can lead to a gross distortion of the picture derived from the quality-related cost analyses. It is also easy to fall into the trap of double counting (Plunkett and Dale, 1985).

Reporting quality-related costs

By knowing where costs are incurred and their magnitude, action can be taken to control and reduce them. Quality costs should be collected and recorded separately and not absorbed into a variety of overheads and budgets or otherwise hidden, for example by debits in one area that are balanced by credits in another. The objective is to allocate these indirect costs to a specific cost activity.

It is essential to present a financial report to management that is an accurate statement of the costs of failure, the costs of operating quality controls and the quality system, and the costs of quality improvement activities.

For control purposes, it is necessary to allocate quality costs to the accountable area and the use of account codes within cost centres is a convenient method. The allocation of costs is important to the analysis and prevention of failures. Arbitration may be required when accountability is disputed. The decision for allocation of costs should not be made solely by the accountant. Arbitration by an independent technical authority may be needed.

In order to have sufficient impact, the report detailing quality costs should be presented in a similar style to other management accounts and should be supported by financial ratios and trend analysis related to the business of the company, to enable management to allocate the relevant financial resources. Some quality managers pay insufficient attention to the way in which they report quality costs to their senior management. Unfortunately, in a majority of organisations, the lack of sophistication of quality costs collection and measurement is such that it does not allow quality cost reporting to be carried out in the same detail and to the same standard as for other functions.

It is essential that the classification of costs data is relevant and consistent with other accounting practices within the company so that comparisons may be made between costing periods or related activities. Quality costs should be separately recorded within the accounting system and a subsidiary ledger or memorandum account may be found useful for this purpose.

Application of the Pareto method for separation of the 'vital few from the trivial many' will single out the highest contributor to any set of cost figures. The result may be ranked and charted to gain not only a better understanding of what is happening in the business but to aid communication in the reporting of cost data.

BS 6143: Part 2 (1990) recommends that after all costs have been collected, they should be tabulated to give a breakdown of costs by element code. An example of a proforma for quality costs periodic reporting is shown in Appendix D.

The report format and frequency will depend upon the nature of the business and the level of management to which the information is presented. The reports should be relevant to the business objectives and should, therefore, have a consistent basis against which true comparisons can be made. In BS 6143: Part 2 (1990) it is recommended that at least three measurement bases be related initially to quality costs. They should represent the business from different viewpoints and be sensitive to business changes. The following examples are from BS 6143: Part 2 (1990):

> a) a labour base, for example internal failure costs related to total labour or direct labour;
> b) a cost base, for example total failure costs related to manufacturing/operations costs or total material and labour;
> c) a sales base, for example total quality costs related to nett sales billed or value of finished goods transferred to inventory;
> d) a unit base, for example test and inspection costs related to the number of units produced. Quality cost per unit produced has many advantages, but it is necessary to take into account the effect of product mix, volume and value;
> e) a value added base, for example total quality-related costs related to a measure of manufacturing or service activity unaffected by fluctuations in sales and the cost of purchased goods and service.
>
> (BS 6143: Part 2, 1990)

As a matter of caution, measurement bases are only as good as the methods for keeping them consistent. Consideration should be given to such methods and adjustments made, when bases are affected by:

- direct labour replaced by automation;
- manufacturing cost changes due to the use of alternative materials, methods or processes;
- changes in gross margins, selling prices, distribution costs and market demand;
- changes in product mix;
- time scale of numerator that differs from the time scale of denominator.

4.6 Identification, determination and reporting using the process cost model

Part one of BS 6143 provides guidance on the modelling and determination of costs association within any business process in a manner consistent with the pursuit of continuous improvement and the concept and principles of TQM.

The model described in the standard is based in IDEFO. *IDEFO* is a technique for describing processes and has some fundamental similarities to flow diagrams. It was developed for the US Air Force as part of an initiative to improve the efficiency of the aircraft industry through the application of computer integrated manufacturing (CIM). The name is derived from *I*CAM *DEF*inition method, ICAM being the name of the group which undertook the project. IDEFO was placed in the public domain and therefore there are no restrictions on its use. Further details of IDEFO can be found in Ross (1977). A number of people have used IDEFO to model aspects of quality management, for example, Marsh (1989) and Crossfield and Dale (1990).

The process model can be applied equally to the manufacture and service sectors of an industry. The method reduces all organisational activities to processes which have two cost categories: the cost of conformance and the cost of non-conformance.

Definitions

The following definitions are used in the process cost model:

Actual cost: a cost required by the financial system of the organisation to be separately identified and recorded.

Controls: inputs that define, regulate and/or influence the process. Controls embrace procedures, methods, plans, standards, policies, strategy and legislation.

Cost of conformance (COC): the intrinsic cost of providing products or services to declared standards by a given, specified process in a fully effective manner.

Cost of non-conformance (CONC): the cost of wasted time, materials and capacity (resources) associated with a process in the receipt, production, despatch and correction of unsatisfactory goods and services.

Environment: the external and internal conditions that influence the existence, development and performance of the process.

Inputs: material and/or data that is transformed by the process to create outputs.

Outputs: the result of the transformation of inputs. In practice the outputs include:
a) that which conforms to the requirement,
b) that which does not conform,
c) waste,
d) process information.

Process: any activity that transforms inputs into outputs, utilising resources and being subject to particular controls.

Process cost: the total cost of conformance and cost of non-conformance for a particular process.

Process owner: the owner has full responsibility for, and authority over, the process.

Resources: contributing factors which are not transformed to become an output. Resources include persons (individuals or groups), equipment, material, accommodation and environmental requirements.

Synthetic cost: a cost, derived from available relevant data on a clearly established basis. An example of a synthetic cost is

Hours worked × Labour rate.

The process cost model

Fundamentals

Total Quality Management requires the management of processes, not just of outputs. This is fundamental to improving quality and productivity in manufacturing and service enterprises alike. Every person within the organisation contributes to, and operates within, a process, not just those in direct manufacturing activities, and every process must have a process owner, who is responsible for the effectiveness of that process.

It is useful to construct a block diagram to identify all the elements of the process. This focuses attention on the need for the process and a brief statement on this is of value. Essential elements of the model are shown in Figure 4.5.

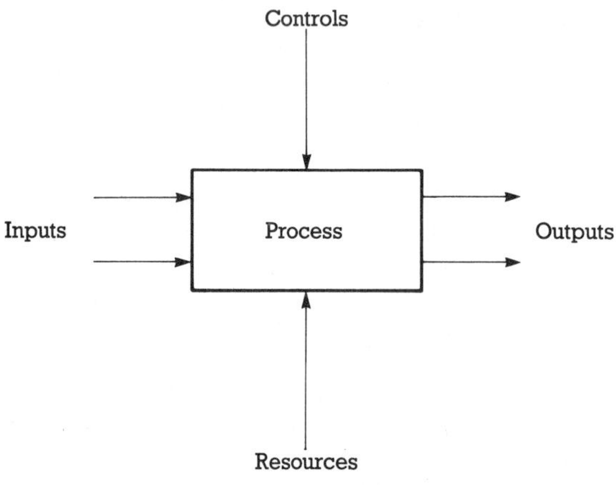

Source: BS 6143: Part 1, 1990

Figure 4.5 Process model

Cost elements associated with the process can be identified and recorded under one of four categories: people, equipment, materials and environment. Each individual cost element can be identified as either a cost of conformance or a cost of non-conformance and the source of the data recorded.

Both areas of cost offer opportunities for improvement. An operator within a process can usually only influence the cost of non-conformance, but he/she can recommend to the process owner changes that may ultimately affect the cost of conformance. The owner of the process should monitor the process and make changes that will impact on both these costs. Some processes exist only because of non-conformance elsewhere and the need for them may disappear if that non-conformance is removed.

Cost of conformance (COC): the cost of operating the process as specified in a 100 per cent effective manner. This does not imply that it is an efficient, nor even a necessary process, but rather that the process, when operated within its specified procedures, cannot be achieved at a lower cost. This is the minimum cost for the process as specified.

Cost of non-conformance (CONC): the cost of inefficiency within the specified process, i.e. over resourcing or excess costs of people, materials and equipment arising from unsatisfactory inputs, errors made, rejected outputs and various other modes of waste. These are considered non-essential process costs.

Preparation of the model

The model may be generated for any process within an organisation. It may be used to identify and monitor process costs within one particular aspect of the organisation. Alternatively, it may be used to monitor the overall cost of a department. Setting up the model is the responsibility of the process owner. This is often done in conjunction with a quality improvement team.

The model is constructed by identifying all of the parameters to be monitored and listing them as either COC or CONC. The source of the data should also be identified. Ideally, this source of data should be from information already collated within the finance function. In some instances, however, it may be necessary to generate synthetic cost data.

An example of a process cost model for a personnel department is given in Appendix D.

Method of preparation

The process should be identified and isolated as a discrete set of activities; it should be given a name and have an owner. The outputs from the process should be identified and each output should be recognised as going to one or more customers. Internally the customer will be the owner of another process. The inputs to a process such as material and data should be identified as should the controls and resources.

Each process will contain a number of key activities. These should be identified. The COC and CONC elements for each activity should be identified and established.

A cost report should be prepared to an agreed format. The report should contain a complete list of the COC and CONC elements. The report should specify:

- identification of all inputs, outputs, controls and resources of the process being considered;
- whether actual or synthetic costs are used;
- the means of calculation for each element of cost;
- the source of cost data.

An example of a cost report for a personnel department is shown in Appendix E.

A programme of improvement activities should be planned based on the information contained in the report and these should be prioritised to maximise the targeted savings. Decisions may be made as to whether the process design or the elimination of waste is the first priority. The process owner should operate a continuous improvement process using teams and individuals and monitor the changes effected to both the COC and CONC.

Uses

The process cost model, in the experience of the authors, has the potential for developing the internal-customer supplier concept, stimulating change in terms of identifying improvement opportunities, empowering ownership for quality improvement and highlighting interal management responsible through process review. This method can have a wider perspective than a traditional quality costing exercise and can provide a firm foundation for departmental purpose analysis and activity based costing.

4.7 Relationship between the traditional (PAF) quality costing and process cost approaches

In the traditional approach to quality cost modelling outlined in Section 4.5, much time is expended in identifying and categorising costs as prevention, appraisal and failure. Such categorisation may be difficult and unsatisfactory for several reasons. For example:

- Many of the costs can be justified as fitting into any one of the three categories. Design reviews, for example, may be considered to be a prevention cost. However, they are essentially a checking stage and, as such, could be considered an appraisal cost; but having been introduced to identify and eliminate design faults at an earlier stage in the process than might otherwise result, they could be considered a failure cost.
- Allocation of costs to prevention, appraisal or failure tends to divert attention from the true purpose of cost reporting which should be the constant drive to lower costs. Thus there is a view that increasing prevention costs indicates an awareness of the costs of quality and should result in a reduction in total costs. While this is true at one level, prevention costs themselves should eventually be a target for reduction. This is to say that the category is unimportant. The true value of cost reporting on a consistent basis is the opportunity to measure process performance, introduce changes and monitor the effects of these changes.

There may however, be a need to link the PAF model with the process cost model, particularly within a business where quality costs have been reported in the traditional manner and are understood and accepted by company personnel. In such a case the COC might initially be considered to compromise prevention and appraisal costs plus the basic process costs, and the CONC to be the failure costs. The COC merely indicates the cost of satisfying the standards declared. It does not indicate an efficient or even necessary process. Therefore, it must be considered as an opportunity for cost improvement.

4.8 Advice on the collection and use of quality costs

The following advice is given in the Recommendations of BS 6143: Part 2 (1990). Further advice may be found in Dale and Plunkett (1991, 1992), together with other papers and books already referred to in this chapter.

Quality improvements and quality cost reductions cannot be dictated by management.

They have to be earned through the processes of data collection, analysis and problem solving.

The first step is the identification of quality problems; a *problem* in this context is defined as an area of significantly high quality costs. Every problem so identified by quality costs provides an opportunity for greater customer satisfaction, and quality and profit improvement.

The quality costs proposals made in BS 6143 form a sound basis for such an approach. Their application will be most effective when conducted within the framework of an appropriate company strategy, backed up by a committed workforce and supported by sound quality costs procedures.

The specific approach adopted by a particular company will depend on many factors. However, there are common key elements to all successful approaches. These include the following:

- Management commitment: the personal commitment of management to attaining product and service quality in the most economical way. The process needs to be led by the chief executive officer and members of the senior management team.
- Quality costs procedure: the devising and implementation of an on-going procedure for the identification, reporting and analysis of quality costs.
- Quality costs action team: the formation of a quality costs action team responsible for overall direction and co-ordination of quality cost exercises, and for ensuring that quality costs saving targets are set and met.
- Training: the inclusion of TQM and quality costing as an integral part of all induction and training schemes. Everyone should understand from the outset the financial implications of quality and recognise that achieving and maintaining a reputation for product and service quality is vital to the success and growth of an organisation and to every individual within it.
- Quality costs awareness promotion: the presentation of significant quality costs/losses in readily understandable terms to all personnel. This might include, for example, displays of defective products and/or services carrying price tags, or charts of errors, rework, complaints, or defective costs per section per day, indicating a possible course of remedial action.
- Quality costs participation: acceptance of the concept that ideas for the reduction of quality costs can emanate from any part of the organisation. Introduce a suitable scheme for achieving maximum participation of employees. This will include the means for promoting, initiating, receiving, discussing, appreciating and acting on these ideas. Quality cost action groups, 'quality circles', corrective action teams, quality improvement groups and problem elimination teams organised throughout the company may well meet this purpose.

4.9 Quality costing: some do's and don'ts

To conclude this chapter a few do's and don'ts, from Dale and Plunkett (1991), which may help companies to avoid some of the difficulties and traps typically encountered in the collection of quality costs are given below.

DO

- Get the purpose and the strategy clear at the start.
- Report only costs produced or endorsed by accounts departments.
- Get data and costs from standard data wherever possible.
- Seek independent corroboration of any data which is doubtful.
- Avoid getting bogged down with trying to understand underlying details.
- Start with failure costs.
- Consider appraisal costs as a target for cost reduction.
- Consider ease of collection and start with the easiest.

- Ensure that any first-off quality costing attempt is soundly based.
- Refine large costs rather than attempt to quantify small unknown costs.
- Concentrate on costs that do or can change with quality improvement action.
- Remember that, from the quality cost collection point of view, rigid systems make for easier cost collection.
- Analyse and report costs clearly in a business context.
- Avoid a multiplicity of quality cost reports.
- Consider reporting warranty and guarantee payments as a separate quality cost category.
- Treat 'economic cost of quality' models with considerable suspicion.
- Forget that there are many complexities and difficulties in the measurement and collection of quality-related costs.

DONT

- Go it alone – seek accounting and technical help as appropriate.
- Expect accountants to take the initiative.
- Expect that standard accounting systems will yield the information needed.
- Expect accountants to arbitrate on what is, or is not, quality-related.
- Underestimate the difficulties with definitions of quality costs.
- Be too ambitious – start small.
- Expect too much from the first attempt.
- Lose sight of the fact that it is primarily a cost collection exercise.
- Agonise over relatively trifling costs.
- Use guesses – not even informed guesses.
- Make quality cost comparisons unless you can guarantee comparability.
- Assume straightforward operations will necessarily be easy to cost.
- Overlook the fact that transactions between companies and their customers and suppliers are often as difficult to cost as in-house transactions.
- Forget that prevention is the most difficult category to cost.
- Deduct from quality costs income from scrap.
- Forget that costs derived from estimates of time or from special intensive studies do not get revised.
- Concentrate exclusively on what is already known.
- Overlook the fact that concessions, document and design changes are a major source of quality-related costs which do not receive the attention they merit.
- Be constrained by the traditional PAF categorisation of quality costs.

4.10 Definitions and terminology

Some useful definitions and terms are given in Sections 4.3 and 4.6 of this chapter.

British Standards

BS 4778 *Quality vocabulary* Part 1:1987 *International terms;* (ISO 8402, 1986) (EN 28402:1991) Part 2: 1991 *Quality concepts and related definitions.*

BS 4891: 1972 *A guide to quality assurance.* (Now withdrawn)

BS 5750: 1987 *Quality systems;* (ISO 9000: 1987) (EN 29000: 1987).

BS 6143: 1981 *Guide to the determination and use of quality-related costs.*

BS 6143 *Guide to the economics of quality;* Part 1: 1992, *Process Cost Model;* Part 2: 1990, *Prevention, appraisal and failure model.*

PD 6470: 1981 Management of design for economic production.

References

Abed M H and Dale B G. 'An attempt to identify quality-related costs in textile manufacturing', *Quality Assurance,* 13(2), pp 41–5, 1987.

Blank L and Solarzarno J. 'Using quality cost analysis for management improvement', *Industrial Engineering,* 10(2), pp 46–51, 1978.

Campanella J (Ed). *Principles of Quality Costs: Principles, Implementation and Use,* ASQC

Quality Press, Milwaukee, 1990.

Cox B. Interface of quality costing and terotechnology'. *The Accountant*, 21 June, pp. 800–1, 1979.

Crossfield R T and Dale B G. 'Mapping quality assurance systems: a methodology'. *Quality and Reliability Engineering International*, 1990.

Dale B G and Plunkett J J. *Quality Costing*. Chapman and Hall, London, UK, 1991.

Dale B G and Plunkett J J. *The Case for Costing Quality*. Department of Trade and Industry, London, UK, 1992.

Feigenbaum A V. 'Total quality control'. *Harvard Business Review*, 34(6), pp 93-101, 1956.

Feigenbaum A V. *Total quality control*, 3rd Edition, McGraw-Hill, New York, USA, 1983.

Marsh J. *Process modelling for quality improvement*, Proceedings of the Second International Conference on Total Quality Management in London. IFS Publications, pp 111–21, 1989.

NEDO. *Quality and value for money*. A report to the NEDC by the Task Force on Quality and Standards, National Economic Development Office, London, UK, 1985.

Plunkett J J and Dale B G. *Some pitfalls and practicalities of quality-related cost collection*, Proceedings of the Institution of Mechanical Engineers. 199(B1) pp 29–33, 1985.

Plunkett J J and Dale B G. 'Quality costs: a critique of some "economic cost of quality" models'. *International Journal of Production Research*, 28(11), pp 1713–26, 1988.

Plunkett J J and Dale B G. 'Quality-related costing: findings from an industry-based research study'. *Engineering Management International*, 4(4), pp 247–57, 1988.

Ross D T. 'Structured analysis: a language for communicating ideas'. *IEE Transactions on Software Engineering*, SE-3(1), 1977.

CHAPTER 5

The marketing function in quality management

5.1 Introduction

The objectives of an effective quality system should be to satisfy customer needs and expectations, whether the customer is the ultimate consumer, user, client, beneficiary or second party, while at the same time serving to protect the company's interests. It is a valuable management resource in the optimisation, control and improvement of product and service quality in relation to risk, cost and benefit considerations.

Risk considerations

For the company, consideration needs to be given to non-conforming products or services which will ultimately lead to loss of image or reputation, loss of market share, complaint claims, liability and wastage of resources in whatever form this takes.

For the customer, risks such as those pertaining to the health and safety of people, dissatisfaction with goods and services, availability, marketing claims and loss of confidence, need to be considered.

Cost considerations

For the company, consideration has to be given to costs due to marketing and design deficiencies, and non-conformances, including unsatisfactory materials, rework, repair, replacement, reprocessing, loss of production, warranties, field repair and product recall campaigns.

The customer will need to consider costs such as safety, acquisition, operating, maintenance, downtime, repair and disposal.

Benefit considerations

The company would expect to see some increased profitability and market share.

For the customer, consideration has to be given to reduced costs, improved fitness for use, increased satisfaction, and growth in confidence in the performance of the supplier.

In addition to carrying out its prime function of selling a product or service in accordance with departmental objectives, the marketing function also has an important role in determining and defining customer needs, expectations, future product and service requirements and benchmarking. Marketing have a key input into an organisation's long and short-term R & D. They have an important role in product and service quality because of their direct relationship with the customer and are at the front end of the product development cycle, being involved with initial identification of market demand, and they should take the lead in establishing quality requirements for the product or service. In fact, market research is the starting point for TQM. The quality philosophy has got to be market-orientated. It is no use having a product or service which is free from non-conformities or whose key quality characteristics and/or parameters are uniform around a nominal or target value, but for which there is no demand. This is the reason why marketing and sales personnel should receive some training in the fundamentals of TQM and quality improvement.

In summary, the marketing function should:

- determine and promote the need and demand for a product or service;
- accurately define the market demand and sector. This is important in determining the grade, quantity, price and timing estimates for the product or service. The market research activity also provides information on what the company's competitors are doing. They should ensure that the production or operations-related functions are consulted and their commitment obtained, with reference to the ability of the producing system to satisfy the suggested quality requirements for the product or service;
- accurately determine customer requirements by a review of contract or market needs; actions include an assessment of consumer tastes, grade of service and reliability expected, availability, unstated expectations or biases held by customers. Where necessary, customers should be assisted in developing a product or service specification in terms of the desired requirements and product characteristics;
- conduct on-going research to examine changing market needs, new technology and the impact of competition;
- in conjunction with customers, try to specify requirements in accordance with established national or international standards. Marketing personnel need to be fully aware of the financial implications of offering to supply to the customer modified or non-standard products or features;
- review legislation (e.g. health, safety and environmental)
- develop a database profile of their customers;
- develop a database profile of competitors and monitor their activities and performance;
- communicate all customer requirements clearly and accurately within the company, in particular, to the design function;
- study cost estimates from all major functions engaged in the project, prior to pricing a product or service;
- arrange visits of company personnel to the customer.

This chapter explores the role of the marketing function in relation to the management of product and service quality.

5.2 The requirements

All requirements should be known or anticipated at the formative stage. The word 'requirements' covers, in particular, functional needs, and in general such things as quality, reliability, durability, safety, maintainability and a good 'appearance'. Acceptable levels, as perceived by the customers, for all these requirements are necessary at minimum cost and 'value for money'. Almost any inter-relationship of product requirements will produce some that tend to augment each other and some requirements that conflict.

In order to determine whether requirements conflict or augment each other, all the relevant circumstances should be studied carefully. These may be collected into two broad categories: first, the product or service characteristics determined by customers' operating requirements, dependent upon market analysis; second, the production/operations requirements with the addition of purchasing, storage and distribution activities, as well as the actual processes of products.

One word, 'cost', reaches right across the second category and indicates the framework within which customers' demands must be met. Clearly, while the excellence of a product or service will depend upon how well all requirements have been satisfied, it is the superior differences between a product or service and competing ones that may encourage customers to buy. In many cases, these differences may appear to be slight and have very little connection with basic performance requirements, but they cannot be ignored. Therefore, company managements are faced, not just with defining all objectives, but also with deciding their relative importance according to agreed market strategies. The characteristics that determine the nature of a product can be summarised as follows:

- All product functions must be known or anticipated because all are related;
- Conditions that influence costs, i.e. those arising not just when making the product or providing the service, but also when operating the entire corporate management system, act as a framework within which all product/service functions must be satisfied;
- The relative importance of each product function must be known, especially in highly competitive markets, because it is the difference between these functions and those of competing products that help to decide sales.

These conditions emerge from the study of the nature of products. They may well be described as the static approach, but they do not meet all the conditions in which good design work involving the philosophy of standardisation will flourish. There is also the dynamic approach, which takes account of the forces acting to cause change and the effect of change on the character of the product.

Forces, such as technological advances, new product or service methods and feedback from manufacturing and field experience, create pressures that management cannot afford to ignore. Neither can they ignore the element of resistance to change. Almost always there is a resistance to change within an organisation due to conservative attitudes that undoubtedly exist. However, this reluctance should not be overstressed. A number of issues must be faced. The investment required to create change, whether for initial development or for modifying production/operational procedures and equipment is a major element of resistance. Existing material and stocks can be additional resistant elements. Customers themselves may sometimes shy away from change.

These issues should be tackled realistically and objectively because reluctance to change is often based on assumptions rather than on realistic estimates. Estimates of the investment required to effect change should be balanced against those of the return it offers. Change is always costly and brings with it a unique set of problems but should be looked upon as a means to facilitate improvement and to motivate employees at all levels of the organisational hierarchy. The assessment of customers' conservatism cannot be properly weighed unless the influence of sales techniques, both by the company and by competitors, is taken into account. In short, it is no good in any situation to sit back and say that nothing can be done. The one constant factor in business is that change is inevitable, but it has to be controlled by careful evaluation and it must be anticipated wherever possible and kept under control. In most markets, customer requirements are becoming increasingly rigorous and the competition is forever improving, this is why companies must pursue a policy of never-ending improvement.

Through recognising the need for new concepts and encouraging their evaluation, enlightened management can promote them, provided that the entire company is working together to the same end. Marketing, design and production or operations, finance and purchasing departments must play their part and must be controlled if the approach is to succeed. Management must encourage close liaison between departments and functions and see that the whole company contributes to the assessment made. New concepts do not just happen, they depend on a wide variety of inputs, such as marketing, production/operating cost data, technological development, details of competitors' achievements, performance measures, and even apparently unrelated happenings that have been found by experience to influence or forecast events in the market under consideration.

Hence, there must be feed forward from all departments of a company so that new concepts can be encouraged and evaluated and feedback through all departments of the company from the customer's experiences. There must be a constant evaluation of the situation throughout the life of the product and service not just during all stages of development. Apart from cost, a customer considers such factors as reliability, durability, the economics of logistic support (spares and ease of maintenance), the adaptability of the product to changed operating requirements, availability and adequate levels of quality conformance. Thus whole life costs must be taken into account.

It is clear that the successful and superior performing companies are those that pursue a 'customers first' strategy and who continually watch the market and pursue changes to meet the demands of the market. Benchmarking is now being used by an increasing number of companies in their search for continuous improvement. Details of benchmarking are given in Camp (1989) and AT and T (1992).

5.3 Product evolution

The idealised evolution of a product is illustrated in Figure 5.1 and the motivation/need stage in this evolution is discussed below.

Product idea

The *product idea* is a brief description of a proposed new product, what it has to do and why it might have potential for the organisation. In many industries this is called the *product concept*.

The idea may be triggered in any of the following ways:

- a need to fill the gap in revenue caused by a reduction in demand for existing products;
- a specific customer enquiry;
- a response to a perceived market opportunity;
- a research finding, perhaps associated with the development of a new technology;
- a new way of applying existing technology that may result in an innovation;
- a licence agreement that may require further design activity;
- a simply expressed creative thought from any source;
- a change of in-company facilities, such as the replacement of worn-out tooling, that may provide an opportunity to redesign the product.

Each product idea, from any source, should be assessed to establish whether:

- it is compatible with the corporate plans;
- there will be an adequate market demand;
- the product will lead to a worthwhile return that is compatible with the risks involved.

Project proposal

The purpose of a project proposal is to expand the product idea, confirm that it has potential and initiate a feasibility study. The proposal should be requested by a member of senior management and submitted to them for approval. A budget should be created and monitored to meet the financial plan.

The project proposal should include first statements or estimates of the following:

- the objectives,
- the market for the proposed product,
- the stage and completion timing,
- the project operating costs and capital requirements,
- the special subcontract requirements,
- the projected contribution to corporate turnover, profit and return on investment.

Feasibility study

Following approval of the project proposal a feasibility study should be carried out to provide sufficient information to allow the whole project to be approved or rejected by senior management.

Design brief

The *brief*, sometimes called the *target design* or *product specification*, should be a definitive statement or instruction to the designer of what is required. It should define all the requirements

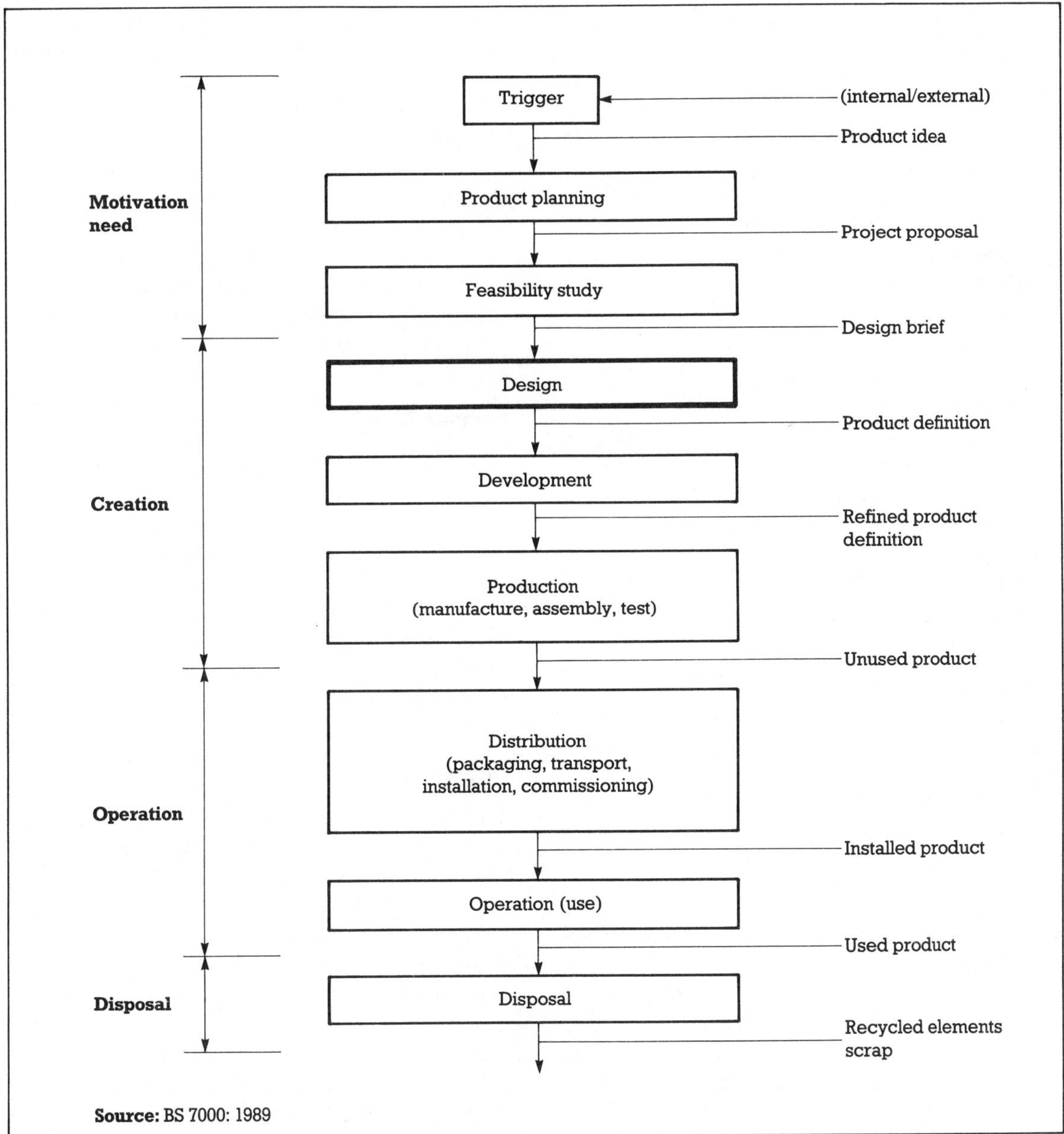

Figure 5.1 *Idealised product evolution*

and constraints, for example standards and regulations that the designer has to observe, but should not impose design solutions. The design brief should be prepared and documented in such a manner as to indicate senior management's requirement clearly to the designer. The documentation of the design brief should be controlled and changes recorded. It should also state the source of requirements and constraints.

It is essential for success in the market that the design brief should be comprehensive and complete, and deal adequately with the requirements in the following three broad categories: performance, cost and timescale.

- Performance requirements (targets) should

include, as appropriate, the following:
appearance and texture,
static requirements, for example size, mass, and colour,
dynamic requirements, for example input and/or output,
ease of use,
environmental conditions of use, for example temperature, humidity and shock,
safety,
reliability,
durability,
maintainability,
disposability.

- Cost requirements should include, as appropriate, the following:
manufacturing costs, including requirements for standardisation and rationalisation,
tooling costs,
maintenance costs,
other product-support costs,
design costs.
- Timescale requirements should include, as appropriate, the following:
quantity, for example number of articles to be produced per unit time,
product launch date,
anticipated warehouse or shelf life,
expected sales life for the product,
anticipated product life.

The brief should receive contributions from many sources and should evolve through a series of iterations. Sources that may be involved include research, design (including packaging), development, quality, marketing, finance, production/operations, manufacturing, distribution, sales and customers.

It is often the responsibility of the project manager to co-ordinate the project and to ensure that differences are resolved and that the final brief is approved by senior management.

The design manager should contribute to the design brief at the drafting stage so that it benefits from his/her specialist knowledge. They may need to obtain information that should be included in the design brief. For example, a policy to aim a product into new export markets may require the application of different technical and environmental requirements. Similarly, a requirement relating to a product's appearance or feel could require translation into limitations on surface roughness.

The design manager should also ensure that the brief contains all the information that is considered essential to undertake the design. It is recommended that a comprehensive checklist be prepared to ensure that the brief contains all the essential elements for the appropriate product group.

Service briefs

In terms of a service organisation once a decision has been made to offer a service, the results of the market research, analysis and the agreed supplier obligations should be incorporated into a service brief. This brief defines the customer's needs and the related service organisation's capabilities as a set of requirements and instructions that form the basis for the design of a service.

Project plans

The project manager should ensure that a resource plan is made. This may take the form of a bar chart or network analysis showing when particular skills and facilities are required.

Figure 5.2 shows a typical cash flow projection for the launch of a new product and it is recommended that a plan of this type be drawn up for each new product.

It is important to spend sufficient time and effort early in the project on evaluating the concept of the product and the approach to be taken, thus avoiding as far as possible any unforeseen problems that could lead to considerable excess time and cost. A progress plan should be used as an important yardstick in subsequent monitoring and controlling.

In many projects, prototype definitions may be expected to appear when about one-quarter of the total cost expenditure and one-third of the total time allowed have elapsed. The design brief is normally established after the first 5% to 10% of cost expenditure.

A plan for communication specific to the

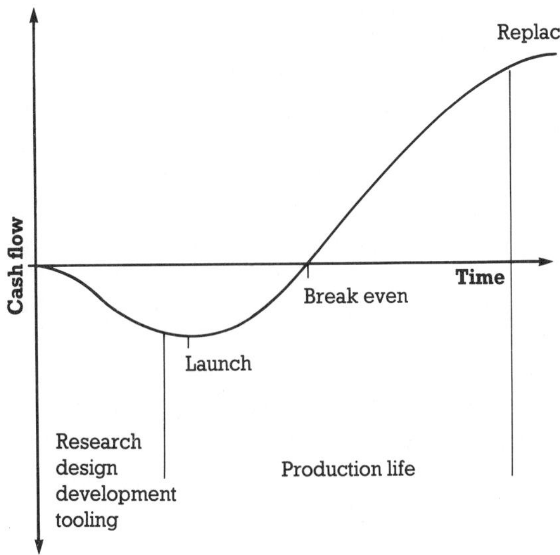

Figure 5.2 Projected net cash flow

project should be established to set out lines of authority, areas of responsibility, customer contact level and other specific internal or external communication systems not provided in the overall procedures of an organisation.

5.4 Marketing and the use of standards

The marketing department has a considerable influence on the customer's use of national and international standards. They should attempt to persuade customers to purchase standard products or options that are already in production and not be too willing to accept orders for special features or non-standard products – standardisation facilitates product and service quality. The marketing function can also contribute to the efficiency of the company by keeping abreast of matters relating to standardisation that affect the company business and influence the customer and designer accordingly. For example, their co-operation is essential for product rationalisation and considerable economies have been made by companies in standardising distribution quantities and sizes and types of pack to suit transport methods and conditions. This is a two-way process and communication from the customer and suppliers should also be used to update company standards.

There is also scope for using standards to reduce the paperwork and improve the corporate image. Standard procedures can be established for operational and training purposes to improve letter writing, answering telephone enquiries and communicating with customers.

5.5 Market readiness review

It is important that a review is carried out to determine whether production and process capability and field support are adequate for the new or redesigned product or service. The marketing and design functions need to liaise closely in conducting such a review. Depending upon the type of product, the review may cover the following points:

- availability and adequacy of installation, operation, maintenance and repair manuals;
- existence of an adequate distribution and customer service organisation;
- training of field personnel;
- availability of replacement products or parts;
- field trials;
- certification of the satisfactory completion of qualification tests;
- physical inspection of initial or sample production units and their packaging and labelling;
- evidence of process capability to meet specification on production or operational equipment.

5.6 Customer feedback information

The transmission of feedback information is an essential feature of a quality improvement process. However, Naybour and Dale (1985) comment that most of the major works on quality management mention feedback and its importance, but very few go farther than that. The marketing and servicing functions form the direct link with the customer and, as such, provide the main channel for the feedback of market reaction to the goods and services supplied. The marketing function should actively gather data (for example, field performance and complaints) on product and service performance from the customers and report this information back to appropriate people in the organisation; then follow up with customers to determine if they are satisfied.

It is important that some form of information monitoring and feedback system is used, on a continuous basis, throughout a product or service life cycle, in order to take advantage of information available for quality improving changes. The 'voice of the customer' should be listened to at all times. All information pertinent to the quality of a product or service should be analysed in detail, collated, interpreted and communicated in accordance with defined procedures. This system should analyse the degree to which the product or service satisfies customer expectations on quality, including safety, availability, reliability and durability. Such information will help to determine the nature and extent of problems in relation to customer experience and expectations.

In addition, feedback information may well provide clues to possible design changes and production control points, as well as appropriate management action. Information on complaints, the occurrence and modes of failure, customer needs and expectations or any problem encountered in use, should be made available for design review and corrective action in the supply and/or use of the item.

In some cases, it is useful to establish an early warning system for reporting instances of product or service failure or shortcomings, as appropriate, particularly for newly introduced products and services, to ensure rapid corrective action.

To obtain data on the customers' perceptions of the product and service, a variety of methods can be used to supplement the normal feedback channel. These include workshops and clinics, surveys, interviews, visits to customers, agents and distributors by employees from a variety of positions in the organisational hierarchy and trialing the service using 'mystery' shoppers (i.e. shoppers who are company employees but are unknown to the people from the site in question). However, care must be taken not to accumulate superfluous data and thus create problems with analysis which can result from ill-conceived surveys and questionnaires. It is prudent to seek professional advice regarding the confidence of expectations prior to submitting anything other than the simplest type of request for information to the market, otherwise much time and goodwill may be dissipated at considerable cost.

In conjunction with the design department, the marketing function should perform a periodic re-evaluation of the product or service in order to ensure that the design is still valid with respect to all specified requirements. This should include a review of customer needs and technical specifications in the light of field experiences, field performance surveys or new technology and techniques. The review should also consider process modifications. The quality system should ensure that any product and/or service and field experience indicating the need for design change is fed back for analysis. Care should be taken that design changes do not cause product or service quality to degrade and that proposed changes are evaluated for their impact on all characteristics in the design base line definition.

There is little doubt that companies from within the Pacific Rim have been using, for some years, a variety of means to pick up customer feedback from the marketplace, in order to improve the goodness of fit of their products or services to customer requirements. However, in the UK, there is evidence that suppliers, certainly in the automotive industry, do not go out of their way to obtain information on how their products perform in practice (Egan, 1986, and Lascelles and Dale, 1988). 'If the customer does not return the product, it must be satisfactory' was not an uncommon view. The main findings from some research studies which have touched on the subject of feedback are discussed below.

Duncalf and Dale (1988), reporting on research carried out on quality-related decision making in UK manufacturing companies, claim that few of the companies they studied had formal quality information systems which ensured that processes, procedures and decision making were carried out with the best up-to-date information. Feedback from the marketplace and/or via the customers was often processed in an informal and inadequate manner, and in many of the decisions analysed it was impossible to identify the precise route of this type of information in its circulation within companies. They also found that the feedback system for receiving quality-related information from the marketplace is not easily identified and felt that this state of affairs does bring into question the use of the information in decision making on quality improvement and product or service improvement.

Naybour and Dale (1985), reporting on a study of the sources of performance feedback information which exist in a multinational chemical company and the type of feedback which equipment manufacturers would like to receive, found that few suppliers appeared to receive any feedback information other than warranty claims, on which little performance analysis was carried out. They also pointed out that the data from computerised maintenance history systems could be used as a source of feedback to equipment manufacturers and that if companies wished to see an improvement in the quality of products purchased they should be prepared to expend more effort in feeding back to the suppliers information on how their product or service performs in practice.

Staveley and Dale (1987), reporting on their findings from a study of plant and equipment suppliers, believe that the main reason why the majority of manufacturers have not developed systems to obtain data from users is due to the difficulties encountered in obtaining meaningful information. They found that the main sources of feedback were from technical sales representatives, customer complaints and internal feedback obtained from monitoring recurrent orders for spares. They also made the point that most of the manufacturers they studied would use such feedback data if it was offered.

Lascelles and Dale (1988) claimed there were two types of quality measurement data which relate to customer satisfaction with the quality of a company's product and services, reactive (for example, failure data) and proactive (for example, benchmarking against competitors' products and services). They found that of the 206 companies responding to their survey and claiming to have recorded measures of customer satisfaction, only two reported the use of proactive measures. Their view was that suppliers see customer satisfaction in very simple terms; if the customer does not return the product then quality must be satisfactory. The following are given as examples quoted by respondent companies:

'Continual acceptance of delivered product certificates';
'Monitoring warranty claims';
'Adopting a specific quality management tool or technique'.

However, in relatively recent times some Western companies have started to grasp the value of market-related feedback data in their quality improvement efforts. For example, Jaguar Cars 'telephoned directly 150 new owners in Britain and a similar number in the United States, one month after purchase, and again nine months later' (DTI, 1986). The Ford Motor Company conduct interviews, carry out questionnaire surveys, and hold workshops and clinics to establish how well their products meet customer needs.

5.7 Product support

Dependent upon the type of goods or services supplied, it may be necessary to include support activities such as:

- the provision of 'technical' documentation and education for the user;
- planning and provisioning of adequate stocks of products or parts;
- total productive maintenance (TPM) to improve on equipment efficiency and effectiveness by cleaning, lubrication, adjustment or repair;
- the provision of skilled and prompt attention to all complaints.

In relation to after sales service the following activities are relevant:

- The design and function of special purpose tools or equipment for handling and servicing products during or after installation should be validated.
- Measuring and testing equipment used in field installation and tests needs to be controlled.
- Instructions for use which deal with the assembly and installation, commissioning, operation, spares or parts lists, and servicing of any product should be comprehensive and supplied to the customer in a timely manner. The instructions should be suitable for the intended reader.
- There must be adequate, logistic back-up, to include technical advice, spares or parts supply, and competent servicing. Responsibility should be clearly assigned and agreed among suppliers, distributors and users.
- Servicing personnel must be trained to ensure that they can carry out the required tasks.

Servicing activities, whether carried out by the manufacturer of the product or by a separate agent, need to be properly designed, planned and implemented.

5.8 Internal customers

The closer an organisation is to its customers, the more likely it is to meet their requirements and expectations. Where there is some form of buffer (for example, distributors and stockists) between the producer and the customer, some contact with the marketplace is certain to be lost. Using the same argument, some internal departments are more removed than others from the organisation's final customers. To ensure that every department and individual feels that they are at the front end in satisfying customer expectations and requirements, there is a need for some positive measure(s) of quality performance as perceived by the organisation's customers, to be reflected and translated into performance measures across all internal activities.

Every department of an organisation is a business operation with input from suppliers and output to its customers. The objective of every department should be to ensure that the demands of their individual customers are being met, so that the customer satisfaction test can be applied to every department. If each department within an organisation is satisfying its own internal customers then there is a very good chance that the organisation's final customers will have their expectations met. IBM Havant (Lewis, 1984) and Philips Components (Payne in Dale and Plunkett, 1990) are two organisations which have pioneered an approach to ensure that every internal department is focused on the needs of its customers. At IBM this basic approach is called a department purpose analysis (DPA), while at Philips Components it is called a departmental improvement review (DIR). The approach is beneficial for involving non-manufacturing departments in the quality and improvement process. Payne states that:

> DIR is a formal management improvement procedure having a six-step structure. It is designed to:
> i) identify clearly the purpose of any activity,
> ii) test this purpose of alignment with the aims, objectives and goals of the overall business,
> iii) formally examine the internal customer-supplier relationship,
> iv) identify the major workload elements of the activity,
> v) expose any elements of wasted (i.e. non-value-added) work.
>
> Its major outputs are:
>
> - to establish a package of performance measures reflecting the critical aspects of internal functional performance and those seen as critical by the customers;
> - to establish a project-based improvement plan;
> - to establish the improvement activity as a continuous one by means of a review mechanism.
>
> (Payne in Dale and Plunkett, 1990)

The following are the DPA implementation guidance notes as used by Grace Dearborn Ltd. at their Widnes plant:

1) Define the purpose and aims of the department, and agree with line management that it is consistent with the Company's

mission and vision, i.e. What are we here for?

2) Draw up a list of the main tasks carried out within the department and consolidate to no more than 15 tasks. Prioritise the tasks and agree the top 10 tasks with departmental staff and confirm with line management.
3) List the key skills and activities for each of the top 10 tasks. Where applicable this should be done by task and agreed within the department.
4) For each of these tasks, list who are the customers and who are the suppliers.
5) Within each of these tasks, identify for each supplier what input they provide and who provides it.
6) Within each of these tasks, identify for each customer what output they receive and who receives it.
7) Discuss the input received from each supplier, identify any irregularities and agree specifications for needs.
8) Discuss the output provided with each customer, identify any irregularities and agree specification for needs.
9) Identify any non-added-value time. This is the time spent on tasks carried out which do not meet customer requirements first time and need some reworking, time spent on tasks with no identified customers, etc.
10) Draw up an action plan to achieve agreed specifications and to reduce the non-added-value time. Confirm with line management that the actions and time scales are appropriate.
11) Review the skill requirements to identify any training needs.

Part of a DPA from the Sales Office of Grace Dearborn Ltd (Widnes) is given in Table 5.1 (on pp. 96–7).

5.9 Definitions and terminology

The following are some useful definitions and terms used in this chapter.

Availability: the ability of an item to be in a state to perform a required function under given conditions at a given instant of time or over a given time interval, assuming that the required external resources are provided.

Durability: the ability of an item to perform a required function under given conditions of use and maintenance, until a limiting state is reached.

Maintainability: the ability of an item under given conditions of use, to be retained in, or restored to, a state in which it can perform a required function, when maintenance is performed under given conditions and using stated procedures and resources.

Quality level: any relative quality measure obtained by comparing observed values with the relevant requirements.

Quality system: the organisational structure, responsibilities, procedures, processes and resources for implementing quality management.

Reliability: the ability of an item to perform a required function under stated conditions for a stated period of time.

Safety: the freedom from unacceptable risks of personal harm.

Specification: the document that prescribes the requirements with which the product or service has to conform.

British Standards

BS 4778 *Quality vocabulary:* Part 1: 1987 *International terms* (ISO 8402: 1986) (EN 28402: 1991), Part 2: 1991 *Quality concepts and related definitions.*

BS 5750: Quality systems: Part 1: Section 0.1 1987 *Quality systems – principal, concepts and applications: Guide to selection and use* (ISO 9000: 1987) (EN 29000: 1987).; Part 4: 1990 *Guide to the use of BS 5750;* Part 1, *Specification for design/development, production, installation and servicing;* Part 2, *Specification for production and installation;* Part 3, *Specification for final inspection and test;* Part 8: 1991 *Guide to quality management and quality systems elements for services* (ISO 9004–2: 1991).

BS 7000: *Design management system:* Part 1: 1989 *Guide to managing product design.*

Table 5.1 Departmental Purpose Analysis (**a**) Main tasks – customers

Task	What is the output?	Who receives it?
Taking of orders	An order blank or client order	Sales office
Processing orders	A works order set	Warehouse, stores, production control, purchasing and manufacturing plants
Answering enquiries and liaison with shipping and transport, warehousing and customer services	Fast accurate response	Clients, unit offices, sales persons, credit control, transport and stores
Daily booked order figures	Accurate booked sales figures	Sales management, I. Priestnell, R. Clifford and T.E. Larsen
Outstanding order list – chemicals	That all booked orders are progressed to invoices	Sales office
Outstanding order list – engineering	That all booked orders are progressed to invoices	Sales office
New account raising	The facility to process client orders	Sales office
Process confirmatory orders	Processed client orders	Sales office
Ordering and progress of engineering bought out items	Purchase requisitions and progress sheet	Engineering and purchasing departments
Price list maintenance	Special price lists	Sales office and sales management
Forward order diary	Orders raised to clients requirements	Sales office
Water treatment service and supervisory contracts	Memos annotated with account numbers and account special instruction facility displaying contract	Sales office and accounts department

Source: Grace Dearborn Ltd, Widnes

Table 5.1 *Continued* (b) Main tasks – suppliers

Task	What is the input?	Who provides it?	Is it right?	How can it be modified?
Taking of orders	Phone calls, telexes, fax messages, ansafone, postal orders	Clients, sales, persons, unit offices	In the main yes, but some aspects such as packaging sizes, address detail, order nos, are sometimes given with the assumption we know what is missing	Personnel placing orders could be more explicit with details. Some detail could be checked at unit offices prior to passing to sales office. Ansafone could be replaced by the Wang electronic mail system
Processing orders	Computer via visual display units and internal sales office order input form	Sales office	Yes, within our abilities and constant interruptions by telephone calls and visitors which by causing distractions can lead to errors	A CSP is in the system to assist with efficiency. Sales department could specify if the checking of product programme is required as some require it and others do not
Answering enquiries and liaison with shipping and transport, warehousing and customer stores	Telephone calls to engineering, technical, purchasing, production, credit control, customer stores, shipping & transport and warehousing	Clients, unit offices & sales persons	Generally yes, but clients sometimes require miracles and are annoyed and sometimes abusive if they do not get them	Sales office is manned 9 to 5 pm. Technical back-up and stores are often not available during the working day. Warehouse is unmanned after 4pm which makes transport ineffective as they can only answer in the main based on information from the warehouse
Daily booked order figures	Edit list	Computer department	Yes	Computer could produce the same data but would have to run in parallel for 1 year while it built up a year's record
Outstanding order list – chemicals	Computer listing 106	Computer department	No	Glassware and reagents should be on engineering list. Due date is required
Outstanding order list – engineering	Computer listing 109	Computer department	No	Glassware and reagents should be on this list not on chemical list
New account raising	Orders	Clients, sales persons, unit offices	No	Sales office often get passed around in obtaining territory numbers, responsible sales units/offices should know their own prospects
Process confirmatory orders	Postal orders	Clients, unit offices, sales persons	No	These are confirmatory to verbal instructions, they are not required from unit offices and sales persons

Source: Grace Dearborn Ltd, Widnes

PD 3542: 1991 *The role of standards in company quality management.*

PD 6470: 1981 *The management of design for economic production.*

References

AT and T. *Benchmarking: Focus on World-class Practices*, AT and T Quality Steering Committee, Corporate Quality Office, Indianapolis, 1992.

Camp R C. *Benchmarking: The Search for Best Practices that Lead to Superior Performance.* ASC Quality Press, Milwaukee, USA, 1989.

Dale, B G and Plunkett J J (Ed). 'Managing Quality', Chapter 20 by B J Payne, *The Quality Improvement Process in Service Areas.* Philip Allan, Herts, UK, 1990.

Department of Trade and Industry, *The case for quality.* Department of Trade and Industry, London, 1986 and 1990.

Duncalf A J and Dale B G. *The management of product quality: a study.* Proceedings of the Institution of Mechanical Engineers, 202 (B3), pp 135–41, 1988.

Egan J. *Benefits of Total Quality: a Vehicle Manufacturer's View.* Unpublished paper presented at the Society of Motor Manufacturers and Traders Drive for Total Quality Conference, 5 February 1986.

Lascelles D M and Dale B G. 'A study of the quality management methods employed by UK automotive suppliers.' *Quality and Reliability Engineering International*, 4 (4), 301–9, 1988.

Lewis L. *Quality improvement handbook.* IBM, Hants, UK, 1984.

Naybour P M and Dale B G. 'The relevance of performance information to product quality.' *Engineering Management International*, 3, (2), pp. 175–82, 1985.

Staveley J C and Dale B G. 'Some factors to consider in developing a quality-related feedback system.' *Quality and Reliability Engineering International*, 3 (4), pp 265–71, 1987.

CHAPTER 6

Designing for quality

6.1 Introduction

The best production/operations methods cannot compensate for poor or inadequate design and the design activity is fundamental to the creation of product and/or service quality. Product/service design is the formative stage of the manufacturing/operations process. Any product or service competes in its market according to performance, appearance, price, delivery, reliability, durability, safety and maintainability. All of these factors depend fundamentally upon the design of the product/service.

Quality, reliability and durability cannot be inspected into a product, it must be designed in before manufacture by the effective and accurate translation of customer requirements into practical designs and specifications that permit production, maintenance and servicing to be technically and economically feasible. The rôle of the design function is to translate customer requirements indicated by market research and/or R & D projects from the product/design brief into practical designs and specifications for materials, product and processes. The objective of design management is to provide a product design that meets the design brief. The same is also true of many services, including health care, banking, insurance and legal aid.

The process of designing a service involves converting the service brief into specifications for both the service and its delivery and control, while reflecting the organisation's options (i.e. aims, policies and costs). Design of the service specification, the service delivery specification and quality control specification are interdependent and interact throughout the design process.

In the design phase all concerned must be in agreement on the quality aspects of the design and the specification, this should be unambiguous and adequately define acceptance and rejection criteria.

Failure, in the design stage, to take full account of environmental conditions, or simple errors of judgement can have far reaching consequences and will usually have a greater effect on product and service quality than poor workmanship. For example, a design error reaching production/operations undetected will affect all of the commodity being produced and probably necessitate additional equipment costs. On the other hand, if an effective quality system is in place, a fault or error in production can be recognised at a stage where perhaps only a small percentage of output of whatever form is affected. All the evidence from bodies such as the Design Council indicates that the performance and appearance of many products could be substantially improved, which in turn would have the effect of increasing market appeal and reducing production costs. A poorly designed product may damage a company's reputation and prospects for growth, particularly if the product is unreliable, unsafe or difficult to maintain and repair.

In a number of Japanese companies during the development and design stage, engineers from production preparation and quality assurance departments take up residency in the development and design department. This is to ensure that the product is designed with quality and manufacturing in mind. In the production preparation stage, design engineers take up residency in the production preparation department. This is to ensure design intent, to feed in 'know-how' and experience obtained during the design and development stage, to facilitate producibility and quality, and to promote the implementation of counter-measures against potential abnormalities. This form of concurrent or simultaneous engineering through the use of cross-functional teamwork is now being taken-up by an increasing number of Western organisations.

In general terms the quality of a design is determined by:

- the degree to which the functional requirements have been expressed in the design;
- the degree to which the specification requirements have been realised;
- the degree to which the design permits rational production or operation and marketing;
- the efforts made to attain a target life (or failure rate) with low maintenance costs;
- the speedy feedback of new experience and quality troubles.

The senior management team of the organisation must integrate in an effective manner their objectives in design, development, production/operations and marketing to ensure the quality of the product or service as desired by the customer. To manage design effectively the following information needs to be known:

- what business the organisation is in;
- the quantified targets for growth and profitability;
- the identity and market position sought.

This information should be communicated to, and understood by, all concerned.

This chapter explores the key activities of the design function and highlights the importance of the design activity in TQM. It should be noted that BS 7000 (1989) provides useful guidance on the management of product design and outlines an efficient level of current practice that companies should aim to achieve. The standard emphasises that the design process has to be managed in the same way as other parts of the business. At a seminar to launch BS 7000, the keynote speaker, Geoffrey Constable, made the following points based on statistics collected by the Design Council:

- only 27 per cent of companies have a corporate policy favourable to good design;
- only 20 per cent of designers were adequately briefed;
- only 10 per cent of design projects were subjected to a design brief;
- only 6 per cent of companies had suitable policies for ensuring that their designers were kept up-to-date by appropriate training.

6.2 Design planning and objectives

Responsibilities must be assigned for various design duties to activities inside and/or outside the organisation. It is also important that all those who contribute to design are aware of their responsibilities for achieving and improving product and service quality. The need to identify and control design interfaces with other functions cannot be over-emphasised. Designers need to be free to be creative, but their work needs to be controlled where it affects the work of others. It is essential that the design team is not isolated from the staff of other disciplines and it is important that production/operations, and quality and reliability personnel are involved in the design processes.

The need for a design and development programme will depend upon the nature and complexity of the specified requirements. The programme generally consists of a breakdown of the design processes into separate elements and can be presented as a chart showing the different activities against a time scale. This enables progress to be measured. Key events and design reviews should also be indicated on the chart. The extent of each phase and the stages at which design reviews or evaluations will take place may depend upon the product or service application, its design complexity, the extent of innovation and technology being introduced, the degree of standardisation and similarity with past proven designs.

In addition to customer needs, the designer needs to give due consideration to the requirements relating to safety, environmental and other regulations, including items in the organisation's quality policy which may go beyond existing statutory requirements.

During the design evaluation process lifecycle cost studies should be performed to select the optimum combination of design features. These include, in particular, the maintenance concept and the maintainability characteristics. The trade-off, including lifecycle costs and other studies, provides input to system evaluation resulting in the selection of an optimum design.

The quality aspects of the design should adequately define characteristics important to quality, such as the acceptance and rejection criteria, with both fitness for purpose and safeguards against misuse being important considerations. Product or service definition may also include reliability, durability and maintainability, and include benign failure and safe disposability, if appropriate.

The designer must not prescribe irrational tolerance limits in the specification. While tolerances should be adequate to define the required quality, they should be no more stringent than required. Unduly restricted tolerances can create requirements for equipment and process capabilities, operator skill, or time beyond that which is really essential. Moreover, output designated as non-conforming to such tolerances adds unnecessarily to overall costs. At the same time, the specification tolerances should represent the requirements that may exist for interchangeability. A common argument used for the setting of tight tolerances by the design function is 'If we set realistic tolerances the production/operations function will only claim that they cannot conform to them. Therefore, if they are set deliberately tight at the outset, it will not matter if they are subsequently relaxed.' In the authors' view the way in which tolerances and specifications are established by the design department in some organisations is very debatable.

The design manager should play his/her part in ensuring that the product or service design brief continues to reflect the product or service requirements, and that changes to the brief are authorized by the person responsible for the brief. During the design process many questions and suggestions may occur that reflect on the adequacy or correctness of the brief. The following are typical of such questions and suggestions:

a) Since the brief was written a new material has become available that is not listed as one of the options. Can we use it?
b) Can the requirements for size or shape be relaxed? They can be achieved but only at a high cost.

It is essential that questions such as these are considered as the design progresses.

6.3 The main stages in design and development

The design and development stage normally follows a chronological sequence and is presented in four stages (see Figure 6.1 overleaf) as follows:

- conceptual design;
- embodiment design;
- detail design;
- design for manufacture.

Conceptual design

This is the stage of the design process in which ideas and working principles for the product are conceived. Such ideas only need to contain

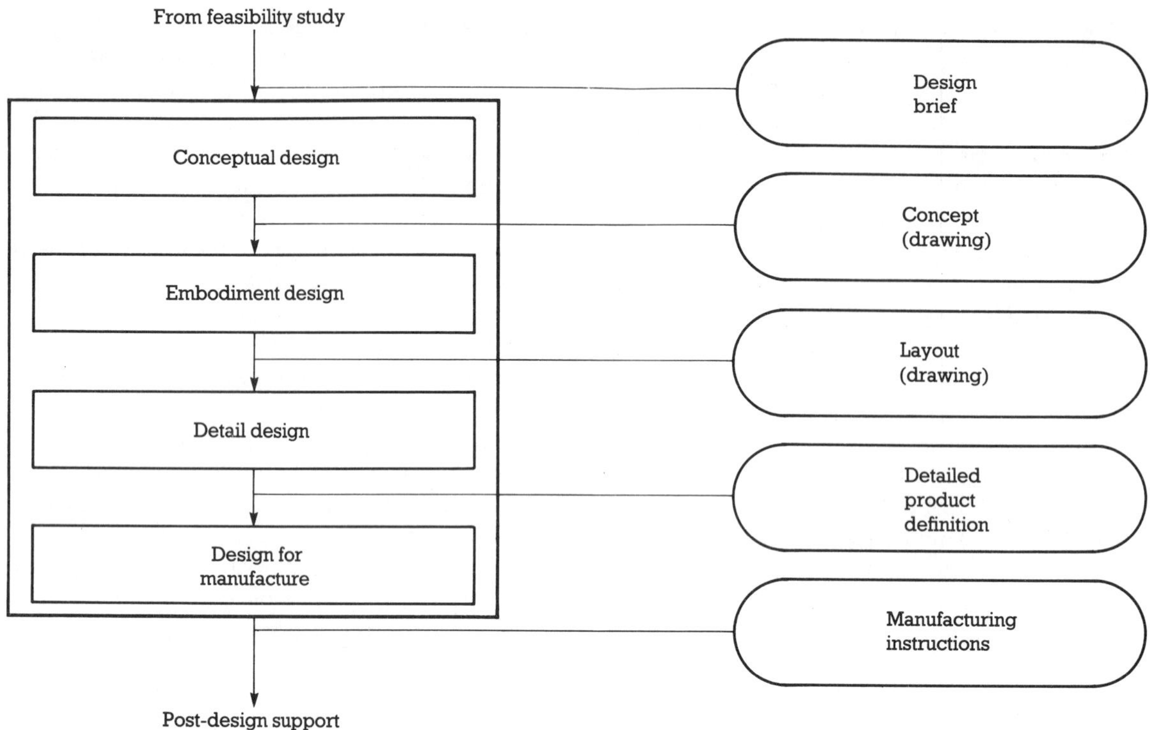

Figure 6.1 Idealised design process

such detail necessary to define the essential elements of the idea or concept.

Embodiment design

This stage lays the foundation for good detail design through a structured development of the concept. At the conclusion of this stage most areas of design uncertainty should have been resolved, the general layout completed and much of the development and model testing carried out. The output will be in the form of data on drawings or other media sufficient for full-scale models to be made, if required, and detail design to be undertaken. It is appropriate to conduct a design review at the completion of this stage.

Detail design

In this stage the final details of the design are completed. Lack of proper attention to detail design can lead to many problems, including delays in the design process and final designs that fail to meet the design brief. Therefore, it is necessary for design management to maintain an involvement and control that is at least as significant as that in the earlier stages. A design review at, or during, the completion of this stage is essential.

Design for manufacture

The completion of the detail design will not necessarily result in instructions suitable for the manufacture of the product. Irrespective of whether these take the form of drawings, written instructions or electronic data, it is essential that manufacturing instructions should be subject to strict discipline.

Some important procedures are as follows:

- control of the interface design (the design of multiple component products by teams needs control to ensure compatibility of, and interface between, components without detriment to product performance);
- control of manufacturing instructions (also known as configuration control);
- checking the manufacturing instructions.

6.4 Quality in design

The following features that enhance the quality in design of a product should be considered from the conceptual stage. (Some of these features will be described in more detail later in this chapter.)

- Avoid unnecessary complexity; simplicity aids manufacture. An easily manufactured product/component gives rise to less risk of process error, additional costs and quality-related troubles. Where appropriate, existing, proven components of known cost and reliability should be used. This reduces the cost of product design and testing.
- Avoid unnecessary variety. Design and specify components for common usage wherever possible because this results in longer production runs of fewer different parts with obvious economic and quality advantages.
- Avoid unnecessary costs. Avoid over-specification of tolerances and materials that will result in a less competitive product.
- Minimise or eliminate features known to cause quality troubles. Whether the product is a one-off or being designed for mass production, feedback from both the manufacturer and the end user should be used to assist in this task. In the one-off case the feedback will come from 'know-how' in related designs.

It is essential to produce a product that is fit for its purpose. Any company that fails to do this by under-specification has little future. A company that over-specifies is wasting money and is likely to be uncompetitive. This is bound to result in a loss of its market share.

6.5 Design for minimum cost

The responsibility for satisfying the product or service brief with a product or service that can be produced at a cost and which allows a profitable return on investment rests primarily with the designer. Product or service costs originate mainly in design and the designer has a prime responsibility to ensure that the project gives optimum value for money. The irreducible cost of the product or service is determined by the designer. A poor design decision may commit a company to many years of producing a design which would have been more profitable had the design been better conceived at the outset.

While the techniques of value engineering in the post-design phase and value analysis in the pre-design stage (described later in the chapter) can often improve the value and reduce the total cost of a well designed product, it is far more difficult to reduce significantly the cost of a badly designed product or service. A major factor is that products or services should be designed for economic production/operations. This can be achieved through the simultaneous design of product, service and process and should be the major objective of the people involved. Cost is just as much an attribute of the design specification as is performance, appearance, reliability, life, safety and time, and is an essential factor to be satisfied by the optimum design solution. A design that fails to meet its cost specification is no better than one that fails to satisfy its performance requirements.

At the same seminar mentioned in the introduction to this chapter, Geoffrey Constable, stated that, based on statistics collected by the Design Council, modern products could, on average, be redesigned to:

- reduce manufacturing costs by 24 per cent;
- improve market demand by 29 per cent;
- reduce the capital tied up in stocks and work-in-progress by 37 per cent.

In today's industrial and commercial climate, the opportunity for cost reduction by good design that permits economic operations is considerable. Whatever organisational approach is adopted to achieve more economic designs it will ultimately depend on people. An additional benefit of management cost control is that it requires the co-operation of all departments: design, production/operations, quality, finance/accounting, purchasing and marketing to achieve success, and thereby opens up more channels of communication and opportunities for co-operation.

This does not mean the benefits are easily

achieved. Marketing and sales personnel may accurately reflect customer difficulties with a particular product or service operation but over-estimate the value of a design modification that increases the costs in all other departments, resulting in little profit being made on the contract. The purchasing manager may know the lower unit cost for larger orders of the same material but this may sacrifice operational efficiency or performance. This is particularly true in the case of just-in-time (JIT). The production or operations manager may know the extra time and cost of generating a fine finish or shorter delivery time but is often unaware of the importance or otherwise to the product or service performance. All relevant personnel should know the extra cost involved of introducing, for example, a new material to the company, in terms of purchasing negotiations, testing and storage, or changing the processing sequence. In other words, cost reduction must be a totally integrated activity. Increasingly then the designers' job is one of co-ordination and accommodation of the, sometimes conflicting, interests of all departments, functions or groups.

The most junior designer, research chemist or technical specialist must realise that a detailed specification is not just an instruction to production/operations, it is a statement on specifications, tolerances, materials and production methods that will demand the inevitable and irrevocable expenditure of sums of money that add to the cost of the finished product or service. The published document PD 6470 (1992) contains some useful cost data pertaining to design for economic production.

6.6 Design and maintainability

As already mentioned, the designer is responsible for the achievement of operational requirements including maintainability requirements in design within the usual constraints of schedules and costs. In order to satisfy these requirements, maintainability should be specified at the beginning of the design process and maintainability studies, as appropriate, should be performed during this process.

BS 6548: Part 2 (1992) provides guidance on studies which should be carried out during the design phase and on the relationship of these studies to maintainability and maintenance support tasks. The purpose of maintainability studies is to assist design decision-making, to predict the quantitative maintainability characteristics of an item and to help in the evaluation of alternative design options.

Maintainability studies should be developed and integrated with the design process to meet the stated system operational requirements. To ensure that these requirements are met, maintainability studies should be carried out during all phases of design, and their results should provide inputs to design decision-making.

Maintainability analysis, an integral part of maintainability studies, is a process which translates operational requirements into detailed qualitative and quantitative maintainability requirements and design criteria. It provides inputs to the design process by means of documentation under the following headings:

- specific maintainability requirements to be met in the design;
- design guidelines and check-lists to ensure that the required maintainability features are included in the design;
- a summary of basic maintenance functions and support requirements.

Maintainability analyses are involved in iterative design trade-off studies, a number of which may be required before the optimum design is selected. They should also be used to evaluate the extent of achievement of the maintainability design requirements.

Figure 6.2 illustrated the way in which maintainability studies in design and their sequences relate to design tasks.

6.7 Safety

Safety relates to the freedom from risks that are harmful to a person, or group of persons, either local to the hazard, nationally or even

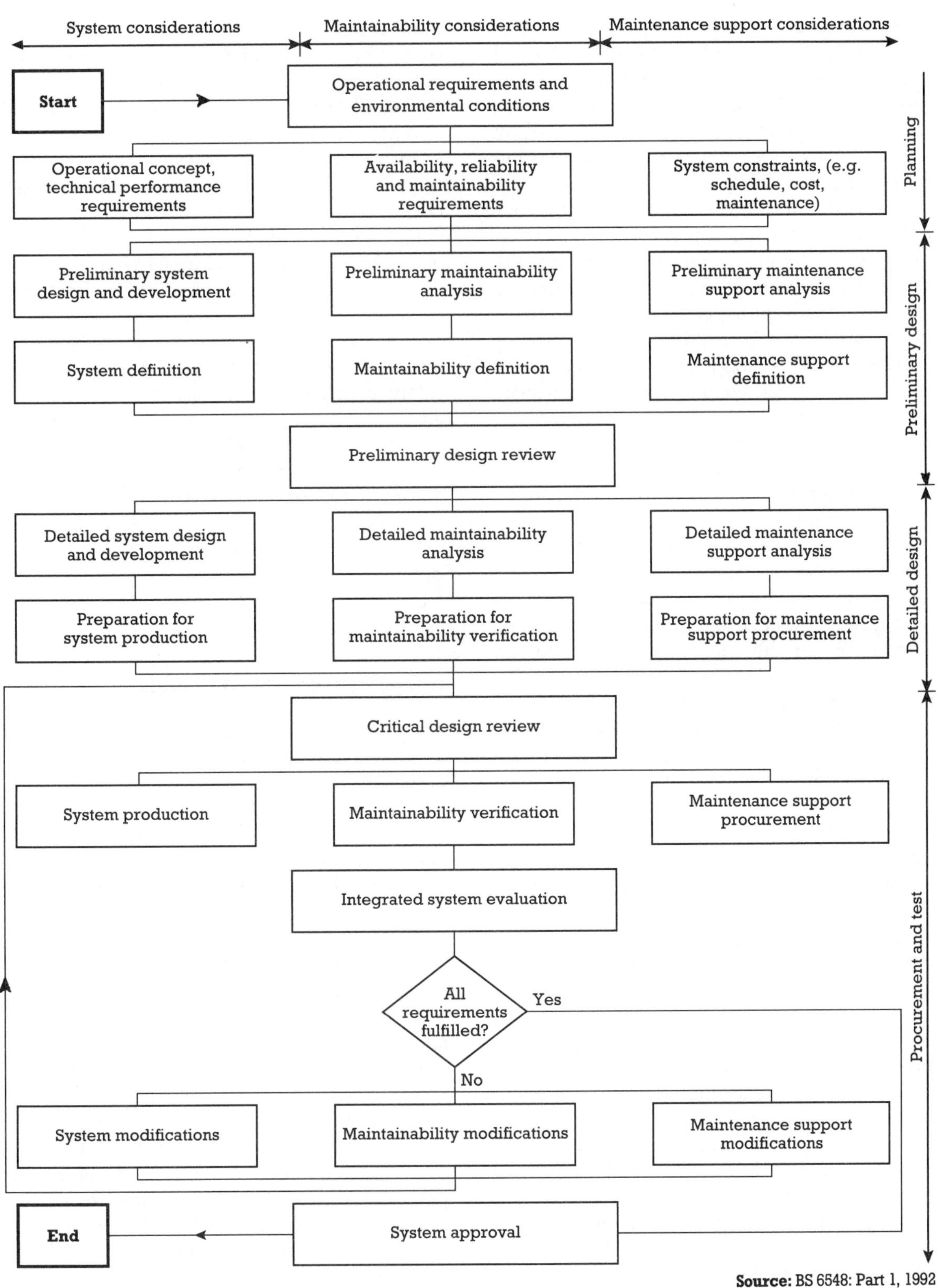

Source: BS 6548: Part 1, 1992

Figure 6.2 Maintainability studies in the design process

worldwide. It is implied that for the consequences of an event to be defined as a hazard (i.e. a potential for causing harm) there is some risk to the human population and therefore safety could not be guaranteed, even if the risk is accepted when judged against some criterion of acceptability.

National and international legal requirements that may place constraints on designs and designers must be identified at the outset of the design process. These are not only concerned with the aspect of health and safety of material but also with the avoidance of danger to persons and property when material is being used, stored, transported or tested. Today, there is an increasing amount of international legislation which places certain constraints on designs, which must be taken into account prior to the production of products and services for sale.

In the UK, the Consumer Protection Act, 1987 has introduced a major legal requirement for product safety and product liability. It strengthens existing legislation and increases safeguards for the consumer. This makes it easier for the consumer or user of a product to put forward a claim against a manufacturer, if they are injured or suffer a loss due to defective goods. It places a clear responsibility on the manufacturer to ensure that they supply safe products and services to the marketplace. The issue of strict product liability will cause a manufacturer to ensure that their quality system, traceability system and procedures, and advanced quality planning methods are efficient and effective.

Regardless of this new Act, a supplier has always been held responsible under the common law of tort if they distributed products or services which present hazards to the public (if professional negligence can be proven). Certain risks, for example cutting edges of knives or folding parts of chairs, are commonly accepted. However, with more complex equipment, it is necessary for the design function to recognise factors that may have concealed danger potential. As far as possible such elements should be eliminated from the design or be in accordance with fail-safe principles. For example, when a hazard is imminent an appliance immediately ceases to operate, pending the correct positioning of a particular guard on the equipment.

Hazards can be classified according to the severity of their potential effects, either in terms of safety, economics or other consequences. Different industries use different classifications. Such classifications are purely subjective and usually require qualification and quantification, by definition of the precise form of the hazard and a quantified evaluation of the consequences.

The increasing use of new materials and performance specifications can present certain safety problems for designers. For example, although mechanical performance figures quoted for metallic and non-metallic items may be identical, a non-metallic component may require a flammability test if used at elevated temperatures, whereas a metallic component might require corrosion tests if used in adverse climatic conditions.

6.8 Standards in design

The time span between a good, practical idea and the manufacture of a marketable product is and always will be uncertain. Many products have reached the market place too late. BS 7000 is about using a methodology to improve the systematic designing, developing, market researching, planning and development of the manufacturing process. Used as an audit tool and aide-memoir it can help in the design process. One of the key factors in the management of product design is the drafting and management of clear, accurate and comprehensive specifications (see BS 7373 (1991) for details).

The earliest point at which component, material or even manufacturing process, standardization can be applied is at the design stage. This is where specifications and drawings originate. Naturally it is the design department who will be responsible for the specification of materials and components used. Change control will also have to be standardized at this stage.

Company standards are drawn up to ensure

that all these aspects are specified unambiguously. Involving standardization as a function in new designs can result in constructive suggestions that are unlikely to be made otherwise. Design staff will, for example, be comparing the proposals against existing standards and be considering their effect on current practices without departmental bias. Manufacturing data will originate from design, but purchasing, planning and inspection will also be involved. Company standards should be the only issued authority to official information. Other instructions, particularly those in the form of memoranda or handwritten notes, should have no authority for manufacturing/operational purposes. They should complement the drawings or any other documents by establishing and recording the standards of design, manufacture/operation and quality control throughout the organisation as well as comprising the 'drawing office handbook' or other standard manuals.

6.9 Design and standardisation philosophy

Standardisation is the result of the compromise between the opposing forces of customer demand and economic necessity. It is now a prime requirement in economic design and production. Further, it must be a principal aim carried right through a company's organisational structure. The aims and results of standardisation are shown in Figure 6.3.

Management must be concerned constantly with adapting resources to take account of the foreseeable needs of the marketplace. Resources are not being used economically if they have to be readjusted for each individual demand that is made upon them. An efficient and effective management team tries to regularise procedures and develop techniques that may be called into play quickly and without fuss. In other words, it aims at standardisation.

This aim depends upon the way in which the

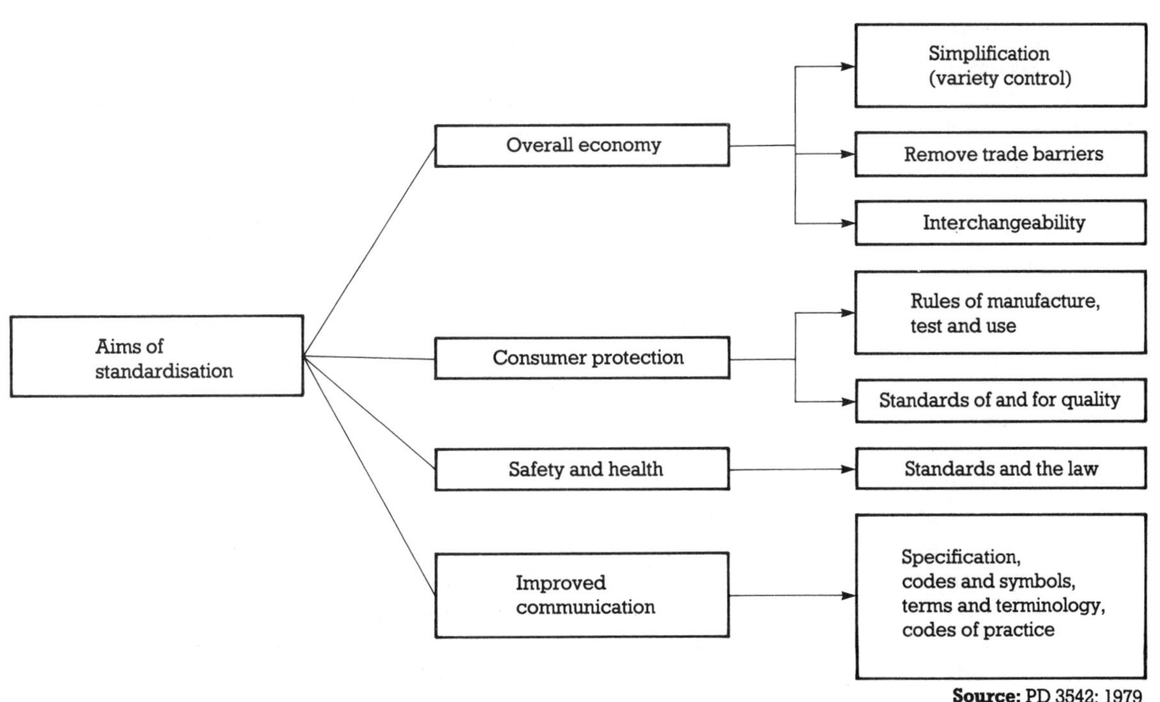

Figure 6.3 Aims and results of standardisation

products or services are designed. Unnecessary design variations cause unnecessary variation in the use of production or operations resources, in the purchase and storage of materials, the operation of processes, and indeed in managerial and design work. Since variations of one kind or another may have crept into a company's products or services, processes and procedures over a period of years, they are not always easily eliminated unless a significant external influence is brought to bear. The majority of new designs are evolved rather than invented and an organisation cannot afford to keep on rediscovering the wheel. As the rate of new discovery and the depth of past experience increases, so does the importance of recording and retaining the best practices to ensure consistency in approach and methods used in the future. Quality troubles caused by abnormalities can be prevented in future designs and production or operations by the standardisation of counter-measures.

As the user, as well as the creator, of materials, the designer is expected to incorporate those features and parameters which have an assured availability and quality. The rationalisation of specifications is essential to improve availability by dimensional and non-dimensional interchangeability. It is most important that national and international standards be incorporated at company level. The person in the company responsible for standards can assist the designer by obtaining the background information on the relevant standards and ensure that this information is communicated effectively, perhaps in a current awareness bulletin or by circulating notices on particular topics as they arise.

Standardisation, in its broadest sense, is the discipline of using the minimum number of different materials and parts for the maximum number of purposes, produced by the most economical manufacturing processes, of the appropriate quality to give reliable and acceptable performance at minimum (whole life) cost. Within this broad definition, standardisation becomes a powerful tool in producing effective products or services with the maximum economy. It is an essential tool for use when organisations diversify in order to spread the risk over a wider sector of the market, since, if control is not applied, the increased variety of materials can undo the beneficial effects.

The application of a standardisation philosophy will give economies in money, manpower and time, and will lead to increased competitiveness. To achieve this, the threefold aim should be to minimise the number of products or services to satisfy the market, and the number of different materials and services to satisfy the range of products and services.

The theoretical absolute limit of standardisation is achieved when an organisation offers a product or service in which all components are identical and are all generated in an identical manner. However, in product or service design, this ideal situation will never be reached. There are many products and services that, while having similar functions, must be offered in a range of forms, sizes or capacities, while others may have a generic similarity but perform different tasks. In the first category come such products as motors and pumps, and services such as bank accounts and hospitality. In the second category are such products as machine tools and electronic equipment, and services such as health care and legal aid. Finally, there are products and services that are dissimilar in character but may contain common features.

Variations in products and services are obviously not being created by organisations out of sheer perversity. They arise from real efforts to satisfy customers. Consequently, when given the opportunity to start again, the product or service should be designed and broken down into its elemental components in such a way that there is:

- the maximum possibility of multiple use for the elemental components;
- maximum flexibility in meeting customer requirements and likely future requirements.

It is essential that an organisation's senior management team establish their product or service policy, together with procedures aimed at the most economical use of resources consistent with meeting market requirements as fully as possible.

The department or function responsible for

standards can complement the work of the design department by establishing and recording the standards for design, production or operations and quality assurance throughout the organisation. The success or failure of standardisation will be reflected in the work of the design department. Therefore, it is essential that design personnel are fully aware of the scope and benefits and that they ensure that standards are implemented. This is usually achieved by having available organisation manuals or handbooks specifying the company's policies and methods in both manufacture and design (e.g. tolerances, standard tooling, equipment design, finishes and preferred sizes).

It is important that the company policy on the use of external and internal standards is clear. Management has a duty to guide the designer in these respects and it can do this by means of codes of practice on the design policy to be followed. The scope and benefits of standards in design are to:

- provide a storage facility capable of accumulating a good knowledge of key aspects of product design, so reducing prototype costs;
- ensure that unproven new materials and methods do not proliferate without prohibiting controlled development to exploit technological change;
- simplify the communication of the necessary technical requirements to the production/operations department and improve project scheduling.

Designers have a significant rôle in the effective use of standards. Their rôle is to:

- implement national, international and company standards;
- initiate product standards which promote good design and economic production/operations activities;
- consolidate existing designs and allow the free movement of design services to other areas;
- initiate the setting of quality standards and methods of testing, checking, etc.

Some examples of the application of standardisation philosophy in design are given in PD 6470 (1981) along with examples of variety prevention. This published document also contains a useful checklist for standardisation.

A method is given in PD 6495 (1992) for deciding whether a *standardisation project* (a project which is to be carried out in a planned manner involving the use of existing standards and/or the creation of new standards) is worthwhile. This is done by assessing its effects on all aspects of the company's operations and, where practical, by expressing them in monetary terms.

6.10 The standards manual

Standards are of importance to companies as a means of removing barriers to trade, of achieving economies in production/operations, of regularising procedures, and of specifying performance and quality. Furthermore, standards are sometimes referred to in legislation either in contractual use or in trade descriptions. Hence, every organisation needs to establish standards that will harmonise with, and make use of, relevant national and international standards, and which will improve productivity through better design, reduced variety, improved quality and lower unit costs.

These standards must be documented so that they are available for reference by all personnel. They need to be classified according to their subject and type, and published in a company standards manual. Such a manual is of particular use in the design process. The scope of the manual may include all areas of company activity, typically they cover materials, bought out items, manufactured parts, design practices, quality and inspection procedures, and production/operations processes.

The primary purpose of a company standards manual is to communicate standards information so as to derive the benefits available from:

- the control of unnecessary variety;
- improved management control;
- improved quality assurance;

- the provision of a central source of information;
- the promotion of value engineering;
- the provision of on-the-job reference information;
- the clarification of responsibilities;
- improved product or service safety;
- information for training new staff;
- uniform interpretation of policies;
- a constant review of standards;
- the auditing of procedures;
- visible proof of standardisation and organisation;
- the demonstration of the company's quality system to customers.

Although most companies recognise the need for standardisation they sometimes have no form of standards manual and, in many cases, there is little or no obvious evidence that any standards exist. In such situations, 'quick fixes' are applied and no long-term corrective measures are put into place, resulting in the problem(s) reoccurring at some future date. Sometimes standards information is passed on verbally. In such cases, the various versions of the standards are likely to be different. The only satisfactory way to communicate standards information is via a company standards manual. Published document PD 6489 (1980) provides useful guidance on the preparation of a company standards manual.

6.11 Variety control

Considerable costs can be incurred by lack of attention to variety control at the design stage. The introduction of each new part, material or method will be reflected by increased costs in design, production or operations planning, equipment management, purchasing, stores and inspection, and assembly. Variety is usually the result of random or uncontrolled specification or lack of adequate retrieval systems. To avoid these, manufactured and purchased parts should be classified, coded and catalogued so that they can be identified easily at a later date, and the introduction of a new part, where there is an existing one, can be avoided.

Some very sophisticated methods exist for classifying and coding materials, parts and commodities so that they can be retrieved at a later date. This avoids the introduction of new parts or materials, where satisfactory ones exist. The cost of such systems and their degree of sophistication should be weighed against the benefits, which may depend to some extent on the size, complexity and type of industry or operation. In most cases, the use of a simple classification system can separate items or materials that are likely to be repeated. The cataloging and coding of materials and parts also has the advantage that the code can be used instead of the full description. A useful description of the factors to be considered in the design of a classification and coding system is given in PD 3542 (1991).

Variety cannot be controlled effectively without some written guidance for the specifier or user. Standard specifications and codes of practice are essential tools for variety control.

The scope and benefits of variety control in the design department may be summarised as:

- provision of standardised data to reduce design time and improve quality;
- provision of a design manual as a training aid and source of basic standards;
- coding and cataloging of all materials and parts including purchase specifications;
- design and control of company coding systems;
- formulation of design and production/operations codes of practice to simplify specification information;
- preparation of company standards based on retrospective variety reduction exercises;
- a technical information service and advice on national and international standards.

On the other hand, variety reduction is a retrospective operation to reduce existing variety. This can be expensive because of the effect on existing designs, specification, planning layouts and existing material in stores. It is much better therefore to control variety by prior organisation and discipline. Even with the best means of variety control, periodic exercises of this kind may still be needed, perhaps because of the development of production or operational facilities, a modification to the product or service range, or supply difficulties. First, the existing variety should be identified by the coding system. This should then be compared with the company standards. Finally, any necessary changes should be implemented and this requires knowledge of where various materials are used.

6.12 Quality function deployment

The *quality function deployment (QFD)* methodology was developed in Japan at Kobe Shipyard, Mitsubishi Heavy Industries, Kobe, Japan. It arose out of the need to achieve simultaneously a competitive advantage in quality, cost and delivery. QFD is a planning and analysis system and is a means of translating the customer requirements (the customer needs are expressed in their original words and translated into the technical language of the organisation) into the appropriate technical requirements for each stage of marketing, product planning, product design, manufacturing engineering, production/operations, sales and service. It also helps to identify the design requirements to be optimised and the quality characteristics to be controlled. QFD offers a logical method of examining the interrelationships between critical characteristics. These are usually displayed in pictorial form to enable a reasoned judgement to be made at the design stage.

When used as part of a company's overall management system, QFD reinforces the horizontal flow of information and interaction between the departments so as to ensure that customer requirements and wants are not lost. Focusing on the voice of the customer, QFD improves teamwork between departments and facilitates more effective project management. It is also a means of systematically assigning responsibilities and focusing on product/service and process development. The following is an overview of the steps in carrying out QFD.

The starting point is a list of customer objectives or a wants list ('voice of the customer'). A list is then developed of the technical requirements of how to satisfy the customer objectives or wants ('voice of the company'). The data is usually grouped in a planning matrix which is known as the *house of quality* (see Figure 6.4 overleaf). The relative importance of the relationships is assessed and a comparative analysis is performed between competitive products/services. The required features are then listed and design requirements which relate to the customer wants are identified. A technical evaluation is then performed to indicate how well competitive products/services meet the design requirements. This is followed by determining the relative degree of difficulty for the design requirements. The correlations between the design requirements are defined and the relationships between the wants and requirements are ranked. Value weights for the design requirements are calculated and finally target values are set for the design requirements.

QFD is a relatively simple process to apply but requires considerable resources to supply, collect and analyse the information which the method requires. The benefits typically claimed for QFD include:

- reduction in product introduction times;
- reduction in design and document changes;
- reduction in overall costs of design and production;
- reduction in warranty claims;
- improved product and service quality and reliability;
- improved internal communications.
- improved advanced quality planning;
- improved teamwork;
- improved market share and profitability.

A full description of QFD is outside the scope of this book, but further information may be found in Burn in Dale (1994), Akao (1990), Eureka and Ryan (1988) and Ryan (1988).

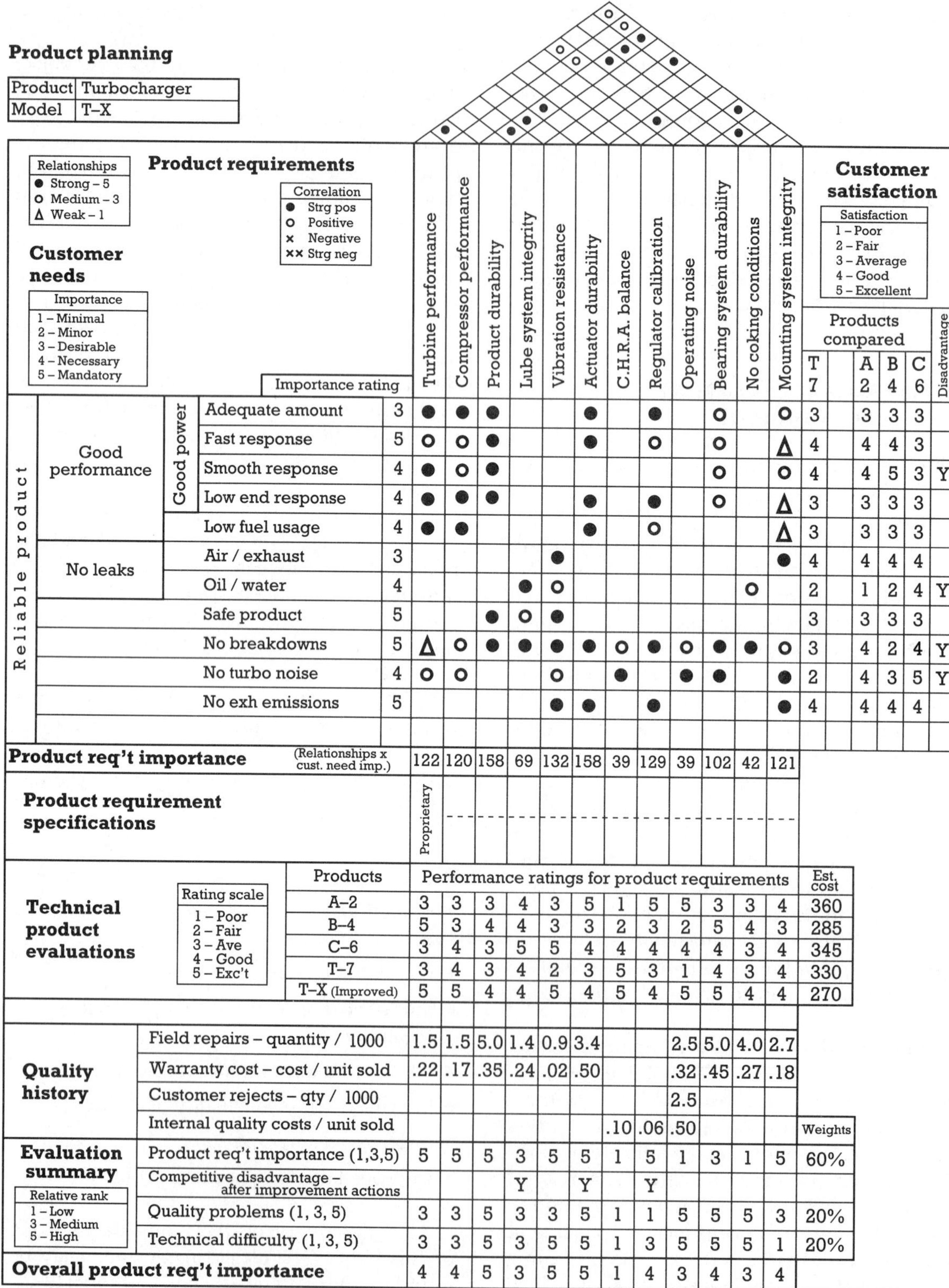

Product planning

Product	Turbocharger
Model	T–X

Relationships: ● Strong – 5; o Medium – 3; Δ Weak – 1

Correlation: ● Strg pos; o Positive; × Negative; ×× Strg neg

Customer needs – Importance: 1 – Minimal; 2 – Minor; 3 – Desirable; 4 – Necessary; 5 – Mandatory

Customer satisfaction – Satisfaction: 1 – Poor; 2 – Fair; 3 – Average; 4 – Good; 5 – Excellent

Product requirements

Customer needs				Importance rating	Turbine performance	Compressor performance	Product durability	Lube system integrity	Vibration resistance	Actuator durability	C.H.R.A. balance	Regulator calibration	Operating noise	Bearing system durability	No coking conditions	Mounting system integrity	T 7		A 2	B 4	C 6	Disadvantage
Reliable product	Good performance	Good power	Adequate amount	3	●	●	●			●		●		o		o	3		3	3	3	
			Fast response	5	o	o	●			●		o		o		Δ	4		4	4	3	
			Smooth response	4	●	o	●							o		o	4		4	5	3	Y
			Low end response	4	●	●	●			●		●		o		Δ	3		3	3	3	
			Low fuel usage	4	●	●				●		o				Δ	3		3	3	3	
	No leaks		Air / exhaust	3					●							●	4		4	4	4	
			Oil / water	4				●	o						o		2		1	2	4	Y
			Safe product	5			●	o	●								3		3	3	3	
			No breakdowns	5	Δ	o	●	●	●	●	o	●	o	●	●	o	3		4	2	4	Y
			No turbo noise	4	o	o			o		●		●	●		●	2		4	3	5	Y
			No exh emissions	5					●	●		●				●	4		4	4	4	
Product req't importance (Relationships x cust. need imp.)					122	120	158	69	132	158	39	129	39	102	42	121						
Product requirement specifications					Proprietary																	

Technical product evaluations (Rating scale: 1 – Poor; 2 – Fair; 3 – Ave; 4 – Good; 5 – Exc't)

Performance ratings for product requirements

Products	Turbine performance	Compressor performance	Product durability	Lube system integrity	Vibration resistance	Actuator durability	C.H.R.A. balance	Regulator calibration	Operating noise	Bearing system durability	No coking conditions	Mounting system integrity	Est. cost
A–2	3	3	3	4	3	5	1	5	5	3	3	4	360
B–4	5	3	4	4	3	3	2	3	2	5	4	3	285
C–6	3	4	3	5	5	4	4	4	4	4	3	4	345
T–7	3	4	3	4	2	3	5	3	1	4	3	4	330
T–X (Improved)	5	5	4	4	5	4	5	4	5	5	4	4	270

		Turbine performance	Compressor performance	Product durability	Lube system integrity	Vibration resistance	Actuator durability	C.H.R.A. balance	Regulator calibration	Operating noise	Bearing system durability	No coking conditions	Mounting system integrity	Weights
Quality history	Field repairs – quantity / 1000	1.5	1.5	5.0	1.4	0.9	3.4			2.5	5.0	4.0	2.7	
	Warranty cost – cost / unit sold	.22	.17	.35	.24	.02	.50			.32	.45	.27	.18	
	Customer rejects – qty / 1000									2.5				
	Internal quality costs / unit sold							.10	.06	.50				
Evaluation summary (Relative rank: 1 – Low; 3 – Medium; 5 – High)	Product req't importance (1,3,5)	5	5	5	3	5	5	1	5	1	3	1	5	60%
	Competitive disadvantage – after improvement actions				Y		Y		Y					
	Quality problems (1, 3, 5)	3	3	5	3	3	5	1	1	5	5	5	3	20%
	Technical difficulty (1, 3, 5)	3	3	5	3	5	5	1	3	5	5	5	1	20%
Overall product req't importance		4	4	5	3	5	5	1	4	3	4	3	4	

Figure 6.4 Quality Function deployment – 'house of quality' **Source:** Garrett Automotive

6.13 Off-line quality control methods

In recent times, considerable enthusiasm among Western manufacturing companies has developed for what are termed off-line quality control methods. These methods are employed at the stages of product design and process design, and have the objective of reducing the sensitivity of the product/service and processes to the variation in inputs. The aim is to design a product or service and its production/operation processes together in order to produce robust products/services. By this means the producibility and reliability of the product or service will be improved, along with a reduction in the development and life cycle costs. These methods of product/service and process design are commonplace in Japanese industry.

The interest in off-line quality control methods has followed the resurgence of interest in recent years for statistical process control (SPC). While the roots of SPC can be traced back to the work of Shewhart (1931) in the 1920s, likewise the ideas of statistically-based experimental design (an important part of off-line quality control methods) can be attributed to the work of R A Fisher, who was carrying out his research at the same time as Shewhart.

The off-line control methods of Taguchi (1986) have received the most attention and there is little doubt that he has increased industry's awareness about the techniques of design of experiments. Genichi Taguchi is a statistician and electrical engineer who was involved in rebuilding the Japanese telephone system. He was contracted to provide statistical assistance and design of experiment support. Taguchi rejected the classical approach to design of experiments as being too impractical for industrial situations and revised these methods to develop his own approach to design of experiments. He has been applying Taguchi design of experiments in the Japanese electronics industry for over 25 years. His ideas fall into two main related areas known as *the loss function* and *off-line quality control*. Taguchi writes that 'The quality of a product is the loss imparted to the society from the time the product is shipped.' Among the losses he includes consumers' dissatisfaction, warranty and guarantee costs, loss of reputation and, ultimately, loss of market share.

Taguchi maintains that a product does not start causing loss only when it is out of specification but when it deviates from the target value. In most cases the loss to society can be represented by a quadratic function. This leads to the conclusion that quality (as defined by Taguchi) is achieved most economically by minimising variance rather than by strict conformance to specification.

This conclusion provides the basis for Taguchi's ideas for off-line quality control. By *off-line quality control* he means optimising production processes and product parameters in such a way as to minimise item-to-item variations in the product and its performance. This clearly focuses attention on the design process, particularly parameter design. Underlying the parameter design process is the concept that process and product performance are defined by two different kinds of factor: control factors, which can be controlled easily, and noise factors, which are difficult, impossible or expensive to control. Taguchi's methods look for a set of control factors which will produce a process or product insensitive to the effects of noise factors. One goal of a good design is that the product should be robust to all types of processing and user conditions.

When seeking to optimise production processes and product or service parameters it is frequently necessary to determine the effects of varying the parameter values experimentally. This can be a very expensive and time-consuming process which may produce a lot of redundant information. By using fractional factorial experiments, renamed by Taguchi 'orthogonal arrays', the number of experiments required to identify the main effects and potential interactions can be reduced drastically. This allows for a large number of factors to be given an initial assessment, with future experimentation concentrating on the factors which have been identified as the most important.

Taguchi offers a new way of measuring quality (the loss function), a tangible goal which will maximise quality (elimination of variation) and a strategy for working towards it (attention to parameter design and quantification of the effects of control factors).

The attention given to what are commonly termed 'Taguchi methods' has been largely responsible for some organisations examining the usefulness of experimental design both in quality planning and in tackling quality problems.

6.14 The seven new quality control tools

The so-called 'seven new tools' of quality control may be used to address the various aspects of the design process. These are:

Relations diagram method (relationship diagram or linkage diagram) – used to identify, understand and clarify complex cause and effect relationships, to find the causes and solutions to a problem and to determine the key factors in the situation under study. They are also employed to identify the key issues to some desired result. Relations diagrams are used when the causes are non-hierarchic and when there are multiple interrelated problems. They allow the problem to be analysed from a wide perspective as a specific framework is not employed. Relations diagrams can be considered to be a more free and broader version of cause and effect diagrams.

Affinity diagram method (Kawakita Jiro or KJ method) – used to categorise verbal data about previously unexplored issues, problems and themes which are hazy and difficult to understand, helping to create order out of chaos. This type of diagram uses the natural affinity between opinions and partial data from a variety of situations to help understand and structure the problem. It helps, perhaps in a less logical manner than the relations diagram, to organise data and ideas for decision-making and to reach solutions about previously unresolved problems.

Systematic diagram method (tree diagram) – used to examine, in a systematic manner, the most appropriate and effective means of planning to accomplish a task or solving a problem; events are represented in the form of a root and branch relationship. It is used when the causes that influence the problem are known, but a plan and method for resolving the problem have not been developed. A systematic diagram is usually used to evaluate several different methods and plans for solving a problem.

Matrix diagram method – used to clarify the relationship between results and causes or between objectives and methods and to indicate their relative importance. The factors are arranged in rows and columns on a chart with the intersections identifying the problem and its concentration; the intersecting points are the base for future action. Seeing the complete problem and its essential characteristics is of considerable help in developing a strategy for solving it. Symbols are used to depict the presence and strength of a relationship between sets of data. There are a number of types of matrix diagrams (e.g. L-type, T-type, Y-type), each having a specific range of applications.

Matrix data analysis method – used to quantify and arrange the data presented in a matrix diagram in a clear manner. It is a numerical analysis method and employs techniques such as multivariate analysis.

Process decision program chart (PDPC) method – used to select the best processes to obtain the desired outcome from a problem statement by evaluating all possible events and conceivable outcomes. Considering the system as a whole it is used to anticipate unexpected events and develop plans, counter-measures and actions for such outcomes. In this it is similar to FMEA and FTA. However, it is claimed to be more dynamic than these two methods since the relationship between the initiating condition/event and terminating condition/event has been thought out and mapped. It is based on a systematic diagram and uses a questioning technique of, for example 'What could go wrong?', 'What are the alternatives?' and the listing of actions or counter-measures accordingly. The PDPC has no prescribed set of rules.

Arrow diagram method – used to establish the most suitable plan for a series of activities in a project, and to monitor its progress in an efficient manner. The sequence of the steps involved and their relations to each other are indicated by arrows and in this way a network is developed. This method, its form of construction, calculations and identification of critical path are well known and used in project management in relation to critical path analysis and programme evaluation and review techniques.

Further information on these tools can be found in Appendix M, Barker (1989), Dale (1994), Mizuno (1988), Oakland (1990) and Ozeki and Asaka (1990).

6.15 Value engineering

The technique and philosophy of value engineering on a product/service being designed or value analysis on an existing product/service is based on simple concepts, but its effective use can be realised only through the co-ordinated effort of a team of specialists. There are six steps to all value engineering exercises. These are listed below.

Selection
Selection of the product or service, or part thereof, sub-assembly or component for investigation. The product/service or operation under scrutiny must offer a benefit. Identification of high absolute cost outputs, comparison with competitors' products, or a sudden material price rise or shortage can all aid selection.

Information
This stage involves collecting all the relevant facts about the product, part or service including design criteria, production/operations methods, detailed costs, customer usage, expected product/service lifetime and maintenance. It requires the full co-operation of all those involved in the design, production/operations, quality assurance and marketing of the product or service.

Analysis
The next step is to analyse the functions the product/service performs, to rank these in order of priority and to assign as accurately as possible the costs attributable to each function. A grid or matrix may be used for this function/cost analysis. The purpose is to identify items of poor value for further investigation.

Speculation
Speculation on ways of improving poor value items requires a broad knowledge of alternative design strategies, materials and production/operations techniques. Although this activity may be called brainstorming, creative or lateral thinking, it is important that such thinking includes more mundane but equally vital ideas such as standardisation of materials or parts, elimination of unnecessary variety and grouping of components or service elements. It is generally agreed that this stage should be as unconstrained as possible.

Evaluation
Most effort is normally expended at this stage because the reward for correct evaluation of a good idea can be great, and the penalty for a mistake can be even greater. Detailed information is required on the performance, cost and availability of alternative materials or methods required. Similarly the dependence of costs on tolerance, grade, size, shape, level of service and quantities must be ascertained.

Implementation
If the value engineering investigation has been an integrated company activity then this stage will be relatively simple. Monitoring of the results is in any event a necessary final step in the value engineering exercise.

A convenient aide memoire for the steps in value engineering is:

- What is it?
- What does it do?
- What does it cost?
- What else will do the job?
- What does that cost?

Whatever the precise techniques, value engineering is much more than cost reduction. Value, measured in terms of quality, performance and reliability at an acceptable price or, in other words, customer satisfaction and customer delight is the overall aim.

6.16 Design practice and procedures documentation

The design responsibilities and interfaces can be included in the quality manual or by reference to it in appropriate design control documentation; this documentation identifies design practices and procedures. In either case, the aim is to ensure that the design organisation has a prescribed management system to assure the required quality. Design control documentation also provides a basis against which the design organisation can be audited. Most designers need to review a considerable amount of information before producing a working specification for production or operations. In general, they require data on materials, processes and tolerances and it is helpful to include such information in a manual. Procedures, whether developed inhouse or in nationally available standard documents, need to be laid down to ensure the orderly and controlled preparation of the design. Design documentation consists of specifications, instructions and relevant output documents.

The documentation typically contained in the design department's manual includes:

- departmental instructions;
- specifications and conventions;
- relevant national and international standards and statutory regulations;
- formats and systems;
- coding of design documents;
- general design data;
- standard, preferred and common parts, and materials;
- material specifications;
- production/operations processes specifications;
- reference tables, if appropriate;
- sources of data on basic and specialist design information.

6.17 Design qualification and validation

It is important that the design process provides periodic evaluation, including an analysis of the reliability implications of all parts, materials and processes, of the design at significant stages in its development. Such evaluation can take the form of analytical methods, such as failure modes and effects analysis (FMEA), and fault tree analysis (FTA) or risk assessment, as well as inspection or testing of prototype models or services and actual output samples. The amount and degree of such examination is related to the risks identified in the design plan. Independent evaluation may be employed, as appropriate, to verify original calculations, provide alternative calculations or perform tests. To prove statistical confidence in the results, adequate numbers of samples must be examined by testing, checking or inspecting. The tests can include the following activities:

- evaluation of performance, durability, safety, reliability and maintainability under expected storage and operational conditions;
- inspections to verify that all design features are as intended and that all authorised design changes have been accomplished and recorded;
- validation of computer systems and software.

6.18 Failure modes, effects and criticality analysis (FMEA and FMECA)

Introduction: general

Failure modes and effects analysis (FMEA) and failure modes, effects and criticality analysis (FMECA) are methods of reliability analysis to identify failures which have consequences affecting the functioning of a system within the limits of a given application, thus enabling priorities for action to be set. They are important techniques for reliability assurance and quality planning and can be applied to a wide range of problems which may occur in any form of system or process.

FMEA or FMECA is a systematic and analytical quality planning tool for identifying at the product and process design stages what might go wrong either during the manufacture of a product or during its use by the end customer. It was developed in the aerospace and defence industries. There are two categories of FMEA which can be distinguished – design and process. The former addresses the issues of what could go wrong with the product in both service and manufacturing operations as a consequence of a weakness in the design. The latter concentrates on the reasons for potential failure during manufacture and in service as a consequence of a non-compliance to specification and/or design intent.

From the design FMEA the potential causes of failure should be studied and actions taken before designs and drawings are finalised. Likewise with the process FMEA, actions must be put into place before the process is set up. Used properly, FMEA prevents potential failures occurring in the production/operation and delivery processes or end product in use and will ensure that designs and processes are more robust and reliable. However, it is important that the technique is seen not just as a catalogue of potential failures but as a tool for pursuing improvement.

The concept and procedures involved with FMEA are not new; every forward-thinking person carries out in an informal manner, various aspects of FMEA. However, this mental analysis is rarely committed to paper. What FMEA does is to provide a planned systematic method of capturing and documenting this knowledge. It also forces people to use a disciplined approach and is a vehicle for obtaining collective knowledge and experience through a team process.

This section now concentrates on design FMEA, process FMEA is discussed in Chapter 10.

Introduction: design FMEA and FMECA

The analysis is carried out in a limited way during the conception, planning and definition phases and more fully in the design and development phase. The FMEA should be updated as the project progresses and as designs are modified. At the end of the project, FMEA is used to check the design and may be essential for demonstration of conformity of a designed system to the required standards, regulations and users' requirements.

FMEA begins at the item or sub-assembly level for which the basic failure criteria (primary failure modes) are available. Starting from the basic failure characteristics of the elements and the functional structure of the system, the FMEA indicates the relationship between element failures and malfunctions, operational constraints and degradation of performance or integrity of the system.

Criticality is a measure which combines the concepts of severity of consequences of failure and rate of occurrence or probability of occurrence of failure in a defined period. Severity is usually measured by placing a failure mode in one of a number of categories according to the consequences. Probability or rate of occurrence may also need to be dealt with in this way if numerical data are not available. Criticality is then measured by combining these indices in a defined manner.

All the general qualitative considerations presented for FMEA also apply to FMECA. However, FMEA and FMECA are different in the sense that FMEA can be performed on its own, whereas criticality analysis has to be carried out in conjunction with FMEA.

The reasons for undertaking FMEA (or FMECA) may include the following:

- to identify those failures which have unwanted effects on system operation (e.g. safety critical failures);
- to satisfy contractual conditions that FMEA should be completed;
- where appropriate, to quantify the reliability and/or safety of the system;
- to allow improvements of the system's reliability and/or safety (e.g. by design or quality assurance actions);
- to produce aids to fault diagnosis;
- to allow improvement of the system's maintainability (by highlighting areas of risk or non-conformance for maintainability).

In view of these reasons the objectives of FMEA (or FMECA) may include the following:

- a comprehensive identification and evaluation of all the unwanted effects within the defined boundaries of the system or process being analysed, and the sequence of events brought about by each identified item failure mode, from whatever cause, at various levels of the system's functional hierarchy (a failure mode refers to the effect by which a failure is observed by an operator as a change in performance);
- the determination of the significance (or criticality) of each failure mode with respect to the system's correct function or performance and the impact on the reliability and/or safety of the process concerned;
- a classification of identified failure modes according to relevant characteristics, including detectability, diagnosability, testability, item replaceability, compensating and operating provisions (repair, maintenance and logistics);
- an estimation of measures of the significance and probability of failure.

Failure modes and effects analysis

Some of the detailed applications and benefits of FMEA are listed below:

- to avoid costly modifications by the early identification of design deficiencies;
- to identify failures which, when they occur alone or in combination, have unacceptable or significant effects, and to determine the failure modes which may seriously affect the expected or required operation;
- to determine the need for the following:
  - redundancy;
  - design improvement;
  - more generous stress allowances (derating);
  - screening of items;
  - design of features that ensure that the system fails in a preferred failure mode (e.g. 'fail-safe' outcomes of failures);
  - selection of alternative materials, parts, devices and components;
- to identify serious failure consequences and hence the need for changes in design and/or operational rules;
- to provide the logic model required to evaluate the probability or rate of occurrence of anomalous operating conditions of the system in preparation for criticality analysis;
- to disclose safety hazard and product liability problem areas, or non-compliance with regulatory requirements;
- to ensure that the development test programme can detect potential failure modes;
- to focus upon key areas in which to concentrate quality control, statistical process control, inspection and manufacturing process controls;
- to assist in defining various aspects of the general maintenance strategy, such as:
  - establishing the need for data recording and condition monitoring during testing, checking-out and use;
  - provision of information for development of trouble-shooting guides;
  - establishing maintenance cycles which anticipate and avoid wear-out failures;
  - the selection of preventative or corrective maintenance schedules, facilities, equipment and staff;
  - selection of built-in test equipment and suitable test points;
- to provide a systematic and rigorous approach to the study of the installation in which the system is embedded;
- to facilitate or support the determination of test criteria, test plans and diagnostic procedures (for example performance testing, reliability testing);
- to identify parts and assemblies requiring worst case analysis;
- to support the design of fault isolation sequences and to support the planning for alternative modes of operation and reconfiguration;
- to facilitate communication between general and specialized engineers, the equipment manufacturer and his suppliers, the system user and the designer or manufacturer;

- to enhance the analyst's knowledge and understanding of the behaviour of the equipment studied;
- to provide designers with an understanding of the factors which influence the reliability of the system;
- to provide a final document that is proof of the fact that (and of the extent to which) care has been taken to ensure that the design will meet its specification in service. (This is especially important in the case of product liability).

Procedure

The wide variation in complexity of system designs and applications may require the development of highly individualized FMEA procedures consistent with the information available. Traditionally there have been wide variations in the manner in which FMEA is conducted and presented. However, the analysis is usually done in a standard manner and presented on a worksheet that contains a core of essential information which can be developed and extended to suit the particular system or project to which it is applied. A typical example of a worksheet is shown in Figure 6.5 (overleaf). The core information is as follows:

- the name of the item in the system being analysed;
- function performed by the item;
- identification number of the item;
- failure modes of the item;
- failure causes;
- failure effects on the system;
- failure detection methods;
- compensating provisions;
- severity of effects;
- remarks.

The procedure involved in the development of an FMEA is iterative. In brief, it starts by focusing on the function of the product, it then identifies potential failures, assesses the effects of each potential failure, examines the causes of potential failure, reviews current controls, determines a risk or action priority number, recommends the corrective action which should be taken to help eliminate potential concerns, and finally monitors the corrective actions and counter-measures.

The FMEA procedure consists of the following four main stages:

- preparatory definition and understanding of the system including the design, functional, operational maintenance and environmental requirements; flow charts, functional diagrams and other system drawings are normally necessary for this understanding;
- establishment of the basic principles and purposes of the FMEA and the form of its presentation;
- carrying out the FMEA using an appropriate worksheet;
- reporting of the complete analysis including any conclusions and recommendations made.

Procedural steps needed to perform an analysis are as follows:

- decide whether FMEA or FMECA is required;
- define system boundaries for analysis;
- understand system requirements and function;
- define failure/success criteria;
- determine each item's failure modes and their failure effects and record these;
- summarize each failure effect;
- report findings.

A system FMEA can be carried out without reference to any particular application and could then be adapted subsequently for project use. This applies to relatively small assemblies that might themselves be regarded as generic components (for example an electronic amplifier, an electronic motor, a mechanical valve). However, it is more usual to develop a project-specific FMEA and to have regard to the particular consequences of system failure. It might be necessary to categorize the effects of failures on the system according to the consequences of these failures, for example, fail-safe, fail-danger, repairable failure, non-repairable

FMEA

Indenture level: Sheet no: Mission phase:					Design by: Item: Issue:			Prepared by: Approved by: Date:				
Item ref.	Item description/ function	Failure entry code	Failure mode	Possible failure causes	Symptom detected by	Local effect	Effect on unit output	Compensating provision against failure	Severity class	Failure rate (F/Mhr)	Data source	Recommendations and actions taken

Figure 6.5 Example of the format of an FMEA worksheet

Source: BS 5760: Part 5 (1991)

failure, mission degraded, mission failed, effects on individuals, groups or society generally.

The need to relate an FMEA to the ultimate consequences of system failure will depend on the project and the relationship between the FMEA and other forms of analysis, such as fault trees (see Section 6.19).

The usual requirement and purpose of an FMEA is to identify the effects of all failure modes of all constituent items at the lowest level in the system. To achieve this the worksheet should be used in the following manner.

- Identify all items in the system or subsystem, each of which is to have its failure modes and effects analysed. The system of identification by name and number should be such that no items will be omitted.
- Select the first item for analysis and enter the item name and identification number in the appropriate columns of the worksheet. Determine the function of that item in the system and enter it on the worksheet.
- Deduce all the possible failure modes of the item due to any possible cause and individually enter these modes on the worksheet.
- Postulate the most likely failure causes for each failure mode of the item and enter these on the worksheet.
- Deduce the effects of the failure on the subsystem and system.
- Complete the remaining columns of the worksheet for the first failure mode of the first item.
- Repeat the above steps for all other failure modes of the first item.
- Repeat for all other items.

The last worksheet entry should give any pertinent remarks to clarify other entries. Possible future actions such as recommendations for improvements should be recorded and then amplified in the report. This column may also include the following:

- any unusual conditions;
- effects of redundant element failures;
- recognition of specially critical design features;
- any remarks to amplify the entry;
- references to other entries for sequential failure analysis;
- significant maintenance requirements;
- dominant failure causes;
- dominant failure effects;
- decisions taken, e.g. at design review.

The procedures for identifying failure modes, their causes and effects can be effectively enhanced by the preparation of a list of failure modes anticipated in the light of the following:

- the use of the system;
- the particular system element involved;
- the mode of operation;
- the pertinent operational specifications;
- the time constraints;
- the environment.

Failure modes such as those listed in Table 6.1 can describe the failure of any system element in sufficiently specific terms. It should be noted that a given failure mode may have several causes. To assist with the identification of failure modes, typical failure mode data can be sought from the following areas:

- For new items, reference can be made to other items with similar function and structure and to the results of tests performed on them under appropriate stress levels.
- For items in use, in-service records and failure data may be consulted.
- Potential failure modes can be deduced from functional and physical parameters typical of the operation of the item.

It is important that item failure modes are not omitted for lack of data and that initial estimates are improved by test results and design progression. The FMEA should be modified to allow for new information, or changed assumptions or approximations; it should always be updated for each design review milestone.

The identification of failure modes and where necessary the determination of remedial design

Table 6.1 Examples of failure modes

1	Cracked/fractured	21	Binding/jamming
2	Distorted	22	Loose
3	Undersize	23	Incorrect adjustment
4	Oversize	24	Seized
5	Fails to open	25	Worn
6	Fails to close	26	Sticking
7	Fails open	27	Overheated
8	Fails closed	28	False response
9	Internal leakage	29	Displaced
10	External leakage	30	Delayed operation
11	Fails to stop	31	Burned
12	Fails to start	32	Collapsed
13	Corroded	33	Overloaded
14	Contaminated	34	Omitted
15	Intermittent operation	35	Incorrect assembly
16	Open circuit	36	Scored
17	Short circuit	37	Noisy
18	Out of tolerance (drifted)	38	Arcing
19	Fails to operate	39	Unstable
20	Operates prematurely	40	Chafed

Note: This is an example only. The modes contained in the list cannot be applied to all items and the list is not exhaustive.

Source: BS 5760: Part 5 (1991)

actions, preventative quality assurance actions or preventative maintenance actions is of prime importance. It is more important to identify and, if possible, design out failure modes than to know their rate of occurrence. When it is difficult to assign priorities, criticality analysis may be required.

The possible causes associated with each possible failure mode should be identified and described. The causes of each failure mode are identified in order to estimate its probability of occurrence, to uncover secondary effects and to devise recommended corrective action. Since a failure mode can have more than one cause, all potential independent causes for each failure mode need to be identified and described. The list given in Table 6.2 illustrates how a more specific definition of failure causes can be developed.

The methods for detection of the failure mode should be described. Failure modes other than the one being considered which give rise to an identical manifestation should be analysed and listed. The need for separate detection of failure or redundant elements during operation should be considered.

Criticality analysis

The fundamental steps in the procedure for FMECA are the same as those for FMEA, however FMECA requires additional steps as follows:

- determine system severity classes;
- establish item failure mode severity;
- determine item failure mode and effect frequencies;

- determine event frequencies;
- draw up criticality matrix for item failure modes;
- summarize the criticality of failure effects from the criticality matrix;
- draw up criticality matrix for system failure effects;
- report findings at all levels of analysis.

Table 6.2 Possible failure causes

Type	Examples
Specification	Omitted statements Erroneous statements Support system failure
Design	Misapplication Design error Design omission Support equipment failure
Manufacture	Omitted action Erroneous action Procedural error Manufacturing equipment failure
Installation	Omitted action Erroneous action Procedural error Installation equipment failure
Operation	Omitted action Erroneous action Procedural error Off-line equipment failure
Maintenance	Omitted action Erroneous action Procedural error Maintenance equipment failure
Environment	Temperature Humidity Vibration Corrosion
Uncontrollable forces	Fire Flood Earthquake Explosion

Source: BS 5760: Part 5 (1991)

Criticality is a combination of the severity of an effect and the probability or expected frequency of its occurrence. When associated with, for example, a failure mode the criticality of the effect is spoken of as the criticality of the failure mode. It may be desirable to quantify criticality as an aid to decision-making on the corrective actions needed and their priorities.

The purpose of a criticality analysis is to quantify the relative importance of each failure effect, so that priorities for action to eliminate or contain the failures may be set. Criticality is evaluated by a subjective measure of the severity of the effect and an estimate of the probability of expected frequency of its occurrence. When the estimate of probability of frequency is based on trustworthy data the analysis may be used as a basis for judging whether or not the likelihood of a particular effect is acceptably small.

Criticality analysis is applied as an extension of FMEA, to give a failure modes, effects and criticality analysis (FMECA). A set of severity classes ranging from catastrophic to trivial should be drawn up first, with particular reference to the range of possible damage to people, plant and economics resulting from the failure of the item under analysis. Using the failure effects identified by the FMEA each effect is allocated to an appropriate severity class. A probability or frequency for the event is calculated from failure data for the part concerned and modifying factors such as environment, the probability of the system failing as a consequence of the failure mode and the

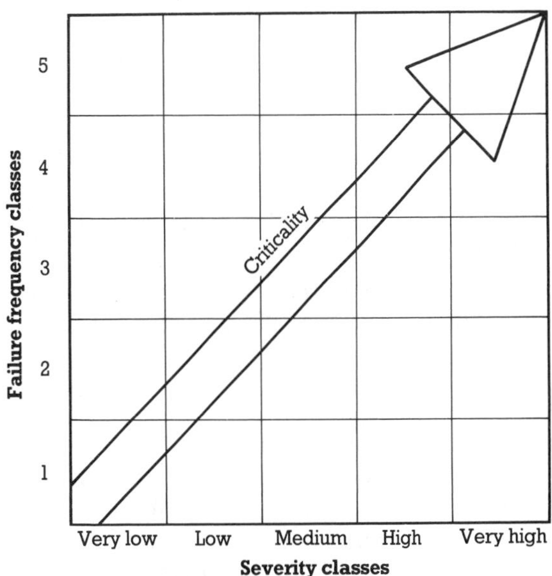

Source: BS 5760: Part 6 (1991)

Figure 6.6 Example of a criticality grid

proportion of elapsed time during which the part is at risk. The severity class and frequency or probability for each effect together constitute the criticality of the effect. They can be presented on a criticality grid, as shown in Figure 6.6; where they can be placed in criticality bands, or presented in the form of ranked contributions to the total frequency of each severity class.

An example of applying FMECA to the subsystem of a motor generator set is given in Appendix F.

6.19 Fault tree analysis (FTA)

Fault tree analysis is concerned with the identification and analysis of conditions and factors which cause or contribute to the occurrence of a defined undesirable event, usually one which significantly affects system performance, economy, safety or other required characteristics. It is suitable for the analyses of single failure modes involving complex failure logic and redundancy.

The fault tree is an organised graphical representation of the conditions or other factors causing or contributing to the occurrence of a defined undesirable event, referred to as the 'top event'. The representation is in a form which can be understood, analysed and, as necessary, rearranged to facilitate the identification of:

- factors affecting the reliability and performance characteristics of the system, for example component fault modes, operator mistakes, environmental conditions, software faults;
- conflicting requirements or specifications which may affect reliable performance;
- common events affecting more than one functional component, which would cancel the benefits of specific redundancies.

FTA is basically a deductive (top-down) method of analysis aimed at pinpointing the causes or combinations of causes that can lead to the defined top event. The analysis is mainly qualitative but, depending on certain conditions, it may also be quantitative.

There are several reasons for performing FTA independently of, or in conjunction with, other dependability analyses. These include:

- the identification of the causes or combinations of causes leading to the top event;
- the determination of whether a particular system reliability measure meets a stated requirement;
- the demonstration that assumptions made in other analyses, regarding the independence of systems and non-relevance of failures, are not violated;
- the determination of the factor(s) which most seriously affect a particular reliability measure and the changes required to improve that measure;
- the identification of common events or common cause failures.

The fault tree is particularly suited to the analysis of complex systems comprising several functionally related or dependent sub-systems with different performance objectives. This is especially true whenever the system design requires the collaboration of many specialized technical design groups. Examples of systems to which FTA is commonly applied include nuclear power generating stations, aeroplanes, communication systems, chemical and other industrial processes.

Principles

The development of the fault tree should start early in the system design stage. The growth of the fault tree should be such that it reflects the progress of the design. Thus an increased understanding of the fault modes will be obtained as the design proceeds. The 'analysis concurrent with design' allows for early systems design changes as significant fault modes are identified. Fault tree events are not confined solely to software or hardware faults, but include all conditions or other factors which are relevant to the top event for the system concerned.

In order to use the fault tree technique effectively as a method for system analysis, the procedure should consist of at least the following steps:

- definition of the scope of the analysis;
- familiarization with the design, functions and operation of the system;
- definition of the top event;
- construction of the fault tree;
- analysis of the fault tree logic;
- reporting on the results of the analysis.

If a numerical analysis is planned, it will be necessary to define a technique for numerical assessment.

Each system should be defined by a description of the system function and by an identification of the system interfaces. Such a definition should include:

- a summary of the design intent;
- the boundaries of the system, such as electrical, mechanical and operational interfaces; such boundaries will be governed by the interaction and interfaces with other systems and should be described by identifying the particular functions (e.g. power supply) and parts (e.g. fuse), which form the interfaces;
- the physical structure of the system, as opposed to the functional structure;
- the identification of operational modes together with a description of system operation and the expected or acceptable performance in each operation mode;
- the system's environmental conditions, and relevant human aspects;
- a list of applicable documents, for example drawings, specifications, operating manuals, which give details of the equipment design and operation. Task duration, time interval between (periodic) tests, as well as time available for corrective maintenance actions should be known, as should the support equipment and personnel involved. Specific information on prescribed operating conditions during each operational phase is also required.

Events arising from all causes should be included in the fault tree. Such causes should include the effects of all environmental or other conditions to which the item might be subjected including those which are possible during operation, even if outside the design specification. Where relevant, fault trees should take into account the effects of mistakes and of deficiencies in computer software including that used for control and status monitoring.

Events which the analyst has considered, but excluded from further analysis as not applicable, should be documented but not included in the final fault tree.

If the fault tree highlights a system performance problem caused by an existing fault, then the event describing that fault should be included in the fault tree. It should be marked as an event which already exists. This should be done in order to consider the effect and order of multiple faults.

Fault tree development starts with the definition of the top event. The top event is the output of the top gate, while the corresponding input events identify possible causes and conditions for the occurrence of the top event. Each input event may itself be an output event of a lower level gate.

If the output event of a gate defines the inability to perform a function, the corresponding input events could be hardware faults or performance limitations. If the output event defines a hardware fault, the corresponding input events could be hardware faults, lack of control and lack of essential supplies, if applicable and not already included as part of the performance limitations.

The development of a particular fault tree branch terminates after any one or more of the following have been reached:

- basic events, i.e. independent events for which the relevant characteristics can be defined by means other than a fault tree;
- events which need not be developed further, as defined by the analyst;
- events which have been or will be developed further in another fault tree; if an event is developed further such an event must bear the same identification as the corresponding event on the other fault tree so that the latter tree effectively forms a continuation of the former.

Procedure

FTA proceeds in steps. The specific steps followed for a particular system may not be exactly the same as those followed for another system. However, the following fundamental steps are common to all fault tree analyses.

Scope of analysis

The definition of the scope should include the definition of the system to be analysed, the purpose and extent of the analysis and the basic assumptions made. These assumptions should include those related to the expected operating and maintenance conditions as well as to system performance under all possible conditions of use.

System familiarization

In order that FTA may be carried out successfully, a detailed knowledge of the system is required. However, some systems may be too complex to be understood fully by one person. In this case, the process of familiarization requires that the necessary specialized knowledge be obtained and incorporated as appropriate into the FTA.

Top event identification

The top event is the focus of the entire analysis. Such an event may be the onset or existence of a dangerous condition, or the inability of the system to provide a desired performance. Whenever possible it should be defined in measurable units.

Fault tree construction

Fault trees may be drawn either vertically or horizontally. If the vertical arrangement is used, the top event should be at the top of the page and the basic event at the bottom. If the horizontal arrangement is used, the top event may be on the left or right of the page. Each event in the fault tree needs to be uniquely identified. The top event is the undesirable event which is the primary reason for undertaking the FTA. A typical code should contain information relating to system identification, component identification and fault mode. The fault tree is in effect a diagram in which the events are linked by logic gates. Each gate has one output event but one or more input events. The input events identify possible causes and conditions for the occurrence of the output events.

An example of a fault tree is shown in Figure 6.7. It can be seen that symbols are used to show the development of representation of a fault tree. The basic fault tree uses 'AND', 'OR' and 'NOT' gates. Alternative routes are combined through 'OR' gates while events and states that have to be confident are combined through 'AND' gates. An event which represents a condition which is an inverse of the condition defined by the input gate is a 'NOT' gate. For complex systems analysis, additional gate symbols may be required to assure that the fault trees are readable ad as simple as possible. Annex A of BS 5760: Part 7 (1991) gives the standardised basic symbols in accordance with BS 3939: Part 12 (1985) together with possible

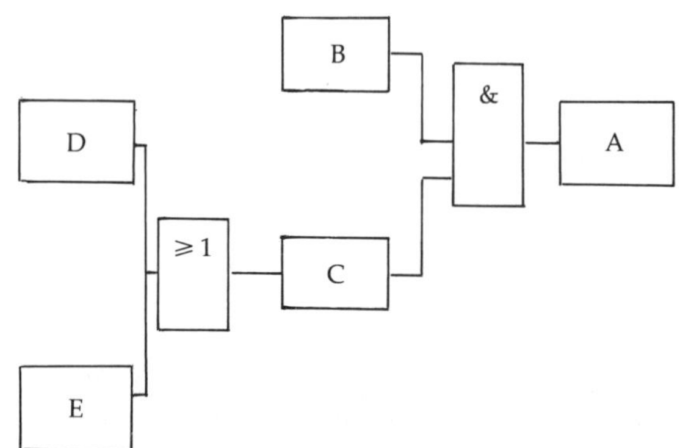

Event A will occur only if both events B and C occur. Event C is present if either event D or E occurs.

Note: For each event, A, B, etc., information to be included in the event description box includes

- event code;
- probability of occurrence (if required);
- name or description of event.

Function	Description
AND gate	Event occurs only if all input events occur simultaneously
OR gate	Event occurs if any of the input events occur, either alone or in any combination

Source: BS 5760: Part 7 (1991)

Figure 6.7 Example of a fault tree

alternatives. A detailed write-up of construction procedures for FTA is contained in BS 5760: Part 7 (1991).

Fault tree evaluation

The primary purposes of logical (qualitative) and numerical (quantitative) analyses of a system are:

- identification of events which can directly cause a system failure, and the probability of such events;
- assessment of fault tolerance of the system (ability to function even after a specified number of lower level failures or events contributing to the occurrence of a system failure have happened);
- verification of the independence of failure of systems, sub-systems or components;
- assessment of data to locate critical components and failure mechanisms;
- identification of device failure diagnostics, inputs to repair and maintenance strategies.

An example of a FTA for a hypothetical chemical reactor is given in Appendix G.

6.20 Design review

Purpose and organisation

A design review can be defined as a formal, documented and systematic critical study of a design proposal by specialists who are not necessarily engaged in the design process. This review is different from a project progress meeting, which is primarily concerned with time and cost. The prime objective of a design review procedure is to provide a preventive evaluation. The aim is to identify and anticipate problem areas and inadequacies, and initiate corrective actions to ensure that the final design and supporting data meet customer requirements. It can also encourage constructive participation of an optimum design without usurping the responsibility of the design function. The design review procedure can prove advantageous both for the supplier and customer, particularly on large-scale projects where it may not be possible to prove the design by comprehensive R & D work.

At the conclusion of each phase of the design development cycle – from initial conception to the issuing of operations instructions and specifications to a production/operations department – a review of the design should be conducted. For example:

- preliminary reviews held at the time of product or service concept and planning proposal, bid, or request for funds, and also when the contract or authorisation is received;
- intermediate reviews held when the following are completed – block or function diagram, flow design, equipment design, styling and development model tests;
- final reviews held when material lists and specifications are complete or when pre-production units are tested and analysed.

The participants at the design review generally include representatives of all functions affecting product and service quality as appropriate to the phase being reviewed. In addition to the chairman, it is usual to have membership from the quality assurance department, specialists on reliability, development and industrial engineering, as well as the designers responsible for the product or service in question. Representatives from the purchasing, production/operations, marketing and service departments might attend as appropriate and customer representatives would normally attend a final design review.

The extent of design review, the methods to be used and the composition of the review team will depend upon the nature of the product/service application, its design complexity, the degree of standardisation, the state-of-the-art situation, the competence of the design originator and the degree of similarity with past proven designs.

A review is normally initiated by the chairman who will generally wish to appoint a secretary from within the group to deal with the procedural matters, such as the preparation and circulation of terms of reference, calling notices, agendas and minutes of the meetings, indicating what actions need to be taken, by whom and by what specified date.

Following completion of a review it is usual for a final report to be submitted to the responsible executive to summarise the recommendations made and any modifications subsequently incorporated in a design. However, the final authority for design decisions rests with the designer and his or her design manager.

Elements of design reviews

It is useful to establish a checklist of factors for the design review, as appropriate to the design phase and product or service. The following are typical of the elements to be considered.

Items pertaining to customer needs and satisfaction:

- Comparison of customer needs expressed in the product/service brief with specifications for materials, products or services and processes;
- validation of the design through prototype tests or trials;
- ability to perform under expected conditions of use and environment;
- considerations of unintended uses and misuses;
- safety and environmental compatibility;
- compliance with regulatory requirements, national and international standards, and corporate practices;
- comparisons with competitive designs;
- comparison with similar designs, especially analysis of internal and external problem history to avoid repeating problems.

Items pertaining to product specification and service requirements:

- reliability, durability, serviceability and maintainability requirements;
- permissible specification tolerances and comparison with process capabilities;
- product/service acceptance/rejection criteria;
- ease of assembly and installation, storage needs, shelf-life and disposability (if applicable);
- benign failure and fail-safe characteristics;
- aesthetic specifications and acceptance criteria;
- FMEA and FTA;
- ability to diagnose and correct problems;
- labelling, warnings, identification, traceability requirements and user instructions (if applicable);
- review and use of standard materials or parts.

Items pertaining to process specifications and service requirements:

- producability of the design, including special process needs, mechanisation, automations, assembly and installation of components (where applicable);
- capability to inspect and check out the design, including any special inspections and check requirements;
- specification of materials, including approved supplies and suppliers, as well as availability;
- packaging, handling, storage and shelf-life requirements, especially safety factors relating to incoming and outgoing materials or items (if applicable).

Figure 6.8 shows a typical design review checklist as used by the Garrett Automotive group (Muninger, 1987).

Design verification

Design verification may be undertaken independently or in support of design reviews by applying the following methods:

- alternative calculations, made to verify the correctness of the original calculations and analyses;
- testing, for example by model or prototype tests or trials of the service;
- independent verification, to verify the correctness of the original calculations and/or other design activities.

1 Is the turbocharger especially developed for this particular customer?
2 How many critical, major, and non-critical parts and characteristics are in the total unit?
3 Do we have all data used for selecting particular parts, can a commercial version off the shelf part be used?
4 Have the individual parts been checked for strength?
5 Have we had problems in similar designs? In what areas? Have we implemented corrective action? Has the problem been solved successfully?
6 Is it likely that problems encountered in other applications apply in this design?
7 If anything is to fail, what is most likely to be the failure mode? List them by order.
8 What is the known data of failure modes from field returns and green runs?
9 Were the detected problems resolved and/or what is currently taking place to resolve the identified problems?
10 Can this design introduce new failure modes?
11 Does our design differ from others in the market? Do we know the strength and weaknesses of that design? Is our new design better? Does it provide solutions in the market for the known problematic units?
12 What is the reliability of the design/process to produce the parts?
13 How does the unit go into function (life path, condition and environments units to be subjected to)?
14 Is this the simplest design to accommodate engineering's needs?
15 Have we used, as much as possible, common parts from other units?
16 Have we completed a thorough tolerance study?
17 Are parts manufacturable using inexpensive methods?
18 How will these units behave in different parts of the world? Under different environmental conditions and operators (i.e., temperature, humidity, dust, vibration, etc.). Will the driving pattern or mode affect the unit performance or life expectancy?
19 Human engineering – has it been considered for finished assembly?
20 Is the design cost effective?

Source: Muninger, 1987

Figure 6.8 A typical design review checklist

6.21 Design audit

It is usual to carry out a critical examination of the design in order to ensure that there will be an acceptable level of reliability and maintainability in operational use. This is carried out by staff who are independent of the design process, and the audit should cover all activities from the design concept to testing, installation, operation, degradation of performance in service and maintenance. The audit will help to identify any design weaknesses requiring modifications but it should not offer a solution; this is the province of the designer.

6.22 Design baseline and production/operations release

The results of the final design review need to be appropriately documented in specifications and drawings that define the design baseline. The total document package that defines the design baseline will require approval at appropriate levels of management affected by, or contributing to, the product or service. This approval constitutes the production/operations release and signifies that the design can be realised.

An objective of the design process is to produce clear and comprehensive data that contains the information necessary for purchasing, production/operations, inspection, tests, checks and maintenance. This data usually consists of specifications and instructions. Procedures are also prescribed for the identification and revision status of design documents, records of changes made and their distribution, control and recall. The procedures provide for approval, by the organisation or person responsible for the design, of all documents and changes to documents in which the design is defined.

6.23 Product testing and measurement

Testing is a normal part of any product development for reasons such as improvements in performance, function and quality, and optimization of clearances. It is usual to include an analysis of materials and processes proposed in the design during the design and development phase, with regard to the known reliability and producibility of such parts. If innovation in materials or techniques is proposed, then the desirability from both design and operational standpoints should be analysed and/or tested in order to justify their adoption in preference to established alternatives.

Although tests to destruction are neither possible nor feasible with certain products, one of the more successful ways of ensuring the quality and in particular the reliability of systems, equipment and parts is through R & D. With this, attempts are made to simulate actual operational and environmental conditions on a test basis, the samples of product or operations being representative of the envisaged or actual product or service. When used in the preventive rather than the assessment sense, development can be most rewarding, especially where the quality assurance function is working in conjunction with design and development functions to monitor and feedback the necessary data as a basis for future modifications.

The methods of measurement, checking and testing, and the acceptance criteria applied to evaluate the product, service and processes, during both the design and production/operations phases need to be specified. Parameters include the following:

- performance target values, tolerances and attributed features;
- acceptance and rejection criteria;
- testing, checking and measurement methods, equipment, bias and precision requirements, and computer software considerations.

6.24 Evaluation of the design process

An evaluation of the actual product design process should be carried out to establish if the plans made to achieve the objectives set out in the design brief were adequate, if estimated times and costs were accurate and if the general management of the product design function was satisfactory. A review of the progress of the design project will reveal areas where improvements can be made for the next product design venture. The evaluation of the design process should examine both company procedures and those that are specific to the project. It is essential to record data during the progress of the project so that evaluation does not rely on memory alone.

The person responsible for the design function should examine the following questions when evaluating a specific design activity:

- Were all the objectives achieved?
- Was the planning comprehensive?
- Was the work completed within the planned time?
- Were the costs of the activity within the budget?
- Were the design staff under-stretched or over-stretched?
- Were training needs identified?
- Were recruitment needs identified?
- Were the procedures specific to the project adequate and did they interface properly with the standard procedures?

6.25 Document (or design) change control

It is necessary for an organisation to have in place a procedure for controlling the release, change and use of documents that define the design base line (resultant product or service configuration) and for authorising the necessary work to be performed to implement changes that may affect the product or service during its entire life cycle. All design modifications made after the design has reached the point of release for production/operations are regarded as changes. These also should be governed by design change control measures, if the achieved and demonstrated reliability is not to be unacceptably reduced by later design changes made for non-reliability reasons. The later in the process the change is made the more difficult and costly it will be. The use of QFD helps to reduce the number of design and document changes.

Before permitting a change the following questions should be considered:

- Does the product or service still conform to the design specification?
- Is the fitness for purpose affected?

- Are changes to the specification possible in order to accommodate the change?
- Are associated parts of the product or system affected by the change?
- Is there a need for further interface design (i.e. physical contact with other components in a product or the interaction of two or more finite procedures in a system or service)?
- Does the change create problems in manufacture, installation or use which may affect the plan?
- Does the product or service still remain verifiable?

In industries where innovation, redesign, and product improvement are continuously practised, control of changes is of critical importance to product or service quality and reliability. However, it should not be forgotten that the main reason why organisations face problematical engineering changes is that the design was a problem to begin with.

Dale (1982) gives the following reasons for design and document changes:

- in the launch of a new product design, essential design changes usually arise in the development and manufacture to make the product work, to help the product achieve its specification and make it possible to manufacture it;
- to take advantage of improvements in manufacturing technology during the product's life cycle;
- the need to improve the life, quality conformance, reliability, maintainability, serviceability, safety and attractiveness of the product;
- other optional design changes include those intended to reduce production costs, to facilitate changes in supplier, to improve the flexibility of sourcing and to reduce distribution costs;
- an unavoidable cause of design changes is the permanent loss of supply for a component or material. A single-source manufacturer may discontinue the production of a part or a type of grade of raw material from an overseas source may become unavailable owing to political events.

The design (or document) change procedure should provide for various necessary approvals, specified points and times for implementing changes, removing obsolete drawings and specifications from work areas, and verification that changes are made at the appointed times and places.

There are a number of factors to consider in design change procedure, including: how the change is to be classified; the subject of interchangeability; the structure, organisation and responsibility of the design change committee; determining when the change is to be implemented; and the change procedure itself, along with the relevant documentation.

Balcerak and Dale (1992) have carried out research into design change control, the main findings of their work are summarised below:

- Engineering changes can be usefully and objectively classified by two separate criteria, namely type (which indicates the impact of the change on the various departments of the company) and grade (which indicates the urgency with which a change should be processed).
- For each engineering change, it is the responsibility of the engineering change committee to answer two questions. Is the engineering change commercially justifiable? If it is, then when should it be implemented?
- Six determinants of engineering change effectively were identified – market forces, drawing office work, availability of replacement parts or raw materials, stock run out, availability of replacement tools and tool wear. All but the simplest engineering changes require more than one determinant to be considered, when deciding the optimum effectivity date for putting the changes into place.
- Feedback from manufacturing areas is essential to the success of an engineering change procedure. It provides information on the status of individual changes, a measure of the performance of the engineering change procedure and experience, based upon which effectivity estimating can be improved in the future.

6.26 The use made of feedback data

It is important that the experience gained from previous designs and user experience is employed in current and future designs. For this to be effective, accurate notes need to be kept, all data must be analysed and the analysis fed back to design and production/operations so that the necessary corrective action can be planned and implemented as quickly and as economically as practicable. The analysis, and particularly the categorisation of failures, in terms of relevance, responsibility and proposed corrective action, should ideally be prepared in conjunction with the appropriate design, development, production/operations and quality assurance personnel. To facilitate this, a procedure is often established to encompass recording, reporting, analysis and distribution of information gained during production or operations, assembly, installation, commissioning, servicing and field use. There must be a constant evaluation of the situation throughout the life of the product/service not just during the stages of development.

6.27 Definitions and terminology

The following are some useful definitions and terms used in this chapter.

Catalogue: a published list of information on equipment, parts or materials. Presented primarily for the retrieval of information, it usually incorporates the code, and sufficient information for the user to identify his requirements.

Classification: a grouping set in order shown, i.e. alphabetically into categories or classes, of parts or materials that share common attributes.

Code of practice: a document that recommends practices or procedures for the design, manufacture, installation, maintenance or utilisation of equipment, structures or products.

Coding: the designation of items by reference numbers or letters in place of the full description. A code may be allocated according to a classification system, but this is not essential. The simplest code may be allocated by consecutive accession to a list.

Concession; waiver: written authorisation to use or release a quantity of material, components or stores already produced but which do not conform to the special requirements.

Conceptual design: the design process in which concepts are generated with a view to fulfilling the objectives.

Configuration: the complete technical description required to make, test, accept, install, operate, maintain and logistically support an item.

Criticality: a combination of the severity of an effect and the probability (or expected frequency) of its occurrence.

Design: the process of task recognition and problem solving with the object of fulfilling needs by the creation of products and services.

Design review: a formal, documented, comprehensive and systematic examination of a design to evaluate the design requirements and the capability of the design to meet these requirements and to identify problems and propose solutions.

Detail design: the process in which the precise shape, dimension and tolerances are specified, the material selection is confirmed and the method of manufacture is considered, for every individual part of the product.

Embodiment design: the design process in which a structured development of the preferred concept is carried out. The preliminary embodiment of all the main functions to be performed by the product is undertaken and the physical processes are clearly established.

Failure effect: the consequence of a failure mode in terms of the operation, function or status of the system.

Failure mode: the effect by which a failure is observed.

Failure modes and effects analysis (FMEA): a qualitative method of reliability analysis which involves the study of the fault modes which can exist in every sub-item of the item and the determination of the effects of each fault mode on other sub-items of the item and on the required functions of the item.

Failure mode, effects and criticality analysis (FMECA): a qualitative method of reliability analysis which involves a fault mode and effects analysis together with a consideration of the probability of their occurrence and of the ranking of the seriousness of the faults.

Fault tree: a logic diagram showing which fault modes of sub-items or external events, or combinations thereof, result in a given fault mode of the item.

Fault tree analysis (FTA): an analysis to determine which fault modes of the sub-items or external events, or combinations thereof, may result in a stated failure mode of the item, presented in the form of a fault tree.

Functional specification: the document that describes in detail the characteristics of the product or service with regard to its intended use.

Hazard: a situation that could occur during the lifetime of a product, system or plant that has the potential for human injury, damage to property, damage to the environment or economic loss.

Maintainability: the ability of an item, under given conditions of use, to be retained in, or restored to, a state in which it can perform a required function, when maintenance is performed under given conditions and using stated procedures and resources.

Procedure: a specified method of carrying out a particular task.

Product liability: a generic term used to describe the onus on a producer or others to make restitution for loss related to personal injury, property damage or other harm caused by a product or service.

Quality level: any relative quality measure obtained by comparing observed values with the relevant requirements.

Rationalisation: the procedure for reducing variety by the simplification of existing ranges.

Reliability: the ability of an item to perform a required function under stated conditions for a stated period of time.

Risk: a combination of the probability, or frequency, of occurrence of a defined hazard and the magnitude of the consequences of the occurrence.

Safety: the freedom from unacceptable risks of personal harm.

Specification: a document that prescribes the requirements with which the product or service has to conform.

Standard: a document, established by consensus and approved by a recognised body, that provides, for common and repeated use, rules, guidelines or characteristics for activities or their results, aimed at the achievement of the optimum degree of order in a given context.

Standardisation: activity of establishing with regard to actual or potential problems, provisions for common and repeated use, aimed at the achievement of the optimum degree of order.

Tolerance: the difference between the upper and lower tolerance limits.

Tolerance interval; tolerance zone: the variate values of the characteristic between and including the tolerance limits.

Tolerance limits; limiting values; specification limits: the specified values of the characteristic giving upper and lower bounds of the permissible value.

Value analysis: a technique applied to an existing product to improve its value and reduce the total cost.

Value engineering: a technique applied in the design stage to improve the value and reduce the total cost of a product.

Variety control: selection of the optimum number of sizes or types of products, processes or services to meet prevailing needs.

British Standards

BS 3939: *Guide to graphical symbols for electrical power, telecommunications and electronic diagrams* Part 12: 1985 *Binary logic elements* (IEC 617–12: 1983).

BS 4778: Part 1: 1987 *Quality vocabulary – International terms* (ISO 8402: 1986) (EN 28402: 1991); Part 2: 1991 *Quality concepts and related definitions;* Part 3: 1991 *Availability, reliability and maintainability terms,* Section 3.1: 1991 *Guide to concepts and related definitions;* Section 3.2: 1991 *Glossary of international terms* (IEC 50(191): 1991).

BS 5750: *Quality systems* Part 0: Section 0.2: 1987 *Quality systems – principal contents and applications; guide to quality management and quality system elements* (ISO 9004: 1987) (EN 29004: 1987); Part 1: 1987 *Specification for design/development, production, installation and servicing;* (ISO 9001: 1987) (EN 29001: 1987); Part 4: 1990 *Guide to the use of BS 5750; Part 1: Specification for design/development, production, installation and servicing; Part 2: Specification for production and installation; Part 3: Specification for final inspection and test.*

BS 5760: *Reliability of systems, equipment and components* Part 1: 1985 *Guide to reliability and maintainability programme management*; Part 2: 1981 *Guide to the assessment of reliability*; Part 3: 1982 *Guide to reliability practices: examples*; Part 5: 1991 *Guide to failure modes, effects and criticality analysis (FMEA and FMECA)*; Part 7: 1991 *Guide to fault tree analysis* (IEC 812: 1991).

BS 6548: *Maintainability of equipment* Part 1: 1984 *Guide to specifying and contracting for maintainability* (IEC 806–1: 1982); Part 2: 1991 *Guide to maintainability studies during the design phase* (IEC 706–2: 1990).

BS 7000: *Design management systems* Part 1: 1989 *Guide to managing product design.*

BS 7373: 1991 *Guide to the preparation of specifications.*

PD 3542: 1991 *The role of standards in company quality management.*

PD 6470: 1981 *The management of design for economic production.*

PD 6489: 1980 *Guide to the preparation of a company standards manual.*

PD 6495: 1992 *IFAN: Guide 1: Method for determining the advantages of (company) standardisation projects.*

References

Akao Y (ed.). *Quality Function Deployment Integrating Customer Requirements into Product Design.* Productivity Press, Cambridge, Ma., USA, 1990.

Allied Signal Inc. *Quality Function Deployment – A guide for Implementation,* Allied Signal Inc., Michigan, 1989.

Balcerak K J and Dale B G. 'Engineering Change Administration: the key issues', *Computer-integrated manufacturing systems,* 5(2), pp 125–132, 1992.

Barker R L. *The seven new QC tools.* Proceedings of the First Conference on Tools and Techniques for TQM, Manchester, IFS Conferences, pp 95–120, 1989.

Dale B G. 'The management of engineering change procedure.' *Engineering Management International,* 1(2), pp 201–8, 1982.

Dale B G (ed.) *Managing Quality,* 2nd edition, Prentice Hall, Oxford, 1994.

Eureka W E and Ryan N E. *The customer-driven company: managerial perspectives on QFD.* ASI Press, Michigan, USA, 1988.

HMSO. *The Consumer Protection Act.* HMSO, London, UK, 1987.

Mizuno S. *Management for quality improvement.* Productivity Press, Cambridge, Ma., USA, 1988.

Muninger B. *Reliability assurance in product development.* Garrett Automotive Group, Reliability Engineering, France, 1987.

Oakland J S. 'The seven new tools of total quality management', in *Total Quality Management,* Denholm Publicity, 1990.

Oakland J S. *Total quality management,* 2nd edition, Butterworth-Heinemann Professional Publishing, Oxford, UK, 1993.

Ozeki K and Asaka T. *Handbook of quality tools: the Japanese approach.* Productivity Press, Cambridge, Ma., USA, 1990.

Ryan N E. *Taguchi methods and QFD.* ASI Press, Michigan, USA, 1988.

Shewhart W A. *Economic control of quality of a manufactured product.* Van Nostrand Company, New York, USA, 1931.

Taguchi G. *Introduction to quality engineering – designing quality into products and processes.* Asian Productivity Organisation, Tokyo, Japan, 1986.

CHAPTER 7

Quality systems

7.1 Introduction

A principal factor in the performance of an organisation and its corporate health is the quality of its products or services. There is a worldwide trend towards more stringent customer expectations with regard to quality and a growing realisation that continual incremental improvements in product and service quality are necessary to achieve and sustain good economic performance. This requires efficient organisation within a company and the determination of all employees to fulfil the needs of its customers and pursue continuous improvement on a long-term basis.

Organisations produce a product or service intended to satisfy a user's needs or requirements. Such requirements are often incorporated in specifications. However, these may not in themselves guarantee that a customer's needs and requirements will be consistently met. For example, there could be deficiencies in the specifications, the communication of the specification or in the organisational system to design and produce the product or service. In today's competitive markets, major purchasers demand proof of a company's ability to produce quality products or provide quality services. The manufacturer needs to demonstrate to the customer and/or an outside party that not only is the product, service or material to specification but also that the manufacturing, operational and associated processes are under control at all times. This has led to the development of quality system standards (for example, the Ministry of Defence DEF STAN 05–21 to 05–29 series (1973–6), the NATO Allied Quality Assurance Publications AQAP–1 to AQAP–9 series (1970–2) and BS 5750: 1987), and guidelines that complement relevant product or service requirements given in the technical specifications. Some of these standards had been developed for commercial use and others for the needs of the military or the nuclear power industry. Some standards were guidance documents and others were for contractual use between purchaser and supplier organisations. The terminology in the standards and in commercial and industrial practice was also inconsistent and confusing.

A major impetus to the debate on standards in the UK was the Warner Report (1977). This report highlighted the contribution which standards can make to competitiveness and pointed to the shortcomings and fragmented nature of the British system of standards. It was recommended that British Standards be produced to provide the single base documents for quality systems. Consequently, BS 5750 quality systems emerged in 1979 as Parts 1, 2 and 3 for the three levels of system; Parts 4, 5 and 6 were published in 1981 as guidance documents to the use of Parts 1, 2 and 3 respectively.

The principles embodied in BS 5750 can be traced back to the use of the Allied Quality Assurance Publications (AQAP) which were used by NATO in defence procurement. These were modified by the Ministry of Defence (MOD) to produce the DEF STAN 05–21 series.

The ISO 9000/BS 5750 series are equivalent with some minor differences to NATO AQAPs 1,4 and 9, which superseded the MOD DEF STAN 0521–29. The ISO 9000 series has now superseded the AQAP series.

Following their publication, the BS 5750 series has rapidly been adopted in a wide variety of industrial sectors. As such they have formed a cornerstone of various government initiatives and are the reference basis for the DTI's *Register of Quality Assessed United Kingdom Companies*. Subsequently, BS 5750: Parts 1, 2 and 3, together with other national standards, such as the Canadian Standard Z 293, were used as the basis for part of the then new series of ISO Standards (ISO 9001, 9002 and 9003). BSI formally proposed the formation of a new technical committee to develop international standards for assurance techniques and practices (ISO/TC176). Some 20 countries participated in the development of the ISO 9000 series.

The series of International Standards (ISO 9000 to ISO 9004 inclusive), which were first published in 1987, embodies a rationalisation of the many and various national approaches in this sphere. They were published in time to meet the growing needs for international standardisation in the quality arena, and the wider scale adoption of third-party quality systems certification. The ISO Standards are heavily based on BS 5750: 1979 but reflect international requirements and eight years of UK user experience, the influence of UK quality management experience and leadership using BS 5750: 1979 is very evident in the ISO Standards. The text of these International Standards has been approved as suitable for publication as a British Standard without deviation – BS 5750: Parts 0 to 3 and Part 8, Part 13 and Part 14. The lowering of European trade barriers which took place in 1992 has given an increased importance to the ISO 9000 Series. The ISO 9000 series of International Standards have now been adopted by CEN-CENELEC (the joint European Standards Institution) as the EN 29000 series. The standards have brought harmonisation on an international scale and have supported the growing impact of quality as a factor in international trade.

In response to the interest in the ISO 9000 series of quality management standards, ISO in 1992 set up an 'ISO 9000 forum'. This service is intended to provide an international communication mechanism to support the implementation of the ISO series of quality standards. An excellent account of the historical background to the development of the ISO 9000 series is provided by Spickernall (1991).

The ISO 9000 series of standards (ISO 9000, ISO 9001, ISO 9002, ISO 9003 and ISO 9004) were published in 1987 and extended to services and software in 1991 as ISO 9000–3 and ISO 9004–2. In 1993, the series was further extended as ISO 9000-4 (BS 5750: Part 14) to dependability management and as ISO 9004-3 to processed materials. Also in 1993, guidelines for the application of ISO 9001, ISO 9002 and ISO 9003 were published as ISO 9004-4. These latter two standards have British Standard counterparts as BS 5750: Part 4 and BS 7850: Part 2. They have now been adopted as national standards in some 50 countries and a third-party and registration process exist, for recognising conformance to ISO 9000 standards, in at least 30 countries.

Major industrial customers, for example, Ford Motor Company (Ford Q-101, 1990), the National Nuclear Corporation (G/7622, 1983), Nissan Motor Manufacturing (UK) (Nissan, 1991) and Rover Group (RG 2000, 1991), have developed their own quality system standards, and a supplier must conform to these requirements, thus imposing a wide variety of extra requirements on their subcontractors or suppliers. However, companies such as Nissan have structured their quality system standard along the lines of the ISO 9000 series, but with additional requirements in terms of quality, cost, housekeeping, site and equipment maintenance, visual management and warranty. These quality system standards are often more specific and demanding than the ISO 9000 series. However, obtaining accreditation to ISO 9000 is a useful foundation leading to development of an organisation's quality system to meet the independent system requirements of customers. Thankfully present trends have seen the rationalisation of many of these systems by concentrating on and contributing to the production of national and international standards.

Assessments of a supplier's quality system are carried out prior to a contract in order to determine the supplier's ability to satisfy the requirements of the relevant quality system standard and, when appropriate, supplementary requirements. In many cases, assessments are performed directly by the purchaser. By agreement between purchaser and supplier, pre-contract assessment may be delegated to an organisation independent of both contracting parties. As part of their supplier rating activities, the supplier's quality system implementation and operation, are reviewed, from time to time, by major customers. Therefore, for contractual, mandatory and assessment purposes, demonstration that identified elements in the system have been implemented is often required.

The quality system of an organisation is influenced by the objectives of the organisation, by the product or service and by the practices specific to the organisation. Therefore, it will vary from one organisation to another. The management of an organisation should also ensure that the quality system will facilitate and promote continuous quality improvement. The quality system should include the objectives, policies, organisational structure, responsibilities, procedures, processes and resources for beginning and developing a process of quality improvement. It should be as comprehensive as necessary to meet the organisation's quality objectives. The organisation should provide confidence to the purchaser that the intended quality is being, or will be, achieved in the delivered product or service provided.

The quality system involves all phases from initial identification to final satisfaction of requirements and customer expectations. These phases and activities may include the following:

- marketing and market research;
- design/specification engineering and product development;
- procurement;
- production preparation, process planning and development;
- production;
- inspection, testing and examination,
- packaging and storage;
- sales and distribution;
- installation and operation;
- technical assistance and maintenance;
- disposal after use.

Figure 7.1 overleaf shows a schematic representation of these phases and activities.

This chapter begins by discussing the advantages to an organisation of obtaining BS 5750 Series registration, and then details some of the general criticisms which have been levelled against this approach. The main elements of the new ISO 9000-4 series (BS 5750: Parts 0 to 3 and Parts 8, 13 and 14) are discussed and this is followed by an outline of how an organisation may obtain registration to the BS 5750 Series.

7.2 Benefits and limitations of the BS 5750/ISO 9000 series

Benefits

From BSI literature, the following is a list of typical benefits claimed for an organisation obtaining BS 5750 registration:

- it is a first class marketing tool, at home and abroad;
- major buyers accept BSI certification and registration as proof of quality and technical expertise;
- customers are much less likely to ask for their own special assessments, and the number or the extent of audits and assessments can be minimised – thus saving time and money;
- confidence for the organisation resulting from the quality system being under independent surveillance;

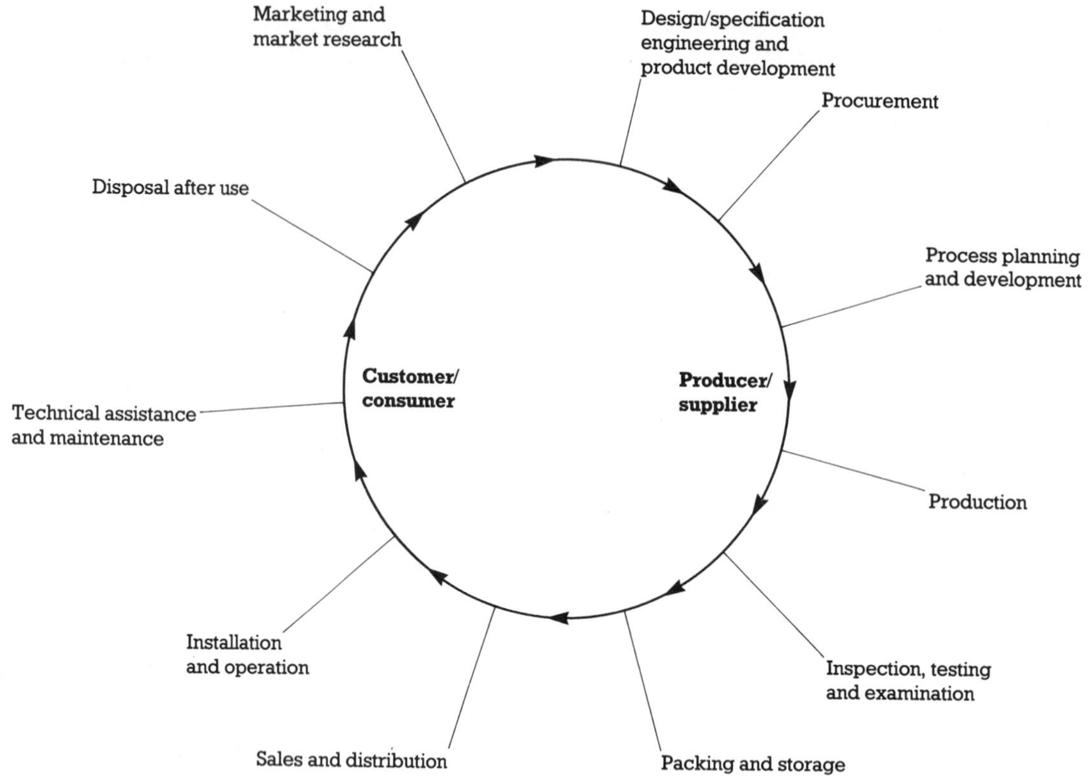

Figure 7.1 Quality loop

Source: BS 5750: 1987

- improvement in quality performance and company morale;
- the cost of lost orders, reworking, extra handling, scrapped production, wastage and senior executive time will all reduce;
- improved customer satisfaction, leading to increased sales, competitiveness and profitability;
- the company's name will appear in the BSI *Buyer's Guide* and in the DTI's *National Register of Quality Assured Companies.* (This register lists the firms whose quality system have been assessed and approved either by major users (formerly government agencies like the MoD and nationalised industries like British Coal) or independent third-party assessment bodies. It also describes the assessment methods used and stresses the measures taken to ensure that listed companies continue to perform to the relevant standards. The Register has a world-wide subscription list and is recognised as a major reference source for public purchasing and procurement authorities and for national industries.)

A survey carried out by PERA International and Salford University Business Services Limited (1992) of 2317 firms who had completed a Quality Consultancy Project under the DTI Enterprise Initiative prior to 31st December, 1990 found the following benefits:

- Overall, 98% of all clients surveyed believed that the introduction of quality management systems had a positive effect on their internal operating efficiency.
- Some 48% of firms claimed increased profitability, 76% improved marketing and 26% improved export sales – all attributed the effect to the introduction of quality management systems.

The report also claimed that:

- Service sector firms compare well with manufacturers and are likely to progress towards certification more quickly.
- On average, certification is attained some 17 months following the commencement of a consultancy project.

Perry (1991), who is IT Assessment Services Manager for BSI QA's IT and Software (PERA International and Salford University Business Services Limited 1992) Engineering Department, makes the following points regarding the benefits of BS 5750/ISO 9000 series registration:

> Our experience shows that if a quality system is installed or an existing one modified to meet the standard there is a one time cost of implementation, but it proves to be a very effective investment. Major benefits from a quality system conforming to ISO 9000 are:
>
> - The company becomes more consistent in its design and manufacturing processes, identifying and eliminating waste.
> - A discipline of internal audits is established.
> - There is a greater chance that the customer will be delivered goods to an agreed specification.
> - The company's organisation will be clarified, employees will know their responsibilities and authorities, and how to carry out their tasks through documented procedures and work instructions.
> - In addition there will be a statement on the company's quality policy, giving a set of company values.
>
> There are hard issues, they can be measured and audited and according to the DTI have resulted in cost savings of up to 25% of sales revenue in average companies, when implemented.
>
> (Perry, 1991)

Perry also goes on to say that the soft issues of management style, leadership, customer satisfaction and continuous improvement are not addressed by the standard yet these also contribute greatly to the quality of the product or service supplied by the company.

These types of benefits are echoed by many writers on the subject, including Atkin (1987), Bulled (1987), De Angelis (1991), Long *et al.* (1991), Marquardt *et al.* (1991) and Rayner and Porter (1990).

The BS 5750 Series is simply a base on which an organisation can build and develop its approach to TQM and these claimed benefits should be considered in the context of this. TQM requires major behaviour and attitude change at all organisational levels and this takes many years and considerable hard work to achieve. Ishikawa (1985), based on the Japanese experience, reports that it takes three to five years from the time the senior management team develop an understanding of quality management, issues policies and shows leadership, to these policies penetrating through to shop floor employees. It does not automatically follow that just because an organisation has a quality system in place considerable cost savings will be made. These savings will only come about once an organisation has committed itself to TQM. Suppliers have a habit of doing what their customers want and there is little doubt that some suppliers have achieved BS 5750 (ISO 9000) series registration just to satisfy the demands of their major customers.

Many major customers are not prepared to accept a supplier's BS 5750 (ISO 9000) series registration and wish to carry out their own full assessment of the supplier's quality system. For example, Dale and Plunkett (1984) reporting on a study carried out in 12 fabrication companies found that most were subjected to about six audits a year. Singer *et al.* (1988) in a study of the impact of quality assurance on 13 suppliers to the nuclear industry found that most companies are audited four or more times each year. Galt and Dale (1991) in a study focusing on the supplier development programs of 10 organisations based in the UK from a variety of industrial sectors found that 'five of the firms relied totally on their own evaluation of suppliers, three considered third-party accreditation a good starting point for their own subsequent evaluation and only two firms accepted third-party recognition as being adequate for their supplier evaluation purposes'. These studies point to the fact that customers are not prepared to accept the approvals of other organisations and this leads to multiple audits and assessments. The industrial sectors covered by these three surveys involve a number of organisations under UK governmental influence and, since it is the policy of government departments to specify BS 5750 series registration, one would expect to encounter less multiple assessments than in other industries (for example, automotive and electronics).

Discussions on the subject with quality assurance managers, with whom the authors have close links, reveal that there are three main benefits from obtaining registration to BS 5750. First, it assists an organisation to get on more bid lists. Secondly, the independent assessment surveillance helps to sharpen up the quality system by improving control and discipline. Finally, if the assessor identifies any system non-conformance, this will be brought to the attention of the organisation's senior management team. Consequently quality assurance managers feel they have more power to implement a change or improvement which they may have been struggling to bring about. For this reason, quality assurance managers in some situations have even asked the assessor to record a non-conformance, where one was not justified. It is also interesting that a number of quality assurance managers feel that the word 'quality' should be replaced by 'management' in the title of the Quality Systems Standard (BS 5750), believing this would encourage line managers to take more responsibility for the operating procedures and systems under their direct control.

Criticisms

A number of writers have articulated some criticisms of the BS 5750 Series. In IBM Havant's *Professional Guide to Vendor Certification* there is a section which compares IBM's approach to that of a BS 5750 Series assessment audit method used in their certification. (It should be noted that their certification programme is based on the BS 5750 Series.) If a vendor holds BS 5750 series registration then IBM do not carry out a readiness audit prior to final audit. The following are two salient comments from this section:

> Nowhere in BS 5750 does it refer to a company's ability to control production.
> If we were to work strictly to BS 5750 we could do so without looking at major areas which we consider contribute to quality.
>
> (IBM, 1985)

Mortiboys (1983) states 'None of the BS 5750 systems are fully cost-effective, because none of them require either extensive employee motivation or involvement, or provide for the implementation of other highly desirable features of the cost-effective management of product quality – market research, quality cost management, extensive training and planning'.

Price states 'Companies are offered financial inducement to install structured quality control systems and thereby become certificated under BS 5750. This Standard is somewhat like a Christian Church without a Christ – all form and no content; but it has the merit of being better than nothing'. (Price in Moores, 1986).

Singer *et al.* reported a variety of criticisms which were levelled at the Standard by 13 suppliers to the nuclear industry.

- The three parts (i.e. Parts 1, 2 and 3) are not entirely compatible in approach or section numbering.
- There are significant differences in terminology within the three parts and in related standards, for example BS 5882 (1980), and BS 4778: Part 1 (1987), even in relation to such basic things as 'quality programme' and 'quality plan'.
- The most common problem experienced, related to how best to interpret the standard to meet the needs of a particular contract or organisation.
- There are a few weaknesses in some of the requirements, for example design control and document control.

(Singer *et al.*, 1988)

Other drawbacks enumerated by Singer *et al.* (1988) include 'cost in terms of time, paperwork and customer involvement; generality leading to interpretation difficulties; and approvals need to be taken with a pinch of salt unless granted by a recognised certification body'. They go on to say that:

> 'In spite of such criticisms the companies believe that essentially the standard is sound and effective, provided it is used with common sense and balanced judgement. Most companies felt that the standard was ideal for applying to suppliers and sub-contractors down the supply chain and for the large-volume manufacturing situation. The commercial benefits of BS 5750 were judged by companies to outweigh the disadvantages. Views about whether the standard should

> be mandatory and backed by legislation were mixed. Some felt that it would not be possible to enforce the standard on every manufacturer, others said it was not applicable in some instances, for example the small jobbing shop. On the other hand, there was a view that the standard should have universal applicability to all manufacturers and producers of goods and services.
>
> (Singer *et al.*, 1988)

Whittington in discussing the results of a survey carried out in 14 manufacturing companies, lists the following points voiced by quality managers.

> i) BS 5750 Quality Systems were replacing what they already had but,
> a) was not necessarily as good,
> b) was at a substantially increased cost;
> ii) BS 5750 did not often result in increased cost;
> iii) BS 5750 did not include SPC. A number of major customers are now requesting that their suppliers provide them with evidence that their processes are in a state of statistical control;
> iv) BS 5750 was useful as a tool to force other managers and employees to work to a quality system;
> v) managers other than quality managers, often did not consider quality as part of their function;
> vi) their reasons for implementing or considering implementing BS 5750 were mainly due to pressure from large company customers;
> vii) the difficulties of attempting to implement BS 5750 are often aggravated by a lack of interest shown by employees.
>
> (Whittington, 1989)

Long *et al.* (1991) writing about a research study which examined the experiences of 68 small companies in relation to the BS 5750/ISO 9000 series, identified the following difficulties in implementation:

> - The time taken in developing, writing and implementing procedures.
> - Understanding the requirements of the standard and its parts and clauses, its terminology and how to adapt it to a particular situation.
> - Making the selection between Part 1 and Part 2 of BS 5750.
> - Meeting the requirements of particular clauses, in particular, identification of materials and product traceability.
> - Poor co-operation among senior personnel in relation to quality responsibility.
>
> (Long *et al.*, 1991)

In addition to criticisms of the BS 5750 Series some writers have outlined the reasons why organisations do not seek registration to the Standard. For example, Deshpande *et al.* in a survey of quality awareness among 300 small companies report:

> Among the 43 per cent who had no intention of applying for registration, were a variety of explanations for the decision (BS 5750 too expensive, BS 5750 not necessary, difficult to justify costs, reluctance to apply until BS 5750 had become recognised nationally and internationally, and registration to existing DEF standard considered adequate).
>
> (Deshpande *et al.*, 1985)

Some writers have also been critical of what they see as too much emphasis given to the BS 5750 Series. For example, Owen (an expert in SPC) discussing the Ford Motor Company's statistical process control training initiative says:

> Meanwhile the BSI presses on with its campaign of promoting BS 5750. Scores of Lead Assessors are being trained, countless quality manuals written and many have hours and much finance allocated to a programme which is system-based rather than people-based. The emphasis is on generating systems, which can be controlled rather than controlling processes and then improving them indefinitely. Only time will tell how effective this will be in comparison with company-wide-quality-improvement programmes such as the Ford initiative in implementing SPC.
>
> (Owen, 1986)

Other writers, including Owen (1988), writing from the chemical industry have criticised the Standard for being too orientated to the engineering industry, while others have argued that the BS 5750 Series is of limited value to their industry.

Writers such as Hersan (1990) have said that the standard 'gives too much weight to inspection, at the expense of preventive measures, that the layout of them could be improved and they omit the motivational aspects of quality management'. Jennings (1992) in a detailed review suggests that a single unified version of the series of standards might be more appropriate.

Sayle (1987), a well-respected quality management consultant and trainer, produced a very critical review of the ISO 9000 series citing a number of criticisms under the broad headings of quality plans and personnel, documents, audit, and design input and output. The feedback he subsequently received, which was published in QA News (the monthly news letter of the Institute of Quality Assurance) was largely critical of his opinions and approach.

The authors of this book feel, however, that many of the criticisms of the standard reflect the narrow way in which it has sometimes been interpreted and used in many organisations. Some people lose sight of the fact that the ISO 9000 series outlines what elements are required to achieve a quality system, whatever the product manufactured or offered, or the service provided, or the technology used. The ISO 9000 series embodies comprehensive quality management concepts and guidance, together with several models of external quality assurance requirements. Using an integrated systems architecture, the standards are packaged under a harmonised, easily memorised, numbering system. The series is not specifically related to any industry, nor to any product or service group. A system, based on the ISO 9000 series, provides only the basic foundation blocks and consideration should be given to how it can be developed to cater for areas which need to be strengthened in relation to the needs of the company in question. In some organisations, a much broader view has been taken and ISO 9000 used as the basis for a process of continuous improvement. For example, Exxon Chemicals have used the Standard throughout Europe to establish process improvements in customer service and business support groups. Clearly, they needed external help in translating the standard into non-engineering, non-manufacturing language, but once this was achieved, the impacts of the approach have been acclaimed inside and outside the company. It must also be said that the majority of the early criticisms relate to the 1979 version of the Standard.

7.3 An overview of the BS 5750/ISO 9000 series

The text of ISO 9000–4 has been approved as suitable for publication as a British Standard (BS 5750). Cross-references between the ISO series and the relevant parts of BS 5750 are as follows:

ISO 9000 Series: 1987	**BS 5750: 1987 Quality Systems**
ISO 9001 Quality systems – Model for quality assurance in design/development, production, installation and servicing	Part 1: Specification for design/development, production, installation and servicing. This is the most comprehensive of the three parts of the standard and is for use when conformance to specified requirements is to be assured by the supplier during the stages of design/development, production or operations, installation and servicing. It has the widest scope of application and contains 20 elements. It is applicable when the contract specifically requires design effort and the product requirements are stated (or need to be established) principally in performance terms; and confidence in product conformance can be

attained by adequate demonstration of the supplier's capabilities in design/development, production or operations, installation and servicing.

ISO 9002
Quality systems – Model for quality assurance in production and installation

Part 2: Specification for production and installation. For use when conformance to specified requirements is to be assured by the supplier during production or operations, and installation. This part consists of 18 elements, excluding design control and servicing.

It is applicable when the specified requirements for the product or service are stated in terms of an established design or specification; and confidence in product conformance can be attained by adequate demonstration of the supplier's capabilities in production or operations, and installation.

ISO 9003
Quality systems – Model for quality assurance in final inspection and test

Part 3: Specification for final inspection and test. For use when conformance to specified requirements is to be assured by the supplier solely at final inspection and test. This contains only 12 of the elements of ISO 9001.

This is applicable when the conformance of the product or service to specified requirements can be shown with adequate confidence, providing that the supplier can satisfactorily demonstrate capabilities for inspection, check or test conducted on the product or service. Clearly this is more difficult in commerce, the public sector and service-type organisations.

ISO 9000
Quality management and quality assurance standards – Guidelines for selection and use

Part 0: Principal concepts and applications.
Part 0, Section 0.1: Guide to selection and use.
ISO 9000 is a guide to the other standards in the series.

ISO 9000-2: 1993 (Quality management and quality assurance standards – Part 2: Generic guidelines for the application of ISO 9001, ISO 9002 and ISO 9003)

Part 4: 1990 Guide to the use of BS 5750. This provides guidance on the implementation of BS 5750: Parts 1, 2 and 3. It highlights important aspects to which attention should be given.

ISO 9000–3 (1991)
Quality management and quality assurance standards – Part 3: Guidelines for the application of ISO 9001 for the development, supply and maintenance of software

Part 13: 1991 Guide to the application of ISO 9001 (BS 5750: Part 1) to the development, supply and maintenance of software.

This sets out guidelines to facilitate the application of BS 5750: Part 1 (ISO 9001) to organisations developing, supplying and maintaining software. The process of development and maintenance of software is different from that of most other types of industrial products. In

	such a rapidly evolving technology field the arguments are that it is necessary to provide additional guidance for quality systems where software products are involved, taking into account the present state of the technology.
ISO 9000-4: 1993 (Quality management and quality assurance standards – Part 4: Guide to dependability programme management).	Part 14: 1993 Guide to dependability programme management. This provides guidance on dependability programme management. It covers the essential features of a comprehensive dependability programme for the planning, organisation, direction and control of resources to produce products which will be reliable and maintainable. It is applicable to hardware and/or software products, where dependability characteristics are significant during the operation and maintenance phase.
ISO 9004 Quality management and quality system elements – Guidelines	Part 0, Section 0.2: Guide to quality management and quality system elements. ISO 9004 provides general guidelines for developing and implementing the kind of quality management system that meets the requirements of ISO 9001, ISO 9002 and ISO 9003.
ISO 9004–2: 1991 (Quality management and quality system elements – Part 2: Guidelines for services)	Part 8: 1991 Guide to quality management and quality system elements for services. This gives guidance and a comprehensive overview for establishing and implementing a quality system specifically for services.
ISO 9004-3: 1992 (Quality management and quality system elements – Part 3: Guidelines for processed materials)	This part of ISO 9004, which has not yet been accepted for publication as a British Standard, gives guidance on the application of quality management to processed materials.
ISO 9004-4: 1993 (Quality management and quality system elements – Part 4: Guidelines for quality improvement)	This part of ISO 9004 gives management guidelines for implementing continuous quality improvement within an organisation. It is based on BS 7850: Part 2 (1992).

BS 5750 can be classified into two types:

- BS 5750: Parts 0, 4, 8, 13 and 14 give guidance to all organisations for quality management purposes.
- BS 5750: Parts 1, 2 and 3 are used for external quality assurance purposes in contractual situations. These three distinct models, which are based on the 'functional or organisation capability', are suitable for two-party contractual purposes. They can be used for assessment of a supplier's quality system.

The purposes of BS 5750: Part 0, Section 0.1 are:

- to clarify the distinctions and interrelationships among the principal quality concepts;
- to provide guidelines for the selection and

use of quality systems that can be used for internal quality purposes (BS 5750: Part 0, Section 0.2) and for external quality purposes (BS 5750: Parts 1, 2 and 3).

After BS 5750: Part 0, Section 0.1 (ISO 9000) has been consulted, reference should then be made to BS 5750: Part 0, Section 0.2 (ISO 9004) in order to develop and implement a quality system and to determine the extent to which each quality system element is applicable; it should be considered as the base set of building blocks. The purpose of BS 5750: Part 0, Section 0.2, which is a generic standard a company can use to manage its quality system, is to provide guidance on the technical, administrative and human factors affecting the quality of products or services, at all stages of the quality loop from detection of need to customer satisfaction. It describes a basic set of elements by which

Table 7.1 Cross-reference list of quality system elements

Clause (or sub-clause) no. in ISO 9004	Title	Corresponding clause (or sub-clause) nos. in		
		ISO 9001	ISO 9002	ISO 9003
4	Management responsibility	4.1 ●	4.1 ◐	4.1 ○
5	Quality system principles	4.2 ●	4.2 ●	4.2 ◐
5.4	Auditing the quality system (internal)	4.17 ●	4.16 ◐	—
6	Economics – quality-related cost considerations	—	—	—
7	Quality in marketing (contract review)	4.3 ●	4.3 ●	—
8	Quality in specification and design (design control)	4.4 ●	—	—
9	Quality in procurement (purchasing)	4.6 ●	4.5 ●	—
10	Quality in production (process control)	4.9 ●	4.8 ●	—
11	Control of production	4.9 ●	4.8 ●	—
11.2	Material control and traceability (product identification and traceability)	4.8 ●	4.7 ●	4.4 ◐
11.7	Control of verification status (inspection and test status)	4.12 ●	4.11 ●	4.7 ◐
12	Product verification (inspection and testing)	4.10 ●	4.9 ●	4.5 ◐
13	Control of measuring and test equipment (inspection, measuring and test equipment)	4.11 ●	4.10 ●	4.6 ◐
14	Non-conformity (control of non-conforming product)	4.13 ●	4.12 ●	4.8 ◐
15	Corrective action	4.14 ●	4.13 ●	—
16	Handling and post-production functions (handling, storage packaging and delivery)	4.15 ●	4.14 ●	4.9 ◐
16.2	After-sales servicing	4.19 ●	—	—
17	Quality documentation and records (document control)	4.5 ●	4.4 ●	4.3 ◐
17.3	Quality records	4.16 ●	4.15 ●	4.10 ◐
18	Personnel (training)	4.18 ●	4.17 ◐	4.11 ○
19	Product safety and liability	—	—	—
20	Use of statistical methods (statistical techniques)	4.20 ●	4.18 ●	4.12 ◐
—	Purchaser supplied product	4.7 ●	4.6 ●	—

Key

● Full requirement
◐ Less stringent than ISO 9001
○ Less stringent than ISO 9002
— Element not present

Notes

1 The clause (or sub-clause) titles quoted in the table above have been taken from ISO 9004; the titles given in parentheses have been taken from the corresponding clauses and sub-clauses in ISO 9001, ISO 9002 and ISO 9003.

2 Attention is drawn to the fact that the quality system element requirements in ISO 9001, ISO 9002 and ISO 9003 are in many cases, but not in every case, identical.

Source: BS 5750: Part 0, 1987

quality management systems can be developed and implemented for internal quality management purposes. The selection of appropriate elements and the extent to which these elements are adopted and applied by an organisation will depend on factors such as the market being served, nature of product, production processes and customer needs. The standard is not written in a form that lends itself to a checklist but has been written in such a form that it can be assessed. Throughout BS 5750: Part 0, Section 0.2 emphasis is placed on the satisfaction of the customer's need, the establishment of functional responsibilities and the importance of assessing (as far as possible) the potential risks and benefits. All these aspects should be considered in establishing and maintaining an effective quality system. The purchaser and supplier should then refer to BS 5750: Parts 1, 2 and 3 to determine which of them is most relevant to the contract, and what specific adaptations, if any, have to be made, after which Part 4 and, if appropriate, Part 8, Part 13 and/or Part 14 should be consulted. Table 7.1 shows the quality system elements and requirement clauses in each of these three Standards. These elements will be discussed later in the chapter.

This series of Standards on quality systems is intended to be used in two different situations: contractual and non-contractual. In both situations, the supplier's organisation wishes to install and maintain a quality system that will strengthen its own competitiveness and achieve the required product and service quality in a cost-effective way. In the contractual situation, the purchaser is interested in certain elements of the supplier's quality system which affect the ability to produce consistently the product or service to the specified requirements, and the associated risks. Therefore, the purchaser contractually requires that these elements be part of the supplier's quality system. It should also be noted that the standards only indicate what is required and do not provide intricate guidance on how to put into place what is required.

Organisations can use the Standards when setting up their own quality systems; customers may specify that the quality of goods and services they are purchasing shall comply with the Standard; and customers or third parties may use it as a basis for assessing a supplier's quality system.

Careful study of the ISO 9000 Series of standards, as released in 1987, by major groups of users or potential users identified a number of needs that were not easily met within the ISO 9000 Series contractual standards in what was then their present form.

Table 7.2 Generic product categories

Generic product category	Kinds of products
Hardware	Products consisting of manufactured pieces and parts, or assemblies thereof.
Software	Products, such as computer software, consisting of written, or otherwise recordable information, concepts, transactions or procedures.
Processed materials	Products (final or intermediate) consisting of solids, liquids, gases or combinations thereof, including particulate materials, ingots, filaments or sheet structures. NOTE – Processed materials typically are delivered (packaged) in containers such as drums, bags, tanks, cans, pipelines, or rolls.
Services	Intangible products which may be the entire or principal offering, or incorporated features of the offering, relating to activities such as planning, selling, directing, delivering, improving, evaluating, training, operating or servicing for a tangible product. NOTE – All generic product categories provide value to the customer only at the times and places the customer interfaces with, and perceives benefits from, the product. However, the value from a service often is provided primarily by activities at a particular time and place of interface with the customer.

Source: PD 6538: 1993

Four generic product categories were identified – hardware, software, processed materials and services – and are described in Table 7.2. Consideration was also given to the industry/economic sector in which the product is present. A development path for the ISO 9000 Series architecture was mapped out, which took this into account. It was believed that the path was sufficiently flexible to meet the needs of users in all generic product categories and all industry/economic sectors. In more recent times this has resulted in the publication of ISO 9000-3 (1991), ISO 9004-2 (1991) and ISO 9004-3 (1993). Details of these developments are outlined in PD 6538 (1993). In this Vision 2000 document four strategic goals for the ISO 9000 Series standards and their related ISO 10000 Series standards were outlined:

- universal acceptance
- current compatability
- forward compatibility
- forward flexibility.

Figure 7.2 overleaf shows how the evolving system of standards meets the combined needs for quality management and quality assurance from both the producer's and purchaser's viewpoints. As outlined earlier, guidance documents for software, processed materials and services have already been released. This trend will continue through the 1990s with the intention of implementing Vision 2000.

ISO standards must be reaffirmed or revised at approximately five-year intervals. The ISO/TC 176 has reviewed and revised the five standards (ISO 9000, ISO 9001, ISO 9002, ISO 9003 and ISO 9004). They are currently being balloted as draft international standards (DIS). The revisions incorporate changes that do not alter the basic approach and structure of the existing standards but instead increase their usability.

7.4 The need for a quality system

Establishing a quality system is well worth doing. Most companies are already doing the right things but lack the formality of written standards and records. Indeed, in many small companies having little or no formal documentation, the provision of a quality system can produce improvements. A quality system is no more than good management and should cover all aspects of the company's operations because there is no sense in having one system for quality matters and another for the remaining operations.

A quality system should be developed and implemented for the purpose of accomplishing the objectives set out in a company's quality policies. Each element (or requirement) in the system will vary in importance from one type of activity to another and from one product or service to another. In order to achieve maximum effectiveness and to satisfy customer expectations, it is essential that the quality system be appropriate to the type of activity and to the product or service being offered.

More organisations outside of mainstream manufacturing are looking to meet the requirements of the BS 5750 series. For example, Girobank have been assessed and registered to BS 5750: Part 2 and are the first financial institution to be awarded British Registration to the BS 5750 Series. The award of BS 5750 covers Girobank's transaction processing operations in its main centre at Bootle, Merseyside, and at its cheque processing centre in London. At the present time 15% of the bank is currently awaiting registration to the BS 5750 Series. Exxon Chemicals' UK Customer Service Unit were the first service department of a manufacturing company in Europe to be assessed and registered to the BS 5750 Series by BSI Quality Assurance Services. Table 7.3 overleaf gives examples of services to which the ISO 9000 series can be applied.

Major public purchasing authorities are tending to place more emphasis on quality assurance and guarantees of satisfactory procedures are requested in many of the contracts they draw up.

The Local Government Act 1987 includes a requirement that, if local authorities wish to carry out certain defined activities using direct labour services, then they must put out contracts to competitive tender. This is called compulsory competitive tendering (CCT). The essential conditions of the Act require that the invitation to tender includes detailed specification of the work to be carried out, and that, if the local authority direct labour unit is awarded the contract, it fully complies with the specification. The result is that local authority

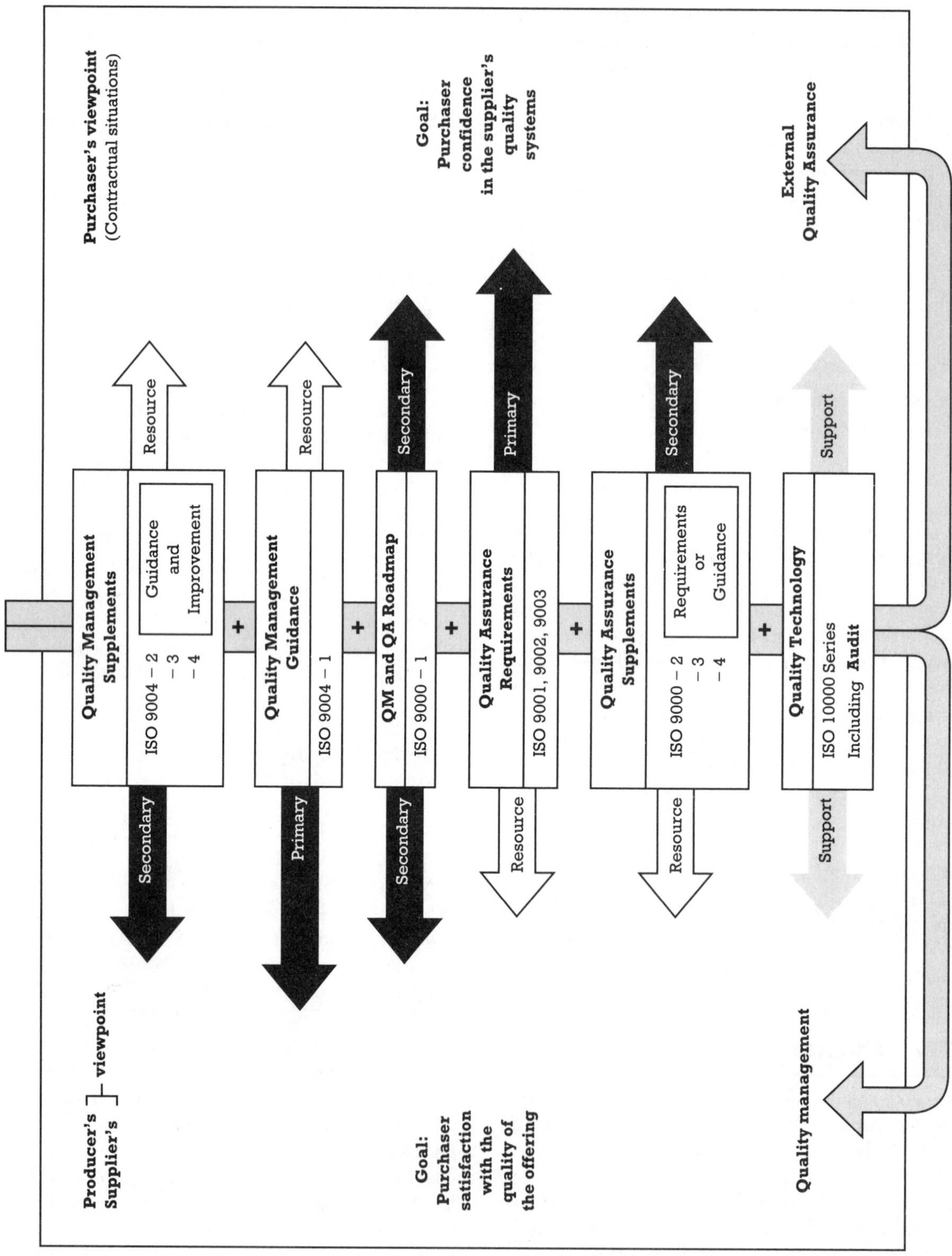

Source: PD 6538: 1993

Figure 7.2 International quality standardisation in the 1990s

Table 7.3 Examples of services to which ISO 9004–2/BS 5750: Part 8 may be applied

Hospitality services Catering, hotels, tourism, entertainment, radio, television, leisure	**Financial** Banking, insurance, pensions, property services, accounting
Communications Airports and airlines, road, rail and sea transport, telecommunications, postal, data	**Professional** Building design (architects), surveying, legal, law enforcement, security, engineering, project management, quality management, consultancy, training and education
Health services Medical staff/doctors, hospitals, ambulances, medical laboratories, dentists, opticians	**Administration** Personnel, computing, office services
Maintenance Electrical, mechanical, vehicles, heating systems, air conditioning, buildings, computers	**Technical** Consultancy, photography, test laboratories
Utilities Cleansing, waste management, water supply, grounds maintenance, electricity, gas and energy supply, fire, police, public services	**Purchasing** Contracting, inventory management and distribution
Trading Wholesale, retail, stockist, distributor, marketing, packaging	**Scientific** Research, development, studies, decision aids

Source: BS 5750: Part 8 (1991)

direct labour services will function more like industrial businesses seeking approval to the BS 5750 Series or from NAMAS. They therefore need to become as efficient and competitive as possible and registration to the BS 5750 Series could be a means of ensuring that organisations are competing on equal terms.

The areas in which registration is being considered are:

- collection of refuse;
- cleaning of buildings;
- other cleaning (litter);
- catering (school, homes, public buildings);
- repair and maintenance of buildings;
- ground maintenance (grass);
- highway maintenance;
- fencing;
- emergency services.

A quality system has two interrelated aspects. First, the company needs to attain and to maintain the desired quality at an optimum cost. The fulfilment of this quality aspect is related to the planned and efficient utilisation of the technological, human and material resources available to them. Secondly, the customer needs to have confidence in the ability of the company to deliver consistently the desired product and/or service quality. Each of these aspects of a quality system requires information and data concerning the quality of the system and the quality of the company's products.

7.5 What should a quality system consist of?

The three most important aspects of a quality system are availability of documentation, control of purchasing and calibration of measuring and test equipment.

There are a few basic points about documentation to consider. The purpose is to convey the information which people need to carry out their job effectively. It is axiomatic that the documentation must be easy to read and understand; if it is not, nobody will bother to read or use it. This means that documents should be short and to the point. To meet the requirements of the BS 5750 Series, documents may be categorized as belonging to one of three groups: quality manuals, sets of procedures and work instructions.

A quality manual comprises about eight pages and gives a short description of the company and its capabilities together with statements of its quality policy and systems, workmanship, control of amendments and reissues, and the organisation and authority for implementing the quality system. The quality manual ends with a precis of each of the procedures. As well as meeting the requirements of the standard, such a quality manual can form a brochure for sending to prospective customers providing the reasons why they should buy the company's products and/or services.

A set of procedures is required which describes how the company operates, who has the responsibility for what actions and what books and forms are used and for what purpose. The procedures should not contain detailed information which is only of concern to a few. Such information should be contained in a group of work instructions. These support the procedures and need only be issued to those concerned whereas the procedures are the concern of all personnel.

The first step is to find out and record in writing how the company operates; information is needed from all departments and sections to obtain a true picture. As people are naturally resistant to change and probably will have been doing the right things anyway, it is sensible in the initial stages to restrict changes to those essential to the requirements of the part of the standard for which registration is sought. Further improvements will undoubtedly be possible but they can be deferred until the benefits of the quality system become obvious. There is no doubt that seeing in writing what happens has a very salutary effect and can lead to staff making their own proposals and plans for improvement.

Procedures need to meet the requirements of the standard in a way which will improve, not hinder, the functioning of the organisation. They should allow room for manoeuvre wherever it is sensible to do so, in order to meet changing situations which arise. After all, the purpose is to increase the competitiveness of the company not to cripple it with unnecessary additional costs. Procedures must be introduced with common sense and it is not feasible to cover every possible situation. However, they will need updating regularly to meet changing circumstances such as market forces, process development, and personnel turnover as well as improved control revealed by retrospective examination of the procedure in use.

The work instructions which largely comprise the technical know-how should provide information which the operative is unlikely to know from his normal training or may need to be reminded of because of its complexity (e.g. instructions for internal calibrations, instructions on how to operate a special machine, packaging instructions to ensure safe delivery).

7.6 Selecting a quality system model

The following six factors are fundamental in the selection of the appropriate quality system model for a product or service:

- design-process complexity – the difficulty of designing the product or service;
- design maturity – the extent to which the total design is known and proven, either by performance testing or field experience;
- production or operations process complexity – this factor deals with:
  - i) the availability of proven production or operations processes,
  - ii) the need for development of new processes,
  - iii) the number and variety of processes required,
  - iv) the impact of the process(es) on the performance of the product or service;
- product or service characteristics – the complexity of the product or service, the number of interrelated characteristics, and the criticality of each characteristic for performance;
- product or service safety – the risk of the occurrence of failure and the consequences of such failure;
- economics – the economic costs, to both supplier and purchaser, of the above five factors weighed against costs due to nonconformities in the product or service.

7.7 Quality system requirements

In this section, an outline is given from which a quality system can be developed and implemented. A number of the issues touched upon here will be discussed in further detail in subsequent chapters. The selection of appropriate elements and the extent to which they are adopted and applied depends upon factors such as the market being served, the nature of the product, production or operations processes, and consumer needs.

Management responsibility

The responsibility for, and commitment to, a quality policy must be accepted by an organisation's senior management team. They need to develop, state and communicate their corporate quality policy. This policy should be consistent with other company policies. Management should take all necessary measures to ensure that its corporate quality policy is understood, implemented, and maintained at all levels in the organisation. Deployment of the quality policy, with improvement objectives and targets established and agreed at all levels of the organisational hierarchy is a key aspect in the process of quality improvement.

The senior management team is ultimately responsible for decisions concerning the initiation, development, implementation and maintenance of the quality system. It is normal to appoint a management representative who, irrespective of other responsibilities, has defined authority and responsibility for the quality function. The organisational structure pertaining to the quality system needs to be clearly established.

The responsibility, authority, and the interrelations of all personnel who manage, perform and verify work affecting quality, need to be defined, particularly for personnel who:

- initiate action to prevent the occurrence of non-conforming product and service;
- identify and record any product and service quality problems;
- initiate, recommend or provide solutions through designated channels;
- verify the implementation of solutions;
- control further processing, delivery or installation of non-conforming product and service until the deficiency or unsatisfactory condition has been corrected.

A management review, which is formal, periodic and independent, of the quality system needs to be undertaken and should include the following two activities:

- A regular review of the documented policies and procedures that define the system. These should be reviewed at specified intervals and updated as necessary to ensure that they reflect the working methods and the business objectives of the organisation. The review should be performed in accordance with a documented procedure and records kept of the reviews and changes made.
- A review of internal audit results to ensure that the defined quality system is implemented and followed as required.

The purpose of these two activities, which are discussed later in this chapter, is to ensure that the system is up-to-date, controlled and effective in both its aim and implementation. Particular emphasis should be placed on the need or opportunity for improvement.

The management review process allows senior management to direct and lead the development and installation of the quality system and to ensure that it supports the process of continuous quality improvement. These reviews should be chaired by the senior site executive.

Quality system principles

As a means of helping to ensure that product or service conforms to specified requirements, it is necessary to establish and maintain a documented quality system. This includes the preparation and the effective implementation of documented quality system procedures and instructions. Documented planning for quality should take place as early as possible, the quality system is not complete unless it is planned and developed in conjunction with all other functions such as design, development, purchasing, manufacturing or operations, and installation (if applicable). Planning for quality should be an integral part of an organisation's corporate planning system. In meeting specified requirements, consideration needs to be given to the following activities:

- the preparation of quality plans and a quality manual in accordance with the specified requirements;
- the identification and acquisition of any controls (including mistake-proofing), processes, inspection equipment, fixtures, total production or operations resources, and skills needed to achieve the required quality;
- the updating, as necessary, of quality control, inspection, measurement, and testing techniques;
- the identification of any measurement and testing requirement involving capability that exceeds the known state-of-the-art, in sufficient time for the required capability to be developed;
- the clarification of standards' acceptability for all features and requirements;
- the compatibility of the design, the production or operations processes, installation (if applicable), inspection and test procedures, and the appropriate documentation;
- the identification and preparation of quality records.

Auditing the quality system

Internal audits should be carried out, on a regular basis, in order to determine whether various elements within a quality system are effective in achieving the stated quality objectives, that the documented procedures are practical, understood and followed and that the training is adequate. For this purpose, an appropriate audit plan should be formulated and established. The schedule established for the audit can be adjusted, based on previous results and experience.

In general, the format of the audit plan covers the following points:

- the specific activities and areas to be audited;
- qualifications of personnel carrying out audits;
- the basis of carrying out audits (for example, organisational changes, reported deficiencies, routine checks and surveys);
- procedures for reporting audit findings, conclusions and recommendations.

It is good practice to submit, in documentary form, audit findings, conclusions and recommendations for consideration by appropriate members of the management team. This typically includes:

- the deficiencies found;
- the corrective action identified;
- the time agreed for corrective action to be carried out;
- the person responsible for carrying out the corrective action.

The customer often wishes to look through the findings of internal audits, so good records need to be maintained. Such records, traceability and actions taken are also a key feature in product liability legislation (see the Consumer Protection Act 1987). The following are typical of the items covered in the reporting and follow-up of audit findings:

- specific examples of non-compliance or deficiencies documented in the audit report, including possible reasons for such deficiencies, where evident;
- appropriate corrective actions and countermeasures to prevent reoccurrence of abnormalities;
- the assessment of implementation and effectiveness of corrective actions suggested in previous audits.

In addition to internal audits, provision should also be made by company management for independent review and evaluation of the quality system (for example, second- and third-party audits). Such reviews should be carried out by appropriate and trained members of management or by competent independent personnel. These include:

- findings of audits centred on various elements of the quality system;
- the overall effectiveness of the quality system

in achieving stated quality objectives;

- considerations for updating the quality system in relation to changes brought about by new technologies, quality concepts, market strategies, and social or environmental conditions.

BS 7229: Part 1 (1991) gives excellent guidance on the auditing of quality systems. It provides audit principles, criteria and requirements for audit practice, and assists in the establishment, planning and execution of audits of quality systems. It is prepared in a general way so that it is applicable to different industries and organisations.

Economics

The impact of quality on profit is significant. It is important, therefore, that the effectiveness of a quality system be measured. The main objective of quality cost reporting is to provide a means for evaluating effectiveness and establishing the basis for a process of continuous improvement.

Quality in marketing

Quality starts in the marketplace. The quality requirements of customers (actual and potential) have to be defined. This is the responsibility of the marketing function and they should:

- determine the need for a product or service;
- accurately define the market demand and sector;
- accurately determine customer requirements by a review of contract or market needs;
- communicate all customer requirements clearly and accurately within the company.

During contract negotiations there is a need to review the contract requirements in a systematic and defined manner to ensure clarity, comprehension, feasibility and reliability prior to a contract being finalised. This review should be conducted against prescribed stages, or steps.

Marketing should provide the company with a formal statement or outline of product or service requirements – a product or service brief. This translates customer requirements and expectations into a preliminary set of specifications, as the basis for subsequent design work. Among the elements that may be included in the product brief are the following requirements:

- performance characteristics (for example, environmental and usage conditions, reliability and durability);
- sensory characteristics (for example, style, colour, taste, smell and time);
- installation configuration or fit;
- applicable standards and statutory regulations;
- packaging (if applicable);
- quality assurance/verification.

The marketing function forms a direct link with the customer and, as such, provides an information monitoring and feedback system on a continuous basis. All information pertinent to the quality of a product or service should be analysed, collated, interpreted and communicated in accordance with defined procedures. Such information will help to determine the nature and extent of product or service problems in relation to customer experience and expectations. In addition, feedback information may provide pointers as to possible design changes as well as appropriate management action.

Quality in specification and design

The best production and operation methods cannot compensate for poor or inadequate design. Quality has to be designed into the product or service before it is produced or generated. The specification and design function are responsible for the translation of customer needs from the product or service brief into technical specifications for materials, product, and processes. This should result in a product or service that provides customer satisfaction at an acceptable price which gives a satisfactory return on investment for the enterprise. The specification and design should result in a product or service which is producible, verifiable, and controllable under the proposed production, installation, commissioning or operational conditions. Management should assign responsibilities for various design duties to activities inside and/or outside the organisation and ensure that all those who contribute to design are aware of their responsibilities for achieving quality.

It is necessary to establish time-phased design programmes with checkpoints appropriate to the nature of the product or service. The extent of each phase and the stages at which design review or evaluations will take place may depend upon the product's application, its design complexity, the extent of innovation and technology being introduced, the degree of standardisation and similarity with past proven designs.

In addition to meeting customer needs, the designer should give due consideration to the requirements relating to safety, environmental and other regulations, including items in the company's quality policy which may go beyond existing statutory requirements.

The quality aspects of the design should be unambiguous and adequately define characteristics important to quality, such as the acceptance and rejection criteria. Both fitness for purpose and safeguards against misuse should be considered. Product or service definition may also include reliability, maintainability and serviceability through a reasonable life expectancy. The methods of measurement, check and test, and the acceptance criteria applied to evaluate the product and processes during both the design and production phases, should also be specified.

The quality system should provide for a review to determine whether production/operations capability and field support are adequate for the new or redesigned product or service. A procedure is also required for controlling the release, change and use of documents that define the design baseline and for authorising the necessary work to be performed to implement changes that may affect the product or service during its entire life cycle.

Quality in procurement

It is necessary to ensure that purchased product conforms to specified requirements. Purchased materials, components and assemblies become part of the company's product or service and directly affect the quality of its output. 'If you have quality problems (addressed to the supplier community), then we have quality problems (referring to the purchaser),' is the philosophy which needs to be used to emphasise this point. The procurement of purchased supplies needs to be planned and controlled with close working relationship and feedback systems developed with the supplier base. In this way, a process of continual quality improvements can be maintained and any quality disputes avoided or settled quickly. This close working relationship and the feedback systems will benefit both the purchaser and the supplier.

The following are typical of the elements contained in a procurement quality improvement process:

- requirements of specifications, drawings and purchase orders;
- selection of qualified suppliers;
- agreement on quality assurance;
- agreement of verification methods;
- provisions for settlement of quality disputes;
- receiving inspection or checking plans;
- receiving controls;
- receiving quality records;
- measurement of performance;
- recognition of superior performing suppliers.

The supplier is responsible for providing goods or services in accordance with an agreed specification. The need for a precise specification cannot be over-emphasised.

When materials, commonly described as 'free issue' are provided by the customer to the supplier the onus for their conformity to specified requirements is that of the customer. The supplier's system should include the provision for verification, proper storage and maintenance of such materials supplied.

Quality in production and operations

The planning of production and service operations in the product or service preparation stage is to ensure that these proceed under controlled conditions in the specified manner and sequence. Controlled conditions include the following:

- documented work instructions defining the manner of production or operation and installation (if applicable);
- monitoring and control of suitable process parameters and product characteristics during production or operations (and installation);
- the approval of processes and equipment;
- criteria for workmanship, stipulated in written standards or by means of representative samples.

Process control in the performance of a service should be maintained in a similar way to that of a product. For example, identification of discrete stages should be observed so that operations are not omitted. Verification and check stages of the service delivery process should be planned. Materials used during the service delivery process should conform to the appropriate specifications and standards. Materials used should be properly stored taking into consideration the declared shelf life and/or storage requirements.

There are processes (special processes), the results of which cannot be fully verified by subsequent checking, inspection or testing of the product or service, and where, for example, processing deficiencies may become apparent only after the product is in use. Accordingly, continuous monitoring and/or compliance with documented procedures is required to ensure that the specified requirements are met.

Material control and traceability

Before being introduced into production or operations, materials, parts and services should conform to appropriate specifications and quality standards. However, in determining the amount of testing, checking and/or inspection necessary, consideration should be given to cost impact and the effect that substandard material quality will have on production flow. Materials should also be appropriately stored, segregated, handled and protected during production or operations. Special consideration being given to shelf-life and deterioration control. Where in-house traceability of material is important to quality, appropriate identification needs to be maintained throughout the procurement and production processes of materials, parts, products and services to ensure traceability to original material identification and quality status. Traceability may be necessary in order that a problem arising at any stage in the supply of a product or service can be analysed and the root cause established.

Control of verification status

There should be a way of identifying the inspection and test status of products or services at all times during the design to delivery stages. The way of achieving this may vary according to the form of the product or service. It may take the form of stamps, tags or notations on material, carriers or vessels, or on inspection records that accompany the product or service. The identification should include the ability to distinguish between verified and unverified material and indication of acceptance at the point of verification and provide traceability to the unit responsible for the operation.

Product verification

This applies to receiving inspection, checking or testing, in-process inspection, measurement and testing, and final inspection, measurement and testing and release of the product or service.

The methods used to ensure the quality of purchased goods and materials will depend on their importance to quality, the state of control and information available from the supplier, the supplier's previous quality performance and the impact on costs. Inspections, checks, measurements or tests should be considered at appropriate points in the process to verify conformity. Location and frequency will depend on the importance of the characteristics and ease of verification at the stage of production or operation. In general, verification of the feature or characteristics should be made as close as possible to the point of production or operation. When considering the overall process of producing a product or service there are three phases where inspection/verification and/or testing may take place:

- on receipt of any purchased or subcontracted items or service;
- during the manufacturing or service delivery process;
- prior to final release to the customer.

Verifications may include the following checks:

- start or set-up and first product/service inspections;
- checks, measurements, inspections or tests by operator(s);
- automatic measurements, inspections or tests;
- fixed inspection stations at intervals through the processes;
- patrol inspections to monitor specified operations.

To augment inspections and tests made during production or operations, two forms of final verification of completed product or service are available. Either or both may be used as appropriate:

- acceptance inspections, checks and measurements, of the finished products or services;
- product or service quality auditing of representative samples of finished products or services.

Acceptance inspection and product quality auditing may be used to ensure that performance and other quality requirements have been met, and to provide rapid feedback for corrective action of products, services and processes.

Control of measuring and test equipment

To provide confidence in decisions or actions based on measurement data, it is important to maintain control over all measurement systems used in the development, manufacture, installation and servicing of a product. The control of measurement consistency needs to be applied to less tangible measures such as auditing, measuring customer satisfaction as well as the physical tools and equipment used in any production process. This extends to all suppliers furnishing goods and services.

Procedures should be established to monitor and maintain the measurement process under statistical control, including equipment, procedures and operator skills. Measurement error should be compared with requirements and appropriate action taken when precision and/or bias requirements are not achieved. The control of measuring and test equipment and test methods includes the following factors:

- correct specification and acquisition, including range, bias, precision, robustness and durability under specified environmental conditions for the intended services;
- initial calibration prior to first use, in order to validate the required bias and precision. The software and procedures controlling automatic test equipment should also be tested;
- periodic recall for adjustment, repair and recalibration while considering the manufacturer's specification, the results of prior calibration, and the method and extent of use, in order to maintain the required accuracy in use.
- documentary evidence covering identification of instruments, frequency of recalibration, calibration status, and procedures for recall, handling and storage, adjustment, repair, calibration, installation and use;
- traceability to reference standards of known accuracy and stability, preferably on a national and international level, or in industries or products where such standards do not exist, to specially developed criteria.

Where measuring processes are found to be out of control or where measuring and test equipment is found to be outside the required calibration limits, corrective action is necessary. Evaluation should then be made to determine the effects on completed work and to what extent reprocessing, retesting, recalibration or complete rejection may be necessary. In addition, investigation of the causes of problems is important in order to avoid recurrence. This may include review of calibration methods and frequency, training and the adequacy of test equipment.

Control of non-conforming products

As production or service delivery processes may yield suspect or defective items, methods for preventing further processing, delivery or installation of such items are necessary. The method of identifying a non-conforming item depends on the nature of the product or service. However, it should be such as to ensure that the identification of the non-conformity should stay in place until a decision regarding further action is made.

When indications occur that materials, completed products and services do not or may not meet the specified requirements, the following are typical of the steps taken:

- Identification – suspected non-conforming items or lots are identified and the occurrence(s) recorded. Whenever possible, provision is made as necessary to examine previous production lots.
- Segregation – the non-conforming items or lots are segregated from conforming ones and adequately identified to prevent their further use, until it is decided how to dispose of them.
- Review – a review of non-conforming items or lots is carried out to determine whether they can be used as they are or whether they should be repaired, reworked, blended, re-classified or scrapped.
- Disposition – disposal of non-conforming items or lots should be taken as soon as practicable in accordance with decisions made in the review. Decisions to pass or downgrade products should always be accompanied by authorised concessions or waivers, with appropriate precautions.
- Prevention of recurrence – appropriate steps should be taken to prevent the recurrence of any non-conformity. For example, establishing a file listing non-conformities in order to help identify those problems having a common source in contrast to those that occur uniquely. This data can often be plotted on a control chart to assist in process control and improvement (see Chapter 15).

Corrective action

Prompt and effective corrective action to eliminate the causes of the non-conforming product or service is essential to a quality system. The implementation of corrective action begins with the detection of a quality-related problem and involves taking measures to eliminate or minimise its recurrence. Corrective action also presupposes the repair, reworking, recall or scrapping of unsatisfactory materials or items. The following are key aspects in a corrective action procedure.

- Assignment of responsibility – the co-ordination, recording and monitoring of corrective action is generally assigned to a particular function within the organisation. The analysis and execution, however, may involve a variety of functions, such as sales, design, production engineering, production/operations, technical, and quality assurance.
- Evaluation of importance – the significance of a problem affecting quality should be evaluated in terms of its potential impact on such aspects as operations/production costs, quality costs, performance, reliability, safety and customer satisfaction.
- Investigation of possible causes – the relationship of cause and effect should be determined, with all potential causes being considered and important variables affecting the capability of the process to meet required standards being identified.
- Analysis of the problem – in the analysis of a quality-related problem, the root cause should be determined before the preventive measures are planned. The need to cure the root cause of a problem rather than a symp-

tom should always be emphasised in management control. Often the root cause is not obvious and careful analysis of the product or service specifications and of all related processes, operations, quality records, service reports and customer complaints is required.

- Preventive action – in order to prevent a future recurrence of a non-conformity, it may be necessary to change an operation, manufacturing, packing, transit or storage, process, revise a product specification, and/or revise the controls.
- Process controls – sufficient controls of processes and procedures are implemented to prevent recurrence of the problem and their effect monitored in order to ensure that desired goals are met.
- Disposition of non-conforming items – for work-in-progress, remedial action is instituted as soon as is practical in order to limit the costs of repair, reworking, waste or scrapping. In addition, it may be necessary to recall completed products. Recall decisions are affected by considerations of safety, product liability and customer satisfaction.
- Permanent changes – permanent changes resulting from corrective action are recorded in work instructions, manufacturing processes, product specifications and/or the quality system. It may also be necessary to revise the procedures used to detect and eliminate potential problems.

Handling, storage, packaging and delivery

The handling of materials during the manufacture of a product or the performance of a service requires proper planning, control and a documented system for incoming materials, materials in process and finished products.

- Handling and storage – the method of handling and storage of materials needs to be considered carefully in order to prevent damage occurring. Material in storage should be checked periodically to check for possible deterioration.
- Identification – it is important to maintain identification from the time of initial receipt to delivery at the final destination, the marking and labelling being adequate to identify a particular product in the event that a recall or special inspection becomes necessary.
- Packing – the choice of packaging can have a significant influence on the quality of the end product as received by the customer and on the quality of supplied materials. It is often the poor packing of material that causes damage in transit.
- Installation – instructional documents contribute to proper installations and should include provision to preclude improper installation or factors degrading the quality, reliability, safety and performance of the product or material.
- Delivery – products with limited shelf-life, or requiring special protection during transport or storage need to be identified and procedures maintained to ensure that deteriorated products are not put into use. For a service the recording, labelling and identification of its delivery or completion is an important fact in providing evidence that the service has been performed, together with a date of delivery or reminder of the likely period following which a further service may be required.

After-sales servicing

Where servicing is specified in the contract, procedures should be established for carrying this out and verifying that it meets the specified requirements. Aspects to be considered include:

- special-purpose equipment for handling and servicing products or services during or after installation should have their design and function validated, as is the case with any new product or service;
- the control of measuring and testing equipment used in field installation and tests;
- instructions dealing with the assembly and installation, commissioning, operation, spares or parts lists, and servicing of any

product. The suitability of instructions for the intended reader should be verified;

- the provision of an adequate logistics back-up, to include technical advice, spares or parts supply, and competent servicing. Responsibility should be clearly assigned and agreed among suppliers, distributors and users;
- servicing personnel should be properly trained to carry out the tasks required.

Quality documentation and records

The quality system elements should be documented and demonstrated. The main document used in drawing up and implementing a quality system is a quality manual. As outlined in Chapter 3, the primary purpose of a quality manual is to provide an adequate description of the quality system while serving as a permanent reference in the implementation and maintenance of that system. Documented work instructions are a means of showing the work to be done and of delegating authority and responsibility, they provide direction to various levels of personnel. Without written guidance, differences in policy and procedures may arise and variations in practice can occur, resulting in confusion and uncertainty.

Policies need to be established concerning availability and access of records to customers and suppliers, and procedure for changes and modifications in various types of documents. The following are examples of the types of document requiring control:

drawings and blueprints,
specifications,
inspection instructions,
test procedures,
work instructions,
operation sheets,
quality manual,
quality plans,
operational procedures,
quality assurance procedures.

Sufficient and adequate records need to be maintained to demonstrate achievement of the required quality and verify effective operation of the quality system. The use and storage of records needs to be systematic so that the data can be readily retrieved and analysed. The following are examples of the types of records requiring control:

inspection reports,
test data,
qualification reports,
validation reports,
audit reports,
material review reports,
calibration data,
quality cost reports,
customer satisfaction reports,
corrective action reports,
suppliers' and subcontractors' performance,
skills and training of personnel.

It is usual to retain quality records for a specified period so that they can be retrieved and analysed in order to identify quality trends and the need for, and effectiveness of, corrective action.

The key to effective documentation is ensuring that it is brief while covering the essential points.

Personnel – training and motivation

It is important that an organisation puts into place a quality-related training and education programme for all its personnel. Organisation's from the Pacific Rim place far more emphasis on this than do Western companies. Lascelles and Dale (1988), reporting on a survey of 300 UK suppliers to the automotive industry, claim that, with the exception of quality staff, first line supervisors and shop floor personnel, less than half the respondent companies had received any formal training on aspects of TQM. They also found that in companies where the directors had received formal quality skills training, personnel from the quality assurance department are more likely to be involved in quality planning and prevention-type activities rather than fire fighting. Van de Wiele *et al.* (1993) found in a survey of 358 European organisations that only 44% of them had a TQM Training Programme. They point out that senior and middle management, quality staff, personnel staff and marketing/sales staff are the main recipients of the training and companies are less likely to provide TQM training for their suppliers, design staff, clerical staff, operations and first-line supervisors.

Education brings awareness of the need for change and provides the means whereby change and development can be accomplished. Important elements in the development of personnel include:

- training executives in quality management, including quality-related costs and evaluation of the effectiveness of the quality system;
- training of personnel (this should not be restricted to those solely concerned with quality responsibilities);
- education of personnel on the organisation's quality policy, objectives and concepts of customer satisfaction;
- a quality-awareness programme which may include instruction and training courses for new recruits in particular, as part of their induction training, and periodic refresher programmes for longer-serving personnel;
- procedures for specifying and verifying that personnel have received suitable training;
- training in process control, data collection and analysis, problem identification and analysis, corrective action and improvement, team working and communication methods;
- the need to assess carefully the personnel requirements for formal qualifications and give appropriate assistance and encouragement where necessary;
- the performance evaluation of personnel to assess their development needs and potential.

A most important resource in any organisation is that of the individual members of personnel involved. This is especially important in a service organisation where the behaviour and performance of individuals directly impacts on the quality of the service.

Motivation of personnel begins with their undertaking of the tasks they are expected to perform and how these tasks support the overall activities. Employees need to be made aware of the advantages of proper job performance at all levels, and of the effects of poor job performance on other employees, customer satisfaction, operating costs and the economic wellbeing of the company. Efforts to motivate employees towards quality of performance should be directed at all personnel from all functions and disciplines.

Accurate, definitive measures of quality achievement attributable to individuals or groups should be publicised to let all employees see for themselves what they, as a group or as individuals, are achieving and to encourage them to produce quality outputs from their processes.

As a spur to the motivation, development, communication and performance of personnel, management should:

- select personnel on the basis of capability to satisfy defined job specifications;
- provide a work environment that fosters excellence and a secure work relationship;
- realise the potential of every member of the organisation by consistent, creative work methods and opportunities for greater involvement;
- ensure that the tasks to be performed and the objectives to be achieved are understood, including how they affect quality improvement;
- see that all personnel feel that they have an involvement and influence on the quality of product and/or service provided to customers;
- encourage contributions which enhance quality by giving due recognition and reward for achievement;
- periodically assess the factors which motivate personnel to provide a quality product and/or service;
- implement career planning and development of personnel;
- establish planned actions for updating the skills of personnel.

The Human Resources function have a key influence in most of the above areas and this list provides an indication of the type of activities the function needs to get involved with; further details of the role of the Human Resources function in TQM are provided by Marchington *et al*. (1993).

Product safety and liability

The aim of enhancing product safety and minimising product liability is paramount. Steps to be taken to limit the risk of product liability and minimise the number of cases include:

- identifying relevant safety standards in order to make the formulation of product or service specifications more effective;
- carrying out design evaluation tests and prototype (or model) testing for safety, and documenting the test results;
- analysing instructions and warnings to the user, keeping maintenance manuals up-to-date and labels and promotional material in order, so as to minimise misinterpretation;
- developing a means of traceability to facilitate product recall if features compromising safety are discovered, and to allow a planned investigation of products or services suspected of having unsafe features.

Use of statistical methods

Correct application of statistical methods is an important element at all stages in the quality improvement process. The use of statistical methods can be beneficial in most aspects of data collection, analysis and application. They assist in making best use of the available data, to gain a better understanding of customer requirements and expectations, in process control, defect avoidance, problem analysis, finding root causes, forecasting, verification, measurement or assessment of quality. As with all such tools, statistical methods have limitations and can only achieve their designated aims when used in the correct way and for the designated objectives.

Specific statistical methods and applications available include the following:

design of experiments/factorial analysis,
analysis of variance/regression analysis,
safety evaluation/risk analysis,
tests of significance,
statistical process control,
statistical sampling inspection.

7.8 Environmental management systems

BS 7750 (1992) *Specification for Environmental Management Systems* has been prepared under the direction of the Environment and Pollution Standards Policy Committee in response to increasing concerns about environmental protection and environmental performance. It contains a specification for an environmental management system for ensuring and demonstrating compliance with stated environmental policies and objectives. It also provides guidance on the specification and its implementation within the overall management system of an organisation. The standard is designed to enable any organisation to establish an effective management system, as a foundation for both sound environmental performance and participation in 'environmental auditing' schemes. Guidance on acceptable levels of environmental management performance for particular sectors will be prepared as sector application guides to explain and amplify the requirements.

This standard shares common management system principles with the BS 5750/ISO 9000 Series of quality management systems standards, and organisations may elect to use an existing management system developed in conformity with the BS 5750 series as a basis for environmental management when sector application guides become available. To achieve equivalence with the requirements of this standard by such means could require the application of a suitable sector application guide. Established procedures for the assessment of compliance with the BS 5750 series should also be capable of extension to deal with the assessment of compliance with BS 7750 (1992) provided that the common assessment team encompasses the appropriate level of environmental expertise and detailed knowledge of BS 7750.

Table 7.4 Links between BS 5750: Part 1 (1987) and BS 7750 (1992)
A cell containing a ● represents a connection between the relevant subclauses of the two standards.

Requirement of BS 5750: Part 1 Subclause	Requirment of BS 7750 Subclause									
	4.1 Management system	4.2 Environmental policy	4.3 Organisation and personnel	4.4 Environmental effects	4.5 Objectives and targets	4.6 Management programme	4.7 Manual and documentation	4.8 Operational control	4.9 Records	4.10 Audits
4.1 Management responsibility	●	●	●							
4.2 Quality system	●						●			
4.3 Contract review				●	●	●				
4.4 Design control						●	●	●		
4.5 Document control							●			
4.6 Purchasing				●				●		
4.7 Purchaser supplied product				●						
4.8 Product identification									●	
4.9 Process control								●		
4.10 Inspection and testing								●		
4.11 Inspection, measuring and test equipment								●		
4.12 Inspection and test status								●		
4.13 Control of non-conforming product								●		
4.14 Corrective action								●		
4.15 Handling, storage, packaging and delivery				●				●		
4.16 Quality records									●	
4.17 Internal quality audits										●
4.18 Training			●							
4.19 Servicing				●				●		
4.20 Statistical techniques								●		

Source: Annex B, BS 7750: 1992

Table 7.4 links the specification of requirements in BS 5750: Part 1 (ISO 9001) to the specification of requirements in BS 7750. This relationship is explained in detail in Annex B of BS 7750.

The elements outlined in the standard to be

incorporated into an organisation's environmental management system are:

- environmental management system;
- environmental policy;
- organisation and personnel;
- environmental effects;
- environmental objectives and targets;
- environmental management programme;
- environmental management manual and documentation;
- operational control;
- environmental management records;
- environmental management audits;
- environmental management reviews.

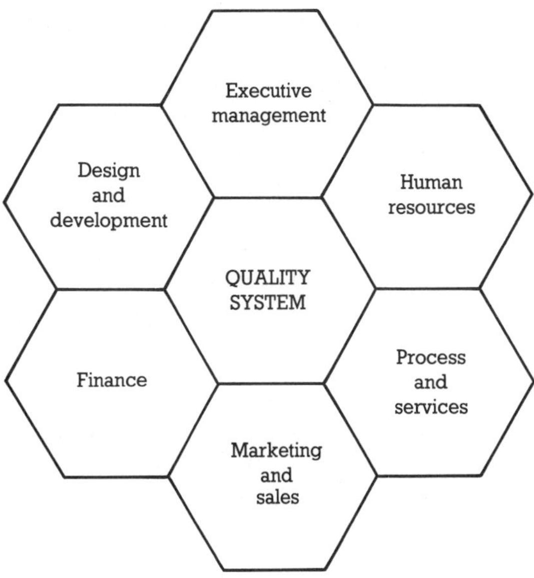

Figure 7.3 Company-wide registration

7.9 Company-wide registration

To date, the vast majority of companies that are registered to the BS 5750/ISO 9000 Series have a scope of registration that covers those activities that have a direct interface with an external customer. In 1991, the British Standards Institution Quality Assurance Service recognised that this is only part of the story and, through company-wide registration, has introduced a service that offers the benefits of quality system accreditation to the whole of the company. Figure 7.3 gives an indication of how company-wide registration applies to an organisation with all business processes encompassed within a fully integrated ISO 9001 (1987) system.

Company-wide registration relies on the introduction of a fully integrated quality system within an organisation. This means that an organisation must have a quality system and the associated procedures not just for the core businesses such as manufacturing, service or customer-facing departments, but also for the supporting functions such as finance, human resources and marketing; every organisation comprises interrelated business processes. It therefore involves the assessment of all business processes, from executive management right through to the administration department. Each individual department within a company is regarded as a business process and each of these processes should have their interfaces with other departments clearly specified and agreed; this concept was outlined in Chapter 5. Individually, these processes work to provide a service to other processes within the company, be it administrative support, finance, marketing, human resources or executive management. Although to some extent these processes act independently, their performance affects other processes with which they have contact. Indeed, the efficiency of the internal structure has a dramatic impact on the overall success of the entire organisation. By assessing the quality system within the company in this way, all business processes can be shown to be working in harmony in order to achieve the company's overall quality goals. Company-wide registration can be thought of as a Total Systems Audit and provides a firm foundation for TQM. It does not, however, address the so-called 'soft issues' of culture, leadership style, motivation and commitment by senior management to quality. Under company-wide registration, each business process is assessed, until the whole organisation has been covered, whereupon a Company-Wide Registration Certificate is issued.

Perry (1991) commenting on the benefits of

company-wide registration makes the point that 'in practice, in a manufacturing company, certification bodies are only likely to enter the Personnel department to view training records as required by the standard. In Marketing perhaps only to discuss contract review and they probably never go near the Finance Department. Yet these three departments along with other functions in the business must behave in a quality way if the business is to be successful.'

One aspect of company structure that it is often very unclear is who has the responsibility and authority for each activity within the organisation. By clearly defining business processes, everyone will be aware of who is responsible for the various activities, how they should be carried out, and the performance levels expected of them. Business process management is simply the encapsulation of common sense in quality management thinking.

Once all the business processes have been clearly defined a typical method of agreeing the interface and performance levels expected between business functions is the establishment of service level agreements. For example, the accounts department may develop an agreement with all other departments/functions of the business (their own internal customers) on the way budgets should be prepared and processed. Similarly, each department may have an agreement with the accounts department on how and when their income and expenditure is reported. These agreements are usually subject to periodic review, to ensure that each business function is receiving the level of service required to fulfil its own obligations. Such agreements provide the vital interface between business functions, and can have a significantly beneficial effect on how well the overall business runs.

BSI claim that the implementation of a company-wide quality system should result in the following benefits:

- breakdown of internal barriers between functions;
- clear agreements between the internal customers and suppliers are fostered;
- clear ownership of business processes is encouraged, so problems can be rapidly resolved by managers with appropriate responsibility and authority.

7.10 Quality system assessment and registration

What follows is a brief outline of the mechanics of independent third-party assessment against the BS 5750 Series, by BSI Quality Assurance Services (BSIQA). See Figure 7.4 for the route to registration. It should be noted that similar assessments are carried out by other certification bodies.

The company must have a documented quality system which complies with the appropriate part (i.e. Parts 1, 2 or 3) of the BS 5750 Series.

Before an assessment is arranged, a detailed appraisal is undertaken of the applicant's documentation. The applicant is required to send system documents in the form of the quality manual to BSIQA for checking to see that all the appropriate parts of the BS 5750 Series are covered. The applicant is then notified of any significant omissions or deviations from the requirements, in order that suitable amendments can be made prior to the on-site assessment. Registration will commence when the assessment team is satisfied that the company is implementing their accepted quality system and has agreed to the required level of audit tests. The team will have been chosen by BSIQA and agreed with the company. The size of the team and time required for assessment depends upon the size of the company, the product or service for which they wish to be registered and the complexity of the technologies involved.

The assessment involves an in-depth appraisal of the organisation's procedures for compliance with the appropriate part of the BS 5750 Series. The company is also required to demonstrate the practical application of its documented procedures. When an assessor discovers a deviation from the requirements or witnesses a non-compliance with the documented procedures, a discrepancy report is

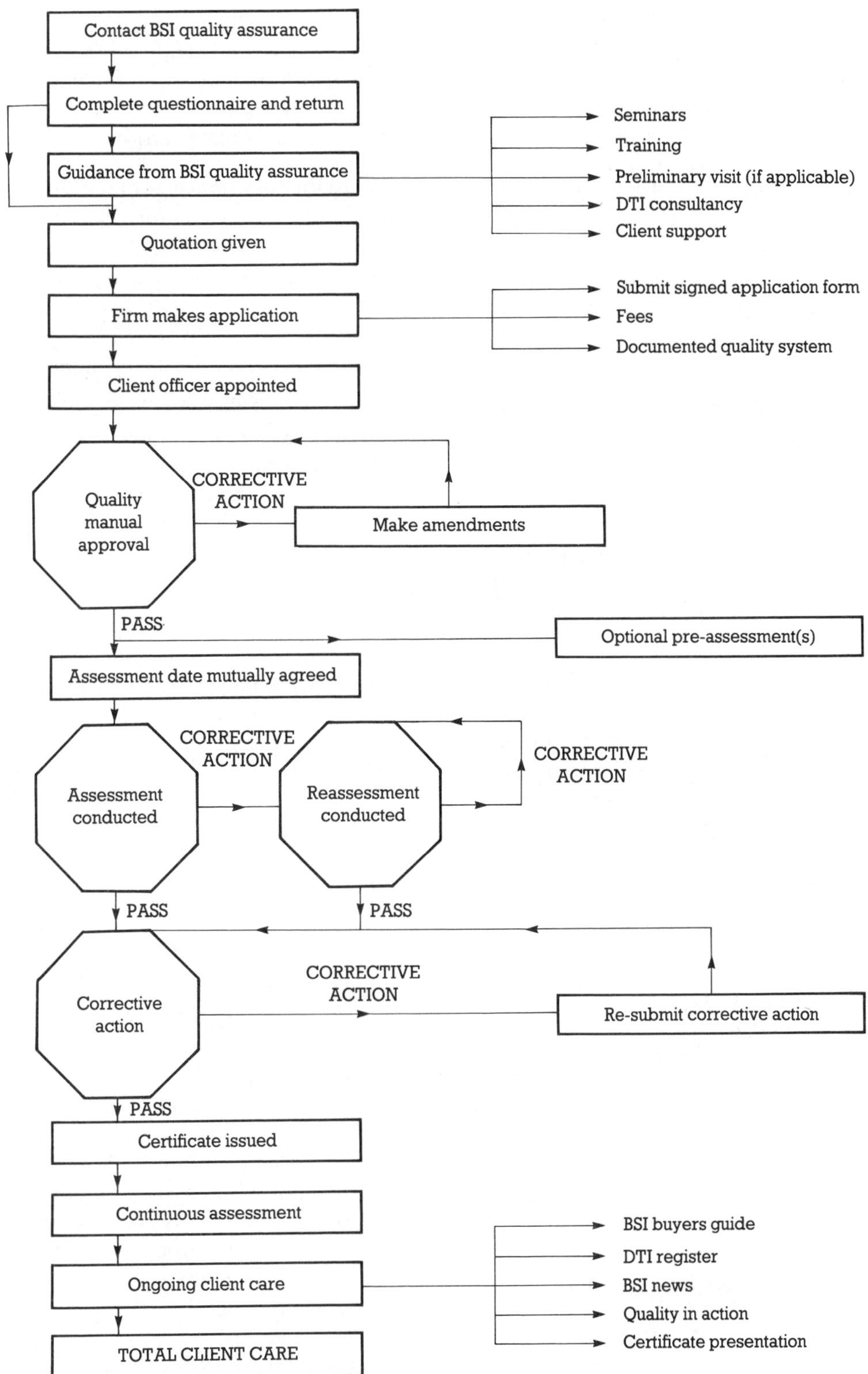

Figure 7.4 The route to BSIQA registration

raised. This describes the deviation, a copy of which is handed to the company's representative who accompanies the assessor.

At the conclusion of the assessment, the so-called lead assessor makes a verbal recommendation on registration at a final meeting with the organisation's representatives. The verbal recommendation is supported by a written summary report and the company is invited to question any discrepancy reports raised.

There are three possible recommendations:

- Unqualified registration – where no discrepancies have been noted;
- Qualified registration – where a number of minor discrepancies, which can be quickly rectified, have been noted and they are neither individually nor cumulatively serious;
- Non-registration – where the lack of procedure or the total breakdown of a procedure has been noted and considerable alteration to the system and/or methods is required.

After the assessment a report, which confirms any discrepancies, is raised and the outcome of the assessment is sent to the company. Where unqualified or qualified registration is granted, a certificate of registration is issued to which is attached an appendix stating the scope of the organisation's registration. A separate certificate is issued to the company for each of its autonomous premises. However, when an organisation has a number of premises which are not autonomous, then a single certificate is used with a separate appendix for each of the premises.

To meet the particular quality needs of an industry or the requirements of a technological discipline, BSIQA is constantly developing documentation, in liaison with industry, in the three main formats outlined below. The essential features of the documentation are agreed with suppliers, purchasers and other interests and consultation takes place in committees under BSI's Quality Assurance Council.

BSI quality assurance specifications

These are documents generated and owned by BSI. They may include additional requirements to those of the BS 5750/ISO 900 Series specific to the industry to which they relate. They therefore contain criteria with which an organisation must conform if Registration is to be granted, and maintained, and which are referenced on the Appendix to the Certificate of Registration.

BSI quality assurance guidance notes

These are primarily for the information of clients and benefit them by:

- providing agreed consistent interpretations of the BS 5750/ISO 9000 Series for a particular industry/sector to assist organisations in developing their quality systems;
- providing clients with an indication of the benchmarks for assessment;
- being promotional documents for BSI indicating to clients and their customers that BSI understands and is committed to the industry/sector;
- being promotional documents for clients to use with their customers.

BSI Quality Assurance Guidance Notes are not referenced on certificates or licences.

Codes of practice

These are owned by Trade Associations or bodies other than BSI. They may include additional requirements to those of the BS 5750/ISO 9000 Series specific to the sector/industry to which they relate. They are for the benefit of the particular sector/industry to which they relate and participation by BSIQA in the development of codes of practice is at the invitation of the industry.

The Quality Assessment Schedules which are now obsolescent are, in some instances, to be converted into one of the above alternative documents, as appropriate.

BSIQA operates continuous assessment visits of which there are a minimum of two per annum. Continuous assessment is planned such that the cumulative effect over a two-year cycle results in the complete audit of a company's quality system.

Announcement of the company's registration takes place in the monthly *BSI News*. BSI also publishes annually, in its *Buyer's Guide*, a list of all registered organisations with an outline of the scope of each registration.

Registration entitles the company to use the BSI registered firm symbol on letter headings, in advertisements and for other promotional purposes other than product marketing.

7.11 Definitions and terminology

The following are some useful definitions and terms used in this chapter.

Accreditation: the formal recognition – against published criteria – of the competence and impartiality of a certification body.

Applicant (for certification): person or body that seeks to obtain a licence from a certification body.

Auditor: A person who has the qualifications and is authorised to perform all or any portion of a quality system audit.

Capability approval: the status given to a supplier for a range of items for which it has been shown that his declared design rules, manufacturing processes and quality system are capable of producing items or services, the quality of which meets the specified requirement.

Certificate of registration: a certificate issued recognising that the quality system operated by a company, having been assessed, is in accordance with these regulations.

Client: a person or organisation requesting an audit.

Customer: ultimate consumer, user, client, beneficiary or second party.

Lead assessor: a person appointed by an assessment organisation to be in charge of a quality system assessment. The assessment may be carried out entirely by the lead assessor, or by a team of assessors under the control of the lead assessor (Institute of Quality Assurance, 1984).

Lead auditor: an auditor who has the qualifications and is authorised to manage a quality system audit.

Non-conformity: the non-fulfilment of specified requirements.

Processed materials: products (final or intermediate) prepared by transformations, consisting of solids, liquids, gases or combinations thereof, including particulate materials, ingots, filaments or sheet structures.

Qualification approval: the status given to a supplier whose product has been shown to meet all the requirements.

Quality assessment schedule: a document, which has been developed by co-operation with a particular industry sector and purchasing and associated interests, which amplifies and particularises the requirements of the BS 5750 Series in relation to a specific range of products, processes or services.

Quality assurance: all those planned and systematic actions necessary to provide adequate confidence that a product or service will satisfy given requirements for quality.

Quality audit: a systematic and independent examination to determine whether quality activities and related results comply with planned arrangements and whether these arrangements are implemented effectively and are suitable to achieve objectives.

Quality control: the operational techniques and activities that are used to fulfil requirements for quality.

Quality loop; quality spiral: conceptual model of interacting activities that influence the quality of a product or service in the various stages ranging from the identification of needs to the assessment of whether those needs have been satisfied.

Quality management: that aspect of the overall management function that determines and implements the quality policy.

Quality manual: a document stating the quality policy and quality practices of an organisation.

Quality plan: a document setting out the specific quality practices, resources and sequence of activities relevant to a particular product, service, contract or project.

Quality policy: the overall quality intentions and direction of an organisation as regards quality, as formally expressed by top management.

Quality programme: a documented set of activities, resources and events serving to implement the system of an organisation.

Quality system: the organisational structure, responsibilities, procedures, processes and resources for implementing quality management.

Quality systems review: a formal evaluation by top management of the status and adequacy of the quality system in relation to quality policy and new objectives resulting from changing circumstances.

Software: intellectual creation comprising the programs, procedures, rules and any associated documentation pertaining to the operation of a data processing system.

Software product: complete set of computer programs, procedures and associated documentation and date designated for delivery to a user.

Specification: the document that prescribes in detail the requirements with which the product or service has to conform.

Traceability: activities such as measuring, examining, testing and gauging one or more characteristics of a product or service and comparing these with specified requirements to determine conformity.

British Standards and other BSI material and International Organisation for Standardisation standards

BS 4778: *Quality vocabulary* Part 1: 1987 *International terms (ISO 8401: 1986; EN 28402: 1991)*; Part 2: 1991 *Quality concepts and related definitions*.

BS 5750: *Quality systems* Part 0: Section 0.1: 1987 *Principle concepts and applications – Guide to selection and use*; (ISO 9000: 1987, EN 29000: 1987); Part 0: Section 0.2: 1987 *Principle concepts and applications – Guide to quality management and quality system elements*; (ISO 9004: 1987, EN 29004: 1987); Part 1: 1987 *Specification for design/development, production, installation and servicing* (ISO 9001: 1987, EN 29001: 1987); Part 2, 1987 *Specification for production and installation*; (ISO 9002: 1987, EN 29001: 1987); Part 3: 1987 *Specification for final inspection and test*; (ISO 9003: 1987, EN 29003: 1987); Part 4: 1990 *Guide to the use of BS 5750: Part 1 Specification for design/development, production, installation and servicing; Part 2 Specification for product and installation; Part 3 Specification for final inspection and test*; Part 8: 1991 *Guide to quality management and quality systems elements to services* (ISO 9004–2: 1991); Part 13: 1991 *Guide to the application of BS 5750: Part 1 to the development, supply and maintenance of software* (ISO 9000–3: 1991); Part 14: 1993 *Guide to dependability programme management* (SIO 9000–4: 1993, IEC 3001: 1993).

BS 5882: 1990 *Specification for a Total Quality Assurance Programme for Nuclear Installations*.

BS 7229: *Quality systems auditing* Part 1: 1991 *Auditing* (ISO 10111–1: 1990).

BS 7511: 1989 *General criteria for certification bodies operating product certification* (EN 4501: 1989).

BS 7750: 1992 *Specification for environmental management systems*.

BS 7850 *Total quality management* Part 2: 1992 *Guide to quality improvement methods*.

PD 3542: 1991 *The role of standards in company quality management*.

PD 6538: 1992 *Vision 2000 A strategy for international standards' implementation in the quality arena during the 1990s*.

British Standards Institution. *The Way to Capture New Markets – a Guide to BSI Quality Assurance*, 1991.

British Standards Institution. *Assessment and Registration*. PAD 900044, Issue 6, February, 1987.

British Standards Institution. *BS 5750, ISO 9000: 1987, a Positive Contribution to Better Business*, 1987.

British Standards Institution. *Company-wide registration: a foundation for total quality*, 1991.

ISO 9004–3: 1993 *Quality management and quality system elements* Part 3: *Guidelines for process models*.

ISO 9004–4: 1993 *Qaulity management and quality system elements* Part 4: *Guidelines for quality improvement*.

References

Allied Quality Assurance Publications. *AQAP–1, NATO Quality Control System Requirements for Industry*. MOD, London, UK, 1972; *AQAP–4, NATO Inspection System Requirements for Industry*. MOD, London, UK, 1970; *AQAP–9, NATO Basic Inspection Requirements for Industry*. MOD, London, UK, 1970.

Atkin G. 'BS 5750 – Practical Benefits in the Factory', *Works Management*, pp 38–42, November, 1987.

Bulled J. W. 'BS 5750 – Quality Management, Systems and Assessment', *General Engineer*, pp 271–280, November, 1987.

Dale B G and Plunkett J J. 'A study of audits, inspection and quality costs in the pressure vessel fabrication sector of the process plant industry', *Proceedings of the Institution of Mechanical Engineers*, 198, (B2), pp 45–54, 1984.

De Angelis C A. 'ICI Advanced Materials Implements ISO 9000 Programs', *Quality Progress*, 24(11), pp 45–51, 1991.

Deshpande A, Dusting F and Younger A. 'Implementation of Quality-Assurance Systems in Small Companies', *Proceedings of the First National Conference on Production Research*, Kogan Page, London, UK, 1985.

Ford Motor Company. *Worldwide Quality System Standard Q101*, Ford Motor Company, Michigan, USA, 1990.

Galt J D A and Dale B G. 'Supplier Development: A British Case Study', *International Journal of Purchasing and Materials Management*, 27(1), pp 16–22, 1991.

Hersan C H A. 'Critical Analysis of ISO 9000', *Quality Forum*, 16(2), pp 61–65, 1990.

IBM. *Professional Guide to Vendor Certification*. IBM Havant, Hants, UK, 1985.

Institute of Quality Assurance. *Registration Scheme for Lead Assessors of Quality Assurance Management System*. The Institute of Quality Assurance, London, UK, 1984.

Ishikawa K. *What is total quality control? The Japanese Way*, Prentice Hall, N.J., USA, 1985.

Jennings G M. 'ISO 9001/9002, Use, Misuse and Abuse', *Quality Forum*, 18(1), pp 33–35, 1992.

Lascelles D M and Dale B G. 'A Study of the Quality Assurance Methods Employed by UK Automotive Suppliers.' *Quality and Reliability Engineering International*, 4(4), pp. 301–9, 1988.

Long A A, Dale B G and Younger A. 'A Study of BS 5750, Aspirations in Small Companies', *Quality and Reliability Engineering International* 7(1), pp 27–33, 1991.

Marchington M, Wilkinson A and Dale B. G. 'Quality Management and the Human Resource Dimension: The Case Study Report', *Institute of Personnel Management*, London, 1993.

Marquardt D, Chove J, Jensen K E, Petrick K, Pyle J and Strahle D. 'Vision 2000: The Strategy for the ISO 9000 Series Standards in the 90's', *Quality Progress*, 24(5), pp 25–31, 1991.

Ministry of Defence. *DEF STAN 05–21, Quality Control System Requirements for Industry*, 1973; *DEF STAN 05–24 Inspection System Requirements for Industry*, 1976; *DEF STAN 05-29, Basic Inspection Requirements for Industry*, 1976, Ministry of Defence, London, UK.

Moores B (Ed.). *Are They Being Served?* Chapter 3 by F Price, 'How Does Britain Rate on Quality?'. Philip Allan, Herts, UK, 1986.

Mortiboys R J. *Quality Management: a Guide for Chief Executives*, Department of Trade and Industry, London, UK, 1983.

National Nuclear Corporation. *G/7622 – Quality Assurance Requirement*. National Nuclear Corporation Limited, Risley, UK, 1983.

Nissan Motor Manufacturing (UK). *Nissan Quality Standard for suppliers*, Nissan Motor Iberica SA and Nissan Motor Manufacturing (UK) Limited, Washington, UK, 1991.

Owen F. 'Why quality assurance and its implementation in a chemical manufacturing company?', *Chemistry and Industry*, August, pp 491–4, 1988.

Owen M. 'Ford, SPC and BS 5750.' *QA News*, 12 (12), p 323, 1986.

PERA International and Salford University Business Services Ltd. *A Survey of Quality Consultancy Scheme Clients, 1988–1990*, The Enterprise Initiative, DTI, London, 1992.

Perry M. *Company-Wide Registration: A Foundation for Total Quality*, BSI Quality Assurance, British Standards Institution, Milton Keynes,

1991.

Rayner P and Porter L. 'BS 5750/ISO 9000: the Experiences of Small and Medium Sized Firms', *International Journal of Quality and Reliability Management*, 8(6), pp 16–28, 1991.

Rover Group. *Supplier Business Specification RG2000*, Rover Group Purchasing, Coventry, 1991.

Sayle A J. 'ISO 9000 – progression or regression.' *QA News*, 14 (2), pp 50–3, 1987.

Singer A J, Churchill G F and Dale B G. 'Supplier quality assurance systems; a study in the nuclear industry', *Proceedings of the Institution of Mechanical Engineers*, 202 (B4), pp 205–12, 1988.

Spickernall D. G. *The path to ISO 9000.* Third Business Success Seminar, November 1991.

Van de Wiele T, Dale B G, Timmers J, Bertsch B and Williams R T. 'Total Quality Management: A State-of-the-Art Survey of European Industry', *Total Quality Management*, 4 (1), pp. 23–28, 1993.

Warner F E. *Standards and Specifications in the Engineering Industry.* NEDO, London, UK, 1977.

Whittington D. 'Some attitudes to BS 5750: a study.' *International Journal of Quality and Reliability Management*, 6(3), pp 54–8, 1989.

CHAPTER 8

Reliability

8.1 Introduction

No matter what an organisation designs, constructs, manufactures, or generates, the achieved reliability usually has a vital effect upon the product and its life cycle, and the organisation's efficiency, profits and market share. Television sets, video recorders, motorcycles and motor cars are examples where penetration of markets has been achieved by more reliable cost-effective products. The DTI booklet *Caring Enterprises and Winning World Market Share* (1985), lists 30 products for which Japanese companies have more than 50 per cent share of world trade. There is little doubt that this market dominance has been achieved primarily through a much better product quality and reliability performance than the competition.

For a manufacturer, immediate sales are seldom as important as their long-term reputation, upon which the stability of the company and, ultimately, its future depends. Customers may buy once on advertised quality and price, but if the goods do not provide the service and reliability required, the customers will be lost to competitors – perhaps forever. Many organisations now make close comparisons of value for money, usually measured as life cycle cost per year, of existing plant items which they use in projections and specifications for new equipment. Clearly manufacturers must look at reliability from the customer's viewpoint rather than trying to reduce their own costs in production and they should base their actions on reducing the customer's life cycle costs. This places a greater emphasis on reliability.

Satisfactory reliability has traditionally been achieved by the use of codes of practice or methods of working that have been shown by experience to give good results for established products and services. However, the need to satisfy competing constraints (including stricter health, safety and product liability requirements, and legislation), the advent of new materials and pressure to reduce life cycle costs has made people realise that reliability can and should be expressed in quantitative terms if it is to be given its proper importance. Quantitative characteristics of reliability are generally quoted in terms of failure rate or intensity. Failure rate is an expression of how often a component or system fails. It may be defined more rigorously as the probability that failure occurs in a specified time interval, divided by the length of that interval. Knowledge of the failure rate of a system allows predictions of the number of failures that will occur over a given period to be made, although this may be complicated if the failure rate is not constant. Quantitative statements relating to predicted reliability may then be made, accompanied by stipulations that certain codes of practice are followed.

One aspect of quantitative reliability that requires emphasising is that reliability can often be predicted, even for products or projects of new design and high cost, but only if there is sufficient knowledge of the processes, likely to lead to failure. This means that the data should be based on the statistical analysis of the observations of known and similar processes. Accordingly, the onus is on all parties, the designer, supplier, purchaser and any other responsible authority, to ensure that quantitative requirements for performance in service are specified, whenever appropriate.

An integrated reliability programme can show an overall cost benefit to the organisation in terms of reduced costs of technical support, replacement, warranties and other consequences of failure. It can also lead to increased competitiveness and help to prevent product liability claims.

This chapter gives some insights into how the reliability concepts may be applied by an organisation. It examines the basics of reliability and outlines the essential features of a reliability and maintainability programme.

8.2 What is reliability?

Reliability is commonly perceived as the ability of a product to give long periods of satisfactory performance without failure in service and use. In qualitative terms (i.e. comparative) reliability relates to success or failure of performance and unreliability seriously undermines the value or usefulness of a product or service. Reliability is itself an important performance characteristic (see Reliability (1) in Figure 8.1).

Reliability may be expressed quantitatively (i.e. measured) as the probability that a product will operate in a prescribed manner under prescribed conditions without suffering any event predefined as failure (see Reliability (2) in Figure 8.1).

Reliability characteristic terms may be used in respect of what has been observed and what may happen, the latter use being defined in terms of a probability. The characteristics can be either qualitative or quantitative and are:

- reliability;
- mean life;
- failure rate;
- mean time to failure (MTTF);
- mean time between failures (MTBF).

Achieving reliability presents problems throughout the life cycle of an item but particularly during design, development and manufacture. Various specialist analytical and management techniques have been evolved to assist these areas. Reliability programmes employing these techniques may add to the time and cost of development but are essential to achieve a reliable product and ensure economic operation and support in service.

A reliability and maintainability programme sets out to provide products with acceptable levels of reliability and maintainability at an acceptable cost rather than products with improved reliability and maintainability regardless of cost. For this reason the quantitative approach is essential. While the qualitative approach is effective in improving reliability and maintainability, it is difficult to measure and quantify any improvements which have taken place.

Reliability relates to success or failure in service or use. This is attained if the product and service quality provided by the producer is adequate and the customer is satisfied. However, to ensure that the required reliability can be sustained in practice, the user has to meet two criteria:

- the product or service should be used only for the purpose and in the manner for which it was designed;
- the product or service should be maintained in accordance with the specified instructions.

8.3 Organising for reliability

Management

The senior management team must ensure that all necessary actions required to achieve reliability in their company's products or services are carried out. Total quality management

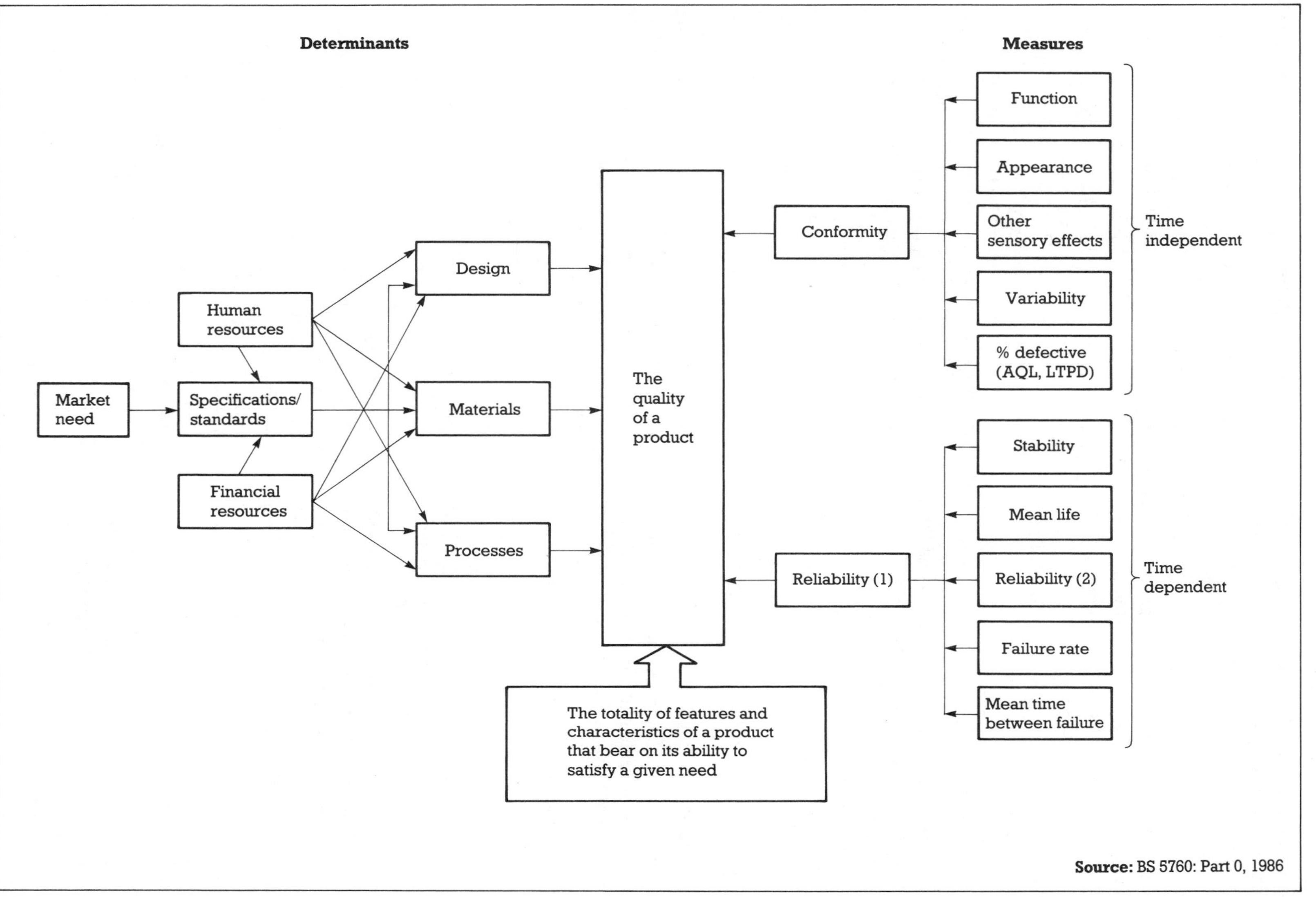

Figure 8.1 The determinants and measures of the quality of a product

provides the framework for the management of reliability, the principles of which may be summarised as:

- An organisation structure is needed in which reliability and quality assurance personnel act in conjunction with the design, product/service and sales/marketing functions but have their own chain of responsibility ending at the board of directors;
- Reliability and quality are every individual's business and responsibility. The typical responsibilities of the various departments towards reliability are shown in Figure 8.2;
- Formal rules are required that recognise the potential contribution of reliability in the design function. These should also recognise the need to learn from the experience of users and to be continuously improving reliability to lead the competition;
- Performance data should be provided by the user to the producer. This partnership should ensure that field failure data is beneficial to both parties;
- The procedures, standards and personal responsibilities for reliability and quality should be documented in a quality manual.

The above principles are represented in Figure 8.3.

Reliability starts as early as the design feasibility study and continues right through to the operation and maintenance phase when the product or service is in use, and reliability technology should make full use of feedback information from users for product improvement. Reliability is mainly determined early on in the product or service cycle, that is in the feasibility, design and development phases. The more firm the design, the more expensive it becomes to make changes and, more importantly, the opportunity for change also diminishes. This is where technique such as quality function deployment can play a key role (see Chapter 6).

It is also important that attention is given by the organisation to putting into place the essential features of a comprehensive dependability programme for the planning, organisation, direction and control of resources to produce products which will be reliable and maintainable. In management terms, this programme is concerned with what has to be done, why, when and how it has to be done. Appropriate guidance on dependability programme management is provided in ISO 9000–4 (1993); it covers both hardware and software products.

Revolutionary and evolutionary designs

If a new design is *revolutionary* (involving new concepts) rather than *evolutionary* (a development of previous designs) the need for a systematic approach to reliability is substantially increased. This is not to say that revolutionary designs should not be attempted, but account should be taken of the number of inventions that have not been successful due to inattention to reliability principles in the development phase. The reliability of novel product designs and new materials is particularly difficult to predict, in particular, when used in new products; in this field the principal need is for appropriate prototypes for intensive testing to find the inevitable weak points of the new design. It is vital that tests are designed to identify critical weaknesses and, when this is achieved, that they are corrected and precluded from reappearance in future designs.

Reliability, performance, maintenance, maintainability and environment

Many good designs have failed in the marketplace by increasing performance levels at the expense of reliability. In mechanical and electrical/electronic products for example failure rate is extremely sensitive to stress levels and stresses should not be increased without further tests. Unsatisfactory components and materials may require only minimum strengthening to make their reliability acceptable.

Maintenance and environmental factors can have a profound effect upon the achieved and the acceptable reliability. Maintenance is the process of maintaining an item in an operational state by either preventing a transition to a failed state or by restoring it to an operational state following failure. Ease of maintenance (maintainability) can make unreliability slightly

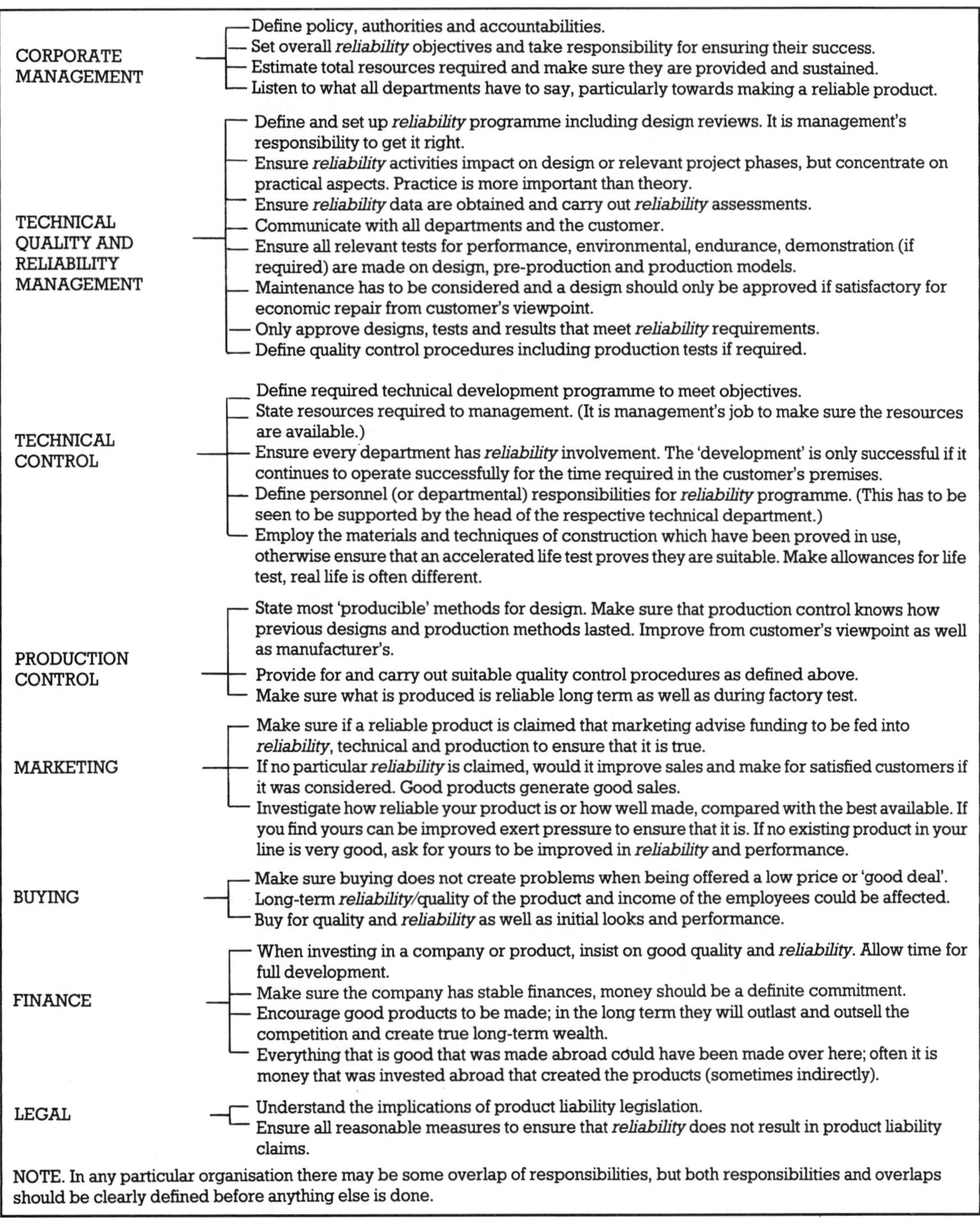

CORPORATE MANAGEMENT

- Define policy, authorities and accountabilities.
- Set overall *reliability* objectives and take responsibility for ensuring their success.
- Estimate total resources required and make sure they are provided and sustained.
- Listen to what all departments have to say, particularly towards making a reliable product.

TECHNICAL QUALITY AND RELIABILITY MANAGEMENT

- Define and set up *reliability* programme including design reviews. It is management's responsibility to get it right.
- Ensure *reliability* activities impact on design or relevant project phases, but concentrate on practical aspects. Practice is more important than theory.
- Ensure *reliability* data are obtained and carry out *reliability* assessments.
- Communicate with all departments and the customer.
- Ensure all relevant tests for performance, environmental, endurance, demonstration (if required) are made on design, pre-production and production models.
- Maintenance has to be considered and a design should only be approved if satisfactory for economic repair from customer's viewpoint.
- Only approve designs, tests and results that meet *reliability* requirements.
- Define quality control procedures including production tests if required.

TECHNICAL CONTROL

- Define required technical development programme to meet objectives.
- State resources required to management. (It is management's job to make sure the resources are available.)
- Ensure every department has *reliability* involvement. The 'development' is only successful if it continues to operate successfully for the time required in the customer's premises.
- Define personnel (or departmental) responsibilities for *reliability* programme. (This has to be seen to be supported by the head of the respective technical department.)
- Employ the materials and techniques of construction which have been proved in use, otherwise ensure that an accelerated life test proves they are suitable. Make allowances for life test, real life is often different.

PRODUCTION CONTROL

- State most 'producible' methods for design. Make sure that production control knows how previous designs and production methods lasted. Improve from customer's viewpoint as well as manufacturer's.
- Provide for and carry out suitable quality control procedures as defined above.
- Make sure what is produced is reliable long term as well as during factory test.

MARKETING

- Make sure if a reliable product is claimed that marketing advise funding to be fed into *reliability*, technical and production to ensure that it is true.
- If no particular *reliability* is claimed, would it improve sales and make for satisfied customers if it was considered. Good products generate good sales.
- Investigate how reliable your product is or how well made, compared with the best available. If you find yours can be improved exert pressure to ensure that it is. If no existing product in your line is very good, ask for yours to be improved in *reliability* and performance.

BUYING

- Make sure buying does not create problems when being offered a low price or 'good deal'.
- Long-term *reliability*/quality of the product and income of the employees could be affected.
- Buy for quality and *reliability* as well as initial looks and performance.

FINANCE

- When investing in a company or product, insist on good quality and *reliability*. Allow time for full development.
- Make sure the company has stable finances, money should be a definite commitment.
- Encourage good products to be made; in the long term they will outlast and outsell the competition and create true long-term wealth.
- Everything that is good that was made abroad could have been made over here; often it is money that was invested abroad that created the products (sometimes indirectly).

LEGAL

- Understand the implications of product liability legislation.
- Ensure all reasonable measures to ensure that *reliability* does not result in product liability claims.

NOTE. In any particular organisation there may be some overlap of responsibilities, but both responsibilities and overlaps should be clearly defined before anything else is done.

Source: BS 5760: Part 0, 1986

Figure 8.2 Responsibilities for reliability

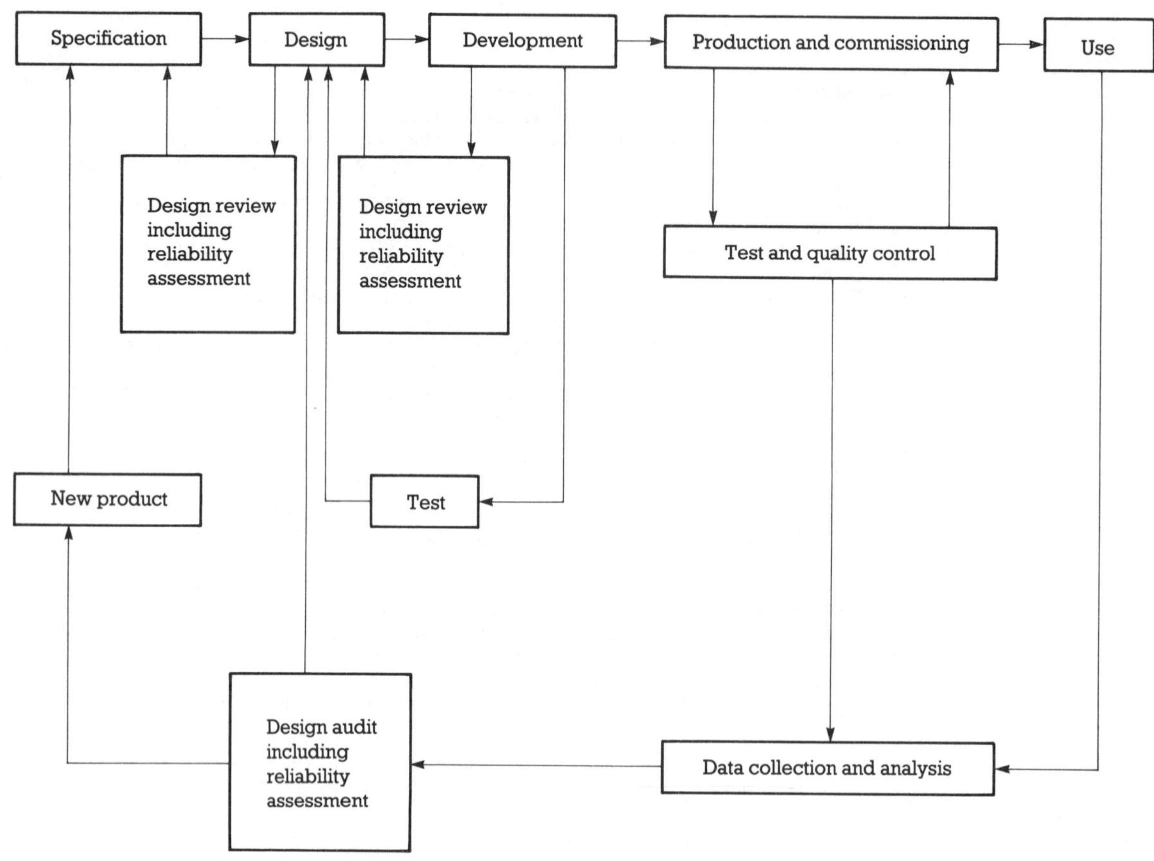

Source: BS 5760: Part 0, 1986

Figure 8.3 Simplified reliability programme concept

more acceptable and, to some extent, the two can be traded off. Preventive maintenance is carried out to make an item less vulnerable to causal influences by restoring the quality to an acceptable level following operational degradation with time. Restorative action following failure will require some form of corrective maintenance. It can save money and time as well as failures and, as an added bonus, tends to extend the durability of the product. These trade off principles can be extended to the elements of the quality equation and then back to those of the value equation. For example, an expensive gold-plated pen is expected to last a lifetime, whereas a cheap plastic ballpoint is probably satisfactory if it writes for about a month after which it is discarded. Both pens are, of course, expected to write legibly and not leave ink on the fingers.

A summary of the various forms of maintenance is shown in Figure 8.4. The most significant subdivision is that maintenance action is either planned in advance, and therefore controlled to a much greater extent by the user, or it is unplanned, usually due to its unpredictability. Planned maintenance is usually linked to known time-dependent failure mechanisms while unplanned maintenance is normally linked to random failure mechanisms.

Planned maintenance may be based on time alone and scheduled to be done at regular intervals (scheduled maintenance). Alternatively, if degradation is known to be more dependent upon the extent or severity of usage than elapsed time, alternative criteria such as running hours, distance travelled or output may be used to determine the intervals between

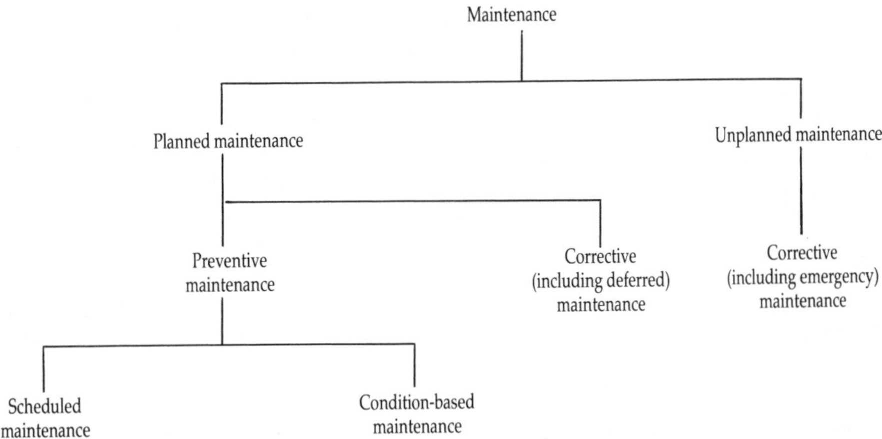

Figure 8.4 Forms of maintenance

Source: BS 4778: Section 3.1 (1991)

maintenance actions. A more efficient and controlled strategy is to base preventive maintenance on measurements of the degree of degradation, i.e. condition-based maintenance. By this means unnecessary maintenance effort and cost may be avoided and suitable shutdown opportunities in the operational programme may be exploited.

It is generally recognised that a strong relationship exists between the areas of maintainability and maintenance. Achieving an item's maintainability objectives during the operational phase is largely dependent on appropriate maintenance and maintenance support procedures, and the provision of adequate maintenance resources. Efforts to reduce the active maintenance time by maintainability programme activities (for details of such programmes see BS 6548: Part 1 (1984)) should be accompanied by corresponding efforts to reduce the non-active maintenance time elements caused by technical, logistic and administrative delays.

Maintenance and maintenance support resources have a major influence on the life-cycle costs of an item, which should be considered throughout the planning process. Maintainability and maintenance support planning tasks should therefore be closely co-ordinated and performed iteratively.

Useful guidance on the definition of maintainability requirements and on the programmes needed to achieve them is given in BS 6548: Parts 1, 2 and 3 (1992) and Part 4 (1993).

The concepts of hazard and risk in relation to reliability can also apply to the environment, either locally, nationally or worldwide. They include the consequences of some hazardous events that do not directly cause personnel harm or economic loss associated with the particular industrial plant, but do more generally affect the environment. The consequences of such an event can therefore directly affect anything outside the boundary of the plant and only indirectly affect human safety or the economics of the plant at the source of the event (e.g. atmospheric pollution affecting vegetation).

8.4 Being objective about reliability

In everyday affairs reliability is often looked at in a somewhat subjective way, but can be treated objectively. The key to the objective approach is recognising the importance of the concept of success and failure. Recording failures in relation to the total population and time-in-use makes an objective approach possible.

Apart from one-shot devices such as ammunition and missiles, products or services are designed, produced, generated and constructed to ensure for a period of time, a number of cycles, a distance run or some other appropriate variable. Usually reliability is estimated in one of two ways:

- as a probability of non-failure over a specified period;
- as a *mean time to failure (MTTF)*, or *mean time between failures (MTBF)* or its reciprocal, which is *failure rate*.

Owing to the variations in the production, operations, assembly and construction of a series of nominally identical products, processes or services, and further variability of treatment in use, times to or between failures exhibit variation. Frequency analysis shows some sections of the possible range of times to occur more frequently than others. BS 5760: Part 2 (1981) provides considerable guidance on the quantitative aspects of reliability.

The statistical distribution of times to failure of a single failure mode will be characteristic of that mode. When analysing failure data, the more modes that have to be considered together, the more the individual characteristic distribution will be disguised. It is not always possible to obtain data precise enough to identify every individual mode, or even to be certain, from the most detailed data, that all the models have been correctly identified. Initial classification of failure distributions may be the hazard function which shows how the failure rate varies with time. An example is the well known 'bath tub' concept (see Figure 8.5). The bathtub model consists of three phases – decreasing failure rate, constant failure rate and increasing failure rate.

During the working life of a product or service, the failure rate usually starts at a higher level than is achieved after initial quality nonconformities have been eliminated or design and specification errors have been rectified. It is common to test products to eliminate the congenially weak areas before they are sold or incorporated into other products and services. Many complete products are tested briefly between construction and sale for the same purpose. The flat part of the bath tub curve may not

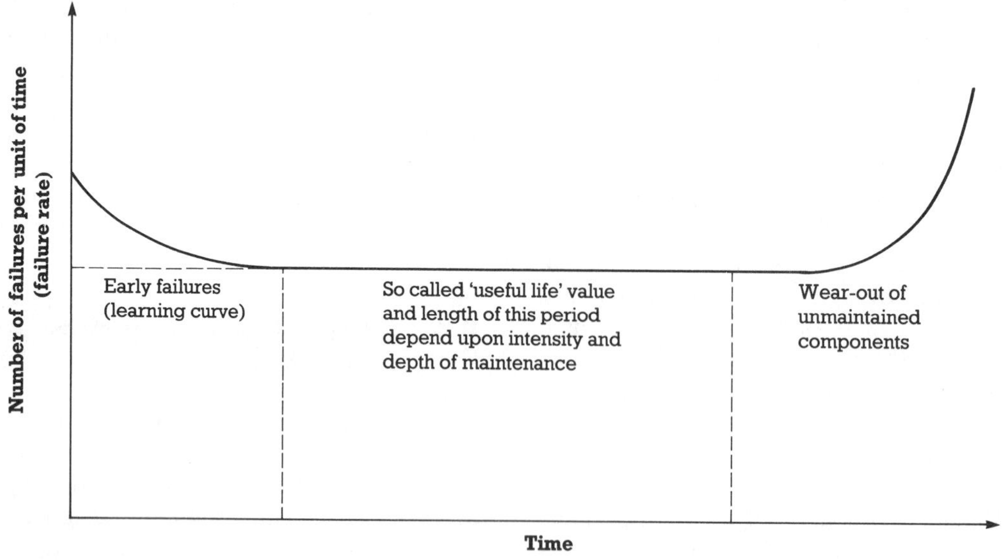

Notes

1 More frequent maintenance lowers the bottom of the curve subject to diminishing returns.

2 Taking more components into maintenance prolongs the flat portion.

3 Scheduled preventive maintenance correctly carried out acts on *components* to reduce average failure rate of the *system*.

Source: BS 5760: Part 0, 1986

Figure 8.5 Bath tub curve showing the relationship of number of failures against time

exist for some products but, if it does, it is likely to be due to random external effects including the consequential effects of failures to other products or components, combined with delay in the onset of the wear-out effects which cause the final part of the curve to rise. For maintained systems, the random effects of service, product or component ages by previously corrected failures produces a constant rate that can be further reduced and extended by preventive maintenance.

Reliability, in most systems, can be improved by proper servicing. Failures can be avoided and equipment reliability restored after failure, by correction or renewal of components, products or parts of systems.

Any system can be made to last forever if all its parts are considered renewable. Therefore, *durability* depends upon the maintenance policy and the quality of the corrective action work. This means that it depends upon costs that would be incurred if preventive maintenance were increased and upon the operator's appreciation of these costs. This means collecting and analysing data, for without sufficient data it is difficult to demonstrate that preventive maintenance does save money, or to make any sensible decisions. With comprehensive failure and cost data, mathematical models can be constructed, the use of which can lead to cost optimisation of preventive maintenance and the determination of renewal intervals or other corrective actions. The objective is usually to minimise life cycle costs to the customer over an agreed period. Additional information on the effect of maintenance on downtime and costs is given in BS 5760: Part 2 (1981).

8.5 A reliability programme

The aims of a reliability programme

Reliability should be considered in a manner similar to any other characteristic of a product, system, piece of equipment or service from its design conception to the end of its working life. Of vital importance is that the reliability experience of one generation of products, services technical specialists or technology is used by the next. This requires that each factor which affects reliability at any stage in the life of a product or service be identified and considered in its relationship to the other factors. This procedure can be formalised into a reliability programme. It may be necessary to divide such a programme into two parts, one of which may be the concern of the designer and the producer/operator, and the other the concern of the user.

The aims of a reliability programme are to ensure that adequate and effective effort is brought to bear on reliability during all phases of the life cycle of a product or service and that the activities which contribute to reliability are properly integrated with other contract/specification activities. A reliability programme should provide continuous study of both quantitative and qualitative requirements throughout all phases of a project. Reliability assessments should be updated, specified requirements should be verified and the reliability activities should be integrated with other elements of the development, production and operation programme. In many projects there are no sharp demarcations between the definition, design and development, and production and operation phases. The activities appropriate to the difference phases are shown in flow diagram form in Figure 8.6.

It is not possible to predict accurately the relative effectiveness of each activity on improving reliability. The choice of activities and the resources to be expended on each should be based on past experience of similar projects. The following recommendations are offered as a general guide.

- The earlier a design change can be agreed, the lower the total cost is likely to be. The cost of making a design change at the production or use stage is usually many times the cost of doing so at the initial design and development stages. This is most important with shrinking product life cycles and product development times.
- For complex items, design evaluation and review, use of proven parts and processes, and the use of redundancy with the design

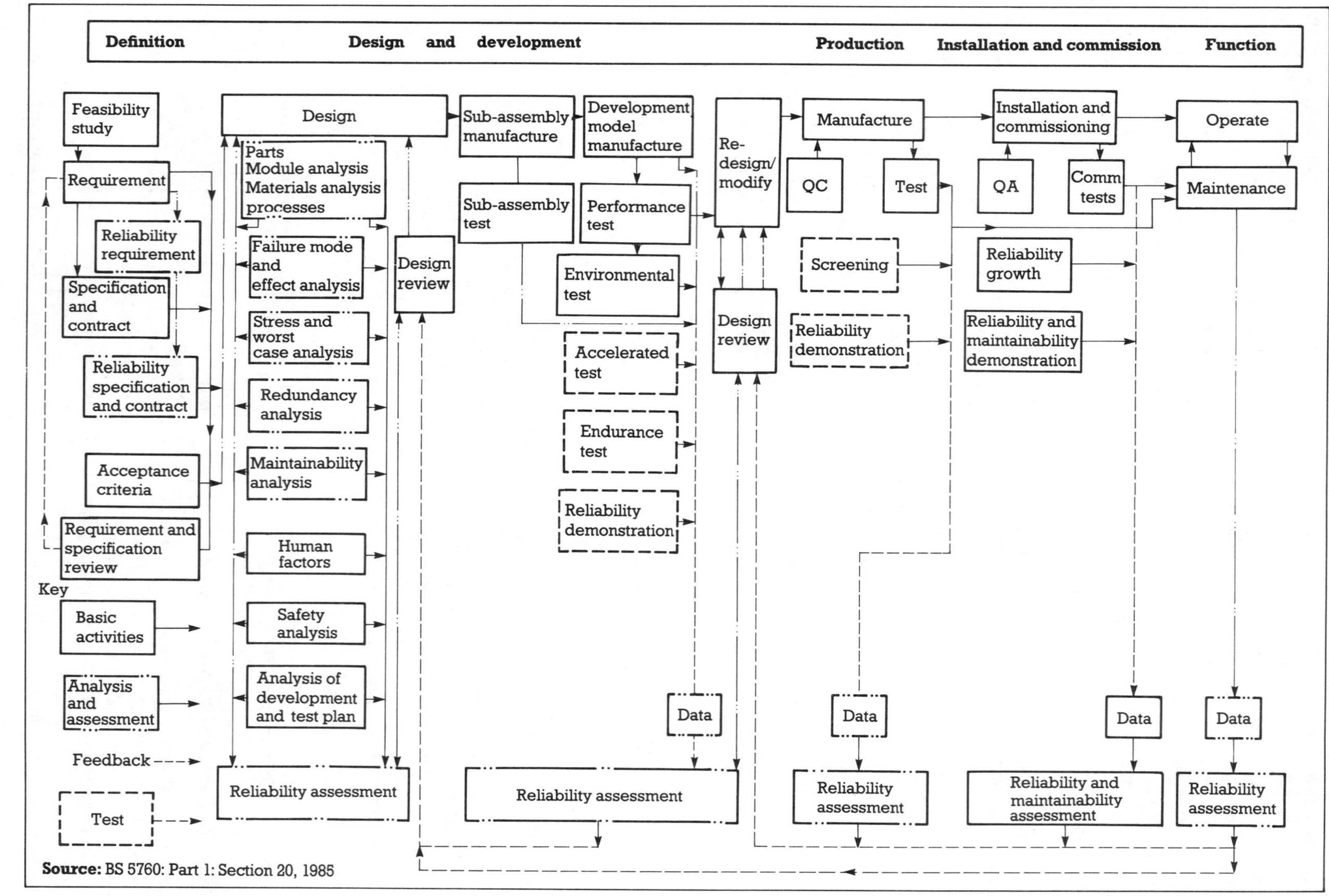

Source: BS 5760: Part 1: Section 20, 1985

Figure 8.6 Reliability and maintainability programme concept

can greatly enhance system reliability. Large-scale use of system redundancy can greatly improve overall system reliability, but at an increase in initial cost and maintenance load. It should be noted that the useful system redundancy may be limited by common mode or common cause failures.

- Reliability testing, including corrective action, carried out during the development and production or operational phases, is an effective means of increasing the reliability of complex products or services, as well as increasing confidence that the required level has been attained. BS 5760: Part 10 (1993) provides guidance on general principles, procedures and considerations for reliability testing in the laboratory and in the field. Guidance is also provided on techniques for availability performance testing.
- Reliability improvement depends on several factors, such as the effectiveness of procedures for identifying, reporting and taking action on failures, the way the programme is managed and the use to which the data from failure analyses is put.

  Reliability improvement by a growth programme should be part of an overall reliability activity in the development of a product. This is especially true for a design which uses novel or unproven techniques or component parts or a substantial content of software. In such a case the programme may expose, over a period of time, many types of weaknesses having design-related causes. It is essential to reduce the probability of failure due to these weaknesses to the greatest extent possible to prevent their later appearance in formal tests or in the field. At that late stage, design correction is often highly inconvenient, costly and time-consuming.

  In a programme of reliability growth, laboratory or field testing is used to stimulate the exposure of weaknesses and improve the reliability of a system, equipment, component part or similar item. When a failure occurs it should be diagnosed, repair and/or replacement carried out and testing continued. Concurrently with testing, past failures should be analysed to find their basic causes and, where appropriate, corrective modifications should be introduced into designs or other procedures, resulting in progressive reliability growth.

  BS 5760: Part 6 (1991) specifies requirements and gives guidelines for the exposure and removal of weaknesses in hardware and software items for the purpose of reliability growth.

Programme activities

An overview of the programme activities shown in Figure 8.6 is now given. The reader should refer to BS 5760: Part 3 (1982) which shows, by way of some examples, how some of the principles in each of the main phases of a reliability programme are applied.

Definition phase

At the definition phase, the originator of the requirement should consider the reliability characteristic that will be required of the product or service in its different phases and the factors that influence this. These factors include:

- the complexity of the product or service;
- the stage of development of similar products/services and of the ones to be used;
- the method of use of the product/service, such as duty cycles, maintenance and expected life;
- the environmental conditions expected – these should cover operating and non-operating conditions, as well as packaging, transport and storage;
- the constraints imposed by other requirements, for example performance, size, mass, time, safety and costs;
- provision for changes in requirements during the life of the system.

When the feasibility of each relevant reliability characteristic has been determined and its value set and agreed, it should be stated as the specific reliability for the product/service that is to be achieved and demonstrated. This requirement or objective should then be included in a specification or contract.

Design and development phase

Table 8.1 shows those activities which, during the design and development (including initial manufacturing) stages, can be carried out by the supplier or by an independent assessor, or as may be required by the purchaser. Owing to the complexity of some systems, the level at which analyses are carried out should be carefully selected, taking into account costs, complexity of analysis and potential benefits. The activities, analysis and tests are described in detail in BS 5760: Part 1 (1985) and Part 2 (1981) and examples showing how they are applied in industry are given in Part 3 (1982). It should be noted that these are written in manufacturing and engineering-type language.

Table 8.1 Design and development phase activities

Analysis of parts, materials and processes
Analysis of established and novel features
Failure mode and effect analysis (FMEA)
Incident sequence analysis (fault tree analysis)
Stress and worse case analysis
Redundancy analysis
Human factors
Design change control
Design review
Design audit
Safety programme
Maintainability programme
Parts and sub-assembly testing
Performance testing
Environmental testing
Accelerated testing
Endurance testing
Reliability growth testing
Reliability demonstration
Data collection, analysis and feedback

Production/operations phase

The following are the activities which take place during the production/operations phase of the reliability programme (a full description is given in BS 5760: Part 1 (1985)):

- preservation of reliability achievement – the procedures to be followed during the production of systems and equipment in order to prevent departure from the achieved and demonstrated reliability;
- quality conformance verification – to ensure that the quality control on reliability is fully effective, it should be integrated with the reliability programme and its planning;
- screening (run-in, bed-in or burn-in) of products, components, intermediate parts and assemblies;
- production/operations reliability demonstration testing – this should be planned as the assurance, on final release, that the finished product/service has met the reliability specification requirement, i.e. that the achieved and demonstrated reliability requirement has been maintained prior to delivery or operation;
- additional software check – it is important that there is a plan to ensure that the production/operation phase for systems containing software does not contribute to a reduction in reliability.

Installation and commissioning phase

The following are the activities which take place during the installation and commissioning phase of the reliability programme; a full description is given in BS 5760: Part 1 (1985).

- System acceptance – the installation phase of the reliability programme should be planned and controlled so that the reliability from the operations or production phase is not degraded.
- Commissioning tests – reliability testing on systems and sub-systems should be performed to define existing weaknesses and problem areas.
- Quality assurance – this function should provide assurance that the detailed requirements for the commissioning tests are met, that the procedures laid down are followed precisely and any variations are properly recorded and witnessed.
- Reliability growth – any design weaknesses that become evident as a result of the commissioning tests should be brought to the attention of the designer so that the appropriate action may be taken.
- Reliability and maintainability demonstration – reliability and maintainability demonstration tests should be primarily

directed at demonstrating that the reliability and maintainability specifications have been achieved. The maintainability aspect should further demonstrate the ease of maintenance, the need for any spares allocation and the prediction of mean times to repairment or replacement; for details see BS 6548: Part 4 (1993).

- Data collection – the test programme should contain detailed data sheets to ensure that all desired data, both input and output are recorded.
- Reliability and maintainability assessment – the detailed data sheets should ensure that all failures are recorded and that the failure reports should provide sufficient information to enable the subsequent analysis to define the failure adequately.

Function and maintenance phase

There are two main activities which take place during this phase. The first is information and data collection, analysis, feedback, and redesign/modification. During the warranty, guarantee or hand-over stages of the product/service, reliability information, such as in-service information, provides a vital feedback function to the producer. Therefore, data collection, analysis and feedback should be continued and followed up by redesign and modification, if further reliability improvement is required. Even if it is not planned to introduce further changes in the product or service, the analysis of operational failure data can be used to ascertain the correlation between reliability testing and operational failure data, so that future demonstration specifications can be better related to the operational requirement.

The second activity is maintenance. Maintenance of equipment in operation obviously affects reliability of products and services, and maintenance should be based on their reliability characteristics. Basic preventive maintenance reduces the rate and severity of such failure causes as wear and corrosion. Preventive maintenance should also be related to the existence of known time-dependent failure modes so that maintenance is minimised while still providing adequate protection. It should be noted that a number of companies are pursuing total productive maintenance (TPM) which is a development of preventive maintenance. The philosophy of TPM recognises that it is the machines and equipment which are the key determinants of product and service quality, and it is people who maintain machines and improve their efficiency and effectiveness. TPM encourages the involvement of everyone through small group activities in maintenance. For further details of TPM see Nakajima (1988).

8.6 System considerations

A chain is as strong as its weakest link. In systems, all components of the chain affect the reliability with the weakest link causing the most system failures; often just a few components cause most of the trouble. Reliability analysis of systems at the design stage can identify such potential failures so that a redesign of the system can reduce or identify them. If this analysis is used with a target reliability performance, the result can be used to limit analysis and redesign. A useful measure of target reliability is mean time between failures (MTBF).

One way to improve reliability is to duplicate less reliable components or those whose failure could result in serious consequences. This measure is known as redundancy. To achieve system fault tolerance, redundancy is the provision of more providers of a function than would be needed if they never failed. If all such providers operate when available this is called *active redundancy*; if they are kept in passive reserve until needed this is called *standby redundancy*. The merits of, and calculation methods for, these two forms of redundancy are given in BS 5760: Part 2 (1981). Again the methods given are described for use in a manufacturing and engineering environment.

Mean time to repair (MTTR) and *repair rate* are used in much the same way as mean time between failures (MTBF) and failure rate. The implication is that repair times vary even for narrowly defined work and that they have a statistical distribution. To take account of preventive maintenance a figure for *mean time for preventive maintenance (MTPM)* is also required.

The concept of system availability combines reliability and maintainability. For example, steady state or long-term average availability may be defined as:

$$\text{Availability} = \frac{\text{MTBF}}{\text{MTBF} + \text{MTTR} + \text{MTPM}}$$

For maintainable systems, such as bank services (e.g. cash dispensing machines), motor cars, power stations, equipment, legal aid, hospitality (hotels, restaurants), plant and buildings, availability is one of the most important measures, certainly in terms of customer satisfaction.

Systems with embedded software require special consideration with respect to reliability. An almost separate science of software reliability is growing up which takes account not only of mistakes in the original software but of further faults induced by imperfect corrections to programs and operating and maintenance instructions. BS 5760: Part 1 (1981) outlines the managerial techniques required in this field.

8.7 Software reliability

Software, unlike electronic hardware, does not exhibit a 'wear-out' mechanism; its individual components (statements) do not deteriorate in service. Therefore it can be argued that software does not exhibit reliability since it cannot wear out and always performs as at delivery. Software faults are either present in the code or not, and, providing that the software is not modified, no further faults will be generated. Software can only fail when the inputs to the software exercise the part of the code that contains the faults. This explains the fact that a program can run for an exceedingly long period of time, perform correctly (as specified), and then suddenly exhibit a behaviour which contravenes its specification. The meaning of software reliability can best be understood from the viewpoint of a user. Having accepted the system containing software into service, he will almost certainly observe later that it sometimes performs 'not as expected'. If the precise condition that reveals such unexpected performance had existed as a test case, then the software could have been rejected, corrected or at least the condition noted as one that produced an unacceptable result.

Users, suppliers and maintenance organisations are interested in methods of predicting the likelihood of such unexpected performance. The user's criteria for deciding whether system performance is 'not acceptable' or 'not as expected' may well dictate the prediction method used and the nature of the data input to it. The classification of performance into these categories will probably have to be made on an individual basis since a software fault which causes the system to stop functioning may be considered acceptable by one user (providing the cause is known) but to another user operating a real-time system, the same fault may be a severe embarrassment. Errors in documentation (which could affect speed of modification or repair) may also affect users to different degrees. In some systems, certain parts of the software may be used more intensively than others and the user may wish to focus interest on those areas in which faults are most likely to occur. The importance of a fault to a user will be governed by such factors as the accessibility of the software for correction and the severity and immediacy of the consequences. The following list gives examples of applications where such factors are important:

- software is unavailable for correction, e.g. guided missiles, computer microcode;
- software is not readily available for correction, e.g. washing machines;
- software is not to mislead users, e.g. teaching software for safety critical systems;
- errors are not to lead to major system malfunction, e.g. real-time systems, railway switching systems;
- software is to function when required, e.g. nuclear reactor shutdown.

Certain classes of software are required to have extremely high reliability. These include systems affecting safety, such as flight critical avionics systems, and systems controlling dangerous industrial processes. Some commercial systems may also have very high reliability requirements, for example those used in on-line banking where failure could lead to unacceptable financial loss.

The widely accepted approach to achieving software reliability is one of using techniques to avoid faults. Given that this is not always perfect, the technique of fault removal by analysis and/or testing is effective in trapping some of the faults that are not avoided. Since exhaustive testing/analysis is impossible to realise practically, some faults will inevitably remain. The effects of these can be reduced by the use of appropriate fault tolerance techniques.

Techniques for measuring and predicting the reliability of hardware are already widely applied. With the increasing use of computers there is a need to establish equivalent methods for evaluating the reliability of systems containing software. However, as mentioned earlier the failure mechanism of software is not a physical process but lies in the emergence, during use, of logical errors in definition, design or development. Such errors occur in hardware systems as well but, except in the case of complex systems, are assumed (albeit often inadvisedly) to have been removed in the early life of an item and are therefore discounted in the prediction of reliability.

It is possible to assess software reliability using failure data gathered from the system under consideration but the demonstration of extremely low failure probabilities poses severe practical difficulties. If the failure rate is high enough to be measured, then it is too high. Other possible ways of predicting software reliability include methods based on knowledge of the program structure, the use of parts having a known service history, and the employment of fault-tolerant design techniques using diverse redundant parts. Research is also being done into the estimation of in-service reliability from records of non-random testing, and methods based on this approach may become available.

Methods of modelling the reliability characteristics of software in a system are still at an early stage of development and no single method has gained wide acceptance. Organisations producing and using software may nevertheless find it advantageous to collect and analyse reliability data albeit initially at a simple level.

Figure 8.7 illustrates the feedback of information from analysis of data collected on software. The simplest reliability analysis generally involves the use of historical data to estimate current reliability performance only; any prediction of future reliability on this basis would hinge primarily upon the continuation of existing trends. Comprehensive and robust methods of reliability prediction could provide relationships between achievable reliability and, for example, the use of methods and tools such as structured design, formal specifications and particular compilers. The ability of individual organisations to provide data in the quantity and range needed to develop such comprehensive models may well be limited but these limitations could be reduced if several organisations or parts of an organisation co-operate to create a shared database of information.

A revolution is now occurring within the

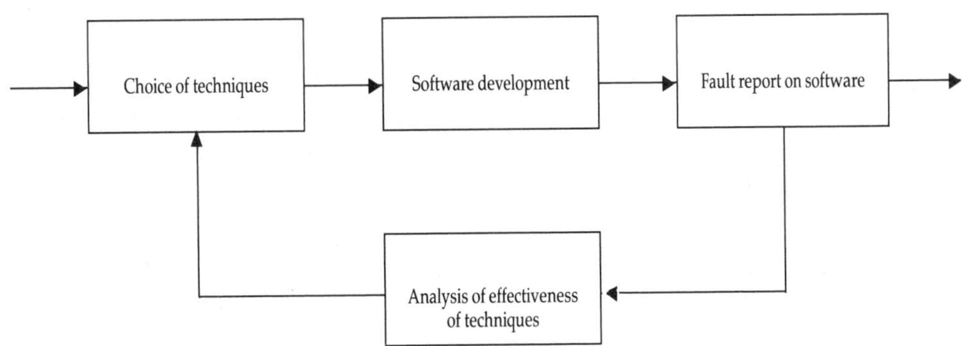

Figure 8.7 Software data feedback

Source: DO 198 (1991)

software fraternity, the aim being to prove mathematically that a program is correct with respect to its specification. However, there are claims that formal proofs cannot deal with all aspects of specifications, and that the complexity of the proofs gives rise to greatly increased costs. These aspects are being actively addressed, and it is possible that formal methods will gain popularity in high reliability/ safety related applications.

DD 198 (1991) explores some of the techniques that are available for assessing the reliability of systems containing software and provides appropriate guidance.

It is clear from the above discussion of software reliability that for the achievement of quality in software it is necessary to satisfy three principle aims:

1) a clear definition of what is to be achieved and when (specifications and plans);
2) a description of the activities and functions that need to be performed (codes of practice);
3) the control and monitoring of the way in which activities/functions are performed (quality control).

BS 7165 (1991) provides guidance as to how these aims may be achieved to help those responsible for software-based projects to meet their commitments effectively, efficiently and economically. The degree and formality of implementation and the extent of the quality activities will vary according to the needs of the project. This standard also gives recommendations for a software quality control system to meet the requirements of the BS 5750 series and BS 5750: Part 13 (1991) sets out guidelines to facilitate the application of ISO 9001 (1987) to organisations developing, supplying and maintaining software.

8.8 Human factors

Human performance, and particularly human reliability, is an important consideration in the safe and predictable operation of increasingly complex industrial processes. The main purpose in addressing human performance is to maximize reliability, principally by reducing error-likely situations (using human factors engineering methods), thereby minimizing the so-called human error failures which affect public safety and process economics. A secondary consideration is to quantify the risks associated with human activities throughout the life-cycle of industrial processes, particularly in design, operation and maintenance.

To facilitate this, techniques have been (and continue to be) developed to assess human reliability including the causes/consequences of human error. Resort has to be made to assessment techniques since comprehensive, validated human reliability databases are few. However, it is possible from a wide range of techniques to select one (or several in combination) to estimate the likelihood of human error.

A major difficulty with human reliability is its variability compared with mechanical/electrical components, even when environmental conditions remain constant. However, more is now known of the so-called performance-shaping factors and their impact on reliable performance. These are increasingly being incorporated into human factors guidelines to ensure that the tasks allocated to the human are matched to the person's abilities.

Unlike plant items it would be difficult (and probably not of benefit) to provide a quantitative target for human performance which would be included in a functional specification. Human reliability is implicit in the failure rates of plant items/components since it is possible (in the final analysis) to construe all failures as resulting from human actions; from incorrect specification of materials to misoperation. This is not helpful and it is now considered that human reliability improvement is achieved best by the systematic application of traditional qualitative human factors methods at the process/system design stage.

Human failure is the basic term denoting the termination (or non-achievement) of a required function. It is applied to all tasks required of the human to achieve the required function under all circumstances.

The possibility of human error leading to unreliability should be considered throughout the life cycle of products, services and systems.

In particular, careful consideration should be given to the way in which reliability of a product, service or system may be reduced by the following:

- Poor communication. Good communication is essential for reliability throughout the life cycle of products, services and systems. One of the most difficult communication phases occurs when a design specification for a product or service is being created. Comprehensive communications are required between all parties early in the process, but they have to become more rigid in order to produce precise verifiable statements. The design process, as well as the other phases of a system's life cycle, should be visible or communicated to those involved and affected. However, communication interfaces occur throughout a product or service life cycle. It is important to ensure that all critical communication is safeguarded, for example, by redundancy, feedback, examples and routine checks.

- Poor design. Care should be given to the structure of both the design and the design teams so that at every level the logic of the design can be checked. Nevertheless, in the design phase human error produces faults. To eliminate these errors, methods of fault detection and well structured procedures are required, for example, specification, inspection, computer program 'walk-through', simulation and task analysis.

- Poor operation. Careful consideration should be given to the way in which the reliability of the product or service may be increased by the reliability of the operation. This requires an analysis of operator function, the information needs, the way in which the information is provided, the operator response required, the physical actions required to respond and the response time allowed. Where the analysis reveals unsatisfactory features, design changes may be necessary. In some cases it may be possible to quantify the element of human (personnel) unreliability in the total system, but in general this analysis is usually qualitative.

8.9 Specification of reliability

The form of reliability specification can vary considerably. It may comprise a statement that defines the required test programme to meet the purchaser's requirements, or it may be a formal specification that defines the complete management structure and sets standards for all aspects, from operating environment, demands for life testing, and details defining environmental or functional testing.

A specification may, for example, be prepared by an ultimate user as a statement of the true needs, or it may be a design specification prepared by a supplier in conjunction with the user, as a detailed statement of the product or service quality to aim for in production, or as an operation defining the desired performance in service. The detail written into a specification depends on the nature of the product or service, its purpose and the market for which it is intended.

Before any quantitative reliability statement can be made, the following prerequisites must be specified:

- a task (time or other measure of usage), against which a probability can be expressed;
- the performance at which the product or service function ceases to be satisfactory, i.e. the criterion of failure;
- the conditions under which the product or service is to function.

Where adequate failure data are available, there is normally no difficulty in writing a quantitative specification of reliability. The designer's confidence that the reliability requirements will be met is dependent on the adequacy of the data available concerning failure. These data can only be obtained from reliability testing, from field data or from knowledge of the physical processes leading to failure. The greater the volume of data, the greater the confidence, providing the corresponding data analysis is available and appropriate.

When reliability is specified qualitatively, the methods used to assure reliability should be clearly described in the specification. The criteria against which reliability may be judged should be stated. Where possible, it is advisable for the customer to agree the specification with the supplier, as well as the extent of reliability assurance to be carried out.

A written reliability specification should consist of a series of clauses; the following are typical:

- the function or functions of product or service;
- the criteria for failure of the product or service;
- the reliability characteristic or characteristics (for example, MTBF or MTTF) that are appropriate to the circumstances.
- the required value of the reliability characteristic and, if known, the distribution of failures in time;
- the time during which, and the conditions in which, the product/service is required to perform its function or functions;
- the means by which reliability assurance is to be attained.

The clauses in a reliability specification state the reliability required, without which the product/service may not be purchased. They lay down detailed targets for design, development, production, operations, installation and commissioning, and state the reliability that may be expected in service.

Reliability clauses normally contain three elements;

- the objective or required value of the relevant reliability characteristics expressed in performance terms;
- the conditions of use, storage and maintenance, and the life of the product or service during which this reliability is required;
- the means by which the required reliability is to be, or has been, assured.

8.10 Assessment and prediction of reliability

Reliability assessment is the process by which a quantitative value is assigned to reliability. An essential part of a reliability programme is the

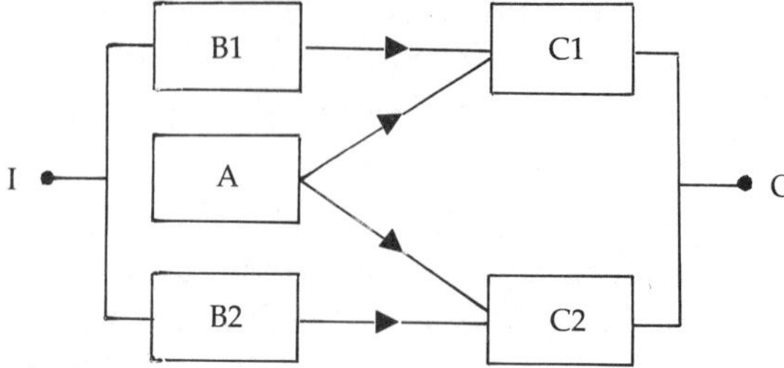

Source: BS 5760: Part 9 (1992)

Figure 8.8 A reliability block diagram. This could represent the fuel supply to the engines of a light aircraft. Item B1 represents the supply to the port engine (C1), item B2 the supply to the starboard engine (C2) and item A a back-up supply to both engines. The system fault definition is that both engines must fail before the aircraft fails.

prediction or measurement of the reliability of a product or service.

Different analytical methods of dependability analysis are available; of these the reliability block diagram (RPD), is one. An RPD is a pictorial representation of a system's reliability performance and shows the logical connection of (functioning) components needed for system success. Figure 8.8 is an example of an RPD. BS 5760: Part 9 (1992) describes procedures for modelling the dependability of a system and for using the model to calculate reliability and availability measures.

Reliability assessment is required in the following circumstances:

- in establishing the reliability required of a product or service;
- in predicting the reliability of a product or service that is still in the design, development or pre-production/pre-operations stage:
- in establishing whether a product or service that is in service has performed or is performing in such a way as to satisfy the specified value of the reliability characteristics (for example, failure rate, mean life and mean time to failure) and whether it is likely to continue to do so for the rest of its design life;
- in establishing the safety of a product or service.

The customer for a product/service may require a demonstration that the reliability requirement has been or will be complied with. This is a major aim of a comprehensive reliability programme. During the design, development and production/operations phases, reliability assessment is a predictive process that relies on techniques, such as the use of reliability models, FMEA, evaluation or parts, systems, materials and processes, and on the testing of development models, methods and prototypes. It also relies on the provision of failure data in order to investigate specific failure modes and thus provide recipes for remedial action. In service, the user may wish to measure reliability by observation.

Reliability assessment requires first a reliability model for the product or service to represent its reliability in an appropriate mathematical form, and secondly the necessary reliability data. The precise way in which the model is developed and the data are collected will depend on the circumstances surrounding the product/service and the stage it has reached in its life cycle. A model could be used in the following circumstances:

- reliability prediction and measurement;
- reliability demonstration;
- formulation of choice of test plans.

The mathematical treatment of reliability modelling is discussed in detail for manufacturing and engineering in BS 5760: Part 2 (1981).

Reliability assessment can vary enormously in the techniques used, from the very simple to the complex. Methods by which reliability data are collected for a particular product or service that can be tested will vary, because development testing may initially be the only source of data, while test data on the typical product or service will subsequently be available. After the product/service goes into operation, the source of data will be acquired from field experience.

When the nature of a product or service is such that it cannot be tested before being put into service, it is necessary to obtain data by testing separately the components of the product/service or, if this is not possible, to adopt the physics of failure methods or to obtain relevant failure data from other circumstances.

The data used in reliability prediction can be gathered from various sources. The acquisition of field data on the product or service itself is obviously the best source since there is no substitute for operating experience. The reliability statistics can be obtained from the recorded operating data. Where a product or service is under development, data can be obtained from development or production/operations tests. Where there is neither test nor physics of failure data available for a product/service, reliability data can be obtained from data on those of comparable function, but not necessarily of the same design or subject to the same characteristics.

8.11 Reliability demonstration and testing

Reliability demonstration is the process by which it is shown that a product or service has characteristics that meet a particular requirement. It is important to be able to describe the ability of the product/service to do this; this ability is termed *compliance*. Normally this is indicated by the use of appropriate test procedures during the development, preproduction, production and operational phases.

Generally, the aims of a test programme are to:

- ensure, as far as practicable, that the product/service, with its operational and design documentation, meets the specified performance or operational requirements including reliability;
- ensure, as far as practicable, that production/operations non-conformances and non-conforming components are eliminated;
- highlight systematic errors so that deficiencies in design are corrected;
- contribute information that can be used to determine reliability characteristics;
- verify that changes, such as those affecting design, including value analysis, modification, operations processes or sources of supply, have not reduced reliability below an acceptable level.

These aims normally apply whatever the stage

in the life of the product or service to which they refer.

It is not always possible or economical to test a complete system; it may be necessary to test components, or specific design features and to use the data in a reliability model to predict the behaviour of the complete system.

There is a wide variety of test programmes, some of the main types are:

- *condition terminated tests* – the test terminates when a predetermined condition is met or failure occurs;
- *fixed time or sequential tests* – these are based on specified acceptable values of the reliability characteristic, and their rules enable decisions to be made on whether the equipment or system is to be accepted or rejected, or whether the test is continued;
- *accelerated testing* – the primary purpose of an accelerated test is to provide failure data more quickly than if the product or service were tested under normal conditions.

These tests are described in detail in BS 5760: Part 2 (1981).

The analysis of reliability test data, which may be limited to a low number of observed failures, will evaluate the true reliability only at a low level of confidence. Bayesian statistics can be used in this situation, using prior information obtained from earlier tests on the same or similar items, sometimes combined with judgement to produce an estimate of reliability. Bayesian techniques are discussed more fully in BS 5760: Part 2 (1981).

8.12 Production/operations, flow, analysis and interpretation of data

The knowledge of the behaviour of a product or service, or of a fixed installation or plant during its life is necessary so that the following conditions are satisfied:

- Effective action can be taken to improve reliability. Periodic reliability reports for a product/service, a fixed installation or plant are necessary to determine whether reliability goals have been achieved. Where modifications to improve the reliability or the life of a product or system in service are necessary, such reports are useful in monitoring the effects of the modifications. Where warranty or guarantee clauses are in operation, reliability data can be used to monitor trends in claims. Reliability data feedback is vital to effective product/service quality assurance.
- Improvements can be incorporated in future designs. The design of future generations of items can be improved if a detailed knowledge of achieved reliability is obtained from the present generation of the items. This can lead to commercial advantage for both customer and supplier.
- Improvements can be made to design documentation in order to improve the efficiency of carrying out software changes or correction.
- An effective and efficient support organisation, which can forecast any spares requirements, and control stores inventories and software change effort can be provided.
- Where hazardous operations are involved, the degree of hazard or risk may be reduced by improvement of the design or operating procedures.
- Collection and analysis of data are important parts of safety programmes.
- Operational procedures, operational documentation and maintenance schedules can be improved.

The systematic means of collecting, recording, processing, and analysing data should be centred on a suitable department within the organisation concerned. Many organisations have an established information collection system (for example, a quality management information system) that provides management with data for normal control purposes. Consideration should be given to the extra cost of adapting any such system so that additional data or reliability, maintainability and availability can be collected.

In considering the collection, analysis and use of reliability data, organisations should not overlook the advantages that may be gained from subscribing to one or more of the available databank services. The use of computers to store and retrieve reliability data may also be appropriate, especially where large quantities of data are to be handled, but in each case the cost effectiveness should be considered.

The data to be recorded for an event should include the nature of the event and additional details taken from routine operating records. These records should include the following:

- specification and description of product and service (location, nature, design, size, time/current configuration);
- operating history, including any installation data, the maintenance regime, condition monitoring, calibration data tests and environment;
- fault/failure history that should include a complete listing of events, causes, consequences, event times, returns to operation, maintenance data, test data, calibration data.

It is important to define clearly the products, services, system components and the boundaries implied. Configuration changes should be taken into account in relation to the levels of data recording. The precision and limitations of the data should be clearly indicated.

Reliability, maintainability and availability can be derived from the operating history of a product or service. Typical sources of historical data include: previous operating experience, design and development, operations, production, tests, guarantee and/or warranty, product liability test reports, supply of replacement parts, repair and field information, demonstration or commissioning tests and data collected from user reporting systems.

Attention must be paid at all times to the integrity of data. For example, prototype of systems are rarely identical with those that are eventually produced. Results obtained from testing prototypes should be extrapolated with extreme caution if they are to be used for assessing the field potential of the product or service. The validity of results obtained from tests under simulated conditions depends on how well the simulation approximates real conditions. It is important to ensure that spurious failure modes are not induced under test, giving a misleading picture.

In addition to product manufacture or service operation, care should be taken into account when incorporating into reliability calculations data provided by suppliers and also that obtained from field data retrieval programmes.

The timely analysis of all discrepancy or failure reports by a team formally constituted by management enables the basis or underlying causes of failure in system, components, parts, materials, processes and procedures to be determined. The analysis should include failures in design, production/operations, procurement, quality control, maintenance, and operation. The resulting failure analyses should be fed back to design, production or operations, and management personnel for action.

It is essential that the route by which data are fed back is clearly defined. Some means should be established to co-ordinate all those concerned with the investigation of failures and the follow-up actions necessary. Reports flowing from user or purchaser areas may emanate from two quite different sources – those from the operating authority or user, and those prepared by the maintenance department or those responsible for corrective action. It is essential that such reports and reports from all other sources, are brought together and co-ordinated before analysis to avoid multiple reporting of a single fault.

It is generally accepted that the overwhelming majority of failures, down time or costs associated with a product or service are usually associated with relatively few modes of failure. Therefore, a cost-conscious data collection system would collect fairly coarse data on everything, sort them and so pinpoint the major problem areas, and perhaps the principal offenders under each of the three headings: failure rate, down time and cost. These areas can then be more thoroughly investigated by acquiring more comprehensive data. In this way resources can be directed in a cost-effective manner.

With reference to quantitative data, the nature and quality of the data should be firmly established. The degree of sophistication of the analysis should never be more than the intrinsic accuracy which the basic information allows.

Appropriate characteristics of reliability should be chosen, for example useful life, mean time to first failure, MTBF, percentile life, failure rate and availability. A relevant statistical analysis method should be chosen, which may range from merely counting numbers of failures to establishing assessments of characteristics.

The descriptive information should be analysed in terms of failure mechanism, design or production/operations procedures and characteristics. If no quantitative data are available, this information will serve to indicate the nature of any problem that may exist and the seriousness of the effects, but not the extent of the problem.

The main problem associated with interpretation of reliability data is the requirement for the extrapolation of results to other situations. This problem arises, for instance, because:

- differences usually exist between test conditions and field conditions of use, or between the times used in the tests and those used in the field;
- it may be necessary to use results from tests on one product mark, service grade or type to assess another product mark, service grade or type;
- an assessment of the potential of a new design may be required from historical data.

The analysis should demonstrate, as far as possible, the effects and validity of extrapolation and should take account of the levels of understanding of the intended users and of the uses to which the data may be put.

8.13 Definitions and terminology

The following are some useful definitions and terms used in this chapter.

Availability: the ability of an item to be in a state to perform a required function at a given instant of time or over a given time interval, assuming that the required external resources are provided.

Bath tub curve: a conceptual model for the instantaneous failure of a system over its whole life.

Constant failure rate period: that period, if any, in the life of a non-repaired item during which the failure is approximately constant.

Dependability: the collective term used to describe the availability performance and its influencing factors: reliability performance, maintainability performance and maintenance support performance.

Dependability programme: the organisational structure, responsibilities, procedures, processes and resources used for managing dependability.

Durability: the ability of an item to perform a required function under given conditions of use and maintenance, until a limiting state is reached.

Early failure period: that early period, if any, in the life of an item, beginning at a given instant of time and during which the instantaneous failure intensity for a repaired item or the instantaneous failure rate for a non-repaired item is considerably higher than that of the subsequent period.

Error: a discrepancy between a computed, observed or measured value or condition and the true, specified or theoretically correct value or condition.

Failure: the termination of the ability of a unit to perform a required function.

Failure rate: the limit, if this exists, of the ratio of the conditional probability that the instant of time, T, of a failure of an item falls within a given time interval $(t + T)$ and the length of this interval, t, when t tends to zero, given that the item is in an up state at the beginning of the time interval.

Fault: the state of an item characterised by inability to perform a required function, excluding the inability during preventive maintenance or other planned actions or due to lack of external resources.

Hazard: a situation that could occur during the lifetime of a product, system or plant that has the potential for human injury, damage to property, damage to the environment or economic loss.

Human error: a human action that has the potential to produce an unintended result; ultimately this may result in a failure.

Human reliability: the ability of a person (or personnel) to perform a required function under stated conditions for a stated period of time.

Maintainability: the ability of an item under given conditions of use, to be retained in, or restored to, a state in which it can perform a required function, when maintenance is performed under given conditions and using stated procedures and resources.

Maintainability demonstration: activity performed on individual items or samples to indicate concurrence with a specific maintainability requirement and/or to generate maintainability data.

Maintainability verification: monitoring actions, inspections or both, for the purpose of determining compliance by the contractor with the maintainability requirements specified for an item.

Mean time between failures (MTBF): the expectation of the operating time between failures.

Mean time to failure (MTTF): the expectation of the time to failure.

Maintenance: the combination of all technical administrative functions, including supervisory actions, intended to retain an item in, or restore it to, a state in which it can perform a required function.

Planned maintenance: the maintenance organised and carried out with forethought, control and the use of records to a predetermined plan.

Preventive maintenance: the maintenance carried out at predetermined intervals or according to prescribed criteria and intended to reduce the probability of failure or the degradation of the functioning of an item.

Probability: a real number in a scale of 0 to 1 attached to a random event. It can be related to a long-run relative frequency of occurrence or degree of belief that an event will occur.

Redundancy: in an item, the existence of more than one means of performing a given function.

Reliability: the ability of an item to perform a required function, under stated conditions for a stated period of time.

Reliability growth: a condition characterised by a progressive improvement of a reliability performance measure of an item with time.

Reliability improvement: a process undertaken with the deliberate intention of improving the reliability performance by eliminating causes of systematic failures and/or by reducing the probability of occurrence of other failures.

Risk: a combination of the probability, or frequency, of occurrence of a defined hazard and the magnitude of the consequences of the occurrence.

Safety: the freedom from unacceptable risks of personal harm.

Software: intellectual creation comprising the programs, procedures, rules and any associated documentation pertaining to the operation of a data processing system.

Software product: complete set of computer programs, procedures and associated documentation and data designated for delivery to a user.

Software reliability: ability of a software product to give a long period of satisfactory performance without failure in use.

Unplanned maintenance: maintenance carried out to no predetermined plan.

Wear-out failure period: that final period, if any, in the life of an item during which the instantaneous failure intensity for a repaired item or the instantaneous failure rate for a non-repaired item is considerably higher than that of the preceding period.

British Standards

BS 4778: *Quality Vocabulary* Part 1: 1987 *International Terms*; (ISO 8402: 1986) (EN 28402: 1991); Part 3: 1991 *Availability, Reliability and Maintainability terms*; Section 3:1, 1991 *Guide to concepts and related definitions;* Section 3:2, 1991 *Glossary of international terms* (IEC 50(191): 1991).

BS 5750: *Quality systems* Part 13: 1991 *Guide to the application of BS 5750: Part 1 to the development, supply and maintenance of software* (ISO 9000–3: 1991); Part 0: 1986 *Introductory guide to reliability;* Part 1: 1985 *Guide to reliability and maintainability programme management;* Part 2: 1981 *Guide to the assessment of reliability;* Part 3: 1982 *Guide to reliability practices: examples;* Part 6: 1991 *Guide to programmes for reliability growth* (IEC 1014: 1989); Part 9: 1992 *Guide to the block diagram technique* (IEC 1078: 1991); Part 10 *Guide to reliability testing* Section 10.1: 1993 *General requirements* (IEC 605-1: 1978), Section 10.3 *Compliance test procedures for steady-state availability* (IEC 1070: 1991).

BS 6548: *Maintainability of equipment* Part 1: 1984 *Guide to specifying and contracting for maintainability* (IEC 706–1: 1982); Part 2: 1992 *Guide to maintainability studies during the design phase* (IEC 706–2: 1990) Part 3: 1992 *Guide to maintainability verification, and the collection, analysis and presentation of maintainability data* (IEC 706-3: 1987); Part 4: 1993 *Guide to the planning of maintenance and maintenance support* (IEC 706-4: 1992).

BS 7165: 1991 *Recommendations for achievement of quality in software.*

DD 198: 1991 *Assessment of reliability of systems containing software.*

ISO 9000-4: 1993 *Quality management and quality assurance standards* Part 4: *Guide to dependability programme management.*

References

Department of Trade and Industry. *Caring Enterprise and Winning World Market Share.* Department of Trade and Industry, London, 1985.

Nakajima S. *Introduction to Total Productive Maintenance.* Productivity Press, Massachusetts, USA, 1988.

CHAPTER 9

Purchasing and the importance of supplier development

9.1 Introduction

The basic objective of any purchasing function is to acquire goods and services from suppliers in the most cost-effective manner in order that the needs and expectations of the organisation's customers are met.

There is a world-wide trend towards more stringent customer expectations with regard to product and service quality. Accompanying this trend is a growing realisation that continual improvements in the quality of materials, products and services from the supplier community is necessary for corporate well-being. It is rarely sufficient for an organisation to control only the work done in their own manufacturing sites or service areas, as few businesses are self-contained to the extent that their products or services are generated at a single location from basic inputs or materials. A considerable amount of goods and services are normally purchased from outside sources. In most organisations, at least 50 per cent of sales revenue is spent on buying materials, components, commodities, assemblies or services. With the increasing specialisation of organisations on their core activities and businesses, the volume of bought-out items will inevitably increase. This emphasises the importance of the purchasing activity to the corporate function and the need for a good infrastructure of suppliers. The successful operation of most companies is to a large degree dependent upon the contribution made by their suppliers.

The purchase cycle commences with a statement of need for a particular item. After the requirement has been clearly defined, a search for a suitable source of supply is carried out. This activity usually includes the transmission of an enquiry, assessment of potential suppliers, comparison of quotations and negotiation. Once a supplier has been chosen, the next step is to send out a purchase order, for which some form of acknowledgement and agreement on the conditions of the contract are reached. In some cases there is a need to carry out purchase progressing to ensure that the supplier delivers to the agreed schedule. A check on description, quantity, damage and conformance to requirements may be carried out on the delivered supplies at the goods inwards area. The data collected on the supplier during the course of the purchase cycle, including on-going supplier assessment, is used to update performance records and a formal vendor rating scheme may be used for this activity. With the closer relationships which are now developing between many major customer organisations and their supplier communities, and the increase in single sourcing of supplies and in the number of long-term contracts which are being awarded, some features of the classical purchase cycle are diminishing in importance.

Purchased materials, components, commodities, assemblies and services become part of the company's products or services and directly affect their quality, reliability and performance. Consequently, the quality reputation of any organisation is very much dependent on the quality of its supplier base. In fact, the larger the percentage of purchased part of the goods or service, the more dependent a company becomes on its suppliers. For example, the quotation 'It is not the Ford Motor Company which builds motor cars but Ford and its suppliers' reflects common sense. It is obvious then that the procurement of purchased supplies should be carefully planned and controlled, and this should include those supplies obtained from autonomous units of the company's own organisation. A close working relationship and feedback system needs to be developed with each supplier so that they see themselves as an extension of their customer's operations. In this way a process of continuous quality improvement can be maintained which will benefit both the purchaser and supplier; it is in both their self-interests to strive for never-ending improvement in the quality of products and services.

This chapter discusses the issues involved in the development of suppliers and the role of purchasing and quality assurance departments in this activity.

9.2 Specifications and purchase orders

The successful procurement of supplies begins with a clear definition of the requirements. The purchasing department must ensure that the R & D, design, production/operations, engineering/technical and quality assurance departments are specifying exactly what they want. Usually these requirements are contained in the contract specifications and purchase orders which are provided to the supplier.

The purchasing function should have adequate methods to ensure that the requirements for the supplies are clearly defined, communicated and, most importantly, are completely understood by the supplier. These methods may include written procedures for the preparation of specifications and purchase orders, vendor/purchaser conferences prior to purchase order release, and other methods which are appropriate for the supplies or services being procured.

The purchasing organisation has the right to receive that which it has specified but, in turn, it must make clear to the supplier precisely what is required in a timely manner. A number of the problems encountered in the supply chain stem from poor communication between purchaser and supplier. It is not uncommon to find that supplier non-conformances are caused by incorrect and out-of-date data, and specifications being communicated by the purchaser to supplier or held by the supplier. Procurement problems can also be aggravated by inadequate specifications, restriction of supply sources, or excessive variety. Lines of communication should be established to ensure that changes in orders or specifications are dealt with correctly and implemented and supplier queries answered satisfactorily. It is also important for both parties to reach agreement on the terminology likely to be used during the course of the contract. Crosby (1982) claims that 50 per cent of a company's problems are caused by non-conforming purchased goods and Ishikawa (1985) claims that at least 70 per cent of the blame for this lies with the customer.

The purchasing documents contain data which should clearly describe the product or service ordered. These include:

- the precise identification of type, class, style grades or other forms of identification;
- a complete, unambiguous set of functional requirements;
- the title or other positive identification, and applicable issue of specifications, drawings, process requirements, inspection instructions and other relevant data, including requirements for approval or qualification of product, service procedures, process equipment and personnel;
- the quality system standard to be applied.

British, European or international Standards

should always be considered the preferred method for the ordering of goods, but a careful study is essential before quoting a standard. It is often necessary to quote a grade or type in addition to the standard, and many of the standards include a clause titled 'Information to be supplied by the purchaser' which will give guidance on what is needed.

Where a standard includes a number of grades, or where it is necessary to supply a considerable amount of additional information, it becomes worthwhile to prepare a company standard to avoid lengthy descriptions on drawings and ordering documents. Such a procedure also enables guidance on the choice to be given, thus assisting variety reduction. For instance, to order electric motor commutator bars according to BS 1433 (1970), it is necessary to state, in addition to dimensional information, the following:

- the designation of the material required;
- the method and frequency of sampling for electrical tests;
- whether a certificate of compliance is required;
- whether it is the purchaser's intention to inspect the material at the supplier's works.

By preparing a simple, one-page company standard covering this detail, all that needs to appear on the drawing is 'copper-silver to purchasing specification 15/021'.

The purchasing department should review the accuracy and completeness of purchasing documents before their release to the supplier. In a number of organisations these documents are also sent to the quality assurance department for their comments prior to transmission to the supplier.

The company purchase specification differs from the catalogue in that it specifies one material, component or type as well as limiting factors and additional requirements outside the supplier's normal range. It also specifies requirements that are not appropriately covered by a national, European or international standard.

The purchase specification is a procurement document and should unambiguously specify the requirements. It is usually couched in technical terms and is personally authorised by the manager responsible for purchasing. Purchase specifications reduce the need for detail on the purchase order and record negotiated contract terms. As such they are employed more frequently by companies who subcontract. They may be produced in two parts: one for internal use listing approved suppliers, internal quality control procedures and application notes, and the other for issue to the supplier.

The purchasing organisation should encourage the supplier to recognise and challenge any feature or characteristic of the specification which is unclear or with which they may have difficulty during the course of manufacture or operation. It is also vital that the supplier understands what are the critical quality characteristics and features of the product or service being supplied.

9.3 The use of standards in purchasing

Bought-out materials may be controlled by classifying and cataloguing at the introduction stage, that is at design and development. This facilitates identification, variety control, purchase specification, evaluation of suppliers and manufacturers and provides a ready and reliable means of communicating design and purchasing data throughout the company. An organisation must be prepared to: vet all new introductions by comparing with existing standards, allocating a code for use on drawings and bills of material, producing a purchase description and perhaps adding supplementary data such as shelf-life for materials which deteriorate with age, health and safety information for items covered by COSHH regulations or test instructions for some electrical or electronic components. The data must then be reliably recorded in the database.

Everyone has some influence as a buyer, whether it be of raw materials, electronic components, tools, fasteners, paper, office equipment, clothing, canteen equipment or food. A study of the costs in each person's own area of responsibility will reveal at least one in which variety control and/or proper specification could reduce the expenditure and improve purchasing and stores efficiency. The person responsible for standards should provide a service to the buyer by checking specifications, suppliers' type numbers and subsequent alterations or departures caused by lack of availability.

Standards to assist purchasing, include:

- design selection guides for processes, materials and components. These comprise data sheets incorporating extracts from external standards or suppliers' data sheets. They are intended to indicate a preference to the designer.
- performance standards for evaluation of alternative sources or recording limits and tolerance for application. They specify in a comprehensive manner the ratings and characteristics of the items and their approved sources.
- bought-out components/materials catalogue. This comprises a classified index of all items giving concise data and part code for internal use.

The functions of the catalogue include:

- the communication of data on parts that are in stock or in current use, including:
  - identity code for repetition on parts list and stores locations;
  - purchase specification, to assist the buyer;
  - inspection and test instructions, for checking goods in;
  - design application data, so that the parts are used correctly;
  - health and safety information;
- acting as an index or guide to company preferred or stock items;
- classification to avoid proliferation of similar parts.

Every item must be coded so that the description of the item to be kept up-to-date with the latest standards or amendments of suppliers' type number can be updated by amending the catalogue entry independently of the parts list or drawing calling it up. It also means that suppliers can quickly and easily be added to, or deleted from, items in the catalogue.

The control and specification of bought-out raw materials, components, plant and equipment, spares and consumables require particular attention. Since procurement problems can be aggravated by inadequate specification, restriction of supply sources or excessive variety, improvements in these areas should be considered as a priority.

In areas where standardisation has not been introduced, components may be specified by a development engineer through the design drawing office to production planning and hence to the buyer or procurement. The potential dangers of this chain can be reduced by standardisation of the purchasing description which is specified on the order. This also provides the opportunity to vet new additions so that unnecessary variety is avoided.

Too frequently a buyer is provided with a trade name or single supplier's type number, which restricts the purchasing options. Or it may be that he cannot take advantage of an offer of a better product from a supplier with whom the organisation has a long-term relationship because he cannot locate the specifier.

The appropriate specialists should carry responsibility for the provision of data, but in any event the purchasing department will be involved by:

- maintaining a catalogue of components/materials used;
- compiling an adequate purchasing description;
- comparing with national, European or international standards, wherever possible;
- specifying alternative suppliers;
- specifying quality control procedures;
- providing design guides on preferred components;
- controlling variety;
- providing a code which can be used rather than specifying trade names.

Proper cataloguing of all company purchases can offer many savings as a result of control of variety. Clear and precise specification should be insisted on to obtain:

- reduction in the quantity of purchase orders;
- saving of capital through elimination of unnecessary stock;
- reduction of purchasing paperwork and improvement in efficiency;
- improvement in terms and conditions of purchase;
- reduction of storekeeping and inspection overheads through reduction of the variety of stock items;
- improvements in quality and reliability through more regular usage and accurate specifications.

9.4 Selection of qualified suppliers

Effective purchasing demands the selection of suitable suppliers and sub-contractors. This will involve some form of assessment of the supplier's capability to meet all the requirements of the specifications and purchase order. Failure to find and develop satisfactory relationships with suppliers will necessitate additional quality assurance and control activities on the part of the purchaser.

The methods of establishing this capability may include any combination of the following:

- on-site assessment and evaluation of supplier's commercial, technical, research and development and quality capability, evaluation of the quality system and the commitment of the senior management team to TQM and continuous improvement;
- supplier performance and quality trends;
- past history with similar supplies;
- experience and results with similar supplies;
- experience of other users of the supplier;
- evaluation of product samples or examples of the service.

As the quality of products or services can be most easily controlled at the point of manufacture or operation, purchasers should assess potential suppliers before orders are placed and, wherever possible, measure their performance in complying with the requirements of specification(s). This grading or assessment of the supplier's quality assurance procedures and performance needs to be done on a continuous basis, so that the resultant vendor assessment will give a rating for comparison purposes.

Most enlightened organisations have moved away from placing sole reliance on inspection and checking towards a more rigorous assessment of the supplier's ability to satisfy the purchaser's needs. This involves continuing surveillance of the supplier's quality assurance organisation and procedures, and commitment of the senior management team to TQM. Alternatively, such evaluation and surveillance might be carried out by an independent third party in the form of a certification scheme. This can be particularly advantageous where standardised products or services are involved. For organisations which may not be able to build up elaborate vendor/vendee relationships, third-party certification can also give the purchaser some degree of assurance. The subject of certification has already been discussed in Chapters 2 and 7.

9.5 Agreement on quality assurance

A clear understanding must be developed and reached between supplier and purchaser on the quality assurance for which the supplier is responsible. The purchaser needs to have confidence that the quality is being, or will be, achieved in the delivered product or service provided by the supplier. When contractually required, this provision of confidence may involve a demonstration of requirements. The assurance to be provided by the supplier may vary as follows:

- the purchaser relies on the supplier's quality system;
- submission by the supplier of specified inspection/test data or process control records; this also includes initial samples and records;
- 100 per cent inspection/checking/testing by the supplier;
- lot acceptance inspection/testing by sampling

carried out by the supplier,

- implementation of a formal quality system as specified by the purchaser;
- none – the purchaser relies on receiving inspection, checking or in-house sorting.

The assurance provision will be commensurate with the needs of the purchaser's business. In certain cases, formal quality systems may be involved, as described in Chapter 7. This may include a periodic assessment of the supplier's quality system by the purchaser.

The purchaser and supplier also need to reach agreement on the methods by which conformance to purchasers' requirements will be verified. Such agreements may include the exchange of data with the aim of facilitating quality improvements. Reaching agreement can minimise difficulties in the interpretation of requirements as well as inspection, test or sampling methods. It is not uncommon to find that the customer rejects the product and sends it back to the supplier. The supplier retests it, verifies that it is correct and ships it back to the customer. A frequent cause of supplies going around in this type of circle is often due to different test equipment and methods being used by suppliers and purchasers.

It is important that systems and procedures are in place to allow settlement of quality disputes to be reached between purchaser and supplier, and such provisions should deal with routine and non-routine matters.

9.6 Vendor assessment and rating

Vendor assessment – general

The objective of an assessment is to give the customer a level of confidence in a supplier's capability to supply consistently products or services to the specified requirements. It also gives suppliers an evaluation of their own methods of operation. The purpose of the initial assessment is to judge if the supplier can provide what is required and if a good working relationship can be built up. It also promotes the assurance and control of quality at the point of production or operations. It is important that the vendor knows why they are being assessed in order to get their commitment to the assessment programme.

A vendor assessment and audit should always be carried out in the post-order stage to assess aspects such as: the adequacy of the supplier's quality system, management controls, production/operations facilities and capacity, technical ability, the financial position of the company, industrial relations record, organisation structure, organisational efficiency, management style, ability to ensure continuity of supply and future development plans. Some of the assessment factors will remain relatively static and require little further assessment. However, it is usual to repeat the assessment at regular intervals.

Prior to assessment it is usual to notify the supplier of the scope of the audit, dates, the key people required to be available and the agenda. There are a variety of ways in which the initial assessment can be carried out. In some cases the purchasing department will first undertake, as a screening process, a commercial assessment of the supplier. If satisfactory, the quality assurance department will then examine the supplier's quality assurance procedures, methods and systems. The assessment can also be a team effort carried out jointly by purchasing, quality, and technical/engineering personnel. The current trend is to place more emphasis on the assessment of the supplier's quality system and commitment to TQM than on commercial considerations.

In evaluating a supplier, various factors have to be taken into consideration. This involves a survey of the supplier in which data is collected. The usual means of gathering the data is by some form of check sheet or survey form to give discipline and structure to the approach. One method is to send the supplier the survey form to complete. This helps to minimise the information collected during the on-site visit. Once this is received, it is assessed and evaluated. A visit to the supplier is then arranged, during which the answers provided in the questionnaire are checked and additional data are collected. An alternative method is just to carry out an on-site assessment. The survey form, while it will contain specific questions, is not intended to limit the rôle of the assessors/auditors carrying out the survey.

The on-site assessment activity requires a certain amount of judgement and experience on the part of the assessors and to some degree it needs to be disciplined. The assessors must also develop listening and observatory skills and investigate examples of specific supplier procedures. It should not be forgotten that some suppliers will resort to elaborate methods of camouflage to try and fool the assessor(s). In both methods it is usual, in order to build-up data on the supplier profile, to use secondary sources such as published accounts, private investigators and purchasing intelligence.

The assessment is very much in the hands of the assessors. The conduct of the assessors must be totally professional and personalities must not be allowed to cloud judgements. At IBM, Havant they have stated guidelines for assessment:

> a) The nominated spokesman for the meeting will be the only spokesman for IBM unless other team members are requested by him to contribute.
> b) The team must agree the observations, significances and the general corrective actions that would satisfy IBM prior to meeting with the vendor for final review. This is to avoid internal disputes.
> c) The team must be professional and clear in their statements to the vendor at all times.
> d) The conduct of all auditors must be above reproach.
> e) Once the agenda has been officially agreed it is most important that punctuality is observed and any timing changes officially notified to the vendor.
>
> (Jeffries, 1985)

Stanger *et al.* (1992) in discussing the development of the Assessor Registration Scheme outline the skills and attitudes which are required of an assessor; they make the point that an understanding of the aptitudes outlined forms the basis of any system of qualification. The following key points have been extracted from their paper:

- attitude to people – assessors must understand people and enjoy working with them;
- open-minded;
- fair-minded;
- single-minded;
- good judgement is vital;
- they need courage to make their conclusions known;
- they need lots of integrity.

Vendor assessment – quality

A number of major purchasers have developed their own quality system standard, against which a supplier's ability to comply consistently with the standard is assessed. Others review the supplier's quality system against a national or internationally recognised standard, for example the BS 5750/ISO 9000 Series.

The supplier quality assurance assessment survey is a comprehensive physical review conducted at a supplier's production/operation facility to evaluate the quality system from receipt of purchased goods or services to the delivery of the final product/service. After the initial assessment, and if an order is placed, supplier quality assurance personnel will periodically review the supplier's facilities, product/service characteristics, process parameters, procedures, systems, controls and performance. This is to assure the customer organisation that conformance to the assessed quality system is being maintained at least; more enlightened customers are looking for improvement. The frequency at which reassessments are carried out is dependent upon factors such as the current quality performance of the supplier, vendor rating score, the classification awarded to the supplier, the type of product/service supplied, the volume being supplied, when a major change (for example, change of management, facilities, operations and processes) has occurred at the supplier organisation and at the request of suppliers. The programme of assessments are to help supplier and purchaser to achieve quality improvements through joint activities.

At the end of the assessment a discussion takes place between the interested parties in the customer organisation to consider the potential of the supplier to become a long-term business partner. The final decision to use the supplier is made after due consideration of all the quality and commercial issues. Some form of summary or classification of the supplier assessment is usually produced. These classifications typically relate to commodity/material groups.

Among the major manufacturers in the UK, the Ford Motor Company have been one of the most active in the assessment of their suppliers. Therefore, it may be interesting to readers to consider, in brief, how Ford tackle vendor assessment.

The Ford Motor Company review the supplier's quality system, its implementation and operation as part of an overall supplier rating system. The other elements being supplier senior management awareness and commitment to total quality excellence (Ford's name for TQM) and supplier on-going quality performance. The Ford Supplier Quality System Survey Report is shown in Appendix H (Ford Motor Company, 1990). The degree of adequacy and compliance is measured by assigning a numerical value (maximum 10), to each of the 20 question in the system survey report. The sum of these values is then converted into equivalent points which constitutes the relative weight of this criterion to the overall supplier quality rating. Conformance to Ford Q–101 requires at least a 5 rating on each individual question and at least a 140 overall system survey rating. The supplier quality engineer provides a quality system survey report to the company which outlines, for each question, his or her reasoning and business judgement for the rating given along with a summary of the supplier's procedures and system. When appropriate, a list of recommendations and deficiencies are also given. The SQA engineer reviews the report with appropriate producer management personnel who have the authority to make corrective action commitments.

Assisting suppliers to improve their ability to produce conforming products or services is a prime objective of the supplier quality assistance operation. In certain cases, the system survey may disclose conditions which indicate that the supplier needs assistance from appropriate Ford Motor Company specialists. If any of the items in the system survey were found to be unsatisfactory (less than seven out of ten), they are required to submit to the Ford purchasing department a written, timed corrective action plan within 30 days. The corrective action plan will be agreed by all parties and the supplier's progress will be monitored against the plan.

Vendor rating

Vendor rating is used in the post-contract stage to measure and assess the supplier's actual performance. It should ensure that the best possible sources are used and provides a quantitative base on which to control and improve supplier performance. The comparison of the supplier can be made against a company standard in order to classify a supplier into a particular category. It can also be made against the supplier's previous performance on a past order or against other suppliers' performance from the same commodity grouping. The aspects of supplier performance which are usually measured are: quality conformance, delivery reliability, quantity delivered, price and after-sales service. The schemes are usually administered by the purchasing department. In some organisations it is not unusual to find that the only measure being taken of supplier performance is a quality rating, and when this is the case the measurement and reporting is the responsibility of the quality assurance department.

There are a number of benefits accruing to both parties from measuring supplier performance, including:

- help the Supplier Quality Assurance (SQA) activities to prioritise their efforts in assisting suppliers to improve their performance;
- provide important feedback to suppliers, pin-pointing their shortcomings and areas for improvement;
- evaluate what it has cost the customer organisation to do business with a supplier;
- aid the purchasing department in sourcing decisions;
- help to focus attention on the purchasing and quality assurance department's own performance and inadequacies;
- determine whether or not a supplier has

achieved the status required (a number of organisations are now setting targets, for example 99 per cent conforming batches and deliveries to within plus or minus one day).

The objective of measuring supplier performance is to further the improvement process. The aim should be to use schemes which are fully understood by both parties, and suppliers must be given regular information by the customer organisation about their performance. The use of vendor rating schemes are not without problems. For example, they require a considerable amount of subjective judgement, they can be time-consuming, and care needs to be exercised in ensuring that suppliers are not penalised for inefficiencies in the customer organisation. The following paragraph outlines some recent research evidence on the subject of vendor rating schemes.

In a questionnaire survey of 116 organisations, which focused on quality-related decision making, Duncalf and Dale (1985) found that although 71.6 per cent of the companies laid down conditions on vendors for effective control over quality, only 29.3 per cent of the 116 operated a vendor rating scheme and of these only half of them passed the ratings onto their suppliers. More recently, Lascelles and Dale (1988), in a questionnaire survey of 348 suppliers to the automotive industry, found that 61.5 per cent used a vendor rating scheme. In a questionnaire survey on the introduction and use of SPC in 158 automotive suppliers. Dale *et al.* (1989) found that 51.0 per cent operate a vendor rating scheme, 25.0 per cent said they planned to introduce such a scheme, and a further 18 per cent said they had no firm plans. According to this work, previous performance, a commitment to quality and technical competence were the major criteria used in sourcing decisions by those organisations which did not operate a vendor rating scheme.

A wide variety of vendor rating schemes exist. These range from keeping informal records of supplier performance to formal schemes based on a numerical formulae, and the variety of formulae which can be used is vast. In general, these numerical rating schemes use some form of weighting to indicate the relative importance of the factors of supplier performance which is to be measured. Any reader wishing to investigate the formulae used in these schemes may find it useful to consult the *International Journal of Purchasing and Materials Management*.

In discussing supplier assessment, the system employed by the Ford Motor Company was given as an example. It may be useful then to outline the criterion used by Ford in measuring on-going supplier quality performance.

The performance is measured by an assessment of the quality of supplier product and services as follows:

- at the supplier manufacturing location,
- quality experience upon receipt or use, of products at Ford locations,
- quality experience of a supplier's products as reported by customers who have purchased Ford products or Ford internal evaluations of its products.

This criterion has a maximum attainable rating score of 50 points. Deficiencies in the quality of products and services will be assessed and demerit points (see Table 9.1 overleaf) awarded that are subtracted from the 50 points.

Ford calculate the total quality rating of a supplier by the summation of the rating given for each of the following three individual criteria:

- $$\text{Adequacy of supplier quality system} = \frac{\text{Total system survey rating points}}{200} \times 30$$

  The 30 is the relative weighting.
- Supplier management awareness and commitment. This criterion measures the supplier management awareness and commitment in bringing about continuous improvement in the quality and productivity of products and services and responding to quality concerns. The three factors considered in assessing this element are: understanding/commitment/quality planning; training; and management controls/implementation. This criterion carries 20 points.

Table 9.1 Quality performance factors and demerit points

Factor	Demerit points
Incoming rejections	2 points per incoming rejection
Product audit deficiency, or lot rejection at source	2 points for each incident
Accumulated (line collected) rejects	0 or 1 points/rejection report
– Accumulated rejects for castings and forgings after Ford machining	0/rejection report
Stop shipment, purge action, or serious quality concern	5 points each
Vehicle/unit hold	10 points/incidence
Field service action	10 points each
Customer warranty	5 points/incidence
Use deviation – supplier fault	2 points each
Initial samples/ preliminary process capability study (self-certification anomaly)	2 points, each initial sample, having minor errors or variations from requirements. 5 points, each initial sample, having serious errors or variations from requirements.

- On-going quality performance which carries a 50 point weighting.

Based on the results of the numerical rating of the three criterion outlined above, suppliers will be classified into one of the following categories:

- *Excellent* (85–100): a supplier that maintains for at least 6 months a minimum score of 85 points with all elements being rated acceptable. All questions on the quality system survey must have a score of 7 or above.
- *Satisfactory* (minimum 70): a supplier must achieve a minimum score of 70 points and each element must be rated acceptable. Quality system survey scores must be at least 140 with no questions rated below 5.
- *Unsatisfactory* (below 70): a supplier in this category has failed to achieve a minimum score of 70, or has failed to achieve an acceptable rating for one or more elements, and/or has a score of less than 5 for one or more questions in the systems survey report.

Most major purchasers have a system by which suppliers who have achieved a satisfactory assessment of the quality system and which maintain a particular level of supplied product performance, qualify for direct shipment to the customer, without any receiving inspection. For example Ford Motor Company Q1 Preferred Quality Audit (Ford Motor Company, 1990). The status is related to specific products, services or processes, or to the total operation. This certified or preferred supplier status is recognised and rewarded by plaques, certificates and at ceremonies. Suppliers which have achieved this status are often given preference in future business dealings. It is worth noting that there are competitive advantages for the supplier in being recognised as a preferred source of supply to a major customer.

Responsibilities

The issue of responsibilities relating to suppliers has already been touched upon in this chapter. It is important that regular meetings take place between purchasing, quality and engineering/technical personnel to discuss suppliers and that these functions work closely together. The organisation must ensure consistency and fairness in its dealings with the supplier community.

The typical responsibilities for supplier performance at the Ford Motor Company are as follows:

Supplier quality assessment

- Evaluate suppliers within the responsibility of the supplier quality engineering activity and develop a rating based on the rating criteria.
- Based on the rating results, classify suppliers as excellent, satisfactory or unsatisfactory.
- Communicate the supplier ratings and classifications to the appropriate purchasing

personnel and, as required, product engineering activities.

- In conjunction with purchasing and product engineering (when appropriate), review and evaluate corrective action plans submitted by suppliers who have deficiencies and/or rated unsatisfactory. Advise Ford Purchasing on the adequacy and timeliness of the plans to improve the supplier's quality performance.
- Review all supplier ratings at the specified frequency to assure current status.

Purchasing

- Receive supplier rating results and classifications from SQA activities, and notify suppliers accordingly. Ford purchasing firmly believe that they should share the assessment results with suppliers.
- Follow up with suppliers who have deficiencies and/or rated unsatisfactory to assure timely development of corrective action plans to improve quality performance and rating.
- Use supplier quality ratings when making sourcing decisions. Comparisons of supplier ratings should be made only within a commodity group.
- Develop alternative sourcing plans for suppliers who are unable or unwilling to implement positive actions to achieve a satisfactory level of performance within the prescribed time period.

9.7 Receiving inspection/test, planning and controls

The supplies which have been received need to be properly controlled from receipt through the goods-inward procedure to placing the products or materials into stores, or directly into production. The procedure sometimes includes some form of quarantine area to prevent unqualified supplies being used until they have been verified.

The extent to which receiving inspection or test will be performed by a purchaser needs to be planned carefully. The level of inspection/test, when it is deemed necessary, should be selected with a consideration of the overall costs involved. It should be remembered that any receiving inspection or test is a non-value adding activity. In addition, when the decision has been made to perform an inspection/test, it is necessary to select with care the characteristics to be inspected or tested. The subject of acceptance sampling inspection will be discussed in some detail in Chapter 14.

In determining the amount and nature of inspection applied to the delivered goods, consideration needs to be given to the controls exercised at source by the supplier and the documented evidence of quality conformance. If a supplier has an effective quality system, the purchaser may reduce the level and amount of incoming inspection or test. It should be apparent, however, that the purchaser's knowledge of a supplier's product, service and/or system quality stems primarily from proven performance, the records the supplier furnishes and any previous assessment of the supplier's quality system. As confidence in the supplier's ability is built up, the purchaser can move from sampling inspection to skip lot inspection then to auditing of incoming batches and finally to direct line supply, if this is applicable to the industry and processes concerned.

In discussing goods receiving inspection it is worth mentioning purchaser supplied material. This is material owned by the purchaser and furnished to the supplier for use in meeting the requirements of the contract. When the supplier takes delivery, there is an acceptance of full responsibility for freedom from damage, identification, maintenance, storage, handling and use while the material is the supplier's possession.

It is usual for the supplier to ensure that there are satisfactory arrangements for the following:

- examination of the material upon receipt to check the quantity received and its identity and to detect any damage in transit. The receipting of goods is usually required by a company's auditors;
- periodic inspection during storage to detect any signs of deterioration, to check on limitations of time in storage, to assure maintenance of proper conditions and to determine

the current state of the material;

- compliance with any contractual requirements for reinspection or retest;
- appropriate identification and safeguarding of the supplied material to prevent any unauthorised use or improper disposal.

Procedures should exist detailing the manner in which unsuitability is reported to the purchaser.

9.8 Developments in the purchaser–supplier relationship

Traditional

The traditional relationship between the customer and its supplier community is an adversarial one, with the customer and suppliers having different objectives. The focus always tends to be on negative issues and is characterised by uncertainty. The search for who is to blame in such adversial situations creates a distance between customer and supplier and their people. Suppliers are kept at arms length and provided with only the bare minimum of data on issues such as production schedules, financial information, future work programmes, product or service changes and their own performance ratings. In general, suppliers are regarded with a certain amount of suspicion by the customer. On the other hand, the customer is seen by suppliers as not being concerned about their future business prospects and very much price driven in contractual negotiation; product and service quality is treated as a secondary consideration. If a customer starts to place some emphasis on product and service quality, the typical reaction from suppliers is 'You can have quality but at a higher price.' The situation may be likened to a game of cat and mouse.

In the traditional relationship, if the customer has not provided feedback data on performance, the supplier management team tend to believe that their performance is acceptable to the purchaser. Most suppliers are not encouraged to ask the purchaser how their product or service is performing in practice. Lack of feedback on quality performance is a frequent complaint among suppliers. Suppliers, however, do react to differing demands and prior experience of their customers. An example of this is the grading of products into different quality levels according to individual customer requirements. If a product will not get accepted at Company X, then Company Y will take it – Company X are considered super meticulous.

To protect themselves in this uneasy relationship with suppliers, the customer will employ a multiple-sourcing strategy, resulting in a large supplier base. Writers on the subject of single versus multiple sourcing cite a number of reasons to support the practice of multiple sourcing. The main ones include: it provides some security in the event of strikes, natural disasters and supplier takeovers; it gives some flexibility to cater for changes in demand (increase or decrease) for the supplies; it helps to off-set poor planning in the customer; it reduces stocks; it protects against a monopoly situation; it facilitates competition and price-related reasons – one supplier can be played off against another. A number of these reasons can be classified as defensive.

Another characteristic of the traditional relationship is that the customer will not have clearly defined responsibilities and accountability for the total quality performance of the supplier base. It is not uncommon to find that a number of people and departments are requesting and providing information to suppliers but no single area is taking overall responsibility. The points of contact are frequently ill-defined resulting in uncoordinated data flow. In particular, the allocation of responsibilities between the purchasing department and quality assurance department are not clear; purchasing personnel often view assistance from quality assurance as interference. This results in weaknesses in the communication system and procedures used by the customer in their dealing with suppliers.

Supplier development

Many organisations have come to realise that having a good supplier base is one of the key factors to their achieving corporate improvement and profit goals. Corporate strategies have to be adjusted to take this fact into account. The suppliers should also realise that if their customers are doing well then they will benefit – the purchaser and supplier have a common goal. For the partnership to work it depends on commitment from both customer and supplier. How a customer can develop a good working and mutually beneficial relationship with its supplier base as equal business partners still remains a major issue and this may be approached in a variety of ways by different organisations. Irrespective of the approach used there has to be a new mood of co-operation, trust, openness, guidance and dependency between purchaser and supplier, and this is vital to supplier improvement over the longer term; both parties must recognise that this is a co-operative effort. Clear changes need to take place in the customer/supplier relationship, but they will take time to develop, see Dale *et al.* (1994) and Galt and Dale (1991) for details. Some of these changes are discussed below.

In order for a supplier to provide the supplies which are required, when they are required and of the required quality standard, major customers must make serious attempts to communicate to suppliers this data, provide visibility of potential business, keep them informed of changing requirements and, based on a set of common objectives, to reach a level of understanding with them. This entails a commitment from both parties to learn more about each other's business including problems and frustrations. In this the purchaser must recognise that the supplier has expertise and experience and they must be prepared to use this. The purchaser must encourage the supplier to take initiatives in suggesting methods of quality improvement, to both the product/service and system. There are a number of ways of doing this, including suppliers being involved by the customer at the product development and design stage in order to make use of the supplier's technical ability and to exploit more fully the product/service to be supplied, joint problem-solving activities with supplier and customer striving to improve the product and reduce its cost, supplier days and supplier conferences. During such activities the supplier must demonstrate that they wish to get at the root cause of the problem and are not just putting in quick fixes and curing symptoms.

To assist their suppliers some customers have articulated and documented the fundamental requirements for the control and assurance of quality and achievement of quality improvement. It is a requirement of the purchase order agreement that suppliers must ensure that their product complies with these requests. For example, Ford have published their Ford Q–101 – Quality System Standard (1990) and Nissan Motor Manufacturing (UK) have their Quality Standard (1991). The Nissan Supplier Quality Statement is as follows:

> The Nissan Quality Philosophy is one of commitment to customer satisfaction through continuous improvement in quality, safety and reliability.
>
> The supplier has total responsibility for the delivery of zero defect products and will establish quality systems accordingly. These systems will include the continual review and development of management, product design, material specification and manufacturing processes.
>
> The development of mutual trust and co-operation will bring about quality and productivity improvements to the shared benefit of both supplier and Nissan.
>
> (Nissan Motor Manufacturing (UK), 1991)

Before leaving the subject of communications, it is important to recognise that suppliers know exactly who they should talk to in the customer organisation. Lascelles and Dale (1988) have found the best results are achieved when the chief executive of the respective customer and supplier organisation set up communication links with each other. Open communications can also be promoted through the medium of SPC.

To develop this new relationship, considerable changes in behaviour and attitude are required in the customer and supplier. Customers have to be prepared to develop plans and procedures for working with suppliers and to commit resources to this. On the other hand, suppliers have to accept full responsibility for the quality of their product and services, and not rely on the customer to verify that the product/service is to specification. A requirement of any relationship is that an agreement of understanding is reached between the two parties on how they are going to work together – the ground rules. Presentations are sometimes made by customers to their existing suppliers outlining the desired approach, the quality system standard to be used, and the way that suppliers' performance will be assessed. For example, Ford have produced a video, *Ford Cares About Quality* to assist with this task.

A search is made to find new suppliers with a clear vision on TQM and having the same quality improvement aspirations as the major customer. At Nissan, potential new suppliers attend a meeting where the senior management team outline the Nissan philosophy and requirements on product quality, and encourage suppliers to exchange ideas with them in any areas of concern. IBM, Havant, take considerable care and time in ensuring their suppliers know the exact location and importance of a particular material, part or sub-assembly in the final product. They hold what is termed a 'road show' when they visit suppliers with their product. Supplier personnel are encouraged to examine where any particular item fits into the final product and also to ask questions of the IBM representatives. British Aerospace Defence Dynamics conduct regular review clinics at their R & D site (Stevenage) and manufacturing site (Lostock) (through a video link) with each of the main suppliers. These clinics typically discuss issues pertaining to all three parties, the supplier's delivery and quality ratings and relevant component requirements on new projects.

Customers should develop long-term relationships with their suppliers and, in some organisations, contracts are now awarded for the life of a product/service. A policy of single sourcing helps to foster this relationship. This has largely been responsible for the recent reductions in the size of major customers' supplier communities. Many organisations carefully consider the number of suppliers they need and how to maintain this at an optimum level. The reduction in the supplier base results in benefits such as: less variation in the supplied product/service, the opportunity to give more business to the high-scoring vendors, an increase in the amount of time which SQA and purchasing personnel can devote to the vendors, improved and simplified communications, less paperwork, less transportation, less handling and inspection activity, and reduced cost for both parties.

It is worth mentioning that it is the policy of some customers to take only up to a certain proportion of a supplier's output – the captive supplier issue – and this sometimes results in dual sourcing. In a number of situations (for example, the strategic nature of the product/service, capacity contrasts, the calibre of supplier, technologies and in terms of long-term research and development potential), it is preferable to have a dual-sourcing strategy. For example, in Japan it is usual to dual source on long-term contracts, see Dale (1990). It is easier to develop the long-term relationship if the suppliers are in close proximity to the customer. Consequently, a number of customers are now reversing their international sourcing strategies to develop shorter supply lines. This closeness is also a vital element in the increasing use of JIT purchasing. An additional advantage of the closer relationship is that if a supplier develops any form of problem, the customer gets to know of it earlier than with the traditional approach. This also has implications for distribution systems. Some companies like Exxon Chemical cannot be a close proximity supplier, because their polymer plant is in Antwerp, but they can develop a very good local distribution network.

Once the customer has assessed the adequacy of the supplier's policies, systems, procedures, and production or operational methods, and the supplier has been able to demonstrate the quality of the product/service, the inspection or checking of supplies can be reduced considerably, in some cases down to the ideal situation of direct line supply.

A number of customers have carried out some restructuring to their purchasing, quality assurance and technical departments and organisational structures (e.g. matrix management) to ensure that they have the right skills in assisting suppliers, and that their logistics and accountability are adequate in dealing with the supplier community.

Lloyd *et al*. (1994) in a study carried out on the role of the Supplier Development Team (SDT) concept used by Nissan Motor Manufacturing (UK) Ltd (NMUK) to assist in the development of its suppliers (the SDT concept represents a concentrated resource which is used by NMUK to improve its suppliers) found that suppliers were seeking to emulate the NMUK approach in a number of ways (e.g. changing their management structure, improving the rôle and status of supervisors, introducing team leaders and revising payment systems) and the NMUK approach, even though it was often more exacting, was preferred to that of its competitors. They go on to suggest the following measures which should be considered by companies wishing to develop their suppliers:

- before seeking to develop a team working relationship with suppliers ensure that the philosophy of the organisation supports teamwork;
- evaluate suppliers and make decisions as to which suppliers should be used;
- commit resources to developing suppliers and take a long-term view of the relationship;
- establish a multi-functional approach to purchasing;
- concentrate on achieving good communication links with suppliers;
- enhance trust by the sharing of information and details of plans and schedules;
- develop technological links with suppliers and ensure they are involved in the design process;
- have supplier personnel attend the organisation's training programmes;
- establish awards to recognise the best suppliers.

In general, with this new relationship, while competitive production/operational costs are stressed, less time is being spent during purchaser/supplier discussions on the contract price. The price is negotiable but the quality standard is not; moreover price is less important than the total cost of dealing with a particular supplier (i.e. total cost of acquisition). With some customers the suppliers have to justify a 'standstill' on price; others are looking for a reduction in price because of the efficiency and quality improvements brought about by the long-term relationship, joint problem solving activities and operational improvements. In short, when selecting suppliers, purchasers are being guided by criteria such as: the commitment to quality, delivery reliability, logistical aspects, technical know-how, lines of communication, development potential, ease of co-operation and problem solving ability.

The new relationship also demands a greater and faster exchange of information between supplier and customer. A number of purchasers are now encouraging electronic data interchange (EDI) with their key vendors. The exchanges relate not only to quality but cover technical requirements and specifications, production schedules, programmes, lead time, stocks and invoicing.

9.9 Definitions and terminology

The following are some useful definitions and terms used in this chapter.

Certification: the authoritative act of documenting compliance with requirements.

Certification system: a system having its own rules of procedure and management for carrying out certification.

Compliance: an indication of judgement that the product or service meets the requirements of the relevant specification or regulation; also the state of meeting the requirements.

Instruction: the written and/or spoken direction given with regard to what is to be done, including the information given in training.

Purchase specification: a specification prepared for the purpose of ordering goods and services. This term may be used in place of 'purchase order description' but it usually implies a more comprehensive specification issued as a separate document.

Qualification approval: the status given to a supplier whose product has been shown to meet all the requirements.

Quality audit: a systematic and independent examination to determine whether quality activities and related results comply with planned arrangements and whether these arrangements are implemented effectively and are suitable to achieve objectives.

Quality surveillance: the continuing monitoring and verification of the status of procedures, methods, conditions, processes, products and services, and analysis of records in relation to stated references to ensure that specified requirements for quality are being met.

Quality system: the organisational structure, responsibilities, procedures, processes and resources for implementing quality management.

Quality verification: the provision of evidence or proof that requirements for quality have been met.

Receiving inspection: inspection by the recipient of material or manufactured products as received.

Specification: the document that prescribes the requirements with which the product or service has to comply.

Supplier: the party that is responsible for the product, process or service and is able to ensure that quality assurance is exercised.

Supplier evaluation: assessment of a supplier's control of quality, carried out after placing orders.

Supplier rating: an index of the actual performance of a supplier.

Vendor appraisal: assessment of a potential supplier's capability of controlling quality, carried out before placing orders.

British Standards

BS 1433: 1970 *Specification for copper for electrical purposes. Rod and bar.*

BS 4778: *Quality vocabulary* Part 1: 1987 *International terms* (ISO 8402: 1986) (EN 28402: 1991); Part 2: 1991 *Quality concepts and related definitions.*

BS 5750: *Quality systems* Part 0: Section 0.1, 1987 *Quality systems – principal contents and applications; guide to selection and use* (ISO 9000: 1987) (EN 29000: 1987); Part 0: Section 0.2, 1987 *Quality systems – principal contents and applications: guide to quality management and quality system elements* (ISO 9004: 1987) (EN 29004: 1987); Part 1: 1987 *Specification for design/development, production, installation and servicing* (ISO 9001: 1987) (EN 29001: 1987); Part 4: 1990 *Quality systems: Guide to the use of BS 5750; Part 1, Specification for design/development production, installation and servicing; Part 2, Specification for production and installation; Part 3, Specification for final inspection list*; Part 13: 1991 *Guide to the application of BS 5750: Part 1, to the development, supply and maintenance of software* (ISO 9000–3: 1991).

BS 6548 *Maintainability of equipment* Part 1: 1992 *Guide to specifying and contracting for maintainability* (IEC 706-1: 1990).

PD 3542: 1991 *The role of standards in company quality management.*

References

Crosby P B. 'How to stem the tide of shoddy goods.' *Purchasing*, 92(9), p 51, 1982.

Dale B G. 'Japanese Manufacturing Efficiency: A Study in the Electronics Industry', *IEE Proceedings*, 137A(5), pp. 293–301, 1990.

Dale B G (Ed). *Managing Quality*, 2nd edition, Dale B G, Lascelles D M and Lloyd A, Chapter 13, 'Supplier Chain Management and Development', Prentice Hall, 1994.

Dale B G, Owen M and Shaw P. 'SPC in the motor industry: what is the state-of-the art?', *Occasional Paper Number 8902*, Manchester School of Management, UMIST, 1989.

Duncalf A J and Dale B G. 'How British industry is making decisions on product quality', *Long Range Planning*, 18(5), p 81–8, 1985.

Ford Motor Company. *The Quality System Survey and Scoring Guidelines.* Plymouth, Michigan, USA, 1990.

Ford Motor Company. *Worldwide supplier quality rating system.* Plymouth, Michigan,

USA. 1990.

Ford Motor Company. *Q1 Preferred Quality Award for Suppliers to Ford Motor Company.* Plymouth, Michigan, USA.

Galt J D S and Dale B G. 'Supplier Development: A British Case Study', *International Journal of Purchasing Materials Management*, 27(1), pp. 16–22, 1991.

Ishikawa K. *What is Total Quality Control? the Japanese Way.* Prentice Hall, New York, USA, 1985.

Jeffries M B. *Professional guide to vendor certification.* IBM Havant Procurement Procedure 46, Hamps, UK, 1985.

Lascelles D M and Dale B G. 'A study of the quality management methods employed by UK automotive suppliers. *Quality and Reliability Engineering International*, 4(4), 301–9, 1988.

Lloyd A, Dale B G and Barnes B. 'Supplier Development: A Study of Nissan Motor Manufacturing (UK) and her Suppliers'. *Proceedings of the Institution of Mechanical Engineers*, 208(3D), 1994 (to be published).

Nissan Motor Manufacturing (UK). *Nissan Quality Standard for suppliers*, Nissan Motor Iberica SA and Nissan Motor Manufacturing UK, Washington, UK, 1991.

Stanger D H, Corner P and Spencer R J. 'International Standards in support of lead assessors registration: trends and issues', *The Global Quality congress*, Singapore, June 1992.

CHAPTER 10

Manufacturing procedures

10.1 Introduction

Quality cannot be inspected into a product, first, it must be designed in, after which the manufacturing function is responsible for producing products in accordance with the design requirements. To prevent non-conforming products being made, manufacturing must be carried out under controlled conditions in the specified manner and sequence. Controlled conditions include appropriate controls for materials, production equipment, processes and procedures. In addition, the manufacturing operations should be specified by documented work instructions, good communications are needed, and all manufacturing and related personnel need to be motivated and committed to satisfying their customer needs and expectations, and to continuous quality improvement.

This chapter discusses the subject of manufacturing procedures and relates their importance to TQM.

10.2 Process/materials control

Process quality controls are required on all materials, production processes and equipment used in the manufacture of any product. The omission of a particular operation or process from the scope of such control may result in non-conforming products being made, as will ineffective or incomplete control. Procedures are also required to ensure that all materials and parts used in the manufacturing processes do conform to appropriate specifications and quality standards. This assurance is typically obtained through tests, inspection, SPC and FMEA information, incoming product control and confidence in the supplier's quality system. Where in-plant traceability of material is considered to be important to original material identification and quality status (this will be stated in the quality plan), it is necessary to maintain appropriate identification throughout the production process.

It is important that special consideration is given to production processes in which control is particularly critical to product quality. This may be required for product characteristics that are not easily or economically measured, for special skills required in their operation or maintenance, or for a product or process the results of which cannot be fully verified by subsequent inspection and test. More frequent verification of special processes will be necessary to keep a check on:

- the accuracy and variability of equipment used to make or measure the product, including setting and adjustments;

- the skill, capability and knowledge of operators to achieve the quality requirements;
- special environments, time, temperature or other factors affecting product quality;
- certification records maintained for personnel, processes and equipment, as appropriate.

It is sometimes important to particular quality characteristics of the product, that auxiliary materials and utilities, such as water, compressed air, electric power and chemicals used for processing, need to be controlled and verified periodically to ensure uniformity of effect on the process. Where a production environment, consisting of features such as temperature, humidity and cleanliness, is important to product quality, limits must be specified, controlled and verified for these features.

10.3 Process specification

There are many processes which require close control of the materials and operations, particularly those involving dangerous chemicals.

The objective of a process specification is to prescribe the steps to be taken in the manufacture of a product. A process specification is produced both as a record of the procedures used and as a quality control document to ensure that practices are not being altered without authority. During preparation it may be necessary to observe and record the procedure being used at an operating level.

The specification should be comprehensive, quoting the materials used and listing the operations in sequential order. It should also carry authorizing signatures. A typical process specification should indicate the following:

- specification reference number/identity code – for identification and retrieval;
- title;
- scope and/or notes on intended use;
- relevant specifications (company, BSI, ISO, CEN);
- safety precautions, preferably in distinctive print;
- summary of process;
- process (including inspection and test, if appropriate);
- related documents and references;
- materials and equipment;
- authorizing signatures;
- appendices, possibly providing related information such as frequency of quality checks, details of inspection and test equipment;
- revision notes;
- date of issue.

Apart from its value as an operational guide for an established process, the specification becomes a reference document which may be used for training and quality control purposes. Feedback from these areas is essential to maintain control and keep the process up-to-date with the latest developments in techniques.

An example of a process specification is BS 6446 (1984) which specifies requirements for the manufacture of structural components made from timber products that are glued together in the process of fabrication. Such a process requires the detailed specification of conditions and control of manufacturing and monitoring of individual component properties (e.g. moisture content, as well as definitive specification of appropriate adhesives and nails).

10.4 Process failure modes and effects analysis

The subject of FMEA has been discussed in Chapter 6; here just a brief outline of a process or manufacturing FMEA is given.

A process FMEA is prepared prior to production/operation and process design and involves the listing of potential failure modes and causes. It concentrates on the reasons for potential failure during manufacture and in service as a consequence of a non-compliance to specification and/or design intent. The purpose is to analyse a product's design characteristics relative to the planned manufacturing, assembly and/or clerical processes to ensure the product does meet the customer needs and expectations. The technique identifies potential process failure modes, assesses the effects on the customer of the failure, identifies the potential causes of the failure and identifies significant process variables in order to develop controls for prevention and/or detection of the failure conditions. To prepare a process FMEA a good working knowledge of the relevant processes, be they manufacturing or clerical, is required. It is always helpful to prepare a flow chart of the process which is under study.

A process FMEA helps to anticipate, resolve and/or monitor potential sources of failures and problems that may be inherent in a planned process. The planned process could be the manufacturing planning stages of both new and revised products and parts or the booking of a customer's order by the sales department. In short, it helps to formalise the mental disciplines that engineers and technologists go through in developing processing requirements. A process FMEA is also helpful in that it documents the procedures used in the process under study.

The process FMEA considers each of the processes involved, identifies what could go wrong, what safeguards exist against the failure, how often it might occur and how it might be eliminated by redesign of the item or the process. The objective is to concentrate attention on possible (or known) problems in sustaining or achieving the required quality. Assemblers of complex goods such as motor cars are well advised to insist that their component suppliers carry out such analyses, but the component manufacturers are usually the principal beneficiaries. The exercise forces a re-examination of entrenched methodology in manufacture and seldom fails to lead to cost improvements. Whilst the earlier applications of process FMEA have been in manufacturing situations there is an increasing use being made of them in non-manufacturing situations. For example, Gosling *et al.* (1992) outlines the use of FMEA at the Operations Directorate of Girobank.

The format is basically similar to that for a product FMEA but some changes are forced by the slightly different requirements. A process FMEA examines how non-conformances can arise and reach customers (internal and external), or be found by quality control procedures. It does not examine how the product may fail in service due to wear or maloperation. There is inevitably some overlap, because some defects affect the durability of the components in service, while others cause immediate or early failure.

A process FMEA should not be carried out in isolation by a planning engineer. The preparation of the FMEA should be either the responsibility of a team or the prepared FMEA should be circulated to appropriate staff who are asked to comment. Dale and Shaw (1990) in a survey on the use of FMEA found that the four main people involved with the planning engineer in the preparation of a process FMEA are the quality engineer, production engineer, first-line supervisor and process engineer.

An example of a process FMECA for machined aluminium castings is given in Appendix I.

10.5 Initial sample and first production approvals

More often than not a customer will require an initial sample (a small quantity of production output) from the supplier using production equipment and production processes for all new products, products subject to design change, and after a change in the process, equipment and manufacturing location. This sample of products will be assessed for conformance before production quantities are produced by the supplier. In some cases, initial samples are verified at the supplier's premises. The initial sample of products from the supplier will be supported by documentation such as inspection test reports and capability data – Initial Sample Inspection Reporting (ISIR). When the initial sample is approved the usual procedure is to notify the supplier of this together with instruction about first production shipments. On the other hand, if the sample is found not to conform to requirements, the supplier will be notified of any non-conformance and it is usual to ask for further samples.

Approval of the initial sample gives confidence to the customer when a new product or model has been introduced, or after changes have been made, that purchased products are to the specification at the start of volume production. The production and verification of initial samples helps to identify potential concerns and proves production methods, equipment and processes. A high level of quality non-conformance is often found on products not having initial sample approval. Most major manufacturers, for example Ford Motor Company (1990), outline procedures to their suppliers on how to prepare and submit initial samples.

The importance of the initial sample procedure must be fully understood and appreciated by both customer and supplier personnel. The success of the initial sample approval system also depends on the customer's purchasing and quality assurance departments working to the procedures which have been laid down. The requirement for initial samples will be identified on the purchase order form. Mone *et al.* (1991) found in a study of initial samples at the Leyland Daf truck assembly plant that those suppliers with ISO 9000 Series registration approval or equivalent were more likely to submit samples for the ISIR procedures than those without. However, they also go on to point out that such registered suppliers had some 30% of their initial samples rejected during the period of analysis, constituting 40% of the total suppliers' initial samples rejection.

Where organisations do not adhere to procedures it is frequently found that samples arrive late according to the schedule outlined in the purchase order, and the submitted samples do not conform for one reason or another (for example, a dimensional non-conformance and laboratory test has not been carried out). It is important that the customer ensures that it allows sufficient time in its programme for initial samples, otherwise short-cuts may be taken in obtaining production quantities.

Figure 10.1 (overleaf) from Nissan Motor Manufacturing (UK) Ltd. (1991) illustrates the timing relationship between the trial build pre-production quality assurance (PPQA) and trial build part submissions.

The development process for Nissan Products is divided into development trials and production trials; this is shown in Table 10.1 and explains the terms used in Figure 10.1.

Table 10.1 Trial build explanation

Development	Production
P-Lot: *Preliminary* The first development trial build to confirm basic characteristics, such as vehicle performance etc.	
D-Lot: *Development* The second development trial, for design confirmation and part, component and vehicle testing.	E0: First production trial build by production engineering, using D-Lot parts to study the assembly and manufacturing process.
C-Lot: *Confirmation* The third development trial, for design confirmation testing, including all modifications since D-Lot.	E1: Second production trial build by production engineering, using C-Lot parts to study the assembly and manufacturing process.
	E2: First assembly using the final production site. Off final production tooling.

Source: Nissan Motor Manufacturing (UK) Ltd (1991)

A first production shipment is the first quantity shipment manufactured in full production conditions following functional approval by the customer of the initial sample. During this first production run it is necessary to assess the capability of the significant quality characteristics. These characteristics will have been determined from the design and/or process FMEA and are those for which quality planning actions are summarised in a control plan.

The subject of advanced quality planning was discussed in Chapter 3. It is a crucial feature in the design and manufacturing of quality into the product. The quality planning process is carried through into the production of initial samples and the production of first shipment batches of product, as illustrated in Figure 10.1.

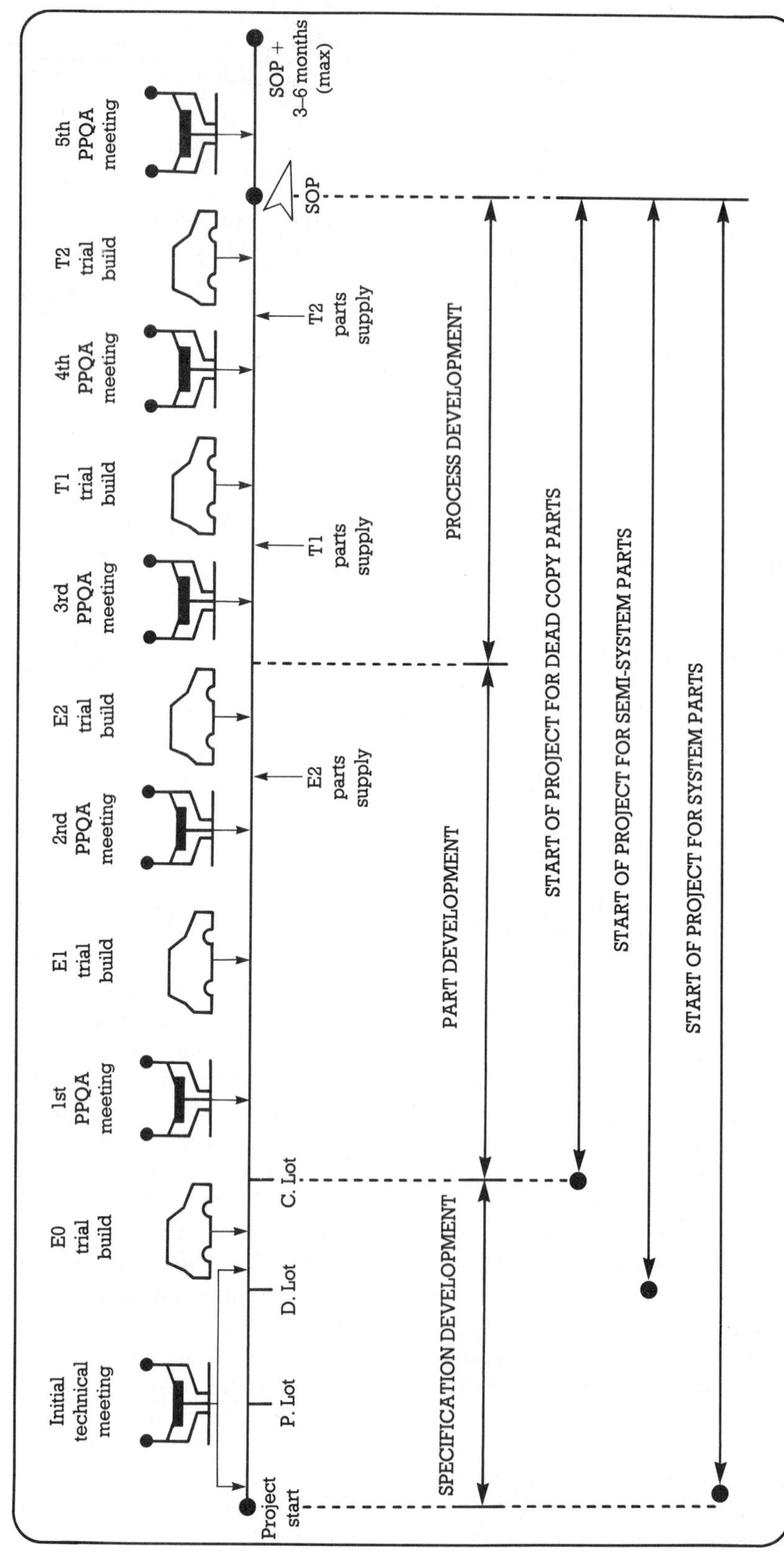

Figure 10.1 Pre-production quality assurance

Source: Nissan Motor Manufacturing (UK) Ltd (1991)

10.6 Process capability

Every operator, machine or process has inherent variability and the extent of this variation is referred to as its process capability. Consequently, there is a need to:

- establish the process capability of work methods in order to ascertain whether a task can be accomplished satisfactorily;
- establish the process capability of existing plant and, where necessary, the need to bring it up to specified requirements;
- control and monitor process capability on a continuous basis to detect and eliminate potential causes of non-conformance and variation.

Process capability is discussed at length in Chapter 15.

10.7 Equipment control and maintenance

The influence which equipment can have on the cost, design and feasibility of production is considerable. It is good practice to see that all such equipment is proved for bias and precision prior to use under production conditions. The equipment needs to be adequately identified and stored in appropriate conditions, be well protected between use, and verified or re-calibrated at appropriate intervals to ensure its bias and precision (see Chapter 12 for additional information on the subject of calibration). In a number of cases, such as a requirement of the purchase contract, equipment will have been loaned to the supplier by the customer and this will specify conditions relating to its care, storage and use. Some organisations have a written procedure where the last item or batch in the production run is inspected along with a check on the condition of the equipment, before it is put into storage awaiting the next production run. This helps to ensure that equipment is kept in good condition at all times.

A programme of preventive maintenance is important in order to ensure continuing process capability, with special attention given to equipment characteristics that contribute to key product quality characteristics. In the Ford Motor Company *Q–101 Quality System Standard* (1990) the following statement is made under the heading of planning and implementation of preventive maintenance:

> Producers must develop and maintain a documented system for routine maintenance of production equipment. Manufacturers' recommendations, tool wear, and SPC data should be considered in developing this system.

10.8 Work procedures and instructions

For controls to be effective they have to be disciplined. The omission of any particular operation or process from the scope of such control may result in the production of non-conforming product; ineffective or incomplete control usually leads to the same result. Personnel, machines and material all require disciplined control. Accordingly, manufacturing operations need to be documented by appropriate work instructions and work conducted as specified in those instructions. The instructions are a means of outlining the work to be done, and of delegating authority and responsibility. Effective communications are a prerequisite of ensuring disciplined controls.

Without written guidelines, differences in policy and procedures may arise along with some variations in practice, this results in confusion and uncertainty. Therefore, to ensure uniform evaluation by production and other personnel, and to provide an objective basis for acceptance and rejection, it is important that standards of workmanship are established. They also provide criteria for assessing the effectiveness of the control being exercised over quality and the levels of conformance of the finished product. These written standards of workmanship also provide clear and precise criteria that distinguish conforming from non-conforming products. This is also the case with samples, models, sketches and photographs. Some companies go to considerable lengths to ensure that standards, work instructions, key product features and inspections to be carried out, are displayed in prominent places in manufacturing areas. This is considered as part of their visual management system.

The procedures and work instructions, and their implementation, should, where appropriate, cover every phase of manufacture, assembly and installation. They identify each operation and, when appropriate, establish the responsibility and suitability of the personnel controlling and performing the work. They describe in detail what is to be done, how it should be done, who should do it, when should it be done, suppliers, services and equipment to be used, and criteria to be satisfied. Satisfactory work instructions include as appropriate:

- identification of the material;
- detailed operations to be performed;
- tools or test equipment required;
- the requirements for operational checks and calibration, and set up of equipment;
- precise method of inspection, check or test;
- environmental conditions to be maintained during the operation or inspection;
- criteria for passing or failing test, or on which workmanship is judged;
- sampling techniques and related decision criteria if applicable.

In addition to detailed work procedures there are often general procedures. These relate to departmental or interdepartmental methods of operation and they normally remain relatively constant within a company, regardless of the product being manufactured.

It should be noted that excessive paperwork is counter-productive and that simplicity plays an important part in efficient operation. One of the prime determinants to be made when considering a documented instruction or the need for one, is what effect the instruction will have on the performance of the work to be carried out. The ultimate test of a procedure is its ability to provide the control to achieve the result for which it was created.

The responsibilities for establishing, issuing and controlling workmanship criteria in the organisation must be clearly defined. Consideration also needs to be given to the facility for training, qualifying and periodic re-examination of personnel, where these factors are essential to workmanship. It is also important that those responsible for authorisation of process changes are clearly designated and, where necessary, approval from the customer sought before such changes are made. As with design changes, all changes to production equipment, materials and processes need to be well documented and controlled.

10.9 Inspection, check and test

It is recognised practice to provide a system of inspection, check or test, to ensure that specified requirements are satisfied. Inspections are normally performed at key points in the production sequence for the purposes of process control (to ensure the acceptability of quality characteristics that cannot be observed or measured at a later point in the process), to minimise the effects of errors or to maximise yields. The location and frequency of the inspection points will depend on the importance of the characteristics and ease of verification at the stage of production in question. When, where and how tests and inspections on completed products are to be conducted must be determined. Among the aspects to be considered are the test procedures and personnel, test equipment including its accuracy and suitability, environmental conditions for testing, and the type, completeness and accuracy of the data to be recorded. The use of control charts and statistical sampling procedures and plans are examples of techniques which can be employed to facilitate production/process control. Verifications at each stage should relate directly to finished product specifications or be an internal requirement, as appropriate. The inspection detail should be described in the quality and control plans. In general, verifications should be made as close as possible to the point of production of feature or characteristic being assessed. Verifications may include the following checks:

- set up and first piece inspection;
- inspection and test by operator;
- automatic inspection and test;

- fixed inspection stations at intervals through the production process;
- patrol inspection by inspectors monitoring specified process parameters and quality characteristics and/or operations.

In addition, it is customary in some situations to perform a final inspection and a test of the completed item/product/batch to obtain an overall measure of its conformance with requirements stipulated in terms of item performance. This includes the inspection of materials, parts and sub-assemblies before they are assembled into larger units. Two forms of final verification of completed product are available as follows:

- Acceptance inspections or tests may be used to ensure that items or batches of work produced have met performance and other quality requirements. Reference may be made to the purchase order to verify that the product to be shipped is to the specification in type and quantity. Examples include screening (100 per cent), lot sampling, skip lot sampling and continuous sampling. Acceptance testing is described in detail in Chapter 14.
- Product quality auditing of sample units, selected as representative of completed production lots, this may be either continuous or periodic.

Either or both forms may be used as appropriate.

Acceptance inspection and product quality auditing may be used to provide rapid feedback for corrective action of the product and/or process. Deficiencies or deviations should be reported, and reworked or repaired, with the modified products being subjected to re-inspection or retest.

As previously mentioned, the inspection may be accomplished in a number of ways – operator control, production line inspection stations and patrol inspection. In carrying out the inspection two basic methods may be utilised, namely:

- Inspection by attributes – each unit of product inspected is classified as conforming or non-conforming, for example 'go' or 'no go' gauging. The degree of conformity is not taken into account.
- Inspection by variables – degree of conformity is taken into account and operates by considering the measurement made.

It is necessary to establish and maintain a system for identifying the inspection status of material and assemblies during all stages of manufacture. It is important to distinguish between inspected and uninspected material by using some suitable identification such as stamps, tags, routing cards, or inspection records, that accompany the product or other control devices. There should be a positive way of knowing at all times whether a product has:

- not been inspected,
- been inspected and accepted, or
- been inspected and rejected.

The means of identification should clearly establish whether the material has undergone any process, partial assembly, final assembly, functional or final inspection. The system should also provide traceability to the unit responsible for the operation.

10.10 Control of non-conforming material

Methods for preventing regular processing, completion or delivery of non-conforming material are essential to the control and improvement of product quality. Procedures include provisions or identification, segregation and disposal to prevent unauthorised use, shipment or intermingling with conforming supplies. It is important that suspected non-conforming product be immediately identified and the occurrence recorded. When this occurs and where possible, previous production batches are examined.

Segregation can be achieved by clearly marking defective items and removing them, where appropriate, from the production line to a special holding area. The method of identifying non-conforming material will depend on the nature of the material. It should be such as to ensure that the identification is not inadvertently removed and that the material remains identified until such a time as it becomes acceptable or is otherwise disposed of. In some cases segregation may involve holding items in quarantine stores to await proof of their compliance with specification. Following inspection, conforming items are sometimes held in bonded stores to signify acceptance. Non-conforming items/batches should be sentenced appropriately for:

- reworking (if economically feasible);
- scrapping (disposal);
- resubmission under concessionary procedures.

The quality procedures will provide instructions for segregation and identification of non-conforming material, the person responsible for doing this and how it will be done. The individual(s) carrying out the review should be competent to evaluate the effects of the non-conforming unit/batch or non-conformity on interchangeability, further processing, performance, reliability, safety and aesthetics. It is important that data is recorded of non-conforming materials, including:

- material identification;
- the stage in the production process;
- the quantity involved;
- the nature and extent of the non-conformity/ non-conformance;
- engineering/technical assessment and decision on disposition;
- the disposition action taken.

The documented procedure should be supported with examples of the format to be used for markers, forms and reports.

In all cases, information concerning non-conforming material should be fed back to the appropriate parties so that action can be taken to establish and correct the cause, and prevent recurrence. The aim should be to record data on non-conformities in such a manner as to help identify those problems having a common source, contrasted with those that are unique occurrences.

It is important that concessionary procedures be clearly defined and, where appropriate, agreed between the supplier and the purchaser or representative. Where a specification has been contractually agreed, neither party has discretionary powers to depart from the agreed requirements. In cases of non-conformance, which may be considered for acceptance under concession, the purchaser's agreement should be obtained, preferably by means of a written procedure (concession form or permit), before the despatch of any products. Any concession granted is valid only for the stated (characteristic(s) and quantity in question and it is vital that it is not taken as a permanent amendment to specification.

10.11 Defect/failure analysis and corrective action

Poor work methods and non-compliance with work instructions are the frequent causes of non-conformance and failures in service. Often poor design or inadequate specifications are also the cause. As the need indicates, remedial action requires:

- changing unsatisfactory designs, specifications and work methods; or
- enforcing compliance with satisfactory designs, specification and work methods.

Prompt, effective, remedial action is essential and the segregation of unacceptable material from acceptable material is not considered to be sufficient on its own.

The significance of a problem affecting product quality should be evaluated in terms of its potential impact on such aspects as production costs, performance, reliability, safety and customer satisfaction. In some organisations it is practice to classify, for inspection purposes, non-conforming product or non-conformities into particular categories such as 'safety/ environmental', 'critical', 'major' and 'minor'.

The concept of failure is primarily related to reliability, which, in general, concerns performance in service, normally under the control of a purchaser, rather than a supplier or a manufacturer. Consequently, the classification of failures can be of particular importance not only for determining causes, but also for the allocation of responsibility for corrective action. Failures are sometimes classified under the following headings:

- cause (misuse, inherent weakness, primary or secondary, or wear out, failures);
- suddenness (whether or not the failure could have been anticipated by prior examination);
- degree (partial, complete or intermittent failures).

Classification of non-conformities and failures can be a useful aid for subsequent analysis of data accumulated and the allocation of total costs as appropriate. The implementation of corrective action begins with the detection of a quality-related problem and involves taking measures to eliminate or minimise the recurrence of the problem. Corrective action also presupposes the repair, reworking, recall or scrapping of unsatisfactory materials or items. This can be immediate involving direct actions to resolve the causes of non-conforming products or services which may be implemented during any stage of the system or operation, or involve more long-term actions.

The following are considered to be important:

- a continuing analysis of rejected products or services to determine the cause, areas of responsibility and action required, for example scrapping, reworking or concessionary procedures;
- a continuing analysis of service reports, customer complaints, or general product support/after-sales service (maintenance) department data to ensure that the performance of the service is in line with market requirements;
- that those responsible for corrective action accomplish their intended purpose at all levels and in all departments with the necessary authority and responsibility.

The responsibility and authority for instituting corrective action should be clearly defined. It is usual to assign the co-ordination, recording and monitoring of corrective action related to all aspects of the organisation or a particular product to a particular function. However, the analysis and execution may involve a variety of functions, such as sales, design, production engineering, technical, production and quality assurance.

It is important that the relationship of cause and effect is determined, with all the potential causes considered. Important variables affecting the capability of the process to meet required standards should also be identified. In the analysis of a quality-related problem, the root cause must be identified before the preventive measures are planned, otherwise there is a tendency to address only the symptoms of the problem. Often the root cause is not obvious and requires careful analysis of the product specifications and of all related processes, operations, quality records, service reports and customer complaints. There are a wide range of statistical methods which can be useful in problem analysis, a number of which are discussed in this book (see Chapters 15 and 17).

In order to prevent a future recurrence of a non-conformity, it may be necessary to change a manufacturing, packing, transit or storage process, change an instruction, revise a product specification and/or revise the quality assurance procedure and/or system. The preventive action and counter-measures put into place must be appropriate to the magnitude of potential problems, with sufficient controls of processes and procedures implemented to prevent recurrence of the problem. In some cases it is necessary to use short-term 'quick fixes', but in all cases these should be replaced by long-term corrective actions. When the preventive measures are implemented, their effect should be monitored in order to ensure that desired goals are met.

If work-in-progress is involved, the remedial action agreed upon must be instituted as soon as practical in order to limit the costs of repair, reworking, or scrapping. In addition, it may be necessary to recall finished products, whether these are in a warehouse, in transit to distributors, in stores or already in field use. Recall decisions are affected by considerations of safety, product liability and customer satisfaction. Manufacturers often use advertisements in newspapers to communicate their recall decisions and campaigns to purchasers and users of the product. This is obviously a costly activity and is in addition to the potential damage to both the product and company credibility.

Permanent changes resulting from corrective action need to be recorded in work instructions, standards, manufacturing processes, product specifications and/or the quality system. It may also be necessary to revise the procedures used to detect and eliminate potential problems.

10.12 Protection and preservation of product quality

The control of material handling is important to the protection of product quality during all phases of manufacture. It requires proper planning, control and procedure. Controls and procedures should ensure that:

- sufficient attention is given to the manner in which the material is handled and protected in process or in movement through the plant;
- special material brought in for a specific job is not mixed with similar material of unknown or dissimilar quality;
- suitable crates, boxes, containers, trucks or other transportation vehicles are used;
- in movement from one location to another adequate protection should be carried out when material is passing through areas where harmful contamination may occur;
- adequate protection for delicate parts between successive processes or in transit is provided (for example, protective covers and preservative coatings);
- when material leaves one processing station it arrives at the next one prescribed and does not miss an operation or inspection;
- the method of controlling the progression of material through the manufacturing process is adequate to prevent loss of identity;
- degradation of the quality of material is prevented.

A number of quality non-conformances are caused by handling damage, and methods, systems and handling aids that help prevent abuse, misuse and deterioration need to be employed. The damage caused by poor handling and storage can often be reduced by increasing employee awareness of the problem through briefing groups, quality improvement group activity, specific instructions, news sheets, providing examples of the damage caused by incorrect handling and similar measures.

It is important that storage areas are kept tidy and protected from undesirable environmental conditions and all sorted material is readily identifiable. Where the material is affected by temperature, humidity and other environmental conditions, these factors must be a key consideration in avoiding possible damage. When special storage conditions are required, packages are marked accordingly. For all areas where materials are held pending use or shipment, it is usual to restrict access to authorised personnel only.

For effective control of the quality of stored product, the following issues are worthy of consideration:

- the provision of quarantine and/or bonded storage areas, where necessary;
- the use of appropriate methods of storage;
- that the material leaves store areas only when properly authorised;
- that storage areas are secure and adequately protected against harmful environments;
- that procedures for rotation of stock, when necessary, are adequate and effective, with due regard being paid to storage life;
- that in order to detect deterioration, the condition of material in stock is periodically assessed. (If a formal system of checking small sections of stock at regular intervals throughout the year is used (cyclical stock checking) so that during the year the whole of the stock is assessed, products with a limited shelf life and subject to deterioration will be checked more frequently than say items of low cost);
- that data are collected and analysed on breakages, spoilage and pilferage in the stores;

- that data are collected and analysed on the frequency of errors (i.e. wrong product or incorrect quantities) made on issue.

BS 5729: Part 5 (1980) describes the functions and key tasks involved in store keeping such as receiving, identifying, storing, issuing, replenishing and accounting.

Materials control does not come to an end when the product has been completed and put into finished storage. As far as is practical, an organisation should ensure for the protection of product during transit to the customer and for ready identification at its final destination. The results of damage to material incurred in transit can be considerable in terms of time, cost and the cost of replacing or repairing damaged plant, equipment and material. BS 1133 (a packaging code consisting of various sections for different materials) provides guidance on the whole range of packaging materials and methods and BS 4672 (1971) gives guidance on transport and storage hazards.

Assurance that acceptable material will be identifiable and in a suitable condition when received by the user depends on the manner in which marking, preservation, packaging and transporting operations are performed. Failure to control these operations properly can negate otherwise effective controls exercised during the manufacturing process and in finished storage areas; arrangements for delivery to the customer include protection against degradation of the product. The following are some of the factors that may need to be considered:

- the nature of the material;
- the type(s) of transport to be used;
- environmental conditions during transit;
- time in transit;
- handing methods en route;
- storage en route and at destination.

While BS 1133 is helpful for the selection and specification of the correct materials, it needs to be supplemented at company level by a code of practice which selects material for particular transit and storage modes. The arrangements should also include protection of any packing and preservation which the purchaser includes in the specified requirements.

Some organisations have developed a packaging handbook which may include the following:

- Packaging specifications: documents for equipment or items being packaged which refer to the preservation standards and container standards to be used;
- Preservation standards: company standards describing the various coating methods, treatments and materials used to provide, for example, primary or corrosion protection;
- Container standards: company standards on containers to be used whenever physical protection of the primary package is required;
- Material standards: catalogue sheets of the preferred sizes of container, and materials which may be specified by the above standards.

The Ford Motor Company's *Q–101 Quality System Standard* (1990), on the subject of packaging, states:

> The choice of packaging could have a significant effect on product quality and is to be considered during feasibility evaluation. Producers must use appropriate packaging, considering the various transport methods and routes that may be employed, to assure that all products arrive at the point of usage without damage or deterioration and that the products can be transported, stored, unpacked, and used efficiently. (Refer to packaging guidelines issued by the Ford customer activity). Shipping trials should be considered to evaluate the ability of the packaging to preserve product quality. For aftermarket products, packaging information should be requested from the appropriate Ford service parts activity.

Ford have a number of brochures to assist their suppliers in developing and establishing the most effective and economical packaging.

10.13 Definitions and terminology

The following are some useful definitions and terms used in this chapter.

Bonded store: a secure place to which access is

restricted to authorised persons only.

Characteristic: a property that helps to distinguish between items of a given population.

Concession; waiver: written authorisation to use or release a quantity of material, components or stores already produced, but which do not conform to the specified requirements.

Defect: the non-fulfilment of intended usage requirements.

Final inspection: the last of several inspections at successive stages during processing.

In-process inspection: product inspection carried out at various stages during processing.

Inspection: activities such as measuring, examining, testing and gauging one or more characteristics of a product or series and comparing these with specified requirements to determine conformity.

Inspection by attributes: inspection wherein certain characteristics are assessed and classified as conforming or not conforming to specified requirements without measurements.

Inspection by variables: inspection which consists of measuring a quantitative characteristic for each item of a population, or for a sample taken from it.

Material specification: the document that describes in detail the materials, components or supplies used in manufacturing the item.

Patrol inspection: inspection carried out during routine or random visits to several production stages.

Product specification: the document that describes, for manufacturing purposes, the product concerned.

Quarantine store: a secure place in which supplies may be held pending a decision on their disposition.

Specification: the document that prescribes the requirements with which the product or service has to conform.

Test: a critical trial or examination of one or more properties or characteristics of a material product or set of observations.

British Standards

BS 0: *A standard for standards* Part 3: 1991 *Guide to the drafting and presentation of British Standards.*

BS 1133 *Packaging Code.* (There are various sections for different materials.)

BS 4672: 1971 *Guide to hazard in the transport and storage of packages.*

BS 4778: *Quality vocabulary* Part 1: 1987 *International terms* (ISO 8402: 1986) (EN 28402: 1991); Part 2: 1991 *Quality vocabulary – quality concepts and related definitions.*

BS 5729: Part 5, 1980 *Storekeeping.*

BS 5750: *Quality systems* Part 0: Section 0.2: 1987 *Quality systems – principal contents and applications: guide to quality management and quality system elements* (ISO 9000: 1987) (EN 29000: 1991); Part 1: 1987 *Specification for design, development, production, installation and servicing* (ISO 9001: 1987) (EN 29001: 1987); Part 4, 1990 *Guide to the use of BS 5750: Part 1, Specification for design, development, production, installation and servicing; Part 2, Specification for production and installation; Part 3, Specification for final inspection and test.*

BS 6446: 1984 *Specification for manufacture of glued structural components of timber and wood based panel products.*

PD 3542: 1991 *The rôle of standards in company quality management.*

PD 6489: 1987 *Guide to the preparation of a company's standards manual.*

References

Dale B G and Shaw P. 'Failure Mode and Effects Analysis: a state-of-the-art study', *Quality and Reliability Engineering International*, 6(3), pp 179–88, 1990.

Ford Motor Company. *Worldwide Quality System Standard, Q–101*, Plymouth, Michigan, USA, 1990.

Ford Motor Company. *The Initial Sample Review Process for Suppliers to Ford Motor Company.* Corporate Quality Office, Michigan, USA, 1990.

Gosling C, Rowe S and Dale B G. 'The use of quality management tools and techniques in financial services: an examination', *Proceedings of the 7th OMA (UK) Conference,*

UMIST, June, Elsevier Science Publishers, pp 285–290, 1992.

Mone J, Hibbert B and Dale B G. 'Initial samples and quality improvement: a study'. *Proceedings of the 7th National Conference on Production Research, Hatfield Polytechnic, September*, Bell and Bain, pp 459–463, 1991.

Nissan Motor Manufacturing (UK) Ltd. *Nissan Quality Standard for Suppliers*, Nissan Motor Iberica SA and Nissan Motor Manufacturing (UK), Washington, 1991.

CHAPTER 11

Service procedures and concepts

11.1 Introduction

Quality and customer satisfaction are important subjects receiving increasing attention worldwide. In response to this awareness companies are seeking to manage the quality aspects of their service activities in a more effective manner. The creation and maintenance of quality service is dependent upon a systematic approach to quality management aimed at ensuring that customer needs are understood and met and, if appropriate, exceeded. The achievement of quality service necessitates a commitment to quality principles at all levels in the organisation and a continual review and improvement of the established system of quality management based on feedback of the customer's perception of the service provided. The successful application of quality management to a service provides significant opportunities for:

- improved service performance and customer satisfaction;
- improved productivity, efficiency, morale and cost reduction;
- improved market share.

To achieve these benefits, it is important to recognise and respond to the human aspects involved in the provision of a service by:

- managing the social processes involved in a service;
- regarding human interactions (customer and service provider) as a crucial part of service quality;
- recognising the importance of a customer's perception of the organisation's image, culture and performance;
- recognising that the customer interaction is an essential part of the service delivery process;
- developing the skills and capability of personnel;
- motivating personnel to improve quality and to meet customer needs and expectations.

This chapter explores some service procedures and concepts within the context of TQM.

11.2 Service and service delivery characteristics

Services come in all shapes and forms, whether solely of a service character or in combination with the manufacture and supply of a product. This can be shown as a continuum ranging from a situation where the service is directly related to a product to a situation where there is little to

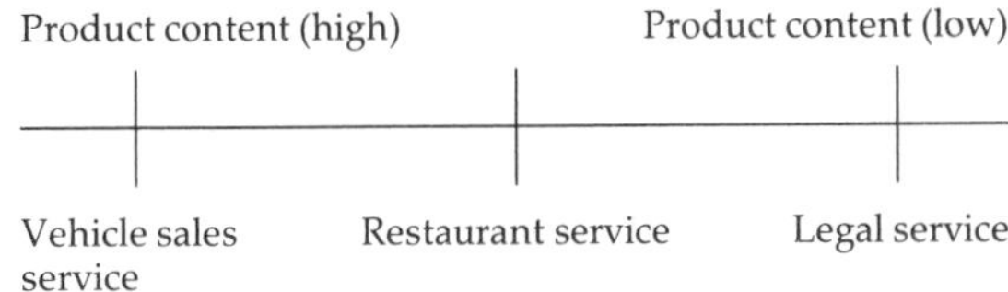

Figure 11.1 Product content in a service continuum
Source: BS 5750: Part 8 (1991)

do with a product. Figure 11.1 illustrates this concept for three different types of service.

The requirements of a service need to be clearly defined in terms of characteristics and parameters that are observable and subject to customer evaluation. The processes that deliver a service also need to be defined in terms of characteristics which may not always be observable by the customer, but which directly affect service performance. Both types of characteristic need to be capable of evaluation by the service organisation against defined standards of acceptability and performance in order to facilitate control and improvement.

A service or service delivery characteristic may be quantitative (measurable) or qualitative (comparable), depending on how it is evaluated and whether the evaluation is done by the service organisation and/or the customer. Many qualitative characteristics which are subjectively evaluated by customers are candidates for quantitative measurement. Examples of characteristics that might be specified include:

- physical facilities, equipment, capacity, number of personnel and quantity of materials;
- waiting time, delivery time and process times;
- hygiene, safety, reliability and security;
- responsiveness, accessibility, courtesy, comfort, aesthetics of environment, competence, dependability, accuracy, completeness, state of the art, credibility, empathy and effective communication.

In most cases the control of service and service delivery characteristics can only be achieved by controlling the process that delivers the service. Process performance measurement and control are therefore essential to achieve and maintain the required service quality. While remedial action is sometimes possible during service delivery, it is usually not possible to rely on final inspection to influence service quality at the customer interface where customer assessment of any non-conformity is often immediate.

The service delivery process may range from being highly mechanized (as in a directly dialled telephone call) to one that is highly personalized (as in services such as legal, medical, hospitality or consultancy). The more definable the process, whether by mechanization or by detailed procedures, the greater the opportunity to apply structured and disciplined quality system principles and quality management techniques such as SPC, FMEA and QFD.

11.3 Quality policy and objectives

Quality policy was explored in Chapter 3 but in relation to a service organisation it should relate to:

- grade of service to be provided;
- the service organisation's image and reputation for quality and reliability;
- objectives for service quality;
- approach to be adopted in pursuit of quality objectives.

The realisation of a quality policy requires the identification of primary goals for establishing quality objectives; these primary goals should include:

- customer satisfaction consistent with professional standards and ethics;
- continuous improvement of the service;
- giving consideration to the requirements of society and the environment;
- efficiency in providing the service.

The primary goals need to be translated into a set of quality objectives and activities. Examples of these are:

- clear definition of customer needs and expectations with appropriate quality performance metrics;

- preventive action and controls to avoid customer dissatisfaction;
- optimizing quality-related costs for the required performance and grade of service;
- creation of a collective commitment to quality;
- continuous review of service requirements and achievements to identify opportunities for service quality improvement;
- prevention of adverse effects on society and the environment.

11.4 Service quality loop

Procedures should be established to specify the performance requirements for all service processes including the three main provisioning processes (marketing, design and service delivery) which can be shown to be operating in a service quality loop, as illustrated in Figure 11.2. The quality of service as seen by the customer is directly influenced by these processes as well as by actions arising from those service quality feedback measures which contribute to service quality improvements, namely:

- supplier's assessment of the service provided;
- customer's assessment of the service received;
- quality audits of the implementation and effectiveness of all elements of the quality system.

Quality feedback should also be established between the interacting elements in the quality loop.

11.5 Customer interfaces

Figure 11.3 illustrates that the customer is the focal point of the three key aspects of a quality system related to the provision of services. It also illustrates that customer satisfaction can only be assured when there is a harmonising of interaction between the management responsibility, the personnel and material resources and the quality system structure.

It is important to establish effective interaction between customers and the organisation's personnel. This is crucial to the quality of service perceived by the customer. Management can influence this perception by creating an appropriate image based on the reality of actions taken to meet customer needs. This image, presented by personnel at all levels, has a primary effect on the service organisation's relationship with the customer. It is important that an organisation's improvement effort does not concentrate solely on customer care; the effort needs to work its way into improving the 'back office' processes.

Personnel with direct customer contact are an important source of information for the ongoing quality improvement process. Communication with customers involves listening to them, using a variety of means, and keeping them informed. The customer's perception of service quality is acquired often through communication with the service organisation personnel and facilities. Difficulties in communication or interactions with customers, including internal customers, need to be given prompt attention; these difficulties provide important information on areas for improvements in the service delivery process. Effective communication with customers involves:

- describing the service, its scope, its availability and timeliness of delivery;
- stating how much the service will cost;
- explaining the interrelationships between service, delivery and cost;
- explaining to customers the effect of any problems, and how they will be resolved, should they arise;
- ensuring that customers are aware of the contribution they can make to service quality, in particular, the service delivery process;
- providing adequate and readily accessible facilities for effective communication;
- determining the relationship between the service offered and the real needs and expectations of the customer(s).

Customer assessment is the ultimate measure of the quality of a service. Customer reaction may be immediate, or it may be

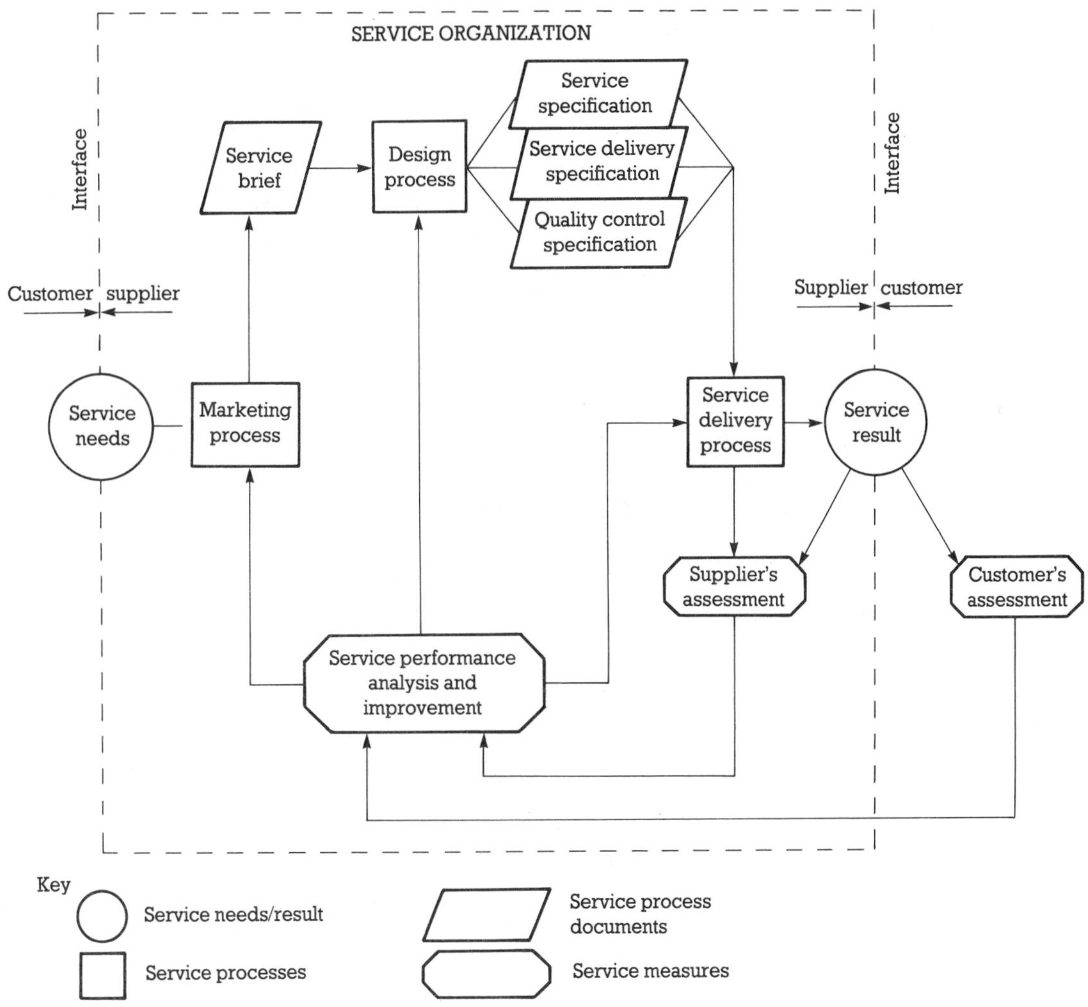

Figure 11.2 Service quality loop

Source: BS 5750: Part 8, 1991

delayed and retrospective. Often subjective evaluation will be the sole factor in a customer's assessment of the service provided. Customers seldom volunteer their assessment of service quality to an organisation. Dissatisfied customers often cease to use or purchase services without giving notice that would permit corrective action to be taken. Reliance on customer complaints as a measure of customer satisfaction can lead to misleading conclusions. The customer service data in Table 11.1 compiled by Mattson and Associates from service sector companies in the USA and quoted by CMC Partnership Ltd (1991) in their survey of 'Attitudes Within British Business to Quality Management Systems' supports these points and makes interesting reading.

It is important that service organisations institute ongoing assessment and measurement of customer satisfaction. These assessments should seek positive as well as negative reactions and their likely effect on future business. The evaluation of customer satisfaction should focus on the extent to which the service brief, specifications and the service delivery process meet the customer(s) needs and expectations. A service organisation often thinks that it is supplying a good service but the customer

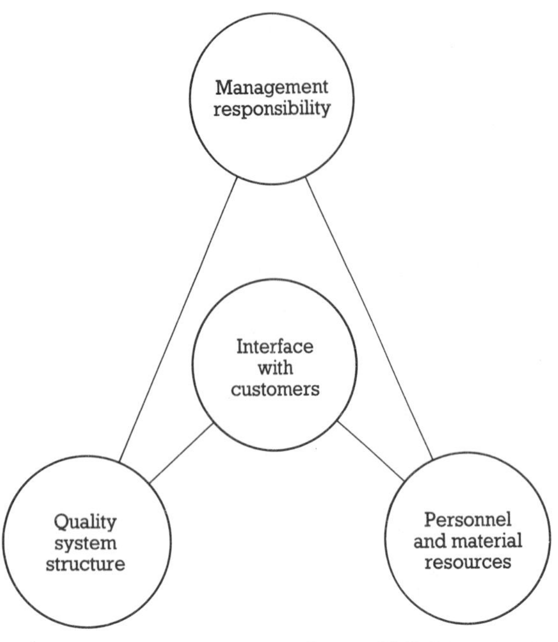

Source: BS 5750: Part 8, 1991

Figure 11.3 Key aspects of a quality system

Table 11.1 Customer service facts

1. If 20 customers are dissatisfied with your service, 19 won't tell you. 14 of the 20 will take their business elsewhere.

2. Dissatisfied customers tell an average of 10 other people about their bad experience; 12 per cent tell up to 20 people.

3. Satisfied customers will tell an average of five people about their positive experience.

4. It costs five times more money to attract a new customer than to keep an existing one.

5. Up to 90 per cent of dissatisfied customers will not buy from you again, and they won't tell you why.

6. In many industries, quality of service is one of the few variables that can distinguish a business from its competition.

7. Providing high quality service can save your business money. The same skills that lead to increased customer satisfaction also lead to increased employee productivity.

8. Customers are willing to pay more to receive better service.

9. 95 per cent of dissatisfied customers will become loyal customers again if their complaints are handled well and quickly.

Source: The CMC Partnership Ltd (1991)

may not agree, indicating inadequate specifications, processes, feedback mechanisms or measures. A comparison should be made of the customer's assessment with the supplier's own perception and assessment of the service provided to evaluate the compatibility of the two and any need for appropriate action for service quality improvement.

11.6 Service specification

Prior to the development of a service, it is important to establish procedures for planning, organising and implementing the launch of the service and where applicable, its eventual withdrawal and replacement, if appropriate. Included in this planning should be a responsibility for ensuring that service requirements and service delivery requirements each contain explicit provision for safety aspects, potential liabilities and appropriate means to minimize risks to personnel, customers and the environment. The service specification should contain a complete and precise statement of the service to be provided, including:

- a clear description of the service characteristics subject to customer evaluation;
- a standard of acceptability for each service characteristic.

The service specification defines the service to be provided, whereas the service delivery specification defines the means and methods used to deliver the service. The quality control specification defines the procedures for evaluating and controlling the service and service delivery characteristics. Design of the service specification, the service delivery specification and quality control specification are interdependent and interact throughout the design process. Flow charts are a useful method to depict all activities, relationships and interdependence.

During design of the service, service delivery and the quality control specifications, it is important to:

- plan for variations in the service demand;

- carry out an analysis to anticipate the effects of possible systematic and random failures and also service failure aspects beyond the supplier's control;
- develop contingency plans for the service.
- ensure that the complete service specification and service delivery specification meet customer requirements;
- ensure that the quality control specification is adequate to provide accurate information about the quality of service delivered.

11.7 Service delivery specification

The service delivery specification should contain service delivery procedures describing the methods to be used in the service delivery process, including:

- a clear description of the service delivery characteristics that directly affect service performance;
- a standard of acceptability for each service delivery characteristic;
- resource requirements detailing the type and quantity of equipment and facilities necessary to fulfil the service specification;
- number and skills of personnel required;
- reliance on sub-contractors for purchased products and services.

The service delivery specification should take account of the mission, vision, aims, policies and capabilities of the service organisation, as well as any health, safety, environmental or other legal requirements which have to be met.

Design of the service delivery process may usefully be achieved by sub-dividing the process into separate work phases supported by procedures describing the activities involved at each phase. Particular attention should be given to the interfaces between separate work phases. Examples of work phases involved in services are:

- providing information about services offered to customers;
- taking orders;
- establishing provisions for the service and delivering the service;
- billing and collecting charges for the service.

Detailed flow charts of the service delivery process can assist in this sub-division.

The provision of an effective service to customers entails:

- adherence to the prescribed service delivery specification;
- monitoring that the service specification is met;
- adjusting the process when deviations occur.

Therefore quality control should form an integral part of the operation of the service delivery process. This includes:

- measurement and verification of the key process activities to avoid undesirable trends and customer dissatisfaction;
- self-inspection by service delivery personnel as an integral part of the process measurements;
- a final supplier assessment at the interface with the customer to provide a supplier perspective of the quality of service delivered.

11.8 Quality control specification

Quality control should be designed as an integral part of each of the service processes – marketing, design and service delivery. The specification developed for quality control should enable the effective control of each service process to ensure that the service consistently satisfies the service specification and the customer. The design of appropriate quality controls involves:

- identifying the key activities in each process which have a significant influence on the specified service;
- analysing the key activities to select those characteristics and/or parameters whose measurement and control will help to ensure service quality;
- defining methods for evaluating the selected characteristics and/or parameters;

- establishing the means to influence or control the characteristics and/or parameters within specified limits.

The application of quality control principles to the service delivery process is illustrated in the following restaurant service example:

a) A key activity to be identified in a restaurant service would be the preparation of a meal and its effect on the timeliness of the meal being served to a customer.
b) A characteristic of the activity requiring measurement would be the time taken to prepare the ingredients for the meal.
c) A method for evaluating the characteristics would be sample checks of the time taken to prepare and serve a meal.
d) The effective deployment of staff and materials would ensure that the service characteristic of timeliness was maintained within its specified limits.

11.9 Service delivery process

New and modified services and their service delivery processes should undergo validation to ensure that they are fully developed and that the service meets the needs of customers under anticipated and adverse conditions. Validation should be defined, planned and completed prior to service implementation and the results documented. Prior to the initial delivery of a service, the following should be reviewed to confirm that:

- the service delivery process is complete;
- resources are available to meet the service obligations, particularly materials and personnel;
- applicable codes of practice, standards, procedures, drawings, photographs and specifications are satisfied;
- information to customers on the use of the service is available and is understandable.

Periodic revalidation should be performed to ensure that the service continues to meet the needs of the customer and conforms to the service specification, and to identify potential improvements in the provision and control of the service. Revalidation should be both a planned and documented activity, and should include considerations of actual field experience, customer feedback – formal and informal, impact of modifications in the service and processes, impact of personnel changes, adequacy of procedures, instructions, guides and proposed modifications.

11.10 Service quality improvement

There should be a process for continuously improving the service quality and the effectiveness and efficiency of the complete service operation, including an effort to identify:

- the characteristic(s) and/or parameter(s) which if improved would most benefit the customer and the service organisation;
- any changing market needs that are likely to affect the grade of service to be provided;
- any deviations from the specified service quality due to ineffective or insufficient quality controls;
- opportunities for reducing cost while maintaining and improving the service quality provided. (This requires systematic methods for estimating the quantitative costs and benefits).

The activities of service quality improvement should address the need for both short-term and longer-term improvement and include:

- identifying relevant data for collection;
- data analysis and giving priority to those activities having the greatest adverse impact on service quality;
- feedback of results of the analysis to operational management with recommendations for immediate service improvement;
- reporting periodically to senior management for a management review of long-term quality improvement recommendations.

Members from different parts of the service organisation working together may be able to offer fruitful ideas that could be directed towards improving quality and reducing cost.

11.11 Definitions and terminology

The following are some useful definitions and terms used in this chapter:

Customer: the recipient of a product or a service.

Organisation: a company, corporation, firm, enterprise or association, or part thereof, whether incorporated or not, public or private, that has its own function(s) and administration.

Quality: the totality of features and characteristics of a product or service that bear on its ability to satisfy stated or implied needs.

Quality management: that aspect of the overall management function that determines and implements the quality policy.

Quality policy: the overall quality intentions and direction of an organisation as regards quality, as formally expressed by top management.

Quality system: the organisational structure, responsibilities, procedures, processes and resources for implementing quality management.

Service: the results generated, by activities at the interface between the supplier and the customer and by internal supplier activities, to meet customer needs.

Service delivery: those supplier activities necessary to provide the service.

Supplier: an organisation that provides a product or a service to a customer.

British standards

BS 5750 *Quality Systems* Part 8: 1991 *Guide to Quality Management and Quality Systems Elements for Services* (ISO 9004–2: 1991).

References

CMC Management Consultants, *Attitudes Within British Business to Quality Management Systems*, The CMC Partnership Ltd., Buckingham, 1991.

CHAPTER 12

Measurement and calibration systems

12.1 The requirement for the control of measuring and test equipment

Manufacturers are increasingly being faced with demands for certification relating to the conformance of their product to a specification. In order to prove conformance to specification, most products require the application of accurate measurement during manufacture. Therefore, demonstration of the quality assurance of products and services is dependent upon measurement. The integrity of measurement work depends on selecting and using, in the correct manner, suitable measuring equipment and validating it by a system of control and calibration. A manufacturer should be able to demonstrate that the measuring equipment (for example, gauges, instruments, sensors and special test equipment) is capable of, and provides, precise measurement, before any assurance of conformance can be given to a customer. Therefore, any organisation working to the requirements of a formal quality system standard, has to be able to demonstrate that measurement is carried out correctly, and to certify that the results obtained can be relied upon. The following are two examples of such requirements.

In BS 5750: Part 1 the requirements for inspection, measuring and test equipment are outlined as:

> The supplier shall control calibrate and maintain inspection, measuring and test equipment, whether owned by the supplier, on loan or provided by the purchaser, to demonstrate the conformance of product to the specified requirements. Equipment shall be used in a manner which ensures that measurement uncertainty is known and is consistent with the required measurement capability.
>
> (BS 5750: Part 1, 1987)

In the section of the Ford Motor Company's *Q–101 Quality System Standard* dealing with the requirements for measuring and testing equipment which must be in a supplier's quality system it is stated that:

> Producers must provide adequate gauges, measuring and testing equipment for process control, approved by the responsible Quality Office or by Ford Product Engineering when so required by the part drawing or specification. Wherever feasible, such equipment must be designed to provide variables data.
>
> Since measuring and testing are processes and sources of variation, evidence is required that appropriate statistical studies have been conducted to determine if the process of measurement is stable. There is no specific threshold for adequate measurement system capability. Variation in the measurement system must be considered in relation to the variability of the process and product tolerance. Measurement

system variation will make it more difficult to stabilise production processes, will reduce the calculated capability of these processes, and will inhibit continuous improvement.

Producers must develop and implement a plan to verify the acceptability of measurement systems at sufficient intervals to protect the integrity of the systems. This plan should be documented and updated as necessary. Traceability to national/international standards should be provided. Where no such standards exist, the basis for calibration shall be documented.

When production tools, fixtures, tool masters, or other such devices are used as gauges, they must be inspected and documented in the same manner as other gauges.

(Ford Motor Company, 1990)

In the Ford Motor Company's *Quality System Survey* of a supplier's quality system, the following questions are asked:

12. Are appropriate gauges, measuring facilities, laboratory equipment, and test equipment available to facilitate process control?
    - Is the selection of significant characteristics effectively incorporated in gauge planning and design?
    - Are gauges and test equipment and personnel appropriately located throughout the producer's operations?
    - Are adequate, well-lit areas available for gauging, measuring, and testing the product?
13. Does the producer have an effective gauge and test equipment maintenance programme?
    - Are new gauges/test equipment inspected to design specifications, calibrated and approved before being used?
    - Do records indicate that gauges and test equipment are periodically inspected and calibrated?
    - Does the producer use statistical methods to determine the stability and capability of gauges, measuring, and test equipment.

(Ford Motor Company, 1990)

BS 5781: Part 1 (1992) has been developed to specify the requirements for a calibration system. In order to ensure that a calibration system will satisfy the requirements of a formal quality system standard, a manufacturer can either set up its own calibration laboratory or sub-contract all metrology requirements to an accredited National Measurement Accreditation Service (NAMAS) calibration laboratory in the UK.

There is little doubt that development in test and measurement technology are assuming greater international importance. With the integration of Europe, agreements between NAMAS and other similar bodies regarding the recognition of calibration and test certificates within the member states of the European Community (EC), are clearly necessary.

Every time a product has to be retested to access a national market it costs time and money. The same is true for services. This is a major burden on organisations and is wasteful of resources. To reduce barriers to trade the EC has introduced a system of mutual recognition of testing and certification. The object of the created organisation, the European Organisation for Testing and Certification (EOTC), is to review the testing certification arrangements in each country of the Community and of EFTA and to decide which of those arrangements are acceptable for mutual recognition throughout the EC and from this reduce and eliminate repetitive testing and service reassessments. According to the EOTC (EOTC, 1991) the ultimate goal is one-stop testing/assessment throughout Europe and in this way it aims to eliminate the differences which restrict trade. This will mean that once technical specifications, such as international or European standards, have been agreed a product or service will only need to be tested or assessed once to be accepted in the wider European market. The policy of the EOTC is to ensure that official recognition is given only to testing and certification carried out by approved bodies.

The objectives of the EOTC (EOTC, 1991) are to constitute the focal point in Europe for all questions relating to conformity assessment issues in particular by:

- encouraging, fostering and managing the development of European certification systems and of mutual recognition agreements for test reports and certificates on the basis of coherent principles and processes which will attract the confidence of all interested parties;
- providing the appropriate framework for the non-regulatory sphere with regard to

conformity assessment issues, whilst operating in such a manner as to give technical support to legislation for the EC and the EFTA countries and assisting the Commission of the European Communities and the EFTA countries regarding conformity assessment in the regulatory sphere;
- assisting the Commission of the European Communities and the EFTA countries in the definition of the technical conditions for furthering mutual recognition agreements;
- providing information and exchange of experience;
- assisting and complementing the European standardisation process in the fields of conformity assessment.

The terms of testing, certification and accreditation are set out in the EN 45000 series. The identical British Standards are BS 7501 (1989) (EN 45001), BS 7502 (1989) (EN 45002), BS 7503 (1989) (EN 45003), BS 7511 (1989) (EN 45011), BS 7512 (1989) (EN 45012), BS 7513 (1989) (EN 45013) and BS 7514 (1989) (EN 45014).

The criteria for the technical and management competence of testing laboratories are set out in BS 7501 (EN 45001) which covers the same basic requirements as the ISO/IEC Guide 25 on laboratory accreditation. Its scope is as follows:

- it is the standard with which a laboratory has to demonstrate that it operates if it is to be recognised as competent in carrying out specific calibrations or tests;
- it is for use by calibration and testing laboratories in the development and implementation of their quality systems;
- it is also to be used by accreditation, certification and inspection bodies as well as those concerned with the competence of laboratories.

The standard covers the following areas:

- impartiality, independence and integrity;
- technical competence:
  - management and organisation;
  - personnel;
  - premises and equipment:
    - availability;
    - premises and environment;
    - equipment;
  - working procedures:
    - test methods and procedures;
    - quality system;
    - test reports;
    - records;
    - handling of test samples or items;
    - confidentiality and security;
    - sub-contracting;
- co-operation:
  - co-operation with clients;
  - co-operation with bodies granting accreditation;
  - co-operation with other laboratories and with bodies producing standards and regulations;
- duties resulting from accreditation.

BS 7502 (EN 45002) specifies general criteria for the procedures used in the assessment of testing laboratories, including calibration laboratories. It is intended for the use of testing laboratories and their accreditation bodies as well as other bodies concerned with recognising the competence of testing laboratories. The accreditation process includes:

- the gathering of information needed for the evaluation of the applicant laboratory;
- the appointment of one or more qualified assessors designated to assess the applicant laboratory;
- the on-site assessment of the applicant laboratory;
- the review of all evaluation material collected;
- the decision, if any, to grant accreditation to the applicant laboratory, with or without conditions, and the definition of the scope of that accreditation or the decision to refuse accreditation to the applicant laboratory.

BS 7503 (EN 45003) specifies general criteria for laboratory accreditation bodies and is intended for the use of testing laboratories and their accreditation bodies.

This chapter examines the main features of measurement and calibration systems.

12.2 The case for regular calibration

Any measuring equipment will at some time during its operating life have been adjusted or graduated to the required accuracy, within known limits. For almost all measuring equipment, this will have occurred as one of the final steps of the manufacturing process. If, in addition, its errors have been determined and recorded, this activity constitutes a calibration.

In order to achieve consistency between measurements made in different locations and using different measuring equipment, equipment should initially have been correctly adjusted using traceable values.

Unfortunately, this by itself is rarely sufficient as almost everything is subject to change. Some of these changes are slow ageing drifts, as are common with resistors and capacitors; some are caused by wear, such as usually occurs with gauge blocks and micrometers; the others are associated with wear out, such as failures that can occur with valves and electrolytic capacitors. In addition, some changes are caused by abuse such as overloading or shock loading, and some erratic changes are caused by either defective design and/or faulty construction.

Therefore, it should not be assumed that just because a device was once correct it will remain so for ever. The chance of its doing so are increased if it is simple, rugged and well treated and maintained. For example, a master gauge block, kept in a controlled environment and used only on rare occasions by a skilled operator, is much more likely to remain unchanged than a voltmeter used by a variety of partially trained personnel in a department responsible for field trials. A problem which occurs with some measuring equipment is that it can become seriously erroneous but still appear to be functioning correctly. Suspicion may fall on a piece of equipment because it produces results different from other similar equipment but, if it is the only one of its kind and range available, it may continue to be used with completely unjustified confidence. The cost to an organisation as a result of such a situation can be considerable. It may involve recalling products, in order to modify or adjust them, and it can have an adverse effect on the reputation of the organisation.

For equipment in regular use, either installed in connection with some process or in use in a factory or laboratory, checking at regular time intervals provides a good assurance that measurements taken with it will be satisfactory. The intervals at which calibration is desirable will vary with the nature of the device, the conditions under which it is used and the seriousness of the consequences if it produces incorrect results.

A very useful check that a measuring instrument continues to measure correctly is obtained by the use of a checking measurement standard, applied to the instrument by the user. This will demonstrate if, at the value or values checked and under the conditions of the check, the instrument is still functioning correctly. The checking measurement standard itself needs to be calibrated and confirmed; in order that the results obtained by its use can with confidence be attributed to the instrument and not to changes in the checking measurement standard, it usually has to be simple and robust. The use of a checking measurement standard is in no way a substitute for regular calibration and confirmation of the instrument, but its use may prevent the use of an instrument which, within the interval between two formal confirmations, ceases to conform to specification.

The magnitude of errors and their rapidity of occurrence in a piece of equipment will vary according to its design and construction, whether it has an inherent wear-out process, or is subject to wear in use. Some instruments incorporate components that alter their properties with changes in temperature, humidity, time lapse or duration of use. All of these factors may significantly affect the uncertainty of the measurement. For the purpose of assessing the calibration interval, it is the time-dependent phenomena that should be considered. For example, a hardened steel gauge block can be expected to be very stable and be subject to very little wear with normal use. On the other hand, a cast iron gauge block can be expected to show the usual growth phenomenon of cast iron and so be unstable. A mild steel gauge block would probably wear significantly in use and become inaccurate.

Irrespective of the apparent stability of a piece of equipment, there is always the possibility of damage causing either a step change or random variability in the error. For example, some damage is often not apparent, such as over-heating a sealed resistor or overloading a Weston cell, and the resultant errors may be completely unsuspected. Such damage may be random in its time of occurrence, but is likely to be more frequent the lower the grade of personnel using it and the more arduous the conditions of use.

12.3 Calibration systems

The intention of a confirmation system is to ensure that the risk of measuring equipment producing results having unacceptable errors remains within acceptable bounds. The error attributable to calibration should be as small as possible. In most areas of measurement, it should be no more than one third and preferably one tenth of the permissible error of the confirmed equipment. Appropriate statistical methods for analysing the results of preceding calibrations, for assessing the results of calibrations of several similar items of measuring equipment and for predicting cumulative uncertainties should be used.

Any measurement work is valueless unless its results are known to be valid and sufficiently accurate for the intended purpose. The provision of a measurement facility necessitates the selection of suitable equipment with instructions for its use, the availability of appropriate skills and means of establishing the initial and continuing validity of the measurement processes. Experience indicates that, in general, ad hoc arrangements for dealing with the calibration of equipment often results in unintentional neglect. The likely consequences are out-of-date calibrations, lack of traceability to standards of reference and inadequate records, leading to loss of confidence in product or service compliance with customer requirements.

Validation of measurement work is best achieved by operating an orderly system in which responsibility for controlling the calibration of all measuring equipment and measurement standards used is assigned to designated personnel. The system should include documents and records to provide evidence of measurement integrity, of any limitations of use and of occurrences affecting confidence in the serviceability of the equipment.

The documentary evidence covers factors such as: identification of instruments; frequency of recalibration; calibration status; and procedures for recall, handling and storage, adjustment, repair, calibration, installation and use. Such records are a valuable reference in cases of dispute, for example, relating to measurement or product rejection by the customer, particularly in relation to product liability, and warranty and guarantee aspects. These records are also useful in assessing drift, wear and other variations in equipment performance. Such data provides a basis for decisions on equipment maintenance, repair and replacement economics.

Once a system has been established for the control and calibration of measurement standards and measuring equipment, it is important to ensure its continued effectiveness. This is best carried out by a periodic and systematic review of the system. In order to perform a review adequately, it is essential that procedures be defined; namely, who will perform the review, the period between reviews, how and where the review will be done, how the results will be reported and how the corrective action will be instituted. All results from the review need to be recorded and be available for inspection. Appendix J, from the now withdrawn BS 5781: Part 2 1981 (1988), indicates the type of questions that may be used in the evaluation or review of a measurement and calibration system.

From a review of the literature on the subject, Dale and Perry (1985), uncovered little published information on calibration systems, in particular, calibration intervals. From the papers identified, the following are worth consulting by any reader interested in developing their knowledge on calibration systems - Kamada (1980), Greb (1979), Meckley (1955) and Weller (1967).

12.4 Planning

A significant factor in planning for the inspection of a product, or for the provision of a measurement service, is the determination of what measurement equipment will be required, what its accuracy should be, and when, where and how the necessary measurement and calibration will be performed. In some cases this activity may be undertaken in conjunction with the planning of other functions; therefore, a definitive plan dealing solely with measurement and calibration system may not exist as such. This planning will also reveal cases where the specified requirements cannot be satisfied, either because the measurement requirement exceeds the known state-of-the-art, or because a particular measurement capability is not available.

Other factors which need to be taken into account are the need for controlled environments and the skills required of personnel performing both the measurements and calibration, in particular, when planning for product measurements which require a greater than average level of skill. Many organisations overlook the need for expertise and aptitude in the measurement area and the training for personnel performing calibration functions. On this point, Cardew (1987) devotes an editorial to the case for some certificate of competence for those personnel who are concerned with measurement.

12.5 Measurement limits

Errors and uncertainties are inherent in all measurement processes, whether performed for the purposes of calibrating measuring instruments or measuring product characteristics and/or process parameters. Valid estimates of the amount of error and uncertainty must be made and should be taken into account, as appropriate. This applies not only in the use of measurement standards in subsequent calibrations, but also in the use of measuring equipment when deciding whether measured values of product characteristics and/or process parameters are within specified limits. The total error and the uncertainty may comprise individual errors and uncertainties arising from inaccuracy and lack of repeatability, resolution of the measurement standards and measuring equipment, the methods of measurement, variations in environmental conditions and operator ability.

When a product characteristic and/or process parameter is being assessed for compliance with specified limits, the total error and the uncertainty should be taken into account if their significance in relation to the specification limits is likely to compromise product acceptance.

When it has been demonstrated by a calibration that the measuring equipment is performing correctly (in accordance with its specification), it is usual to assume that the errors produced while the equipment is in use do not exceed its specified limits of permissible error. This is assumed to hold until the equipment is next calibrated and confirmed. This may not be true under the often more arduous conditions of use as compared with the controlled conditions of the calibration. It may therefore be expedient to compensate for this by tightening the product acceptance limits. The amount of this tightening depends on the particular circumstances and is a matter for judgement based on experience.

The use of statistical methods to monitor and control measurement uncertainty on a continuing basis is recommended.

12.6 Documented calibration procedures

Written procedures for the calibration of measurement standards and measuring equipment are essential in order to establish the application of acceptable techniques and practices, and to maintain control over changes in calibration techniques.

Adequately documented calibration procedures should be available for the calibration of all measurement standards and measuring equipment. However, for some equipment, it may not be economical or technically necessary to provide a detailed procedure. The identification of such equipment is a matter of judgement. Similar considerations may apply when the method of calibration consists of basic and simple principles that would be expected to be known and frequently practised by all personnel involved in calibration activities.

If, in developing written procedures, published standard practices or manufacturers' written instructions are utilised, these should then form part of the procedure. However, procedures may be, but are not necessarily, limited to the compilation of published standard measurement practices and an instrument manufacturer's written instructions.

These methods may be elaborated using SPC, whereby measurement standards and measuring instruments are compared in-house, drifts and faults are determined, and any necessary corrective action is taken. SPC is complementary to regular calibration and reinforces confidence in measurement results during the intervals between confirmations.

In developing calibration procedures for some equipment it is well worth consulting the relevant British Standard, for example, BS 969 (1982) *Specification for limits and tolerances on plain limit gauges*. The amount of detail to be included in a procedure will vary, and depend upon the nature of the equipment and its complexity but it should be commensurate with the complexity of the confirmation process. As a guide, it should, as necessary, include:

- identification of the device or group of devices to which the procedure is applicable;
- identification of all standards and accessory equipment to be used to perform the calibration;
- adequate calibration instructions;
- an indication of the measurement or calibration data to be recorded and how such data is to be tabulated and treated;
- the environmental conditions in which the calibration is to be made and the minimum stabilisation period prior to calibration;
- a statement on the estimated uncertainty of the calibration process;
- an issue number and/or date of issue.

The procedures should be available, for reference, to all personnel employed on calibration work. To facilitate this, copies of the calibration procedures relating to all equipment should ideally be kept together in one place – usually in the quality manual.

It is important that any measurement standard, or any measuring equipment used for the assessment of product quality conformance, is maintained in the required state of calibration and is performing within its designated limits. The procedure should provide for the immediate removal, or identification to prevent use, of any measurement standard or measuring equipment that is:

- outside its designated calibration period;
- has failed in operation;
- is suspected of being, or is known to be, outside its designated limits;
- shows evidence of physical damage that may affect its accuracy.

Where measuring processes are found to be out of control or where measuring and test equipment is found to be outside the required calibration limits, corrective action is necessary. Evaluation should be made to determine the effects on completed work and to what extent reprocessing, retesting, recalibration or rejection may be necessary. In addition, investigation into the causes of non-conformance is required in order to prevent recurrence. This may include review of calibration methods and frequency, training and the adequacy of test equipment.

12.7 Records

Records are the evidence by which it can be demonstrated that all measurement standards and measuring equipment are in a known state of calibration. They constitute a history of the calibration of a piece of equipment and should demonstrate the measurement capability of each item of measuring equipment. The records may be evaluated and used as a basis for changing calibration intervals or measurement procedures, or taking other corrective action. The records may be in manuscript, typescript or microfilm form or may be in an electronic or a magnetic memory or on another data medium.

The minimum time for the retention of records is dependent on many factors, such as the purchaser's requirements, regulatory or legal requirements and manufacturer's liability. Records concerned with the principal measurement standards may need to be retained indefinitely.

The retention and analysis of the results obtained from calibrations may indicate the need to reduce, or permit the extension of, calibration intervals. There is an overall requirement for records to be maintained of any errors that exceed designated limits so that appropriate corrective action can be taken. This action may include the investigation of the effect of such errors on the acceptability of products.

The calibration results are recorded in sufficient detail so that the traceability of all the measurements can be demonstrated and any measurement can be reproduced under conditions close to the original conditions, thereby facilitating the resolution of any anomalies. The recorded information includes:

- the description and unique identification of equipment;
- the date on which each confirmation was completed;
- the calibration results obtained after and, where relevant, before any adjustment and repair;
- the assigned confirmation interval;
- identification of the confirmation procedure;
- the designated limits of permissible error;
- the source of the calibration used to obtain traceability;
- the relevant environmental conditions and a statement about any corrections;
- a statement of the uncertainties involved in calibrating the equipment and of their cumulative effect;
- details of any maintenance such as servicing, adjustment, repairs or modifications carried out;
- any limitations in use;
- identification of the person(s) performing the confirmation;
- identification of the person(s) responsible for ensuring the correctness of the recorded information;
- unique identification (such as serial numbers) of any calibration certificates and other relevant documents concerned.

12.8 Non-conforming measuring equipment

Any item of measuring equipment

- that has suffered damage,
- that has been overloaded or mishandled,
- that shows any malfunction,
- whose proper functioning is subject to doubt,
- that has exceeded its designated confirmation interval, or
- the integrity of whose seal has been violated,

should be removed from service by segregation and prominent labelling or marking. Such equipment should not be returned to service until the reasons for its non-conformity have been eliminated and it is again confirmed.

If the results of calibration prior to any adjustment or repair were such as to indicate a risk of significant errors in any of the measurements made with the equipment before the calibration, the necessary corrective action should be taken.

In the case of a multi-function or multi-range instrument, where it can be demonstrated that the instrument remains intact on one or more of its functions or ranges, it may continue to be used on the intact functions and/or ranges, provided that it is prominently labelled to indicate the restrictions on its use.

12.9 Calibration labelling

To provide a means of determining the calibration status of measurement standards and measuring equipment, equipment should be securely and durably labelled, coded or otherwise identified to indicate calibration status. The labelling may be by a secure self-adhesive stick-on label, a tie-on label or by durable marking directly on the measuring equipment. Any confirmation labelling should clearly indicate when the equipment is next due for confirmation and also the date of the most recent confirmation. Any limitation of calibration or restriction of use should be clearly indicated on the equipment. In some cases it is not always practicable or essential to provide a physical identification of calibration status on the equipment. Whatever method is adopted, it should ensure that it is capable of providing ready identification of the calibration status of equipment. The phrase *calibration status* refers to the information that indicates whether or not the measurement standard or measuring equipment was within its designated limits when last calibrated and that it is within its calibration interval. It may also be used to identify the origin of the calibration.

Where any measuring equipment is not in use, calibration need not be carried out. However, in this case, calibration should be undertaken before reuse if the validity of the previous calibration has expired. To ensure that such equipment is not used accidentally, procedures for its control and segregation, if possible, should be maintained and the equipment should be clearly identified, preferably by the use of a label. The calibration records should indicate any equipment that falls into this category.

When it is not intended to use the full capacity of a measurement standard or measuring equipment, because part of the equipment is unserviceable or because of limited calibration, any restriction should be readily apparent to the operator. Examples of use where there is no need for full calibration are:

- on a multi-range instrument where not all ranges are required for use;
- the equipment is used as a null-indicating device;
- the equipment is used only as an indicator and is not used for precise measurement.

12.10 Intervals of calibration

Except with respect to natural physical constants, no measurement standard or measuring equipment remains in a constant state. Even when such devices are stored unused, change may take place through natural, physical or chemical causes. Therefore, all measurement standards and measuring equipment should be calibrated and, if necessary, serviced, adjusted or otherwise reworked at periodic intervals, to preserve the integrity of product measurement.

The interval between calibrations varies from case to case and device to device and largely depends on such factors as the conditions of storage, the method, purpose and extent of use, the precision of measurement required, the age of the equipment, the effect of wear and the inherent stability of the device. Thus, the calibration interval will vary from one piece of equipment to another. The intervals should be such that confirmation is carried out prior to any probable change in accuracy that is of significance in the use of the equipment. When devices are used that are new, the interval of calibration can be assessed only arbitrarily. The equipment supplier can provide some general advice on the calibration interval based on stability, purpose and usage. Experience of using similar devices and the various factors associated with the measurement should also be taken into account. Where there is doubt, the interval should be set shorter than expected, this being updated with information obtained from subsequent calibrations. However over-frequent calibration is both time-consuming and costly and the intervals may be lengthened if the results of previous calibrations provide definite indications that such action will not adversely affect confidence in the accuracy of the equipment. An organisation should have specific objective criteria on which to base decisions affecting the choice of intervals of confirmation. In determining whether the changes in the intervals of confirmation are appropriate all relevant data should be taken into account including those available from SPC.

Dale and Perry (1985) outline an investigation carried out on the setting of calibration intervals, and external micrometers and plug gauges in a mechanical engineering company. Using data from calibration record cards, wear rates were calculated and this resulted in the mean calibration intervals being lengthened. Most organisations are looking to lengthen the period between calibrations. However, there is a lack of guidance and published information on how they might approach this task. Analysis of the data using basic statistics is always the first step to be taken in this exercise.

An organised approach should be taken to the establishment and maintenance of satisfactory intervals for the calibration of the measurement standards and measuring equipment. It is also necessary to remove and isolate from use, any measuring equipment that has not been calibrated within the established interval of calibration.

Useful advice on the choice of confirmation intervals is given in Annex A of BS 5781: Part 1 (1992).

12.11 Sealing for integrity

It is necessary that access to adjustable devices on measurement standards and measuring equipment, which are fixed at the time of calibration, should be sealed or otherwise safeguarded to prevent tampering by unauthorised personnel. The seals need to be so designed that any tampering will destroy them. The purpose of this is to provide an additional safeguard for the integrity of measurement by precluding errors that can occur if calibrated measurement standards or measuring equipment are tampered with. The interpretation of the term 'adjustable devices' is subject to the exercise of common sense and good judgement.

12.12 Storage and handling

Measuring equipment needs to be handled and used carefully, and be stored and transported under conditions compatible with its vulnerability in order to prevent abuse, misuse, damage and changes in dimensional and functional characteristics. Measuring instruments, including measurement standards, may have their performance impaired by careless use (for example, overloading a resistance standard or damaging the anvils of a micrometer), by poor storage conditions (for example, extremes of temperature, humidity causing rusting and/or mould growth, and sunlight causing degrading of plastics) and by vibration, shocks and temperature cycling, or poor transport conditions.

12.13 Traceability

No practical measurement can be exact; accuracy depends on the effect of various sources of error, usually expressed as an uncertainty of measurement, including the error of any measurement standard used as a reference. Similarly, the uncertainty in the value of this depends on that of the measurement standard used to calibrate it.

All measuring equipment should be calibrated using measurement standards that are traceable to international measurement standards, or to national measurement standards that are consistent with the recommendations of the General Conference on Weights and Measures (CGPM). In cases where such international or national measurement standards do not exist (for example, for hardness), traceability should be established to other measurement standards (for example, suitable reference materials, consensus measurement standards or industry measurement standards) that are internationally accepted in the field concerned.

Traceability is provided by an unbroken chain of comparisons through measurement standards of successively better accuracy up to the national measurement standard. The cumulative effect of the uncertainties of each successive stage in a chain of calibrations (a 'chain of calibrations' implies that the value of each measurement standard in the chain has had its value determined using another measurement standard, usually having a smaller uncertainty of measurement, up to an international or national measurement standard) should be taken into account for each measurement standard and item of equipment that is confirmed. Action needs to be taken when the total uncertainty is such that it significantly compromises the ability to make measurements within the limits of permissible error.

It is clear that traceability is essential to meet interface requirements between manufactured products and to provide a common base for the assessment of product quality and performance in accordance with specification. It is not usually necessary for measuring equipment and measurement standards to be calculated directly against national measurement standards. A lower point in the traceability chain having a sufficiently small uncertainty will often satisfy the need. For each item of measuring equipment or measurement standard used for in-house calibration work, traceability should be demonstrated by a calibration certificate issued by an authoritative source. This certificate should be sufficiently recent to have current validity after allowing for drift subsequent to calibration and show a sufficient range of measurement at an appropriately low uncertainty to allow use of the measurement system at the required level of accuracy. As a guide, the following information should be shown on the certificate:

- identification of equipment calibrated;
- results obtained;
- uncertainty of measurement;
- the authority under which the certificate is issued;
- any limitations on use of the equipment,
- date of calibration.

In general, calibration satisfying the dual requirements of authentic certification and traceability is available in several fields of metrology through an accredited NAMAS calibration laboratory in the UK. It is vital for laboratories to have a system of assuring the reliability and accuracy of their calibration, measurement and testing services. NAMAS has been formed by the amalgamation of the British Calibration Service (BCS) and the National Testing Laboratory Accreditation Scheme (NATLAS), the two laboratory accreditation services of the National Physical Laboratory (NPL) which is itself a DTI research establishment. BCS is a national service set up by the UK government to provide authenticated calibration of instruments and other measurement devices, and certification of measurement of all kinds. Under the scheme, laboratories are specially approved for particular measurements, for which they are authorised to issue official calibration certificates. A BCS accredited laboratory provides authenticated certification of the calibration of instruments, gauges and reference standards, with traceability of all measurements to national standards. NATLAS performs the same functions for laboratories carrying out testing. NAMAS in its turn is accredited by the national approval body NACCB.

Laboratories which are found on assessment to satisfy certain requirements are granted certificates of accreditation for defined types of tests. It is claimed by Dean (NPL, 1985) that the amalgamation of BCS and NATLAS to form NAMAS will provide a single interface between laboratory accreditation and other related UK quality assurance schemes involving NACCB and manufacturer's quality assessment schemes based upon the BS 5750 Series. Accreditation by NAMAS provides assurance in the competence of a laboratory and in the validity and interpretation of the calibration or test data requested by clients. There are an increasing number of NAMAS accreditations and NAMAS produces a directory of all BCS and NATLAS laboratories, which is updated twice a year.

As an alternative to establishing its own fully traceable calibration laboratory or standards room, an organisation can sub-contract all of its measurement, testing and calibration requirements to approved commercial laboratories.

12.14 Environmental control

Any measurement is affected to some degree by the environmental conditions under which it is carried out. The attainment of stable environmental conditions can be extremely costly and the nature and degree of environmental control should be chosen to suit the intended application. Due consideration needs to be given to temperature, rate of change of temperature, humidity, lighting, vibration, dust control, cleanliness, electromagnetic interference and other factors affecting the results of measurements. Where pertinent, these factors should be continuously monitored and recorded and, when necessary, correcting compensation applied to measurement results.

If measuring equipment, because of its size or other factors (for example, a coordinate measuring machine), cannot be moved into a controlled environment for calibration, provision should be made for its calibration in situ, and for necessary compensating corrections to be applied. In some circumstances the effect of environmental factors on calibration of measurement accuracy may be mitigated or even discounted. For example, the use of calibration standards or measuring equipment with a precision many times greater than the parameter tolerance being measured may, depending on the stability of the measuring equipment or product characteristic being measured, greatly reduce the impact of the environmental influence on the measurement. This can be achieved by making the correct choice of calibrating equipment and ensuring that all such measurement standards are calibrated in a well controlled environment. However, at the other extreme, environmental factors may necessitate strict control of calibration, measurement and even the test areas in order to achieve valid measurements. If such environmental factors are of importance, they should be monitored, recorded and applied as compensating corrections as appropriate.

12.15 Definitions and terminology

The following are some useful definitions and terms used in this chapter.

Accredited laboratory: testing laboratory to which accreditation has been granted.

Calibration: the set of operations which establish, under specified conditions, the relationship between values indicated by a measuring instrument or measuring system, or values represented by a material measure or a reference material, and the corresponding values of quantity realized by a reference standard.

Drift: the slow variation with time of a metrological characteristic of a measuring instrument.

International (measurement) standard: a standard recognised by an international agreement to serve internationally as the basis for fixing the value of all other standards of the quantity concerned.

Laboratory accreditation: formal recognition that a testing laboratory is competent to carry out specific tests or specific types of tests.

Laboratory accreditation body: body that conducts and administers a laboratory accreditation system and grants accreditation.

Laboratory accreditation system: system that has its own rules of procedure and management for carrying out laboratory accreditation.

Limits of permissible error (of a measuring instrument): the extreme values of an error permitted by specifications, regulations, etc. for a given measuring instrument.

Measuring equipment: all of the measuring instruments, measurement standards, reference materials, auxiliary apparatus and instructions that are necessary to carry out a measurement. This term includes measuring equipment used in the course of testing and inspection, as well as that used in calibration.

Measuring instrument: a device intended to make a measurement, alone or in conjunction with supplementary equipment.

Measurement: the set of operations having the object of determining the value of a quantity.

(Measurement) standard: a material measure, measuring instrument, reference material or system intended to define, realise, conserve or reproduce a unit or one or more values of a quantity in order to transmit them to other measuring instruments by comparison.

National (measurement) standard: a standard recognised by an official national decision to serve, in a country, as the basis for fixing the value of all other standards of the quantity concerned.

Reference conditions: conditions of use for a measuring instrument prescribed for performance testing, or to ensure valid intercomparison of results of measurements.

Specification: the document that prescribes the requirements with which the product or service has to conform.

Test: technical operation that consists of the determination of one or more characteristics of a given product, process or service according to a specified procedure.

Test method: specified technical procedure for performing a test.

Test report: document that presents test results and other information relevant to a test.

Traceability: the ability to trace the history, application or location of an item or activity, or similar items or activities, by means of record identification.

British Standards

BS 969: 1982 *Specification for limits and tolerances on plain limit gauges.*

BS 4778: Part 1 *Quality vocabulary international terms* (ISO 8402: 1986) (EN 28402: 1991).

BS 5233: 1986 *Glossary of terms used in metrology (incorporating BS 2643).*

BS 5750: *Quality Systems* Part 1: 1987 *Specification for design, development, production, installation and servicing* (ISO 9001: 1987) (EN 29001: 1987); Part 0: Section 0.2: 1987 *Quality Systems – guide to quality management and quality system elements* (ISO 9004: 1987) (EN 29004: 1987); Part 4: 1990 *Guide to the use of BS 5750: Part 1 Specification for design, development, production, installation and servicing; Part 2 Specification for production and installation; Part 3 Specification for final inspection and test.*

BS 5781: *Quality assurance requirements for measuring equipment* Part 1: 1992 *Metrological confirmation system for measuring equipment* (ISO 10012–1: 1992).

BS 7501: 1989 *General criteria for the operation of testing laboratories* (ISO/IEC Guides 2, 25, 38, 43, 45 and 49, 1989) (EN 45001: 1989).

BS 7502: 1989 *General criteria for the assessment of testing laboratories* (EN 45002: 1989).

BS 7503: 1989 *General criteria for laboratory accreditation bodies* (EN 45003: 1989).

BS 7511: 1989 *General criteria for certification bodies operating product certification* (ISO/IEC Guides 28 and 40: 1989) (EN 45011: 1989).

BS 7512: 1989 *General criteria for certification bodies operating quality system certification* (ISO/IEC Guides 40 and 48: 1989) (EN 45012: 1989).

BS 7513: 1989 *General criteria for certification bodies operating certification of personnel* (ISO/IEC Guide 40: 1989) (EN 45013: 1989).

BS 7514: 1989 *General criteria for suppliers' declaration of conformity* (ISO/IEC Guide 22: 1989) (EN 45014: 1989).

European Organisation for Testing and Certification (EOTC) European Organisation for Testing and Certification, EOTC Office, Brussels, 1991.

References

Cardew A. 'Editorial – Certification of metrologists'. *Quality Today*, November, p 3, 1987.

Dale B G and Perry G. 'The specification of calibration intervals.' *EOQC Quality*, 29 (2), pp 3–6, 1985.

Ford Motor Company. *World-wide Quality System Standard Q–101*. Michigan, USA, 1990.

Ford Motor Company. *The quality system survey and scoring guidelines*. Michigan, USA, 1990.

Greb D J. 'Calibration intervals specification and instrument quality.' *Journal of Quality Technology*, 29 (2), p 88–94, 1979.

Kamada M. 'Measurement and instrumentation activities for quality control.' *Technocrat*, 3 (2), pp 11–25, 1980.

Meckley D G. 'How to set-up a gauging policy and procedure.' *American Machinist*, March 14, pp 133–44, 1955.

Ministry of Defence. *Defence Standard 05–26, Measurement and calibration system requirements for industry*. London, UK, 1987.

National Physical Laboratory. *Introducing NAMAS*. Middx, UK, 1985.

Weller J A. 'What's happening in inspection, measurement and quality control?' *Canadian Machinery and Metalworking*, February, pp 76–81, 1967.

CHAPTER 13

Sampling methods and procedures

13.1 Introduction

This chapter presents some of the basics of sampling. It does not deal with the specific techniques of acceptance sampling and statistical process control (SPC), these are the subjects of Chapters 14 and 15 respectively.

The chapter begins by outlining the purposes of sampling; it then goes on to discuss sampling plans, the issues involved in sampling and how to deal with data which is not distributed normally; and concludes by defining the terms, relative to sampling methods and procedures, used in the chapter.

13.2 The purposes of sampling

Samples are taken from a much larger collection or population of results in order to examine them and obtain certain information or statistics pertaining to the whole population. The sampling unit is the item, feature or characteristic for which information is sought. For example, it can be a single item, a set of items but with only one test or observation on it, a test result, a length, a weight, or a volume. It need not be the same as the unit of purchase, supply, production or delivery. The principal objectives of sampling can be grouped under four main headings:

- to estimate the mean value of a characteristic,
- to estimate the variability of a characteristic,
- to estimate what proportion of material is defective,
- to determine opinions, or behaviour.

Sampling is necessary when 100 per cent inspection or testing of each unit in a lot or a batch of product is impracticable as, for example, when destructive testing methods are specified. 100 per cent inspection can be a formidable task and in some cases impossible, for example, with a polymerisation process. It is expensive and, unless automated, is not likely to be successful. 100% inspection is generally somewhat less than 100% efficient and the risk of an incorrect result is unknown, except perhaps when the inspection is automated. It often degenerates into a crude filter when sufficient money, time and staff are not available. On the other hand, sampling methods have the disadvantage that some of the units in the lot will not be inspected. But the risks involved, using the schemes based on the mathematical theory of probability, can be calculated and a sampling plan chosen which provides the appropriate level of cover. The two most common errors arising from sampling are:

- the failure of the sample or samples to represent the whole or population. This could, for example, result in the acceptance of bad batches and, conversely, the rejection of good ones;

- inaccuracies in the test result owing to:
  i) failure to apply the appropriate techniques to determine the chosen characteristic of the sample,
  ii) inherent limitations in the test methods used.

The data gathered may be expressed as a measured variable or a counted attribute. A measured variable is one which is expressed quantitatively, for example the viscosity of synthetic rubber. A counted attribute, on the other hand, is one which is expressed by the presence or absence of a particular qualitative characteristic for each unit examined in the sample. For example, the presence or absence of an error or a contaminant, the presence or absence of dinges and dents in a surface, the conformance of a bore when checked using a 'go/no go' plug gauge and absenteeism. Counted attributes are used when measurement on a continuous scale is impossible; they are essentially measures of a particular criterion being met. They do not indicate the degree of variability. Where measurements are possible either approach may be used, but more information is derived from using the data as variables. Among the factors that influence the choice between measured variables and attributes are:

- Type of characteristic – a characteristic may not be measurable on a continuous scale. In this case counted attributes are the only possibility.
- Cost of inspection or test – attributes can be recorded using visual inspection or by gauges, templates and screens. Measurement on a variable scale requires more sophisticated equipment, and may be slower and require higher levels of skills from operators and/or inspectors. Inspection using a variables scheme will usually be more expensive in time and money terms. However, it has a substantial advantage when the inspection process is expensive as in the case of destructive or lengthy testing methods.
- Number of measurements required – a variables scheme becomes less suitable as the number of different measurements to be taken increases, since each product or service characteristic or process parameter has to be considered separately.
- Sample size – measured variables require smaller sample sizes than counted attributes to achieve equal certainty about the quality status of a lot or process.
- Sensitivity – for a given sample size, measured variables give a much higher probability of detecting changes and smaller risks of wrong decisions, than counted attributes. More knowledge is gained of the product or process when the inspection method used is based on measured variables.
- Understanding – an attributes scheme can be more readily understood and accepted. For example, it may at first be difficult to accept that, when inspecting by variables, a lot can be rejected or a process considered out-of-control on measurements taken of a sample that does not contain any non-conforming items.
- Long-term control – the measured variables approach is a means of providing a basis for specification, negotiation with suppliers and analytical evaluation of the effects of actions. Counted attributes are sometimes useful for exposing underlying weaknesses and identifying quality improvement opportunities.

13.3 Sampling plans

It is essential to plan sampling so that the required information is obtained at an acceptable cost. The following are typical factors which affect the choice of a sampling plan once the decision as to the purpose of the sampling has been decided upon:

- The boundaries, physical state and nature of the whole quantity or population to be examined – the unambiguous statement of precisely what material is to be examined requires that boundaries are defined that include all material to be sampled and exclude all others. Frequently the appropriate boundaries are obvious. For example, both vendor and purchaser will usually consider a single consignment as a lot and will require a sampling plan aimed at reporting on such a lot. Similarly the output from a batch production process will frequently be segregated to retain batch identity and each will need to be examined individually.

Continuous production does not offer such natural boundaries and when materials are flowing in continuous streams it is necessary to establish a reference period in terms of time boundaries in order to define the quantity to be examined. For example, one might choose to regard the material moving past a particular point during a specified interval as a single entity. This approach may also be used in the sampling of customers using a particular service.

- The likelihood of contamination or deterioration, or change in quality of the whole quantity during or after production or operations – samples may need to be subjected to an accelerated ageing processes to simulate the state of the product as it will be perceived by the ultimate consumer or user.
- The acceptable sampling error – in all cases, a statement of acceptable error is necessary in order to design the sampling plan. All sampling plans, however well conceived, contain an implied acceptance of error in the final estimate. It is desirable that the economics or other consequences involved in accepting an unsatisfactory or rejecting a satisfactory batch of material, or making an incorrect assumption about a process or service should be assessed and monitored.
- The specification against which the material, process or service is being examined – if the ultimate objective of sampling and analysis is to establish whether or not the quality of the material, process, or service being examined complies with a particular specification, then the specification itself may influence decisions on sampling. Therefore, to some extent the sampling plan begins with the specification, if it exists (for example, sampling for an opinion or estimate of customer satisfaction).
- The specification of the characteristics which are to be used as criteria for the decisions to be made about the material, process or service.
- The precision limits of the test methods (if used) to ascertain the required characteristics.
- The total and intrinsic value of the material.
- The economics of the sampling, and the physical and human resource available.
- The ease of sampling and testing.

13.4 Sampling

In most cases of sampling, a decision on a batch of product, or output from a process or service is made on the quality of a sample. If this is to be a rational procedure, the sample should be representative of the population. Most sampling methods are based on the assumption that the sample of items will be drawn at random (i.e. all have the same chance of being included in the sample), but for some purposes there are methods in which samples are taken systematically in a prescribed way. There is no known way of ensuring that the sample has exactly the same characteristics, unless the nature of the population is already known. Therefore, to meet the objectives set out in a sampling plan, a procedure for taking a representative sample or samples from the output or process, in order to conform to a specified sampling error, must be determined.

A number of British Standards outline procedures for the sampling of certain products and for sampling in specific situations. For example, BS 5309: Part 3 (1976) specifies methods for the sampling of chemical products in the form of mobile liquids, liquids and solids rendered mobile, viscous liquids, multi-phase liquids (including slurries) and liquefied gases. The Standard also deals with sampling from a drum or tank, pipeline and shallow tank. A good example of procedures for sampling in a particular situation is BS 5700 (1984), which outlines aspects of sampling relating to control charting, as used in SPC.

The following are typical of the issues which need to be considered in sampling:

- the product, service, material, or process characteristics to be sampled – some sampling presents more practical difficulties than others. For example, obtaining representative samples of gases and airborne solids is more difficult than taking a sample from a batch of washers in the goods inwards department;
- the characteristic(s) and/or parameters to be measured in the sample;
- the method and technique of taking the sample – in the case of volume piece part manufacture it is straightforward to specify that a sample of size five is taken every hour from the process, and that a specific product characteristic be measured and recorded. However, there are situations where considerable thought needs to be given about the division of a lot into a number of smaller portions for separate examination and also to preparing the sample. Examples arise in the case of multi-spindle or head machines and multi-piece or multi-cavity tooling. In the case of continuous processes, the point, time and rate of sampling are vital to understanding the results. The service industries must also give thought to these and many other aspects of sampling methodology;
- any apparatus and equipment for taking the sample – in cases of hazardous materials or processes, or technical difficulty in sampling, the equipment may be complex and extensive;
- sample size – the optimum sample quantity is the smallest sample capable of giving the necessary information about the lot, material or process it represents. In general terms, the bigger the sample size the lower the risks of arriving at an incorrect decision. In general, the sample size and the frequency of taking a sample have to be a practical compromise between the costs of sampling, testing or inspecting, and the costs of making incorrect decisions;
- structure of the sample – the majority of procedures for sampling, stress that the sample should be random and be representative of the population. In many cases, the sample taken does not affect the composition of the population and all such samples are truly representative. However, for example, in the sampling of moving fluids containing particulate matter, there is considerable risk of obtaining a sample which is biased in respect of concentration of the particulate matter. (This risk may be diminished if isokinetic sampling is practised, as described in BS 5309: Part 1 (1976).)

  In the case of process control the object of taking a sample is usually to assess the current performance of the process. To do this effectively the sample should be of the most recent output or process control parameter possible.

  In some situations it is not practical to make a random selection of the output to be examined. Consider for example a drum containing 50kg of a powdered product from which it is desired to take a 450g sample composed of 15 randomly chosen 30g portions. The drum itself contains nearly 1700 such portions and to make a random selection from these would require first, that each portion could be separately identified and secondly, that each portion could then be handled separately from the rest of the material. In no other way could the criteria of random selection be satisfied and in practical terms this would require that the contents of the drum should be emptied out and divided into 30g portions from which 15 portions are randomly chosen;
- the type of sampling – this may be single, double, multiple, sequential, continuous or stratified sampling (see Section 13.7 for descriptions of these terms);
- frequency of sampling – this is determined by a number of factors such as: the cost of checking, inspection or testing; the cost incurred as a result of non-conforming material or output being accepted; the volume of output; the cost of passing non-conforming product or service to the customer; the nature and stability of the process; the nature of the material, outputs or parameters to be

sampled; and the frequency of changes that may affect quality;

- separating of samples – the samples should be kept separate from the population if possible, until a decision has been reached as to their acceptability or the nature of their characteristics;
- safety – in certain cases the very act of taking a sample exposes the sampler to a risk of personal injury or may give rise to hazardous conditions endangering the safety of others. A number of recommendations are outlined in BS 5309: Part 1 (1976) which are intended to assist those persons engaged in, or directing, the sampling, and also those responsible for premises within which sampling is performed, to ensure that sampling is a safe operation.

13.5 Non-normal data

For any observed data from a process, it is possible to try to fit the data to many different distributions. However, for the sake of simplicity and because the means of samples of small size tend more to normality than the individual observations from which they are drawn, the so called *normal distribution* (see Chapter 15) will be a reasonable first basis for investigation. Many of the statistical methods recommended in the British Standards are based on the assumption that the variables to which the methods apply are independently distributed according to the normal distribution. In a number of practical situations the true shape of the distribution encountered is often non-normal. For example, some special cause of variation distorting the distribution, and measures such as squareness, parallelism, flatness, ovality, eccentricity or pH values, cause the distribution to be skewed. It must be stressed that no process will ever be exactly normal; it is simply that the normal distribution provides an adequate model for the process under study. There are transformations, for example taking logarithms, that can be applied to non-normal variables to make their distributions approximate more closely to a normal distribution.

Some people become quite concerned about whether the data from a process conforms with a normal distribution and the effects of this on the resulting calculations. These people are familiar with the tests for assessing departure from the normal distribution by the use of measures for skewness and kurtosis (a measure of the concentration of a distribution about its mean). Others are oblivious to this and always assume a normal distribution. Dale *et al* (1989) reporting on a study of the use of SPC in the motor industry, found that 97 out of 145 respondents always carry out a check for normality before calculation of process capability; 39 said they did not; and 9 were not aware of the importance of this process.

Calculation of process capability requires that the pattern of variation exhibited by a process is compared to that of a known statistical distribution. The Statistical Methods Council of Ford of Europe, in carrying out an investigation into the way computerised SPC systems dealt with related data, found that many packages do not apply the correct statistical techniques. 'Almost all assume normal distribution and perform calculations based on this assumption. Many even attempt to fit a normal curve to an obviously non-normal histogram' (Ford Motor Company, 1987). Clearly, the distribution of data should be examined using, for example, a tally chart or histogram to determine its shape. This simple method should be one of the first steps in systematic data analysis.

It is interesting to note that there have been a number of practical experiments and considerable research work which have studied the effects of assuming a normal distribution when the data was in fact, non-normal, for example Scherkenbach (1986) quotes Chebyshev's theorem and the findings of Camp and Meidall. The findings from such work were that the errors in assuming a normal distribution were, in the main, not significant.

13.6 Normality tests

BS 2846: Part 7 (1984) provides a selection of tests which may be used to decide whether or not the hypothesis of normality is acceptable.

The simplest way of testing the normality of the distribution of a series of observations is by plotting a graph, using normal linear probability graph paper, of the observations. This transforms the bell-shaped normal distribution into a straight line. By checking if the plotted points lie in a reasonably straight line, it is possible to observe immediately whether the distribution is close to the normal. A non-linear plot indicates non-normality. If the plot is a smooth concave curve, this suggests a log-normal distribution. Although such a graphical representation cannot be considered as a rigorous test, it permits a subjective judgement of the normality of the data, and the summary information that it provides is an essential supplement to any other normality tests. A statistical 'goodness of fit' test may be used for a more objective assessment.

Formal normality tests are a means of checking the hypothesis of normality for statistical purposes. They are a special sort of hypothesis test and consist of the calculation of the function T of the observation, which is called the statistic of the test. The null hypothesis of a normal distribution is then accepted or rejected depending on whether or not the value of T lies within a set of values, near to the ideal value that corresponds to the normal distribution. Chi-squared (χ^2) tests can also be used for such testing.

13.7 Definitions and terminology

The following are some useful terms and definitions used in this chapter.

Continuous sampling: a method of sampling associated with continuous or flow production, where sampling is interrupted by periods of 100 per cent inspection, depending on the results from sampling.

Double sampling: a method of sampling which consists in taking a second sample, according to the information given by the first.

Inspection: activities such as measuring, examining, testing and gauging one or more characteristics of a product or service and comparing these with specified requirements to determine conformity.

Multi-sampling: a type of sampling which consists in taking up to k successive samples, the decision to take the ith sample ($i > k$) being dependent on the information given by the $(i-1)$th sample.

One hundred per cent (100%) inspection: inspection of every item of product or service, i.e. the whole (as contrasted with any form of sampling inspection).

Population: the totality of the product, process and customers, under consideration.

Production batch: a definite quantity of some commodity, or service, produced at one time under conditions that are presumed uniform.

Sample: one or more sampling units taken from a population (lot or process) and intended to provide information on the population (lot or process), and possibly to serve as a basis for making a decision on the population (lot or process).

Sample size: the number of items or units in the sample.

Sampling: the procedure used to draw or constitute a sample.

Sampling inspection: the inspection of products or services using samples (as distinct from 100% inspection).

Sampling plan: a specific plan which states the sample size(s) to be used and the associated criteria for accepting the lot.

Sampling procedure: instructions relating to the use of particular sampling schemes and/or sampling plans.

Sampling scheme: a combination of sampling plans with rules for changing from one plan to another.

Sampling system: a collection of sampling schemes, each with its own rules for changing plans, together with criteria by which appropriate schemes may be chosen.

Sequential sampling: a method of sampling which consists in taking items, or sometimes successive groups of items, but without fixing their number in advance. The decision to accept or reject the lot is taken as soon as the results permit, according to rules laid down in advance.

Simple random sampling: the taking of n items from a population of N items in such a way that all possible combinations of n items have the same probability of being chosen.

Single sampling: a method of sampling which consists in taking only one sample from the lot, batch or process.

Stratified sampling: a type of sampling in which the population is divided into different sub-populations (*strata*) and sampling is then carried out so that specified populations of the sample are drawn from different strata. This is appropriate whenever a lot can be split into sub-batches according to some logical criteria, for example a sample drawn from a batch which has been delivered in two boxes.

British Standards

BS 2846: *Guide to statistical interpretation of data* Part 7: 1984 *Tests for departure from normality* (ISO/DIS 5479: 1984).

BS 2897: 1970 (1985) *Application of statistics to paper testing*.

BS 4778: *Quality vocabulary* Part 1: 1987 *International terms* (ISO 8402: 1986) (EN 28402: 1991); Part 2: 1991 *Quality concepts and related definitions*.

BS 5309: *Methods for sampling chemical products* Part 1: 1976 *Introduction and general principles* (ISO 3165: 1976); Part 2 *Sampling of gases* (ISO 4257: 1976); Part 3 *Sampling of liquids*; Part 4 *Sampling of solids* (ISO 8213: 1976).

BS 5532: *Statistical terminology* Part 1: 1978 *Glossary of terms relating to probability and general terms relating to statistics* (ISO 3534: 1978).

BS 5700: 1984 *Guide to process control using quality control methods and cusum techniques*.

BS 6000: 1972 *Guide to the use of BS 6001, sampling procedures and tables for inspection by attributes* (ISO 2859/Addendum 1: 1972).

BS 6001: *Sampling procedures for inspection by attributes* Part 1: 1991 *Specification for sampling plans indexed by acceptable quality level (AQL) for lot-by-lot inspection* (ISO 2859–1: 1989).

BS 6002: 1979 *Specification for sampling procedures and charts for inspection by variables for percent defective* (ISO 3951: 1979).

References

Dale B G, Owen M and Shaw P. *SPC in the Motor Industry: What is the state-of-the-art?* Occasional Paper No. 8902, Manchester School of Management, UMIST, 1989.

Ford Motor Company. *SPC Newsletter No. 2.* Statistical Methods Office, Manufacturing, Ford Motor Company, Essex, 1987.

Scherkenbach W W. *The Deming Route to Quality and Productivity,* Cee Press, Washington DC, USA, 1986.

CHAPTER 14

Acceptance sampling

14.1 Introduction

Acceptance sampling is an inspection method in which decisions, based on a sample of the batch or product, are made to accept or reject a product. It is employed in situations where there is a continuous flow of batches between supplier and customer. The general assumption is that a manufacturer presents batches to an inspector who accepts or rejects them on behalf of a customer, in the light of clearly defined, laid down requirements. The manufacturer can be a department internal to an organisation or an outside supplier. In the case of the latter the acceptance sampling is generally carried out at the customer's goods inwards department. It is sometimes a requirement of a major customer that a supplier takes regular samples of their production output using acceptance sampling to determine whether or not the product is of the acceptable quality. The customer's quality system standard will outline the circumstances where this is applied along with the sampling plan to be used. To be of value, sampling inspection has to be carried out in a prescribed and disciplined manner (e.g. using the sampling plans and procedures given in BS 6001: Part 1 (1991) and Parts 2 and 3 (1993) and BS 6002 (1979)).

The acceptance procedure can be based on attributes or variables data, the latter having been little used in industry to date. BS 6001: Part 1 (1991) and Parts 2 and 3 (1993) and BS 6002 (1979) deal with the sampling procedures for inspection by attributes and by variables respectively.

The sampling procedures outlined in BS 6001: Parts 1, 2 and 3 were developed following the work of a joint American, British and Canadian working group which led to an 'ABC' agreement in 1962 to standardise the military sampling inspection tables of the three countries. The sampling plans given in BS 6001: Parts 1, 2 and 3 are, of course, only a selection from all possible plans. However, if an organisation is using acceptance sampling the scheme is likely to be based on this Standard.

The purpose of the BS 6001 Series is to induce a supplier through the economic and psychological pressure of lot non-acceptance to maintain a process average at least as good as the specified acceptable quality level (AQL), while at the same time minimizing the risk to the consumer of accepting the occasional poor lot. Sampling plans designated in BS 6001: Part 1 (1991) are applicable, but not limited, to inspection of:

- finished products;
- components and raw materials;
- operations;
- materials in process;

- supplies in storage;
- maintenance operations;
- data or records;
- administrative procedures.

The sampling plans are intended primarily to be used for a continuing series of lots sufficient to allow the switching rules to be applied, which provide for:

- an automatic protection to the consumer, should a deterioration in quality be detected (by a switch to tightened inspection or discontinuance of inspection);
- an incentive to reduce inspection costs (at the discretion of the responsible authority) should consistently good quality be achieved (by a switch to reduced inspection). The responsible authority may be:
  - the quality department within a supplier's organisation (first party);
  - the purchaser or procurement organisation (second party);
  - an independent verification of certification authority (third party).

As already mentioned in this book, the emphasis of any quality system should be on prevention rather than detection. The latter system should help to prevent non-conforming parts from being passed to the customer, but does not stop them being made. Acceptance sampling is a screening technique based on after-the-event detection. The use of acceptance sampling by a customer at goods inward might be seen as diverting some of the responsibility for product quality from supplier to customer. Thus the customer's inspection becomes a vital ingredient in the supplier's quality control system; clearly an unacceptable situation. Furthermore, the idea of employing a certain proportion of defectives as a measure of the quality required in the product goes against the aim of trying to get suppliers to deliver batches of product which are free from nonconformities and also to pursue continuous improvement. It should also be pointed out that inspection of incoming goods is a non-value adding activity.

Companies which are at the leading edge in their quality improvement activities, pursue policies of ship-to-stock ship-to-production line deliveries along with developing closer working relationships with their respective supplier communities. They tend to employ a minimum of incoming inspection to the supplied product. Their confidence in a supplier's ability is based on frequent assessment of the adequacy of the supplier's quality system, measurement and monitoring of supplier performance, and the commitment to TQM as practised by the supplier's senior management team. The quality thinking of such companies is based on quality levels measured in parts per million and in some cases parts per billion. In such situations employing sampling procedures to assess product quality is considered to be impracticable.

However, there are a considerable number of companies in which the behaviour and attitudes of the senior management team is not in line with continuous quality improvement and their quality systems are rudimentary. In these organisations their quality performance is usually measured in terms of per cent nonconformity. Therefore, for these companies, the use of acceptance sampling is a method of sampling consistent with these levels and can be a stepping stone for the customer to build up data on supplier performance, develop confidence in their ability or attempt to change performance by other means. Once this point has been reached the techniques of reduced inspection, skip-lot inspection, audit inspection and finally no inspection at all can be considered.

This chapter presents the main features of acceptance sampling based on the procedures documented in BS 6000 (1972) and BS 6001: Part 1 (1991) and Parts 2 and 3 (1993) and is written around industrial-type situations. However, it is possible to use acceptance sampling in commerce, public organisations and service-type situations (for example, accounts and invoicing).

The authors point out that they do not recommend the use of acceptance sampling as a means of controlling and improving product and service quality.

14.2 The methods of acceptance inspection

The main aim of any acceptance inspection is to see that the customer gets the level of quality (per cent non-conformity units or non-conformities per 100 units) they specify. The three main methods used in performing this task are 100 per cent inspection, acceptance sampling and ad hoc sampling. All three methods are based on discovering defects in a product after processing. Shingo (1986) calls acceptance inspection 'judgement inspections'.

100 per cent inspection

With *100 per cent inspection* every item produced is examined. Today 100 per cent inspection is the exception rather than the rule. This method is expensive and due mainly to human error, is often not 100 per cent effective. However, it does have its place in some quality systems. Automation has greatly reduced the cost of inspection and improved its effectiveness, and in a number of industries it is often necessary to carry out 100 per cent inspection of parts using automated test procedures and equipment, for example, in the aerospace, defence and electronics industries.

Probably the most serious criticism of 100 per cent inspection is that it appears to divert the responsibility for product quality from the producer to the inspector and tends to hide the true causes of non-conformance. There is a feeling that the inspector is there to sort things out, so that, within limits, what happens in production is not of such vital importance. However, there are some items where safety is of critical importance (for example, aircraft structural components and components used in sophisticated weapons) so it is considered that every item made must be examined. Where this is the case a real effort should be made to ensure that a system is devised that clearly places responsibility for quality with the producer. The quality plan will identify the stages of the production process where agreement has been reached with the customer that a 100 per cent inspection or test operation is required.

Acceptance sampling

Acceptance sampling is based on the mathematical theory of probability. Sampling does involve risks which are a feature of the sampling plan criteria. These risks cannot be eliminated but they can be accurately assessed by statistical techniques. With this method the inspector can no longer be regarded as the person who sorts things out. The producer must see that the product quality is right, otherwise much trouble and expense will be incurred with rejected batches being returned. The object of a statistically-designed sampling plan is to ensure that batches of the AQL, or better, have a high probability of acceptance and that batches with higher non-conformity levels will almost certainly be rejected.

It is important that all decisions regarding acceptance or rejection of a batch of product are based on a *random sample*, i.e. the sample should be representative of the entire production run that produced the batch in question. Most sampling schemes relate sample size to batch size because of the need to ensure a representative sample, which becomes increasingly more difficult as the batch size increases. Accordingly, the penalty for rejecting a good batch or accepting a bad batch, based perhaps on insufficient sample data, also increases.

Ad hoc sampling

Ad hoc sampling is not based on the theory of probability and involves the inspection of a fixed percentage, fixed number or spot checking. This method lacks credibility and is certainly not to be recommended since it leads to uncalculated, and often to unjustifiably high, risks. Furthermore, there is no formal basis for making decisions on acceptance or rejection of the product.

Mistake proofing

In writing about inspection it would be remiss not to mention *poka-yoke (mistake-proofing) systems*. The concept of poka-yoke was developed in Japan and involves the use of simple devices to stop defects and errors occurring at source. Management should encourage their designers, production engineers and technical specialists to think along such lines in the design and preparation of products for production. Shingo describes source inspection as 'inspection methods that, rather than stimulating feedback and action in response to defects, are based on the idea of discovering errors in conditions that give rise to defects and performing feedback and action at the error stage so as to keep those errors from turning into defects' (Shingo, 1986). With poka-yoke systems in use, 100 per cent inspections are in fact taking place.

14.3 Developing and operating a single sampling plan

Before developing a sampling plan from the tables given in BS 6001: Part 1 (1991) it is necessary for the person constructing the plan to know five things, these are:

- the acceptable quality level (AQL) – the designated value of per cent non-conforming (or non-conformities per 100 units) that will be accepted most of the time by the sampling scheme to be used;
- the inspection level;
- whether normal, tightened or reduced inspection is to be used. This is decided by studying the sampling results of the last few batches;
- whether single, double, multiple or sequential sampling is to be employed. Usually the same form of sampling will be used for all the successive batches in a production run, but this is not essential – a change may be made when desired;
- the batch size.

Inspection level

The inspection level required for any particular application should be prescribed by the responsible authority. This allows the authority to require greater discrimination for some purposes and less for others. The choice of inspection level is quite separate from normal, reduced, or tightened inspection. Three inspection levels are given in Table 14.1 for general use. Unless otherwise specified, Level II should be used; Level I may be used when less discrimination is needed or Level III when greater discrimination is needed. Four additional special levels, S-1 to S-4 are given in Table 14.1 and may be used where relatively small sample sizes are

Table 14.1 Sample size code letters

Lot or batch size			Special inspection levels				General inspection levels		
			S-1	S-2	S-3	S-4	I	II	III
2	to	8	A	A	A	A	A	A	B
9	to	15	A	A	A	A	A	B	C
16	to	25	A	A	B	B	B	C	D
26	to	50	A	B	B	C	C	D	E
51	to	90	B	B	C	C	C	E	F
91	to	150	B	B	C	D	D	F	G
151	to	280	B	C	D	E	E	G	H
281	to	500	B	C	D	E	F	H	J
501	to	1200	C	C	E	F	G	J	K
1201	to	3200	C	D	E	G	H	K	L
3201	to	10 000	C	D	F	G	J	L	M
10 001	to	35 000	C	D	F	H	K	M	N
35 001	to	150 000	D	E	G	J	L	N	P
150 001	to	500 000	D	E	G	J	M	P	Q
500 001	and	over	D	E	H	K	N	Q	R

Source: BS 6001: Part 1, 1972

necessary and large sampling risks can and should be tolerated.

Acceptable quality level

In developing a sampling plan attention needs to be paid to the choice of AQL. If a customer designates an AQL which is in excess of the producer's process average (assuming this is known), the plan will more than likely accept all the batches submitted. If on the other hand, the designated AQL is less than the process average, the producer will have great difficulty in getting a batch accepted. Almost invariably this will mean a compromise between the quality the customer would like and the quality which can be afforded. The tighter the requirement the more expensive will be the production activities to meet it and the inspection to ensure that it is met. The AQL is the chosen border line between what will be considered as a satisfactory or unsatisfactory process average.

The designation of an AQL does not imply that a proportion of non-conforming items up to this level is wanted, or is completely acceptable; it is always better to have no non-confirming items. The more the proportion can be reduced below the AQL, the better and the greater the probability of accepting each lot. The AQL to be used should be designated in the contract or by, or according to, the responsible authority.

The value of the AQL selected is usually dependent upon physical and economic constraints, such as the natural process limits and the costs of inspection balanced against the costs of failure. Different AQLs may be designated for groups of non-conformities considered collectively or for individual non-conformities.

The AQL alone does not describe the protection to the consumer. It is necessary to refer to the operating characteristic curve of the sampling plan used, or to the average outgoing quality limit (AOQL) of the plan, to ascertain the likely consumer protection.

The AQL is a parameter of the sampling scheme and should not be confused with the process average which describes the operating level of the process. It is expected that the process average will be less than or equal to the AQL to avoid excessive rejections. The designation of an AQL in no way implies that the supplier has the right knowingly to supply any non-conforming unit of product.

It is crucial to the success of a customer–supplier relationship that there is mutual agreement between them on AQL and they both understand the reasoning behind sampling plans.

The values of the AQLs given in the tables of BS 6001: Part 1 (1991) are known as preferred AQLs. If, for any product, an AQL other than a preferred AQL is designated, these tables are not applicable.

In general, the AQL and inspection level will be laid down for a particular product at the beginning of a contract and will remain constant throughout the contract.

Example

The following example will illustrate how a sampling plan is determined. Suppose the AQL is 1.5 per cent, the inspection level is II, the batch size is 6000 and normal single sampling is being used.

The first requirement is to determine the sample size code letter. This is merely an indexing device to enable reference to be made from one part of the tables to another. For a batch size of 6000 and inspection level II, Table 14.1 (relating to Table 1 of BS 6001: Part 1 (1991)) gives the sample size code letter as L. Then using the appropriate table, Table 14.2 (relating to Table II–A of BS 6001: Part 1 (1991)), it is seen that against code letter L, a sample size of 200 is specified; and in the column for an AQL of 1.5 per cent the acceptance and rejection numbers 7 and 8 are found. This gives a sampling plan of:

sample size 200;
acceptance number 7 (the acceptance number is sometimes designated c);
rejection number 8.

The way this plan is operated is to draw a random sample of 200 units of product from the batch of 6000. The sample is then inspected and the number of non-conforming units discovered is counted. If the number of non-conforming units is less than, or equal to, the acceptance number of 7, the entire batch is

Table 14.2 Single sampling plans for normal inspection (master table)

Sample size code letter	Sample size	Acceptable quality levels (normal inspection)																									
		0.010	0.015	0.025	0.040	0.065	0.10	0.15	0.25	0.40	0.65	1.0	1.5	2.5	4.0	6.5	10	15	25	40	65	100	150	250	400	650	1000
		Ac Re	Ac Re	Ac Re	Ac Re	Ac Re	Ac Re	Ac Re	Ac Re	Ac Re	Ac Re	Ac Re	Ac Re	Ac Re	Ac Re	Ac Re	Ac Re	Ac Re	Ac Re	Ac Re	Ac Re	Ac Re	Ac Re	Ac Re	Ac Re	Ac Re	Ac Re
A	2	↓	↓	↓	↓	↓	↓	↓	↓	↓	↓	↓	↓	↓	↓	0 1	↓	↓	1 2	2 3	3 4	5 6	7 8	10 11	14 15	21 22	30 31
B	3	↓	↓	↓	↓	↓	↓	↓	↓	↓	↓	↓	↓	↓	0 1	↑	↓	1 2	2 3	3 4	5 6	7 8	10 11	14 15	21 22	30 31	44 45
C	5	↓	↓	↓	↓	↓	↓	↓	↓	↓	↓	↓	↓	0 1	↑	↓	1 2	2 3	3 4	5 6	7 8	10 11	14 15	21 22	30 31	44 45	↑
D	8	↓	↓	↓	↓	↓	↓	↓	↓	↓	↓	↓	0 1	↑	↓	1 2	2 3	3 4	5 6	7 8	10 11	14 15	21 22	30 31	44 45	↑	↑
E	13	↓	↓	↓	↓	↓	↓	↓	↓	↓	↓	0 1	↑	↓	1 2	2 3	3 4	5 6	7 8	10 11	14 15	21 22	30 31	44 45	↑	↑	↑
F	20	↓	↓	↓	↓	↓	↓	↓	↓	↓	0 1	↑	↓	1 2	2 3	3 4	5 6	7 8	10 11	14 15	21 22	↑	↑	↑	↑	↑	↑
G	32	↓	↓	↓	↓	↓	↓	↓	↓	0 1	↑	↓	1 2	2 3	3 4	5 6	7 8	10 11	14 15	21 22	↑	↑	↑	↑	↑	↑	↑
H	50	↓	↓	↓	↓	↓	↓	↓	0 1	↑	↓	1 2	2 3	3 4	5 6	7 8	10 11	14 15	21 22	↑	↑	↑	↑	↑	↑	↑	↑
J	80	↓	↓	↓	↓	↓	↓	0 1	↑	↓	1 2	2 3	3 4	5 6	7 8	10 11	14 15	21 22	↑	↑	↑	↑	↑	↑	↑	↑	↑
K	125	↓	↓	↓	↓	↓	0 1	↑	↓	1 2	2 3	3 4	5 6	7 8	10 11	14 15	21 22	↑	↑	↑	↑	↑	↑	↑	↑	↑	↑
L	200	↓	↓	↓	↓	0 1	↑	↓	1 2	2 3	3 4	5 6	7 8	10 11	14 15	21 22	↑	↑	↑	↑	↑	↑	↑	↑	↑	↑	↑
M	315	↓	↓	↓	0 1	↑	↓	1 2	2 3	3 4	5 6	7 8	10 11	14 15	21 22	↑	↑	↑	↑	↑	↑	↑	↑	↑	↑	↑	↑
N	500	↓	↓	0 1	↑	↓	1 2	2 3	3 4	5 6	7 8	10 11	14 15	21 22	↑	↑	↑	↑	↑	↑	↑	↑	↑	↑	↑	↑	↑
P	800	↓	0 1	↑	↓	1 2	2 3	3 4	5 6	7 8	10 11	14 15	21 22	↑	↑	↑	↑	↑	↑	↑	↑	↑	↑	↑	↑	↑	↑
Q*	1250	0 1	↑	↓	1 2	2 3	3 4	5 6	7 8	10 11	14 15	21 22	↑	↑	↑	↑	↑	↑	↑	↑	↑	↑	↑	↑	↑	↑	↑
R	2000	↑	↑	1 2	2 3	3 4	5 6	7 8	10 11	14 15	21 22	↑	↑	↑	↑	↑	↑	↑	↑	↑	↑	↑	↑	↑	↑	↑	↑

Notes

↓ = Use first sampling plan below arrow. If sample size equals, or exceeds, lot or batch size, do 100 per cent inspection.

↑ = Use first sampling plan above arrow.

Ac = Acceptance number.

Re = Rejection number.

Source: BS 6001: Part 1, 1972

accepted, with the exception of any units that were found to be non-conforming in the sample – these should be rejected and subsequently replaced with conforming units.

If, on the other hand, the number of non-conforming units is greater than, or equal to, the rejection number of 8, the entire batch is rejected and returned to the manufacturer (unless otherwise agreed).

In a single sampling plan, the rejection number is always one unit greater than the acceptance number (with the exception of reduced inspection). Therefore, a positive decision to accept or reject will always be reached by this procedure.

The *operating characteristics (OC) curve* of this sampling plan is shown in Table 14.3 (relating to Table X–L of BS 6001: Part 1)1991)). An OC curve indicates the percentage of lots or batches which may be expected to be accepted under various sampling plans for a given process quality. The OC curve is marked 1.5 (the AQL value) to distinguish it from the OC curves for other AQLs which are on the same chart. This curve is reproduced in Figure 14.1 (relating to Figure 1 of BS 6000 (1972)) which also shows the method of interpreting any particular point on the curve. For example, suppose it is required to know what will happen if a manufacturer submits a large number of batches all from a process producing 3 per cent non-conformity and this plan is applied to these batches. A vertical line is raised on the graph at the 3 per cent defective point and where it meets the OC curve a horizontal line is projected to see where it meets the vertical scale. In this case, it does so at approximately the 75 per cent point, which shows that about three out of every four batches will be accepted under the given circumstances and about one out of every four rejected. Each point on the curve can be interpreted in a similar way.

It is important to understand what this means. In such a case, the three out of every four batches which are accepted still contain 3 per cent non-conforming. If this is above the AQL, then, when the rate of acceptance of batches falls to 75 per cent, all batches, including those accepted by the scheme, must be quarantined and perhaps subjected to 100

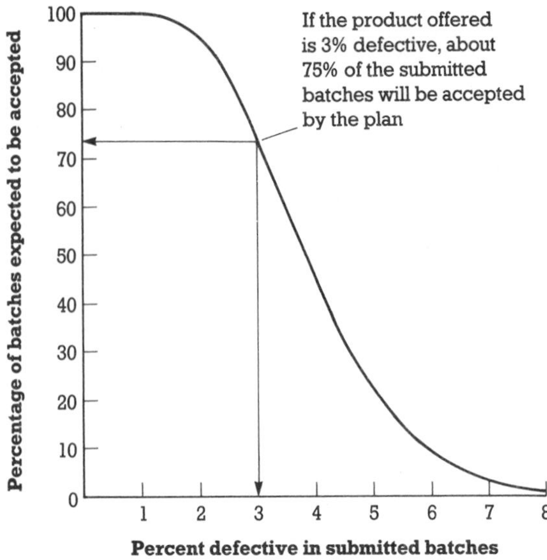

Notes

Sample size	200
Acceptance number	7
Rejection number	8

Source: BS 6000: 1972

Figure 14.1 Operating characteristic curve of a single-sampling plan

per cent screening. It is only by monitoring the acceptance rate of batches in this way that the sampling schemes may be used to detect an increase in the rate of non-conforming units.

In addition to the OC curve Table 14.3 also shows a table (relating to Table X–L–I of BS 6001: Part 1 (1991)), which gives tabulated values from which the curves were drawn. From these, certain points on the curve can be derived more accurately than by eye from the curves themselves. The left-hand column in the table refers to the vertical scale of the charts while the figures given below each AQL value refer to the horizontal scale. For example, in the 1.5 AQL column, it is found that if batches from a process producing 1.99 per cent non-conforming are offered, 95 per cent of them will be accepted if the given plan is used. Whereas if batches from a process producing 5.89 per cent non-conforming are offered, only 10 per cent of them will be accepted.

An increasing trend is for a customer to use a zero acceptance sampling plan (i.e. $c = 0$). The increase in popularity can be explained by the

Table 14.3 Tables for sample size code letter: L

Table X-L – Tables for sample size code letter: L

CHART L – OPERATING CHARACTERISTIC CURVES FOR SINGLE SAMPLING PLANS

(Curves for double and multiple sampling are matched as closely as practicable)

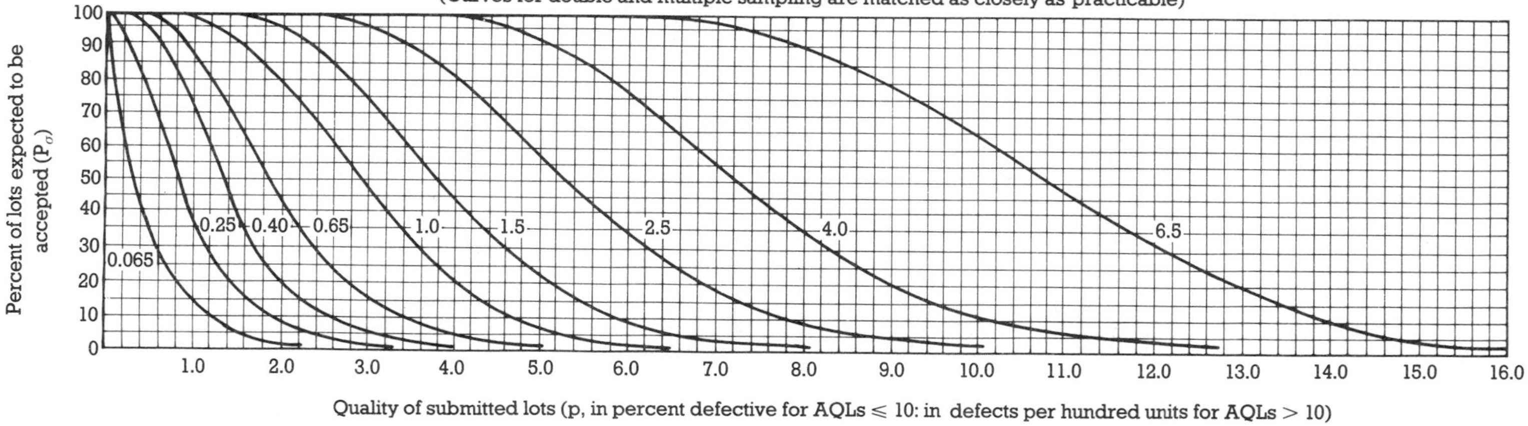

Percent of lots expected to be accepted (P_a)

100 90 80 70 60 50 40 30 20 10 0

0.065 0.25 0.40 0.65 1.0 1.5 2.5 4.0 6.5

1.0 2.0 3.0 4.0 5.0 6.0 7.0 8.0 9.0 10.0 11.0 12.0 13.0 14.0 15.0 16.0

Quality of submitted lots (p, in percent defective for AQLs ⩽ 10: in defects per hundred units for AQLs > 10)

Note: Figures on curves are Acceptable Quality Levels (AQLs) for normal inspection

Source: BS 6001: Part 1, 1972

Table X–L–1 Tabulated values for operating characteristic curves for single sampling plans

P.	Acceptable quality levels (normal inspection)											
	0.065	0.25	0.40	0.65	1.0	1.5	X	2.5	X	4.0	X	6.5
	p (in per cent defective or defects per hundred units)											
99.0	0.0051	0.075	0.218	0.412	0.893	1.45	1.75	2.39	3.05	3.74	5.17	6.29
95.0	0.0256	0.178	0.409	0.683	1.31	1.99	2.35	3.09	3.85	4.62	6.22	7.45
99.0	0.0525	0.266	0.551	0.873	1.58	2.33	2.72	3.51	4.32	5.15	6.84	8.12
75.0	0.144	0.481	0.864	1.27	2.11	2.98	3.42	4.31	5.21	6.12	7.95	9.34
50.0	0.347	0.839	1.34	1.84	2.84	3.84	4.33	5.33	6.33	7.33	9.33	10.8
25.0	0.693	1.35	1.96	2.56	3.71	4.84	5.40	6.51	7.61	8.70	10.9	12.5
10.0	1.15	1.95	2.66	3.34	4.64	5.89	6.50	7.70	8.89	10.1	12.4	14.1
5.0	1.50	2.37	3.15	3.88	5.26	6.57	7.22	8.48	9.72	10.9	13.3	15.1
1.0	2.30	3.32	4.20	5.02	6.55	8.00	8.70	10.1	11.4	12.7	15.3	17.2
	0.10	0.40	0.65	1.0	1.5	X	2.5	X	4.0	X	6.5	X
	Acceptable quality levels (tightened inspection)											

Note: All values given in above table based on poisson distribution as an approximation to the binomial.

Source: BS 6001: Part 1, 1972

following argument. If a scheme with an acceptance number greater than zero is used, it implies that a company is willing to accept batches containing non-conforming product and this is seen as contrary to the concept of zero defects and continuous improvement. However, such a sampling scheme cannot guarantee zero defects.

14.4 Normal, tightened and reduced inspection

Normal inspection

When the AQL has been specified for any particular product, the ideal would be to have a system whereby batches are always accepted when their per cent non-conforming or non-conformities per 100 units is better than the AQL and always rejected when their quality is worse, i.e. an OC curve which descended vertically at the AQL as shown in Figure 14.2 (relating to Figure 3 of BS 6000 (1972)). This ideal is something that no sampling plan can reproduce exactly, so an OC curve has to be accepted that descends at an angle less than the vertical.

An OC curve can cross the ideal vertical line at only one point, and the question is, at what point should it cross? One possible solution is to let the curve cross the vertical line near the bottom of the diagram, as in Figure 14.3 (relating to Figure 4 of BS 6000 (1972)). To choose a sampling plan that does this has the advantage of protecting the customer, since if any batch is submitted with a quality worse than the AQL it will have a high chance of rejection. This sampling plan is unsatisfactory from the manufacturer's point of view. It can be seen from Figure 14.3, that only just over one batch in five would be accepted if the percentage non-conforming were only half the AQL and less than half the batches would be accepted even if the percentage non-conforming were as little as one quarter of the AQL.

An alternative solution is to let the curve cross the vertical line near the top of the diagram, as in Figure 14.4 (relating to Figure 5 of BS 6000 (1972)). This will satisfy the manufacturer, since, if a batch is produced which is as good as, or better than, the AQL, they are almost certain of acceptance. It will now be the customer's turn to complain, for if the manufacturer were to submit batches of a worse quality than the AQL there might be a high probability of them being accepted. For example, in the case illustrated in Figure 14.4, if batches were offered with a percentage non-conforming twice the AQL, then nearly 60 per cent of such batches would be accepted.

To meet the requirements of both manufacturer and customer some compromise is needed, and the one adopted in BS 6001: Part 1 (1991) is that of normal inspection and tightened inspection. With this procedure two sampling plans are specified for any given situation, together with rules for determining when to switch from one to the other and back again.

Normal inspection is designed to protect the manufacturer against having a high proportion of batches rejected even though the quality is better than the AQL. In effect, the manufacturer is being given the benefit of any doubt that may arise due to sampling variability. But the customer needs protection too, and this is achieved by ensuring that the manufacturer is not indiscriminately given the benefit of the

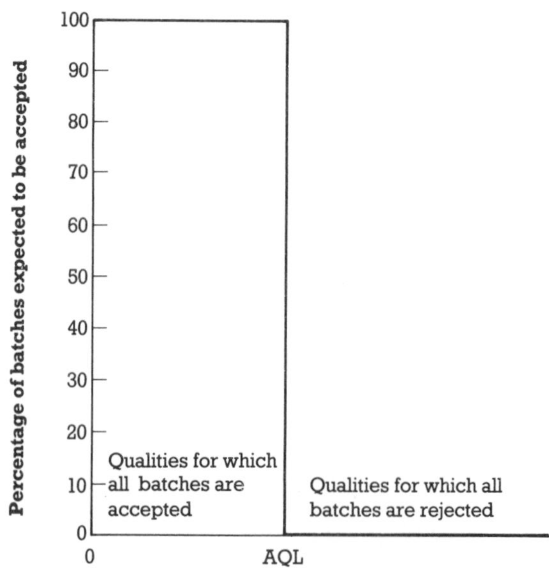

Figure 14.2 The ideal, but unattainable, OC curve

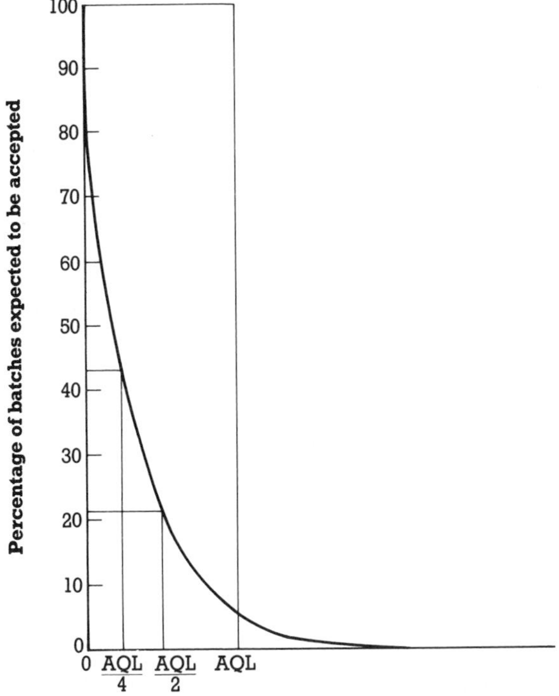

Figure 14.3 TOC curve of a sampling plan designed to give a high probability of rejection if any batch having a quality worse than the AQL is submitted

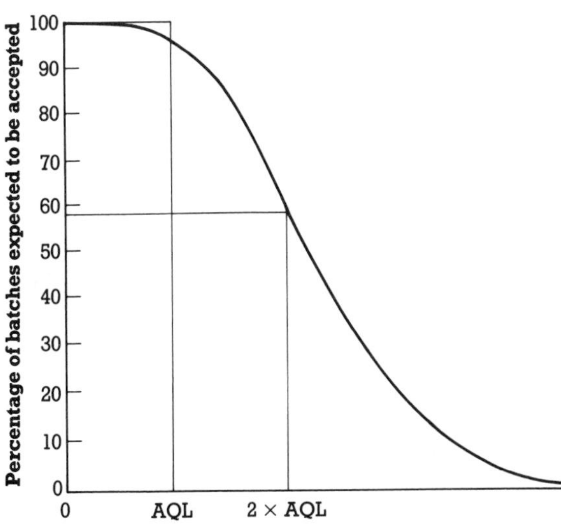

Figure 14.4 OC curve of a sampling plan designed to give a high probability of acceptance if any batch having a quality better than the AQL is submitted

doubt, but only for as long as worthiness is proven. If at any time the sampling results show that quality is probably worse than the AQL, the manufacturer forfeits the right to the benefit of the doubt (that is, the right to normal inspection) and tightened inspection is instituted to protect the customer. Normal inspection, then, has OC curves that cross the vertical line at the AQL near the top, but the exact level at which they cross varies from plan to plan.

Tightened inspection

When tightened inspection is called for, the required plan is drawn from tables (albeit different ones) in just the same way as for normal inspection. In general, it will be found that a tightened plan has the same sample size as the corresponding normal plan but a smaller acceptance number. However, if the normal inspection acceptance number is 1, changing it to zero would lead to an unreasonable degree of tightening, and if the normal inspection acceptance number is 0, no smaller number is available. In both these cases, tightening is performed by keeping the acceptance number the same as for normal inspection while increasing the sample size.

Switching procedures between normal and tightened inspection

The rule used in BS 6001: Part 1 (1991) is that when normal inspection is in effect, tightened inspection be instituted when two out of five consecutive lots have been rejected on original inspection (i.e. ignoring resubmitted lots for this procedure).

When tightened inspection is in effect, normal inspection shall be instituted when five consecutive lots have been considered acceptable on original inspection.

There is one further safeguard for the customer. This is the rule given in BS 6001: Part 1 (1991) that acceptance inspection should be discontinued, pending action to improve the quality, if ten consecutive lots remain on tightened inspection.

Reduced inspection

Sometimes there is evidence that the production quality from a process is consistently better than the AQL. When this happens and there is reason to suppose that this situation will continue, a sampling plan is no longer needed to segregate the good batches from the bad ones, since all the batches will be good ones. However, inspection cannot be dispensed with altogether, since a warning is needed if the production quality worsens. In these circumstances, considerable savings can be made by using reduced inspection sampling plans, which in the majority of cases have sample sizes only two-fifths the size of those of the corresponding normal inspection plans.

The required plan is determined from tables in the same way as for normal inspection and tightened inspection.

Switching procedures between normal and reduced inspection

The use of tightened inspection, when called for by the switching rules, is essential to the use of the BS 6001: Part 1 (1991) scheme, but reduced inspection is entirely optional. Even if the conditions outlined in the switching rules are met, switching need not be introduced. The switching rules are designed to ensure that reduced inspection is not introduced unless the product quality is genuinely good and is likely to continue to be so.

When normal inspection is in effect, reduced inspection shall be instituted provided that all of the following conditions are satisfied:

- The preceding ten lots or more (indicated by the note to Table VIII of BS 6001: Part 1 (1991) corresponding to Table 14.4) have been on normal inspection and none has been rejected on original inspection.
- The total number of non-conforming units or non-conformities in the samples from the preceding ten lots (or other such number as was used for the first condition above) is equal to or less than the applicable number given in Table 14.4. If double or multiple sampling is in use, all samples inspected should be included.
- Production is at a steady rate. Just what is meant by this calls for some interpretation and it may well vary from one industry to another. Basically, the requirement is that there should have been no break in the production operation sufficient to invalidate the argument that the present product quality is of the required level. The precise meaning in any particular case must depend upon technical judgement based upon the consideration of all factors, the variation of which can affect the quality of the product.
- Reduced inspection is considered desirable by the responsible authority.

When reduced inspection is in effect, normal inspection shall be instituted if any of the following occur:

- a lot is rejected;
- the reduced sampling plans have a gap between the acceptance and rejection numbers (for example, acceptance 7, rejection number 10). If the observed number of non-conforming units in the sample falls in the gap (for example, 8 and 9) between these numbers, the batch is accepted but normal inspection must be restored;
- production becomes irregular or delayed;
- other conditions warrant that normal inspection shall be instituted.

Discontinuation of inspection

If the cumulative number of lots not accepted in a sequence of consecutive lots on original tightened inspection reaches five, the acceptance procedures of BS 6001: Part 1 (1991) should be discontinued. Inspection under the provisions of BS 6001: Part 1 (1991) should not be resumed until action has been taken by the supplier to improve the quality of the submitted product or service. The responsible authority should agree that this action is likely to be effective. Tightened inspection should then be used.

The flow chart of Figure 14.5 illustrates the operation of the switching rules between normal, reduced, tightened and discontinued inspection.

Table 14.4 Limit numbers for reduced inspection

Number of sample units from last ten lots or batches	Acceptable quality level																									
	0.010	0.015	0.025	0.040	0.065	0.10	0.15	0.25	0.40	0.65	1.0	1.5	2.5	4.0	6.5	10	15	25	40	65	100	150	250	400	650	1000
20–29	★	★	★	★	★	★	★	★	★	★	★	★	★	★	★	0	0	2	4	8	14	22	40	68	115	181
30–49	★	★	★	★	★	★	★	★	★	★	★	★	★	★	0	0	1	3	7	13	22	36	63	105	178	277
50–79	★	★	★	★	★	★	★	★	★	★	★	★	★	0	0	2	3	7	14	25	40	63	110	181	301	
80–129	★	★	★	★	★	★	★	★	★	★	★	★	0	0	2	4	7	14	24	42	68	105	181	297		
130–199	★	★	★	★	★	★	★	★	★	★	★	★	0	2	4	7	13	25	42	72	115	177	301	490		
200–319	★	★	★	★	★	★	★	★	★	★	0	0	2	4	8	14	22	40	68	115	181	277	471			
320–499	★	★	★	★	★	★	★	★	★	0	0	1	4	8	14	24	39	68	113	189						
500–799	★	★	★	★	★	★	★	★	0	0	2	3	7	14	25	40	63	110	181							
800–1249	★	★	★	★	★	★	★	0	0	2	4	7	14	24	42	68	105	181								
1250–1999	★	★	★	★	★	★	0	0	2	4	7	13	24	40	69	110	169									
2000–3149	★	★	★	★	★	0	0	2	4	8	14	22	40	68	115	181										
3150–4999	★	★	★	★	0	0	1	4	8	14	24	38	67	111	186											
5000–7999	★	★	★	0	0	2	3	7	14	25	40	63	110	181												
8000–12 499	★	★	0	0	2	4	7	14	24	42	68	105	181													
12 500–19 999	★	0	0	2	4	7	13	24	40	69	110	169														
20 000–31 499	0	0	2	4	8	14	22	40	68	115	181															
31 500–49 999	0	1	4	8	14	24	38	67	111	186																
50 000 & over	2	3	7	14	25	40	63	110	181	301																

★ Denotes that the number of sample units from the last ten lots or batches is not sufficient for reduced inspection for this AQL. In this instance more than ten lots or batches may be used for the calculation, provided that the lots or batches used are the most recent ones in sequence, that they have all been on normal inspection, and that none has been rejected while on original inspection.

Source: BS 6001: Part 1, 1991 (Table VIII)

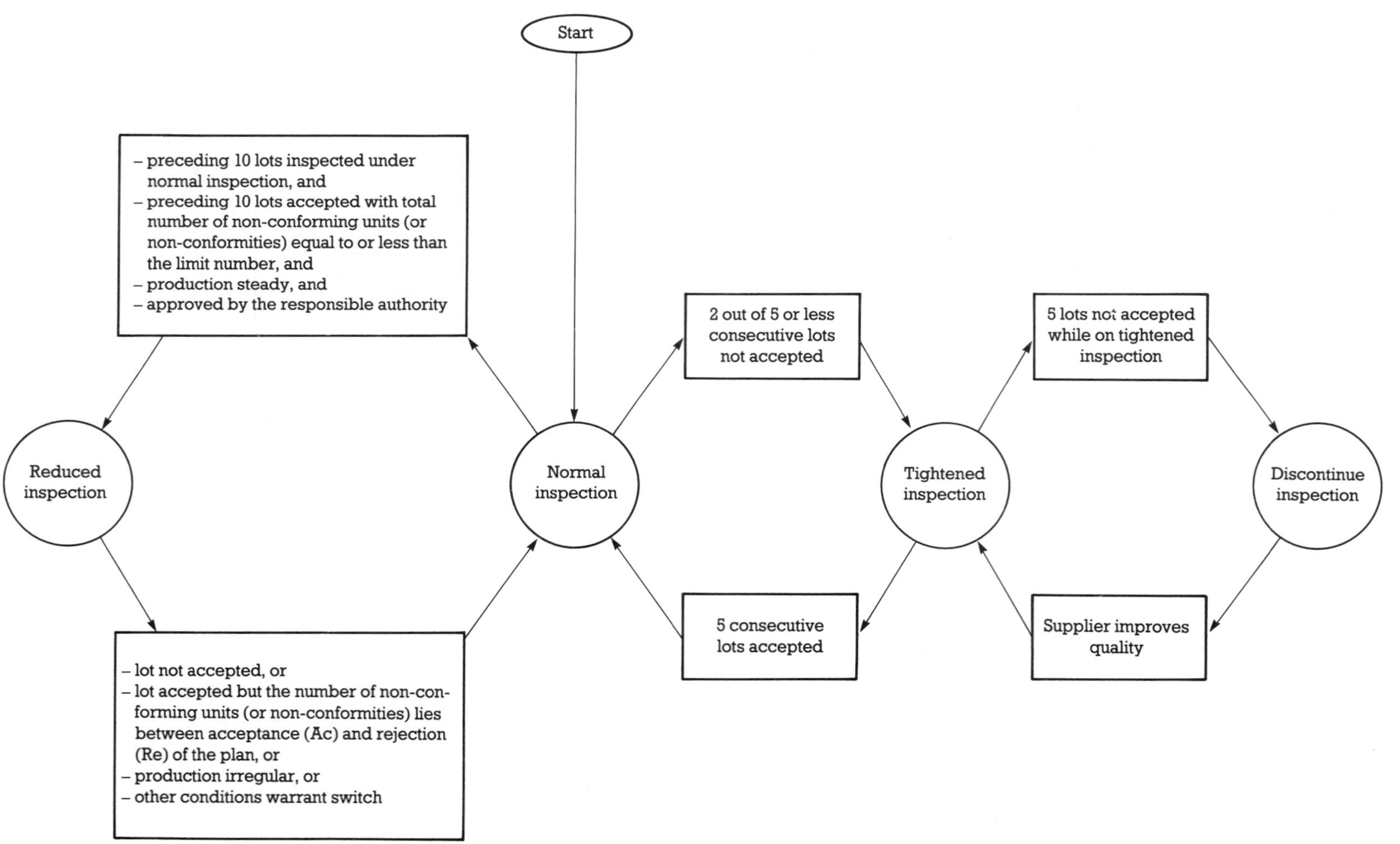

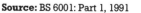

Figure 14.5 Outline of the switching rules

Source: BS 6001: Part 1, 1991

Table 14.5 Double sampling plans for normal inspection (master table)

Sample size code letter	Sample	Sample size	Cumulative sample size	0.010	0.015	0.025	0.040	0.065	0.10	0.15	0.25	0.40	0.65	1.0	1.5	2.5	4.0	6.5	10	15	25	40	65	100	150	250	400	650	1000
				Ac Re	Ac Re	Ac Re	Ac Re	Ac Re	Ac Re	Ac Re	Ac Re	Ac Re	Ac Re	Ac Re	Ac Re	Ac Re	Ac Re	Ac Re	Ac Re	Ac Re	Ac Re	Ac Re	Ac Re	Ac Re	Ac Re	Ac Re	Ac Re	Ac Re	Ac Re
A				↓	↓	↓	↓	↓	↓	↓	↓	↓	↓	↓	↓	↓	↓	★	↓	↓	★	★	★	★	★	★	★	★	★
B	First Second	2 2	2 4	↓	↓	↓	↓	↓	↓	↓	↓	↓	↓	↓	↓	↓	★	↑	↓	0 2 1 2	0 3 3 4	1 4 4 5	2 5 6 7	3 7 8 9	5 9 12 13	7 11 18 19	11 16 26 27	17 22 37 38	25 31 56 57
C	First Second	3 3	3 6	↓	↓	↓	↓	↓	↓	↓	↓	↓	↓	↓	↓	★	↑	↓	0 2 1 2	0 3 3 4	1 4 4 5	2 5 6 7	3 7 8 9	5 9 12 13	7 11 18 19	11 16 26 27	17 22 37 38	25 31 56 57	↑
D	First Second	5 5	5 10	↓	↓	↓	↓	↓	↓	↓	↓	↓	↓	↓	★	↑	↓	0 2 1 2	0 3 3 4	1 4 4 5	2 5 6 7	3 7 8 9	5 9 12 13	7 11 18 19	11 16 26 27	17 22 37 38	25 31 56 57	↑	↑
E	First Second	8 8	8 16	↓	↓	↓	↓	↓	↓	↓	↓	↓	↓	★	↑	↓	0 2 1 2	0 3 3 4	1 4 4 5	2 5 6 7	3 7 8 9	5 9 12 13	7 11 18 19	11 16 26 27	17 22 37 38	25 31 56 57	↑	↑	↑
F	First Second	13 13	13 26	↓	↓	↓	↓	↓	↓	↓	↓	↓	★	↑	↓	0 2 1 2	0 3 3 4	1 4 4 5	2 5 6 7	3 7 8 9	5 9 12 13	7 11 18 19	11 16 26 27	↑	↑	↑	↑	↑	↑
G	First Second	20 20	20 40	↓	↓	↓	↓	↓	↓	↓	↓	★	↑	↓	0 2 1 2	0 3 3 4	1 4 4 5	2 5 6 7	3 7 8 9	5 9 12 13	7 11 18 19	11 16 26 27	↑	↑	↑	↑	↑	↑	↑
H	First Second	32 32	32 64	↓	↓	↓	↓	↓	↓	↓	★	↑	↓	0 2 1 2	0 3 3 4	1 4 4 5	2 5 6 7	3 7 8 9	5 9 12 13	7 11 18 19	11 16 26 27	↑	↑	↑	↑	↑	↑	↑	↑
J	First Second	50 50	50 100	↓	↓	↓	↓	↓	↓	★	↑	↓	0 2 1 2	0 3 3 4	1 4 4 5	2 5 6 7	3 7 8 9	5 9 12 13	7 11 18 19	11 16 26 27	↑	↑	↑	↑	↑	↑	↑	↑	↑
K	First Second	80 80	80 160	↓	↓	↓	↓	↓	★	↑	↓	0 2 1 2	0 3 3 4	1 4 4 5	2 5 6 7	3 7 8 9	5 9 12 13	7 11 18 19	11 16 26 27	↑	↑	↑	↑	↑	↑	↑	↑	↑	↑
L	First Second	125 125	125 250	↓	↓	↓	↓	★	↑	↓	0 2 1 2	0 3 3 4	1 4 4 5	2 5 6 7	3 7 8 9	5 9 12 13	7 11 18 19	11 16 26 27	↑	↑	↑	↑	↑	↑	↑	↑	↑	↑	↑
M	First Second	200 200	200 400	↓	↓	↓	★	↑	↓	0 2 1 2	0 3 3 4	1 4 4 5	2 5 6 7	3 7 8 9	5 9 12 13	7 11 18 19	11 16 26 27	↑	↑	↑	↑	↑	↑	↑	↑	↑	↑	↑	↑
N	First Second	315 315	315 630	↓	↓	★	↑	↓	0 2 1 2	0 3 3 4	1 4 4 5	2 5 6 7	3 7 8 9	5 9 12 13	7 11 18 19	11 16 26 27	↑	↑	↑	↑	↑	↑	↑	↑	↑	↑	↑	↑	↑
P	First Second	500 500	500 1000	↓	★	↑	↓	0 2 1 2	0 3 3 4	1 4 4 5	2 5 6 7	3 7 8 9	5 9 12 13	7 11 18 19	11 16 26 27	↑	↑	↑	↑	↑	↑	↑	↑	↑	↑	↑	↑	↑	↑
Q	First Second	800 800	800 1600	★	↑	↓	0 2 1 2	0 3 3 4	1 4 4 5	2 5 6 7	3 7 8 9	5 9 12 13	7 11 18 19	11 16 26 27	↑	↑	↑	↑	↑	↑	↑	↑	↑	↑	↑	↑	↑	↑	↑
R	First Second	1250 1250	1250 2500	↑	↑	0 2 1 2	0 3 3 4	1 4 4 5	2 5 6 7	3 7 8 9	5 9 12 13	7 11 18 19	11 16 26 27	↑	↑	↑	↑	↑	↑	↑	↑	↑	↑	↑	↑	↑	↑	↑	↑

Notes:

↓ = Use first sampling plan below arrow. If sample size equals or exceeds lot or batch size, carry out 100 per cent inspection.

↑ = Use first sampling plan above arrow.

Ac = Acceptance number.
Re = Rejection number.
★ = Use corresponding single sampling plan (or alternatively, use double sampling plan below, where available).

Source: BS 6001: Part 1, 1991 (Table III-A)

14.5 Double, multiple and sequential sampling

Double sampling

In double sampling, the number of units to be inspected is indicated by the first sample size given by the plan. If the number of non-conforming units found in this first sample is equal to or less than the first acceptance number, the lot is considered acceptable. If the number of non-conforming units found in the first sample is equal to or greater than the first rejection number, the lot is considered not acceptable. If the number of non-conforming units found in the first sample is between the first acceptance and rejection numbers, a second sample of the size given by the plan is inspected. The number of non-conforming units found in the first and second samples are then added together. If the cumulative number of non-conforming units is equal to or less than the second acceptance number, the lot is considered acceptable. If the cumulative number of non-conforming units is equal to or greater than the second rejection number, the lot should be rejected. If this occurs on reduced inspection, normal inspection should be reinstated for the next batch. When reduced inspection is in effect and after inspection of the second sample, the acceptance number has been exceeded but the rejection number has not yet been reached, the batch should be accepted and normal inspection reinstated.

The procedure for double sampling using BS 6001: Part 1 (1991) is the same as for single sampling. The AQL, inspection level and code letter have the same functions as before, but a different set of tables is used. The following example illustrates how a double sampling plan works. The conditions are:

AQL 0.65 per cent non-conforming
inspection level II
batch size 6000
normal inspection
double sampling.

The code letter is found to be L, using Table 14.1. Then using the appropriate table, in this case Table 14.5, the following plan is obtained:

first sample size	125
acceptance number	1 non-conforming unit
rejection number	4 non-conforming units
second sample size	125
combined sample size	250
acceptance number	4 non-conforming units
rejection number	5 non-conforming units.

This means that if none or just one non-conforming unit is found in a first sample of 125 units the batch is accepted without a second sample being taken. If four or more non-conforming units are found, the batch is rejected without inspecting a second sample. If, however, the first sample of 125 contains two or three non-conforming units, a second sample of 125 must be taken and the decision then depends upon the total number of non-conforming units in both samples combined – accepting for four non-conforming units or less and rejecting for five or more non-conforming units.

The flow chart of Figure 14.6 summarises the choice and operation of a double sampling plan.

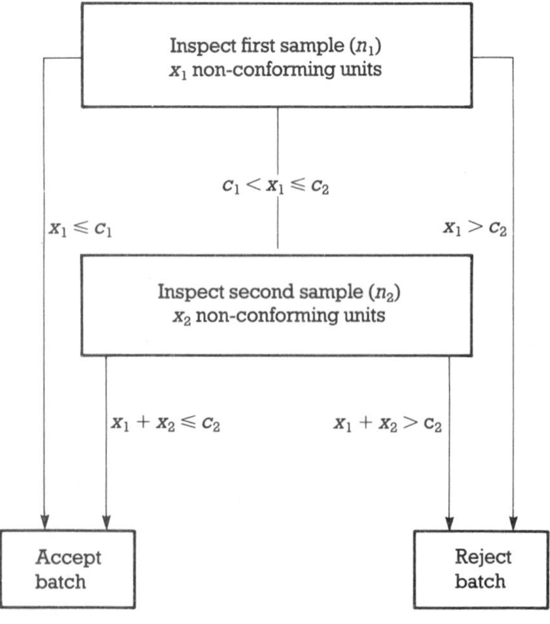

Figure 14.6 Double acceptance sampling plans

Multiple sampling

The principle of multiple sampling is the same as that of double sampling, except that more than two samples may be called for. The multiple plans in BS 6001: Part 1 (1991) are all seven-stage plans and the successive samples are all of equal size. The flow chart of Figure 14.7 illustrates their use.

Sequential sampling

Sequential sampling is a system in which there are no fixed sample sizes, but instead items are examined in sequence as they occur. A decision to accept or reject the batch is taken as soon as the cumulative evidence is sufficiently strong one way or the other. This is done by keeping a score which starts before inspection of the first unit at a value called the handicap (designated *H*). After the inspection of each unit, one point is added to the score if the unit is acceptable, but a value called the penalty (designated *b*) is subtracted from the score if the unit is non-conforming.

$$\text{Score} = \left\{\text{Handicap} + \begin{pmatrix}\text{number of acceptable}\\ \text{units found}\end{pmatrix}\right\} - \left\{\text{Penalty} \times \begin{pmatrix}\text{number of}\\ \text{non-conforming}\\ \text{units found}\end{pmatrix}\right\}$$

The values of *H* and *b* to be used are found in Table 14.6 overleaf (relating to Table Z1 of BS 6001: Part 1 (1991)), where a maximum sample size is also given.

The inspection and the score-keeping continues until either:

- the score reaches the target (equal to twice the handicap – designated as 2*H*), in which case the bach is accepted;
- the score falls to zero or becomes negative in which case the batch is rejected; or

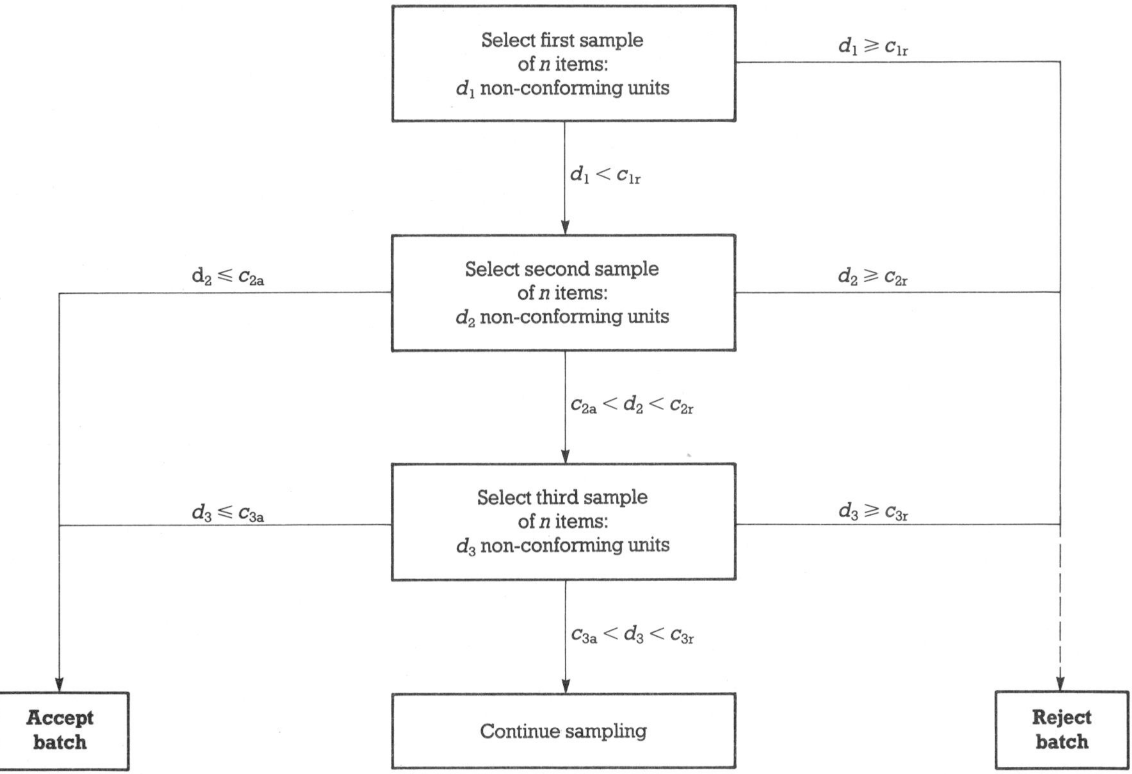

Figure 14.7 Multiple sample plans

Table 14.6 Sequential sampling plans for normal inspection (master table)

Sample size code letter	Minimum sample size		Acceptable quality levels (normal inspection) 0.010	0.015	0.025	0.040	0.065	0.10	0.15	0.25	0.40	0.65	1.0	1.5	2.5	4.0	6.5	10
A B C			↓	↓	↓	↓	↓	↓	↓	↓	↓	↓	↓	↓	↓ ★	↓ ★ ↑	★ ↓↑	↓ ++
D	14	*H* *b*	↓	↓	↓	↓	↓	↓	↓	↓	↓	↓	↓	8 16	↑	↓	6 5	4 2
E	21	*H* *b*	↓	↓	↓	↓	↓	↓	↓	↓	↓	↓	13 26	↑	↓	9 8	8 5	6 8
F	35	*H* *b*	↓	↓	↓	↓	↓	↓	↓	↓	↓	20 40	↑	↓	14 13	10 7	9 5	8 8
G	56	*H* *b*	↓	↓	↓	↓	↓	↓	↓	↓	32 64	↑	↓	22 21	16 12	15 9	11 5	10 8
H	91	*H* *b*	↓	↓	↓	↓	↓	↓	↓	50 100	↑	↓	34 33	26 20	22 14	17 8	16 6	18 4
J	140	*H* *b*	↓	↓	↓	↓	↓	↓	80 160	↑	↓	55 54	40 32	34 23	28 14	24 10	20 7	17 5
K	224	*H* *b*	↓	↓	↓	↓	↓	125 250	↑	↓	86 85	64 53	54 36	43 22	37 16	31 11	28 8	22 5
L	350	*H* *b*	↓	↓	↓	↓	200 400	↑	↓	137 136	103 86	86 59	69 36	60 27	51 19	43 13	36 8	↑
M	560	*H* *b*	↓	↓	↓	315 630	↑	↓	216 215	162 136	136 93	109 58	94 42	80 30	68 21	56 14	↑	↑
N	875	*H* *b*	↓	↓	500 1000	↑	↓	343 342	260 219	216 149	174 93	150 68	127 48	108 34	89 22	↑	↑	↑
P	1400	*H* *b*	↓	800 1600	↑	↓	548 547	410 346	345 238	278 150	239 109	203 77	173 55	142 36	↑	↑	↑	↑
Q	2205	*H* *b*	1250 2500	↑	↓	856 855	651 542	539 373	484 235	374 171	318 121	270 86	223 58	↑	↑	↑	↑	↑
R	3500	*H* *b*	↑	↑	1370 1309	1026 868	862 597	694 376	598 273	508 194	432 139	356 93	↑	↑	↑	↑	↑	↑

Notes

↓ = Use first sampling plan below arrow.
↑ = Use first sampling plan above arrow.
★ = Use corresponding single sampling plan (or alternatively, use sequential plan below)
++ = Use corresponding single or double sampling plan (or alternatively, use sequential plan below).
H = Handicap.
b = Penalty.

Source: BS 6001: Part 1, 1991 (Table Z1)

- the maximum sample size is reached.

The maximum sample size is always the same as the maximum that can be reached by the corresponding multiple sampling plan, and if it is reached during sequential sampling the appropriate table needs to be consulted to determine acceptance or rejection.

Sequential sampling is not available for reduced inspection or for AQL values greater than 10.

Example

The following example will illustrate how a sequential sampling plan works. The conditions are:

AQL 10 per cent non-conforming
inspection level II
batch size 50
normal inspection
sequential inspection

The code letter is found from Table 14.1 to be D. The handicap and penalty are found from Table 14.6 to be $H = 4$ and $b = 2$. The target is $2H = 8$. The maximum sample size is 14.

When sequential sampling plans are used, a smaller average sample size is inspected, but more administrative control is required. If apparatus for semi-automatic use is available, automated sequential sampling offers an opportunity for increased efficiency and economy, particularly when destructive tests are employed.

14.6 Comparing different sampling methods

The factors that need to be considered when adopting a particular sampling method include the following:

- Simplicity – single sampling is the easiest method to understand and administer; double sampling is more complicated; and multiple and sequential sampling are even more complicated.
- Average sample size – the sample size of single sampling is always the same, but for the other types of sampling it varies according to how many samples have to be inspected. For these other types of plans, the sample size has to be considered as an average and this depends upon the quality of the submitted batches, since for some batches more samples will be needed than for others. The average sample size for doubling sampling is nearly always less than the equivalent sample size for single sampling. The average sample size for multiple sampling is usually less than the average for double sampling. The average sample size for sequential sampling is usually close to, but less than, the average for multiple sampling.
- Costs – a double sampling plan will only result in reduced costs if the lots to be inspected have a process average which is not close to the AQL of the sampling plan. If it is close to the AQL then a second sample will almost always be required to be taken. When this is needed, the inspection costs will probably be greater than those of a normal, single sampling plan.
- Variability in sample size – the more the average sample size is reduced, the greater is the variability. Single sampling gives no variability at all, while sequential sampling provides the most variability. Variability can be the cause of difficulties in such cases as the estimation of the labour required for inspection and, in the case of destructive inspection, of the quantity to be ordered to ensure a given quantity after testing.
- Ease of drawing sample units – sometimes it is perfectly simple to take a second sample and to take two samples is no more trouble than to take one sample of the combined size. However, at other times, the situation arises where the drawing of sample units forms a large part of the inspection task and having broken down the batch to take one sample, it is hardly feasible to break it down again to take another one.
- Duration of test – if a test is long and it is possible to apply it to a number of units of product simultaneously, it will usually be better to do so rather than to risk finding that

at the end of the test of a first sample the result is inconclusive and a second, or more of a sample is needed. If only one or two units can be tested at any one time, multiple or sequential sampling may be the preferred method.

- Multiple non-conformities – the more complicated the product in terms of characteristics to be measured, number of possible non-conformities, classes of non-conformities (if used), the more involved multiple or sequential sampling becomes. In cases of complicated product inspection a simple sampling plan is called for.

14.7 Limiting quality

In BS 6001: Part 1 (1991) it is assumed that where a series of batches is offered for acceptance, the upper end of the OC curve is the most important. The production quality must normally be in this region of the curve (i.e. at the AQL) if frequent rejections, tightened inspection and, eventually, discontinuation of inspection pending quality improvement are to be avoided.

However, the lower end of the curve is also important as an indication of the chance of rejection of a single bad batch, should this be encountered in a stream of good batches. It is also important in the case of a single isolated batch, or a very short series of batches, so that the customer is not able to rely upon tightened inspection for extra protection, as there is insufficient scope for switching rules to take effect.

A series of tables in BS 6001: Part 1 (1991) give the quality of the batch, in terms of per cent non-conforming and non-conformities per hundred units, which the OC curve for the selected sampling plan is shown to have a 10 per cent and 5 per cent probability of being accepted. These qualities are called the *limiting quality*. The 10 or 5 per cent probability of acceptance is sometimes referred to as the consumer's risk, at these qualities. The limiting quality at the 10 per cent probability is sometimes termed the *lot tolerance percent defective (LTPD)* as used in the Dodge and Romig sampling tables (Dodge and Romig, 1959). BS 6001: Part 2 (1993) provides details of sampling plans indexed by limiting quality.

14.8 Skip-lot inspection

Skip-lot acceptance sampling procedures are used for reducing the inspection effort on products submitted by those suppliers who have demonstrated their ability to control, in an effective manner, all facets of product quality. With this procedure some lots in a series will be accepted without any inspection by the customer. The procedures are intended only for a continuing series of lots and are not for use with isolated lots. All lots in the series are expected to be of a similar quality and the purchaser should have no reason to believe that the lots which are not inspected are any different to the ones inspected. The skip-lot procedures which are contained in BS 6001: Part 3 (1993) were developed for use in conjunction with the lot-by-lot plans given in BS 6001: Part 1 (1991).

Supplier and product qualification

BS 6001: Part 3 (1993) outlines specific requirements on how the product is manufactured and the systems which a supplier should have in place before skip-lot inspection is employed. These requirements are as follows.

Supplier qualification

The supplier shall have carried out the following:

- implemented and maintained a documented quality system for controlling product quality and design changes, for example, with reference to BS 5750: Parts 1, 2 or 3 (1987);
- instituted a quality system that is capable of detecting and correcting shifts in quality levels and monitoring process changes that may affect quality. The supplier's personnel responsible for the application of the system shall exhibit a clear understanding of the standards, systems and procedures to be followed;

- not have experienced an organisational change that might adversely affect quality.

Product qualification
The product shall be as follows:

- of stable design;
- have been manufactured on an essentially continuous basis for a period mutually agreed by all parties. If no period is pecified, the period shall be six months. Whenever production is halted awaiting sample approval, only the time period after approval and resumption of production shall be included;
- have been on normal and/or reduced inspection or a combination of normal and reduced inspection at general inspection levels I, II or III during the qualification period. A product that has been on tightened inspection at any time during the qualifying period is ineligible for skip-lot inspection.
- have been maintained at the AQL or better (see BS 6001: Part 1) for a period of stability mutually agreed to by both the supplier and the responsible authority. If no period is specified, the period shall be six months.
- comply with the following quality requirements:
  i) the preceding ten or more lots have been accepted;
  ii) the criteria for minimum cumulative sample size as outlined in Table 1 of BS 6001: Part 3 (1993) are met for the preceding ten or more consecutive lots;
  iii) the criteria relating to the acceptance number to continue skip-lot inspection as outlined in Table 2 of BS 6001: Part 3 (1993) are met for each of the last two individual lots.

Skip-lot procedures

These are three basic states in skip-lot procedures:

- state 1 – lot-by-lot inspection;
- state 2 – skip-lot inspection;
- state 3 – skip-lot interrupt.

The inspection procedure for a product starts in state 1, lot-by-lot inspection. When the supplier and product meet the conditions previously described the procedure switches to state 2. Skip-lot inspection may be temporarily interrupted resulting in a transfer to state 3. The product may requalify under less stringent conditions with a transfer of the procedure back to state 2. Alternatively, the product may be disqualified from skip-lot inspection while the procedure is either in state 2 or state 3. In this case, the procedure switches to state 1 and the supplier and product have to again comply with the system and manufacturing requirements. The procedures for interrupt, requalification and disqualification are fully documented in BS 6001: Part 3 (1993).

Throughout the skip-lot procedures, in states 1, 2 and 3, the acceptance/non-acceptance criteria applied to individual lots are those given for the appropriate AQL – sample size combination used on normal inspection as outlined in BS6001: Part 1 (1991).

The lots to be inspected are chosen randomly in accordance with a stated frequency which is called the *skip-lot frequency*. The inspection frequencies that the responsible authority may prescribe are:

- one lot inspected in two submitted (i.e. this means that in the long run the average proportion of inspected lots is 50 per cent of those submitted by the manufacturer);
- one lot inspected in three submitted;
- one lot inspected in four submitted;
- one lot inspected in five submitted (this frequency is not available as an initial frequency).

BS 6001: Part 3 outlines a method for determining both the initial skip-lot frequency and changes to it based on experience of the supplied part. A procedure is also outlined for selecting the lots to be inspected at the authorised skip-lot frequency.

Skip-lot inspection or reduced inspection?

There are three major factors used to decide between skip-lot inspection and reduced inspection as stated in BS 6001: Part 1 (1991). First, the relationship between the supplier and customer. Secondly, the relationship between the fixed cost of inspection and the cost to inspect individual units. If the fixed costs exceed the savings from reduction in the number of units inspected, skip-lot procedures are more economic. Finally, there is the factor of the acceptance number of the sampling plans used during lot-by-lot inspection. If plans with acceptance numbers greater than zero are used, reduced inspection may be more advantageous than skip-lot inspection. When making the decision consideration should be given to the difference between the sample sizes of the non-zero acceptance number plans and the reduced plans.

14.9 Definitions and terminology

The following are some useful definitions and terms in the discussion of this chapter.

Acceptable quality level (AQL): when a continuing series of lots is considered, a quality level which for the purposes of sampling inspection is the limit of a satisfactory process average.

Acceptance: a conclusion that a batch, lot or quantity of product or service satisfies the acceptance criteria.

Acceptance inspection: inspection to determine whether an item, or lot, delivered or offered for delivery is acceptable.

Average outgoing quality (AOQ): the expected average quality level of outgoing product for a given value of incoming product quality.

Average outgoing quality limit (AOQL): the maximum AOQ over all possible values of incoming product quality level for a given acceptance sampling plan and rectification of all non-accepted lots.

Inspection: activities such as measuring, examining, testing and gauging one or more characteristics of a product or service and comparing these with specified requirements to determine conformity.

Inspection by attributes: inspection wherein certain characteristics are assessed and classified as conforming or not conforming to specified requirements without measurements.

Inspection by variables: inspection which consists of measuring a quantitative characteristic for each item of a population, or for a sample taken from it.

Inspection level: an index of the relative amount of inspection of a sampling scheme, chosen in advance and relating the size of samples to the lot size.

Inspection lot: a definite quality of some product, material or service collected together and submitted for examination.

Limiting quality (LQ): when a lot is considered in isolation, a quality level which for the purposes of sampling inspection is limited to a low probability of acceptance.

Lot-by-lot inspection: inspection of product submitted in a series of lots.

Non-acceptance; rejection: a conclusion that a batch, lot or quantity of product or service has not been shown to satisfy the acceptance criteria.

Non-conformity: a departure of a quality characteristic that results in a product process or service not meeting a specified requirement.

Non-conformity per 100 units: the number of non-conformities per 100 units of any given quantity or units of product is 100 times the number of non-conformities contained therein (one or more non-conformities being possible in any unit of product) divided by the total number of units of products, i.e.

$$\text{Non-conformities per 100 units} = \frac{\text{Number of non-conformities} \times 100}{\text{Total number of units}}$$

Normal inspection: the inspection which is used when there is no reason to think that the quality level of the product differs from an acceptable quality level.

One hundred per cent (100%) inspection: inspection of every item of product or service, i.e. the whole (as contrasted with any form of sampling inspection).

Operating characteristic (OC) curve: a graph showing what any particular sampling plan can be expected to do in terms of accepting and rejecting batches.

An OC curve refers to a particular sampling plan. Each possible plan has its own unique curve, and it is the comparison of OC curves that enables one sampling plan to be compared with another. Each point on the curve, for a particular sampling plan, shows against the horizontal scale a value of percentage non-conforming, and against the vertical scale the percentage of batches that may be expected to be accepted if batches from a process producing that percentage non-conforming are offered for acceptance and the sampling plan in question is applied.

Original inspection: the first inspection of a lot, as distinguished from the inspection of a re-submitted lot.

Process average: the process quality level averaged over a defined time period or quantity of production.

Producer's risk: the probability of rejecting a lot whose percentage non-conforming has a value stated by the given sampling plan as acceptable.

Production batch: a definite quantity of some commodity or service produced at one time under conditions that are presumed uniform.

Percentage non-conforming: the percentage non-conforming of any given quantity of units of product is 100 times the number of non-conforming units divided by the total number of units of product, i.e.

$$\text{Percentage non-conformities} = \frac{\text{Number of non-conformities}}{\text{Total number of units}} \times 100$$

Quality level: any relative quality measure obtained by comparing observed values with the relevant requirements.

Reduced inspection: the inspection, less severe than the normal inspection, to which the normal inspection may be switched when the inspection results of a predetermined number of lots indicate that the quality level of the production is better than that specified.

Re-submitted lot: a lot which previously has been designated as not acceptable and which is submitted again for acceptance inspection after having been further tested, sorted and reprocessed.

Sample: one or more sampling units taken from a population (lot or process) and intended to provide information on the population (lot or process) and possibly to serve as a basis for a decision on the population (lot or process).

Sampling inspection: the inspection of products or services, using samples (as distinct from 100% inspection).

Sampling plan: a specific plan which states the sample size(s) to be used and the associated criteria for accepting the lot.

Sampling scheme: a combination of sampling plans with rules for changing from one plan to another.

Sampling system: a collection of sampling schemes, each with its own rules for changing plans, together with criteria by which appropriate schemes may be chosen.

Skip-lot inspection: an acceptance sampling procedure in which some lots in a series are accepted without inspection when the sampling results for a stated number of immediately preceding lots meet stated criteria.

British Standards

BS 4778: *Quality vocabulary* Part 1: 1987 *International terms* (ISO 8402: 1986) (EN 28402: 1991); Part 2: 1991 *Quality concepts and related definitions*.

BS 5750: *Quality systems* Part 1: 1987 *Specification for design/development, production, installation and servicing* (ISO 9001: 1987) (EN 29001: 1987); Part 2: 1987 *Specification for production and installation* (ISO 9002: 1987) (EN 29002: 1987); Part 3: 1987 *Specification for final inspection and test* (ISO 9003: 1987) (EN 29003: 1987).

BS 6000: 1972 *Guide to use of BS 6001, sampling procedures and tables for inspection by attributes* (ISO 2859/Addendum 1: 1972).

BS 6001: *Sampling procedures for inspection by attributes* Part 1: 1991 *Specification for sampling plans indexed by acceptable quality levels (AQL) for lot-by-lot inspection* (ISO 2859–1: 1989); Part 2: 1993 *Specification for sampling plans indexed by limiting quality (LQ) for isolated lot inspection* (ISO 2859–2: 1985); Part 3: 1993 *Specification for skip-lot procedures* (ISO 2859–3: 1991)
BS 6002: 1979 *Specification for sampling procedures and charts for inspection by variables for percent defective* (ISO 3951: 1979).

References

Dodge H F and Romig H G. *Sampling inspection tables*. John Wiley and Sons, New York, USA, 1959.

Shingo, S. *Zero quality control: source inspection and the poka-yoke system*. Productivity Press, Massachusetts, USA, 1986.

CHAPTER 15

Statistical process control

15.1 Introduction

The three words making up statistical process control (SPC) give clues to its meaning. The first word, 'statistical', refers to the collection arrangement and analysis of numerical data. The second word 'process', is a combination of people, machines/equipment, materials, methods and the environment that come together to convert a set of inputs into outputs. The commitment, or lack of it, by senior management to a process of quality improvement can also be considered as an element in the 'process'. The final word, 'control', means to detect changes in some aspects of a process or its product and alter the inputs accordingly.

In simple terms, the objective of SPC is to reduce the variation which is inherent in most processes. To achieve this it is first necessary to establish whether or not a process is in a state of statistical control. If it is not, it must be brought under control by eliminating the so called assignable or special causes of variation. The next task is to reduce and then eliminate the random or common causes of variation so that the output from the process is more closely centred around a nominal or target value. This is an on-going activity in the pursuit of continuous improvement (see Figure 15.1 overleaf).

When SPC is properly applied, it can assist in improving the outgoing product quality, particularly where the number of non-confirming items may be expressed as a low number of parts per million (PPM). The only viable approach to quality in this situation is to institute a preventive methodology in the process to build quality into the product and/or service, adopting a proactive method which allows for the improvement of the process on a continuing basis.

SPC is based upon the prevention of failure, through the application of statistical tools. It does not eliminate the measurement of products and/or services or their parameters; however, statistical analysis will provide insights into the process and opportunities for improvement. As the process improves, there is a reduced need for testing and inspection after the product is completed, with a consequent lowering of the manufacturing/operation cost.

One of the virtues of SPC is its flexibility. Commonsense modifications in procedure to suit local conditions and particular situations can be made, once the principles governing SPC and its function in providing guidance to those responsible for satisfactory production or operation are appreciated.

This chapter outlines the fundamental concepts of SPC, summarises the typical techniques used and concludes with a discussion of how to implement SPC, along with the prob-

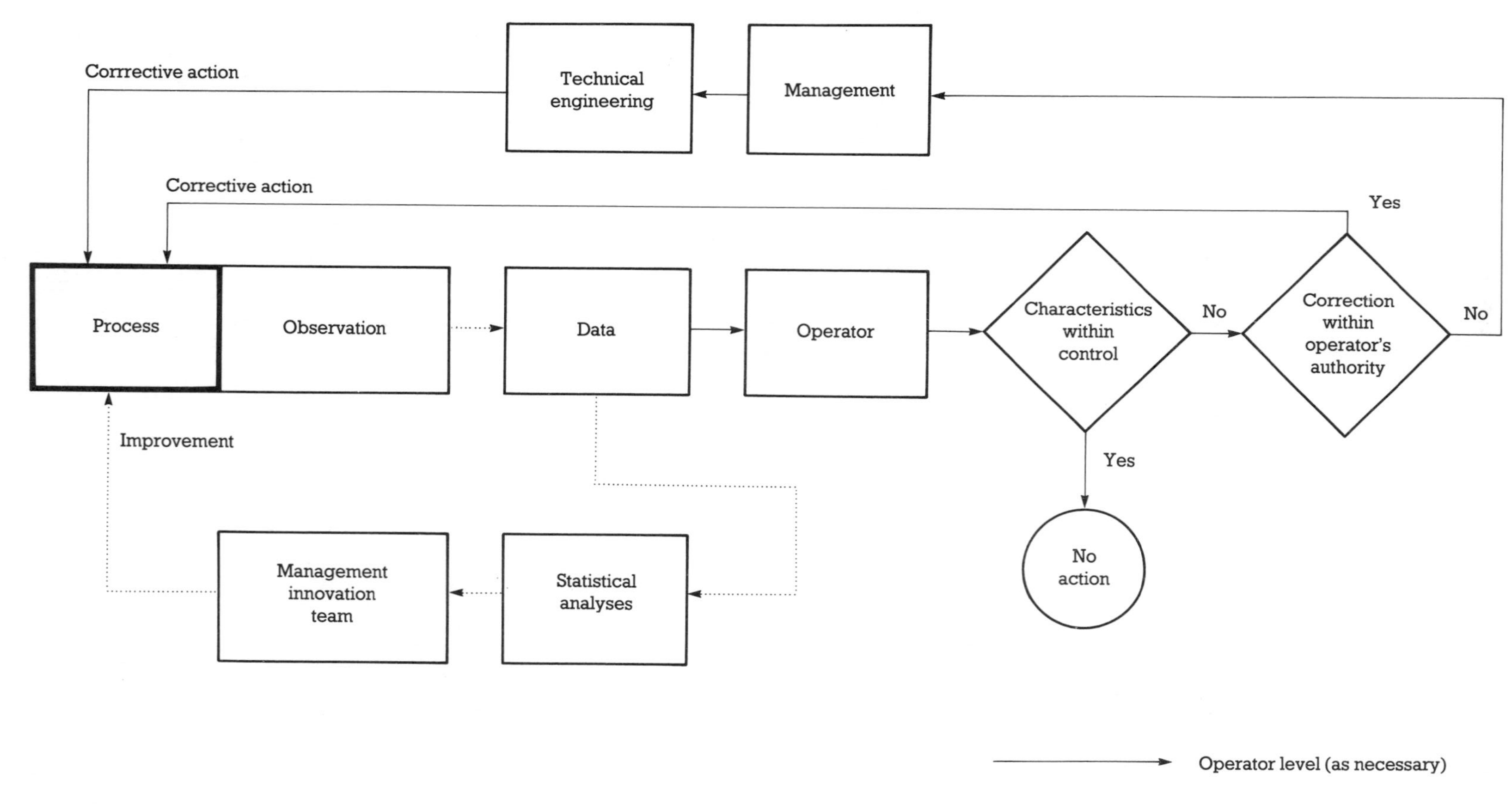

Figure 15.1 SPC loops

lems likely to be encountered in its application and development.

15.2 Why is SPC important?

SPC is now a fashionable buzzword in much of manufacturing industry, but the concept is not a new one. Its roots can be traced back to the work of Shewhart (1931) at Bell Laboratories in the 1920s. Also around this time, Dudding (a British statistician) was also working along similar lines to Shewhart. The control charts developed by Shewhart for distinguishing between controlled and uncontrolled variation are not dissimilar to those in use today.

A British Standard (the first on quality control), BS 600 *The application of statistical methods to industrial standardization and quality* by Pearson, was published in 1935 and another British Standard, BS 600R *Quality control charts* by Dudding and Jennett followed in 1942. The information contained in BS 2564 *Control chart technique when manufacturing to a specification with special reference to articles machined to dimensional tolerances* was first published in 1944 by GEC and reissued in 1955 by BSI in order to supplement the above two standards. Control charts were also used during World War II by US and UK industries in the production of wartime materials. They were used mainly for control and traceability and not for process improvement. A black and white film *Right First Time* produced three decades ago, for the now defunct British Productivity Council, provides an excellent insight to the application of SPC in an engineering environment. Any reader wishing to delve more into the history of SPC will find the work of Duncan (1974) worth studying.

Interest in SPC has witnessed a resurgence in recent years. The 1980s have seen a considerable number of publications on the concepts and their application. A large number of courses, by a wide variety of organisations, are offered on the subject. The trend is such that it would appear to the casual observer that an entire industry has grown up to provide a myriad of SPC consultation services. What then has caused SPC suddenly to become important and to be a vogue quality management technique among manufacturing companies throughout the world?

To seek an answer to this question, one needs to return to the economic recovery of Japan following World War II. The Japanese, stimulated by the teachings of Deming (1982, 1986), became skilled users of the SPC technique. Executives from multinational corporations visited Japan towards the end of the 1970s, the purpose of which was to discover the reasons for the success of Japanese companies in the world marketplace. One issue picked up during the visits, and in the resulting discussions, was the considerable use by all employees of statistical methods. The common view derived was that this was the main reason for the low piece-to-piece variability typically witnessed in their manufactured engineering parts and components. In June 1980, Deming featured in an NBC television documentary said 'If Japan can, why can't we?', and this also helped to generate enthusiasm for SPC among a number of American managers. The interest in SPC was also allied with considerable concern about quality and productivity among manufacturing companies and how this might be improved effectively and economically by the use of SPC.

The motivational effects of SPC upon employees also should not be underestimated. In addition to the direct assistance derived from the use of SPC, it will also encourage an attitude of mind in people associated with the activity – someone is seen to be taking an interest in the process, data are being collected, recorded and used to improve the process. This fostering of positive attitudes is of crucial importance in a process of quality improvement. For example, Dale *et al.* (1989) in a study of 158 automotive suppliers using SPC, reported that the three major benefits of operatives filling in control charts manually were increased operator involvement, the operator feeling more responsible for the process and the operator obtaining an immediate indication of how well the process is performing. The use of SPC will also help people to understand more about statistical methods and give them the confidence to experiment with more advanced methods such as design of experiments and analysis of variance.

The Ford Motor Company have taken several important initiatives on SPC. They have applied the techniques within their own manufacturing plants and have required that their suppliers do the same. The Ford Motor Company have had a considerable influence on the SPC methodology being employed throughout Europe. For example, they have adopted:

- the use of control charts which are based on performance of the process rather than tolerance-based charts;
- the employment of just action limits (or control limits) on the control charts, these not being complemented by warning limits, which is the traditional method currently outlined in the relevant British Standard;
- the use of process capability indices;
- the use of preliminary process capability studies.

The philosophy and methodology developed by the Ford Motor Company has subsequently been adopted by a large part of the automotive supply industry in Europe (SMMT, 1986).

In preparing this chapter the authors have drawn on the data contained in BS 2564 (1955), the BS 5700 Series (1992), the Ford Motor Company *Statistical Process Control Instruction Guide* (1986) and the *Ford Motor Company Statistical Process Control Course Notes* (1985) used on their three-day SPC training course. (Details of the Ford Motor Company SPC training initiative and provided by Dale *et al.* (1989) and Dale and Shaw (1989) and Oakland and Followell (1990).

15.3 What is variation?

It is a matter of common experience that no two parts manufactured to the same specification, under the same process conditions, will be identical. They will differ, albeit slightly, in some way. Similarly, observations or measurements of these items will also differ. This difference is known as variational noise which may arise due to either assignable (special) causes or random (common) causes. The assumption is made that there is a natural (inherent) variability in a process when it is stable and in a state of statistical control. This inherent variability is called the process capability and will be reflected in the variations in observations of samples drawn from a process. The process capability that is typical of a process is due to random or common causes of variability.

Special or assignable causes are unpredictable and appear as unusual patterns of variability on a control chart, for example, a point outside one of the control limits or a run of plotted points. They are usually the result of an individual event or occurrence and, in general, can be detected and corrected without too much difficulty. Typical examples are:

- change in raw material,
- change in the position of equipment or parts of equipment,
- change in the equipment setting,
- damaged equipment,
- errors of an inexperienced operator.

Common or random causes are a regular feature of the process, they are predictable and will remain so unless action is taken to eliminate them. They produce the natural or random pattern observed in data when the process is free of special causes of variation. This natural variability is typical of a process when it is in a state of statistical control. Common causes can be difficult to identify and correct. Typical examples are:

- badly maintained equipment,
- equipment requiring refurbishment or replacement,
- inadequate operating instructions,
- the quality of raw material on which the process is being performed,
- poor operating environment.

To facilitate the improvement of a process, it is necessary to separate special from common causes of variation. The responsibility for elimination of these two causes of variation rests with people from different levels of the organisational hierarchy. Special causes can usually be corrected at source by the operator and/or first-line supervisor but their removal sometimes requires considerable effort by quality engineering, production engineering and maintenance personnel. The removal of common causes requires the attention of management, engineering and technical personnel. It is useful to form a multidisciplinary team which can include operational personnel (for example, SPC teams, quality improvement teams), who have the necessary process knowledge to investigate the reasons for common causes of variation and their eventual elimination.

15.4 Control charts: a description

A control chart is a graphical method, the main purpose of which is to evaluate whether or not a process is in a state of statistical control. This is carried out by comparing the values of a statistical measure of an ordered series of samples of sub-groups with control limits, to determine whether the process is in statistical control. The decision making aspect of control charts is centred on the problem of deciding whether a sample observation is due only to the expected, inherent, common or random causes of variation (in which case no action is required), or whether it is due to the effect of some additional, special or assignable variation (in which case corrective action is usually required). The emphasis is on the process being in statistical control rather than being acceptable with respect to a product or service specification limits. A process can be stable and in statistical control yet be producing a product or service that is not to specification.

The basic objective of any form of control is to detect changes in some aspect of a process or its outputs. Information about the current state of the process is obtained by examination of a sample drawn from recent operation or production. From this sample, data is recorded and, where necessary, acted upon. Some values calculated from the sample (such as its mean, range and number of defective items and depending on the type of control chart are plotted on a graph – the control chart. The positions of these plotted points give rise to decisions about the process.

Figure 15.2 shows control charts in use for a chemical parameter during a stable or 'in-control' period. Figure 15.3 indicates that the process has gone 'out-of-control'.

It should be recognised that the term 'control chart' is itself a misnomer to the extent that the chart is an historical record and does not of itself control or improve the process. It is basically a picture of a series of measurements and is the 'voice' of the process. The essential action of a chart is to sound an alarm when attention to the process is required and to give as much indication as possible of the nature of the change that has occurred, so that remedial action can be taken to restore the process to its in-control state (or to retain the process in its new state if this is more advantageous). SPC is being used properly only when action (which can include no action) is being taken on the data portrayed on the control chart.

Charts should be related, where possible, to individual machines, equipment, operators, shifts or other units and notes should be made on the charts to identify any significant changes in material, personnel or any other external factor.

15.5 Some simple statistical concepts: variables

When a series of measurements of a variable are grouped into a number of sub-divisions covering the complete range of measurements, it is found that they tend to cluster round a central value. The resulting collection of measurements can be described by two values:

- a measure of general magnitude or location, such as the arithmetic mean (μ) (also commonly known as the average), median or mode. This defines the position of the 'middle' or central tendency of the distribution, or the 'setting' of the process.
- a measure of spread or dispersion such as the range (R) or standard deviation (σ). This defines the amount by which the distribution is spread about its location, or the variability of the process.

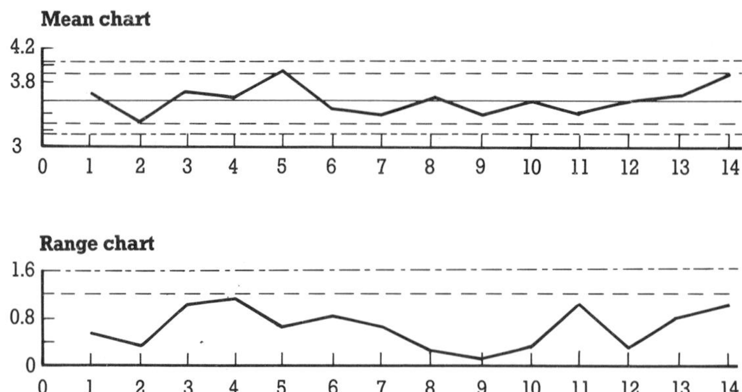

Source: Oakland & Followell, 1990

Figure 15.2 Mean and range charts – stable or 'in-control' period for chemical parameter

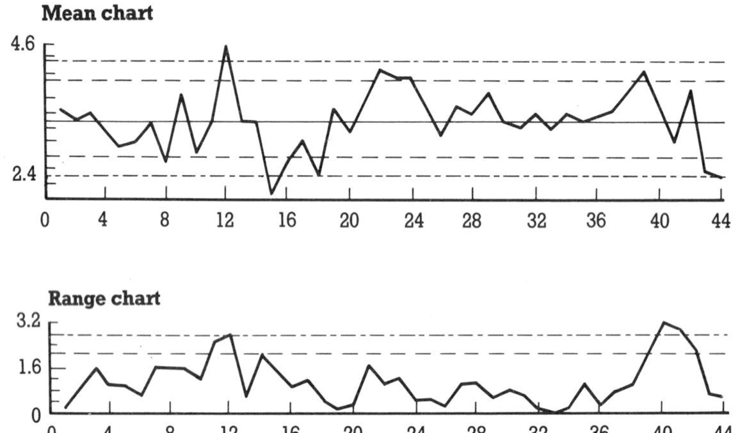

Source: Oakland & Followell, 1990

Figure 15.3 Mean and range charts – chemical parameter from an 'out-of-control' process

Each process has its own inherent pattern (distribution) of variation. There are many types of distributions but the one most commonly encountered for variables is the normal distribution. A knowledge of this distribution allows certain predictions to be made. If the mean and standard deviation of a normal distribution are known it is possible to predict, using normal curve tables, the proportion of the population that will fall within any two limits. For example, as shown in Figure 15.4, 95.44 per cent of the population in the area under the curve will be between the limits set at two standard deviations below the mean and two standard deviations above the mean ($\mu \pm 2\sigma$).

The control charts used for variables make the assumption that the charted product characteristic or process parameter is described by the normal distribution. It is important to note that no process can ever be described exactly by the normal distribution. One simple illustration of this is the fact that the normal distribution covers the range $-\infty$ to $+\infty$, which is impossible for any product or service. However, the normal distribution is an adequate description for a large number of processes. If there are any serious doubts about this adequacy, there are ways of testing the assumption of normality from sample data (BS 2846: Part 7 (1984)). However, minor departures from normality will usually have little effect on the confidence limits for the mean. It is more likely that the distribution of means of samples will be normally distributed than the means of individual measurements. This is derived from the central limits theorem (Oakland and Followell, 1990) and is why

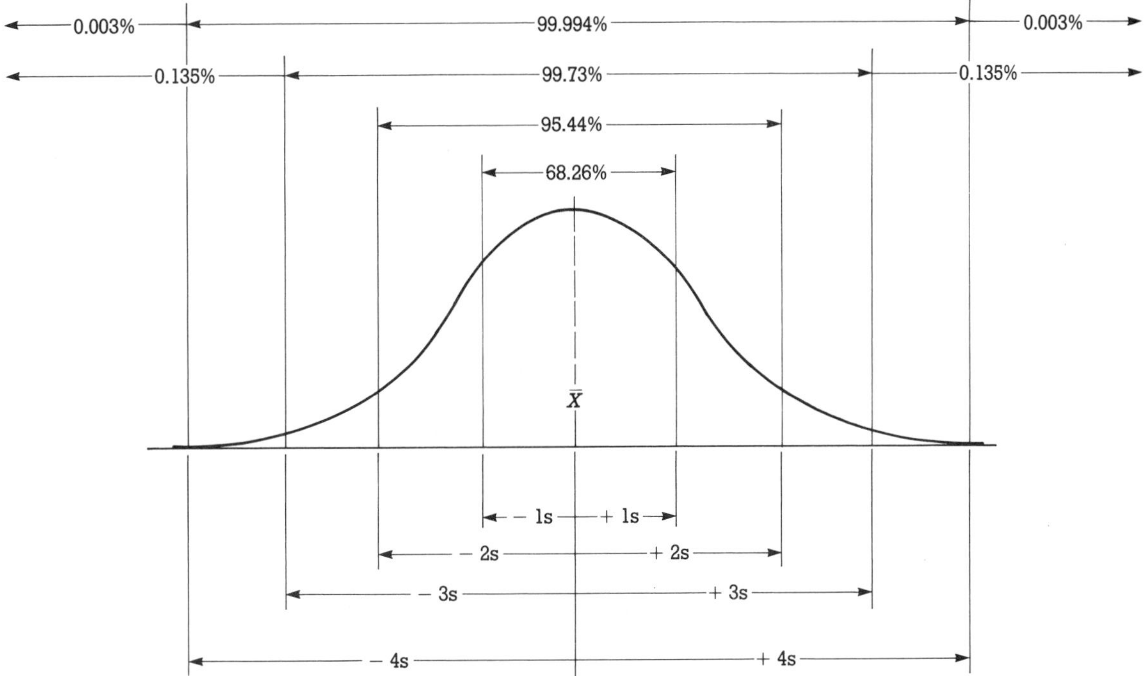

Figure 15.4 Percentages of the normal distribution

calculations for control charts of variables are based on means of samples.

For the small sample sizes of $n = 5$ to 10, which are commonly used in the design of control charts, the distribution of ranges is skewed. The effects of non-normality of the parent population of the range chart will depend on the particular way in which the measured variable departs from the normal distribution. In practice, it has been shown that range charts operate satisfactorily in non-normal situations. From relatively small samples of data, predictions can be made about the population. This means that in SPC the capability of a process can be estimated from samples of data taken from production output.

Useful advice on the routine analysis and presentation of quantitative data is given in BS 2846: Part 1 (1991).

15.6 Data collection

A control chart needs to be designed for the collection and plotting of data. The parameters which need to be selected are sample size, frequency between samples and control limits. Statistical criteria and practical experience are also considered in the design of control charts.

A feature common to all control charting is that of sampling from the process. Therefore, a data gathering plan needs to be developed for collection, recording and the plotting of data on the control chart. The samples are taken from the process at specified intervals and the resulting measurements are used to calculate statistics which are plotted on the control chart. Decisions about the state of the process are made based on the positions of these plotted points.

At this juncture we must mention sampling risks. Because of the variation inherent in sampling, the average levels and the dispersions, as indicated by the samples drawn from the process, will vary from sample to sample, even if the true process average and dispersion are constant. The presence of such a pattern of variation gives rise to two dangers when sample observations are plotted on a control chart. These are:

- Type 1 risk – the risk that a sample will give a spurious 'action' decision when no change has occurred in the process.

- Type 2 risk – the risk that a sample will fail to signal a real change in the process.

The design of a control chart is a compromise between these two opposing risks.

Aspects of sampling that merit general consideration before dealing with specific types of control chart are: frequency of sampling, structure of the sample, size of the sample, number of sub-groups, average run lengths and the holding of production.

Frequency of sampling

The objective of taking samples from the process are to detect any changes in it over a period of time. This is determined by the economics of the process, involving factors such as the stability of the process, the cost of inspection and costs incurred by the production of non-conforming output, and by the frequency of changes made to the process (materials, equipment) that might affect the quality of output. Many formal economic models of control charts have been proposed (Montgomery (1980) gives an excellent review of such models), but a useful rule-of-thumb is to ensure that the sampling interval does not exceed the maximum time that the process could be allowed to operate if it was 'out of control' and producing non-conforming output. Oakland and Followell (1990) also devote a good deal of discussion to this subject and its relationship to the type of process involved.

Whatever the frequency of sampling which has been selected, it should be such that it can reflect any potential changes in the process. If the process exhibits a high level of stability then samples can be taken less frequently.

At this point it is also worth mentioning the costs which should be considered in the design of control charts. For example:

- the costs of taking the sample (and re-samples),
- the cost associated with investigation and correction of assignable causes of variation,
- the cost of non-conforming output,
- the costs of searching for assignable causes, following false alarms.

Structure of the sample

The objective of control charting is usually to assess the performance of the process and to do this effectively the sample should be of the most recent output. This gives the latest news of the process and is the best estimate of process variability. If the sample size is five, these five should be the last five consecutively produced data. However, in some circumstances, the requirement may be to evaluate the product and in such cases a random sample of production since the previous sampling is called for. Such a sample, while being more representative, suffers from the disadvantage that a true measure of the current inherent process variability is not obtained. Therefore, when lack of control is indicated by the control chart, the cause of the undesired variability is more difficult to determine. Whichever method of selecting samples (or sub-groups) is chosen it should be adhered to. The rational groups are groups within which it is believed only chance causes have operated; they should be so chosen that any uncontrolled causes, that it is thought may have operated, will be the same for all observations within a sub-group. Once again, a whole literature exists on the subject of rational sub-grouping.

It has to be noted that any decisions regarding sampling strategy are subject to many practical considerations. There may be circumstances where adherence to one or other of the principles may be impractical or undesirable, as for instance in the control of continuous versus batch chemical production.

Size of the sample (n)

In general terms, the larger the sample size the lower the risk of coming to an incorrect decision, but there are other statistical considerations affecting sample size. In general, sample sizes for attributes charts need to be considerably larger than those for variables charts. The sample size and the frequency of inspection have to be a practical compromise between the costs of inspection and the costs of making incorrect decisions.

The sample size should be such that opportunities for variation within the items in the sample are small. A typical sample size for variables data is five and for attributes data a size of 25 or more is common. When deciding upon the sample size, the effects on the type 2 risk (failure to detect a real change in the process) should be taken into account. In general, the larger the sample size, the smaller the type 2 risk.

Number of sub-groups

In setting up a control chart a sufficient number of sub-groups should be taken during the initial study of the process to be sure that the major sources of variation have had a chance to appear, and the data which have been collected do indeed reflect the performance of the process. It is recommended that as a minimum requirement, 20 sub-groups should be gathered (or 50 to 100 individual datum points be sub-grouped).

Average run lengths (ARL)

The effectiveness of the decision rules associated with a control chart are best described by the *average run length (ARL)*. This is defined as the expected value of the number of samples plotted on the chart up to and including the point that gives rise to an action signal indicating that some assignable causes of variation is present.

If no assignable cause is present, an ARL of infinity is desirable, in other words an 'action' decision is never reached. In the practical circumstance of operating a control chart using sample data, it is not feasible to achieve an infinite ARL, but the objective is to achieve an ARL as large as possible, when no assignable cause is present. Conversely, when a special cause of variation is present, the ideal value for the ARL is 1, i.e. one would expect an 'action' signal on the next sample taken. Whether or not this is achieved depends on the magnitude of the assignable cause, the design of the control chart and its decision procedures. For any particular magnitude of assignable causes of variation the objective in designing control charts is to make the ARL as small as possible. The value of the ARL, when the process is in control, can be decided arbitrarily in the design of control chart procedures. BS 2564 (1955), BS 5700 (1992), BS 5701 (1980) and BS 5703 (1980) contain such arbitrary decisions which are explained in each particular Standard.

Having made this choice, the ARL, when an assignable cause of variability is present, will depend on the magnitude of the change in the process and the size of the sample. For a given chart and a particular magnitude of change due to an assignable cause, an increase in sample size will give a reduction in ARL.

Holding of production

It is essential that any outputs produced when the process was out of control are not dispatched. This means that production may have to be held in quarantine until results on a later sample are available. Because control charts cannot be guaranteed to detect a change when a sample is taken, holding of output or intermediates at an even earlier stage is sometimes advisable. If the next sample indicates that the process is in control, the output can then be released. Otherwise, any appropriate inspection and rectification is restricted to the output held. When loss of control is related only to the economics or subjective acceptability of the process (for example a loss of control which results in the manufacture of overweight packages), decisions on holding production can be made on estimated economic costs and penalties.

A typical SPC flowchart outlining the process of data collection and control is shown in Figure 15.5 overleaf.

15.7 Control chart responsibilities

The responsibility for filling-in control charts should be that of the individual actually controlling the process, whether it be the operator of a machine or a clerk responsible for some administrative process. The control chart should also be displayed as close as possible to the process or activity being monitored. Any employee who has an influence in the outcome of a process should be involved in the control and subsequent improvement of it. When the task of control charting is assigned to quality assurance personnel, some operator control

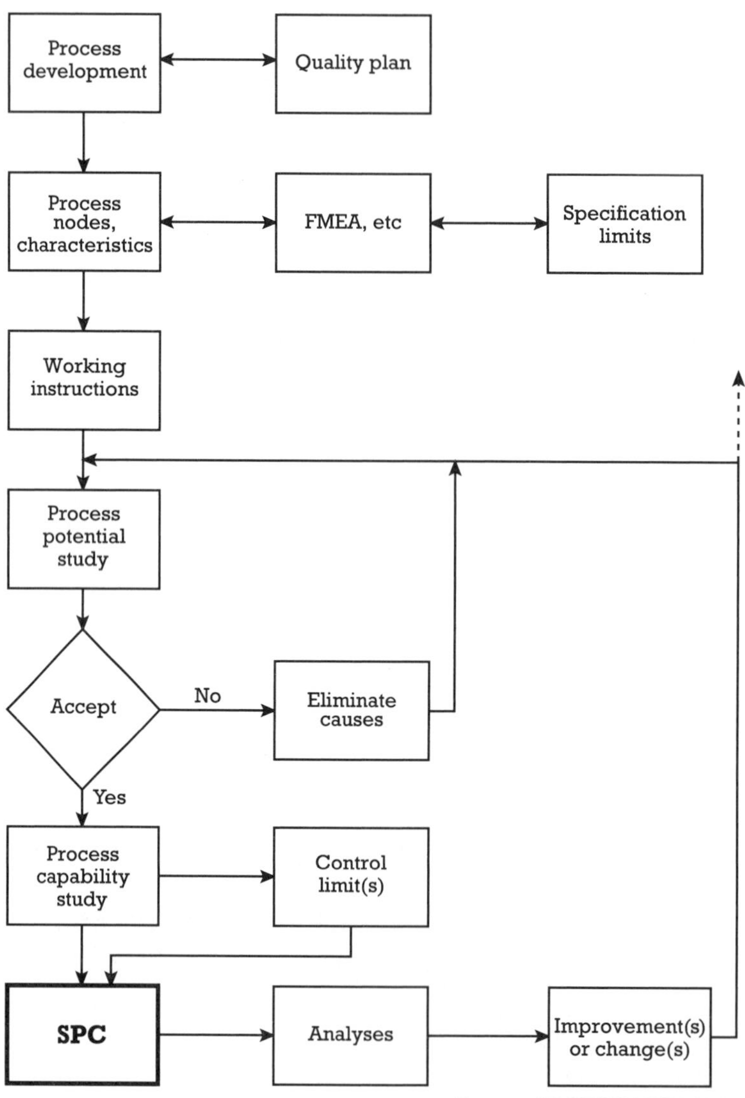

Source: BS/LECC 00016:1991

Figure 15.5 SPC flow chart

and responsibility is certain to be lost.

In some companies there have been difficulties in getting the production personnel to take day-to-day responsibility for SPC, with operatives charting the data. SPC has been delegated, by default, to the quality assurance department. Dale *et al.* (1989) reporting on their SPC survey results found that the patrol inspector, laboratory technician and quality engineer are well represented as persons responsible for filling-in charts. They go on to say that the quality assurance department, laboratory and inspectors' office feature high in the list of places where the control charts are filled-in and that control charts are frequently displayed in the quality assurance department and laboratory.

15.8 Types of control charts

The choice of control chart is dependent upon whether the data is collected as a measured variable or as a counted attribute. The most popular type of variables charts in use are the mean ($\overline{X}$) and range (R) charts, which are used together. Other types of charts, include mean ($\overline{X}$) and standard deviation(s), median ($\tilde{X}$) and range (R), moving mean and moving range, individual value and moving range, and moving mean and standard deviation.

The choice of attributes charts is dependent on whether or not the sample size is kept constant and whether the inspection criterion concerns a non-conforming unit or a non-conformity. For non-conforming units the charts used are proportion or percentage (p chart) and number defective (np chart, samples of constant size). For non-conformities the charts are proportion (u chart) and number (c chart, samples of constant size).

Two probability distributions are used to model the sampling variability in attribute charts. The binomial distribution is appropriate when the sample is measuring non-conforming units, while the poisson distribution is often used when the sample consists of non-conformities.

In choosing a chart appropriate to a particular situation, the use of cusum compared to the above types of traditional control charts also needs to be considered.

15.9 Constructing mean and range charts

Before any study of a process is carried out, all operational personnel (operatives and first-line supervisors) should fully understand what is going on, and calibrated measurement equipment, appropriate to the characteristic/parameter being controlled, be available. The normal operational procedure should not be disturbed, any obvious abnormalities in the process being rectified.

The process under study must be defined as a statistical entity. Once this has been done the relevant product/service characteristics and/or process parameter(s) which influence the quality of the product must be decided upon; these are the characteristics and parameters which will be measured. It is usual to use a separate control chart to monitor the behaviour of each characteristic and parameter. A data gathering plan, in terms of sample size, frequency of sampling and number of sub-groups to be taken, must be developed and used as the basis for collecting, recording and plotting the subsequent data on a control chart. A typical plan is a sample or sub-group size of five consecutive pieces or units every hour from a process (if possible) and that each time a sample is taken it comprises the most recent pieces or units produced by the process. The study of the process should aim to cover approximately 20 sub-groups (or 50 to 100 individual measurements).

The characteristic(s) under study should be measured and the observations noted on a control chart which has been set up for the process. A typical format of a control chart is shown in Figure 15.6 overleaf. It can be seen from this chart that space is available for the individual values of the readings taken, the sum of the readings, the mean ($\overline{X}$) of these individual observations, the range (R) of the observations, and the date, time and sample number (this provides some identification for the sub-group).

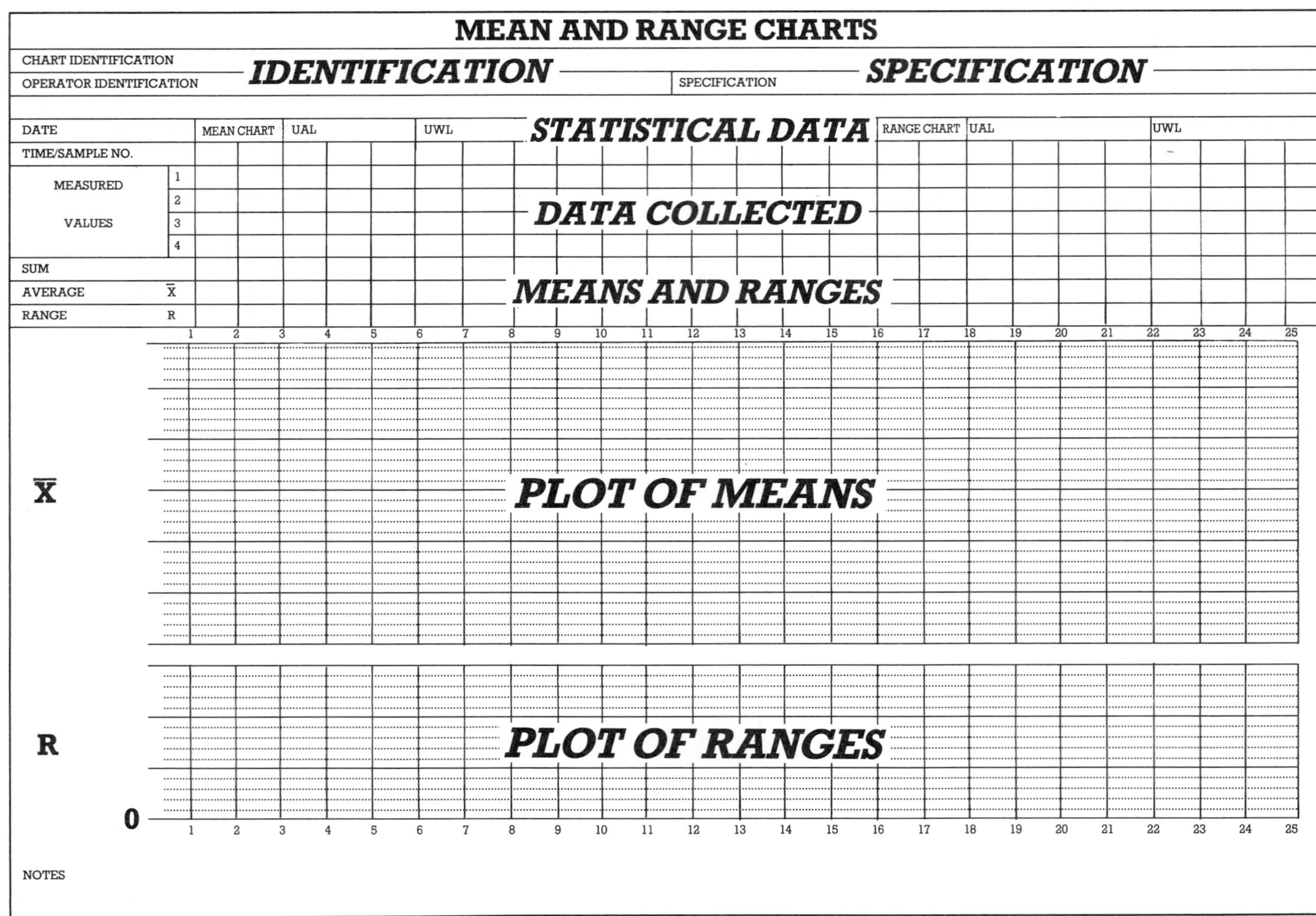

Figure 15.6 Format of a typical control chart

It is essential that control charts are easy to plot, with the minimum of calculation, this is why it is usual to use sample range as a measure of dispersion, rather than standard deviation.

For each sub-group (for example, sub-group size of five), the mean value ($\overline{X}$) (sum of the five readings divided by five) and the range (R) (difference between the extreme readings) are calculated.

Scales need to be selected for the control chart, $\overline{X}$ and R, which portray the data in an adequate manner. Difficult scales should be avoided. The horizontal ordinate is the same for each set and is numbered to correspond with the serial number of the sample or the time at which the sample is taken. The vertical scales are suitably chosen to cover the mean values and the values of the range respectively. The mean chart and the range chart are usually plotted together on one piece of graph paper or chart.

For each individual sub-group the mean and range values are plotted on the control chart. In order to visualise patterns and trends the plotted points should be connected to each other with straight lines. The plotting of individual values is not needed for control purposes, but is useful at the start in helping to understand why, in general, control chart limits for sample means ($\overline{X}$) are narrower than the limits for individual values and more particularly for assessing the capability of the process.

At this stage the control chart is not all that informative, reference values are required. These reference values, the process or grand mean ($\overline{\overline{X}}$) (the sum of the individual averages of the 20 sub-groups divided by 20) and the mean range ($\overline{R}$) (the sum of the individual ranges of the 20 sub-groups divided by 20) are drawn on the control chart as horizontal, heavy broken lines.

The next step is to calculate control limits. The formulae used in current British Standards are as follows:

Mean control chart

Upper action line (UAL) $= \overline{\overline{X}} + \dfrac{3.09\ \sigma}{\sqrt{n}}$

(since $\sigma = \overline{R}/d_n$ or $\overline{R}/d_2$ where d_n or d_2 is a constant (Hartley's constant), $A'_{0.001}$ may be used to simplify the formula:

$$\text{UAL} = \overline{\overline{X}} + A'_{0.001}\,\overline{R}$$

$$\text{where } A'_{0.001} = \frac{3.09}{d_n\ \sqrt{n}}.$$

The constants d_n and $A'_{0.001}$ may be obtained from the tables in British Standard BS 2564 (1955).

Upper warning line (UWL) $= \overline{\overline{X}} + \dfrac{1.96\sigma}{\sqrt{n}}$

(or $\overline{\overline{X}} + A'_{0.025}\,\overline{R}$)

$$\text{where } A'_{0.025} = \frac{1.96}{d_n\ \sqrt{n}}.$$

Lower warning line (LWL) $= (\overline{\overline{X}}) - A'_{0.025}\,\overline{R}$

Lower action line (LAL) $= (\overline{\overline{X}}) - A'_{0.001}\,\overline{R}$

Range control chart

Upper action line (UAL) $= D'_{0.001}\,\overline{R}$
Upper warning line (UWL) $= D'_{0.025}\,\overline{R}$
Lower warning line (LWL) $= D'_{0.975}\,\overline{R}$
Lower action line (LAL) $= D'_{0.999}\,\overline{R}$

As explained above, $A'_{0.001}$, $A'_{0.025}$, $D'_{0.001}$, $D'_{0.025}$, $D'_{0.975}$, $D'_{0.999}$ are constants, consistent with the size of sample, which are taken from the tables in BS 2564 (1955) and which have been reproduced in Appendix K.

The action limits, which are drawn on the chart as horizontal solid lines, are set at approximately three standard errors from the reference value, this may be the nominal value or a target value. The distance the action limits are set out from $\overline{\overline{X}}$, or a nominal or target value, is a reflection of the inherent variability of the process under study. High variability will give wide control limits, while low variability will result in a narrower sets of limits. The limits simply reflect the performance of a process when study data were gathered. These limits, which in the USA are often called control limits, provide indications of the presence of assignable causes of variation.

In the USA and in the Ford Motor Company

system, warning lines are omitted from the charts and simplified control limits are set as follows:

Mean control chart

$$UCL_X = \bar{\bar{X}} + A_2\bar{R}$$

$$LCL_X = \bar{\bar{X}} - A_2\bar{R}$$

Range control chart

$$UCL_R = D_4\bar{R}$$

$$LCL_R = D_3\bar{R}$$

Again, A_2, D_4 and D_3 are constants, reproduced in Appendix L.

It is recommended in BS 2564 (1955) and BS 5700 (1992) that both warning and action limits are used. The tables developed for constants set these limits at 0.025 and 0.001 respectively, i.e. at 1.96 standard errors and 3.09 standard errors respectively. This means that the British Standard action limit is slightly outside the US control limit.

The lower control limits for the range chart are sometimes omitted because it is unlikely that process dispersion will reduce without deliberate intervention or process improvement. One reason for retaining them is to detect spurious precision that appears because of nonconformance in taking the measurements, or to indicate unexpected reductions in variation. It should be noted that for sample sizes below seven, there is no lower control limit if the US method of calculation is used.

15.10 Interpretation of mean and range charts

The sub-group ranges provide an estimate of piece-to-piece variability, consequently the range chart is usually examined before the mean chart. It should be noted that any lack of control in range generally arises for different technical reasons than lack of control in the process mean. The emphasis for process improvement should be to reduce the $\bar{R}$ value. The R control chart should always be run concurrent with the $\bar{X}$ chart, to detect any changes in the variability of the process.

As production proceeds, the patterns of the plotted points for sample mean and range, relative to the control chart limits, indicate whether variation is being introduced above that which occurs in a short period of time. This indicates whether or not production can be considered to be stable. While it is not possible, in all circumstances, to give fixed rules to determine whether the pattern of the points on a control chart indicates a state of instability, the following are typical of the factors which should be considered.

Process state of statistical control

A process is in statistical control when all the variations have been shown to arise from random, chance or common causes and none of the variations are attributable to assignable, non-random or special causes. Many small causes of change are assignable, but it may be uneconomic to consider or control them; if so they should be treated as chance causes.

The randomness of the variations can best be illustrated by collecting at least 50 observations of data and grouping these into samples or sets of at least four observations. Then presenting the results in the form of both mean and range control charts – the limits of which are worked out from the data. If the process from which the data was collected is in statistical control there will be:

- *NO* mean or range values which lie outside the action limits;
- *NO* more than about one in 40 values between the warning and action limits;
- *NO* incidence of two consecutive mean or range values which lie outside the same warning limit on either the mean or the range chart;
- *NO* run or trend of five or more values which also infringes a warning limit;
- *NO* runs of more than six sample means which lie either above or below the grand mean;
- *NO* trends of more than six values of the sample means which are either rising or falling.

If a process is not in statistical control, the assignable causes must be identified and eliminated. The process can then be re-examined to see if it is in statistical control.

If the process is shown to be in Statistical Control the next task is to compare the limits of this control with the tolerance sought.

The Ford Motor Company *Statistical Process Control Instruction Guide* (1986) also provides detailed guidance on interpreting the control chart data for process control. Advice is provided under the broad headings of points beyond the control limits and patterns or trends within the control limits.

It is recommended that notes are made by operational personnel at the appropriate place on the chart and on the process log, to indicate occurrences of technical importance such as adjustment of equipment, tool replacements, coolant adjustment, change of operator, or a new batch of material or components. Such notes will help to identify the source of trouble when the charts indicate that assignable causes of variation are present. All such causes should be eliminated. It is good practice, when taking action to improve a process, to make only one adjustment at a time. By this means it soon becomes evident what improvement, if any, has been effected.

If the special causes of variation have been identified and counter-measures put into place to prevent recurrence, it is usual to exclude these sub-groups and to recalculate the control limits so that the charts portray only variation due to random causes. The control charts can now be used for on-going control. The process is expected to behave as it did when the initial process study was being carried out. The action of eliminating special causes could have resulted in a 'new' process, so caution should be exercised in interpreting data in conjunction with these control limits. The chart indicates to operatives and first-line supervisors when they should be taking action or alternatively when to leave the process alone, and perhaps resample (if warning limits are used).

After a period of operation using these initial control limits, they can be recalculated based on the current performance of the process. These limits need to be reviewed, from time to time, in order that they always reflect the current status of the process.

15.11 Interpretation for process capability

A process which is under control and operating in a controlled environment has limits in its capability to perform its function. These can be measured and presented to provide an indicator of the variability of the process.

This in-control state of any process variable has to be related to what is required of it in terms of the specification. Process capability is a measure of the inherent variability of a process relative to the width of the specification or tolerance for the characteristic or parameter under study. The indices now most commonly used to measure process capability are C*p* which indicates the spread of a process and C*pk* which measures both spread and the setting of a process.

The process capability index (C*p*) =

$$\frac{\text{Total specified tolerance}}{6\hat{\sigma}}$$

where $\hat{\sigma}$ is an estimate of the within-sample process standard deviation. This is calculated from the process study data when only common causes of variation are present using the formula:

$$\hat{\sigma} = \frac{\overline{R}}{d_n} \quad \text{or} \quad \frac{\overline{R}}{d_2}$$

where d_n (d_2) is the conversion factor (Hartley's Constant) depending on the sample size.

The process capability index (C*pk*) is a minimum of:

$$\frac{\text{Upper specified limit} - \overline{\overline{X}}}{3\hat{\sigma}}$$

or

$$\frac{\overline{\overline{X}} - \text{Lower specified limit}}{3\hat{\sigma}}$$

A minimum requirement can be laid down for the spread of a process which should be contained within the specification of the characteristic under study. A C*pk* value of 1.00 is the minimum requirement for ±3 standard deviations within specification. This means that all the specification is equal to 6 standard deviations. The minimum *Cpk* requirement laid down by many motor manufacturers to their suppliers is 1.67.

The ± 3 standard deviation capability is considered to be the natural variation in a process which has not had any improvement activity devoted to it. Improvement in process performance is indicated by an increasing value of *Cpk* and consequently a decreasing number of defects.

In British Standards another term, relative precision index (RPI) is used. The formula for RPI and its relationship to the *Cp* index is as follows:

$$\text{RPI} = \frac{\text{Total specified tolerance}}{\bar{R}} = \frac{6Cp}{d_n}$$

A classification of processes using this index is given in Appendix K (see also Appendix L).

15.12 Machine capability

The minimum requirement for machine capability, when measured by variables, is that $\bar{\bar{X}} \pm 4$ standard deviations are contained within the specification limits. This more stringent requirement is needed if the process is to have any chance of meeting the goal of $\bar{\bar{X}} \pm 3$ standard deviations overall process capability, during normal production when factors other than the machine contribute to variation.

A study to assess machine capability is carried out over a very short period of time. During this reference period it is assumed that all the other inputs are going to be consistent; it is only the performance of the machine which is being assessed. The study will provide an estimate of the variation due only to the machine itself. A sample of 50 consecutive datum points is collected and analysed using a tally chart. The data should then be divided into sub-groups of $n = 4$ or 5, in chronological order, and the subgroups' means and ranges plotted onto 9 $\bar{\bar{X}}$ and R charts to check that the assumption about the stability of the machine is correct. This is particularly important with relatively long cycle times. It is important to also check the pattern of data to see that it conforms approximately to a normal distribution.

The data may then be converted into a cumulative percentage curve which is transposed on to normal probability graph paper. If the data is normally distributed, the resultant graph will approximate to a straight line. Specification limits are superimposed on the graph and if the plotted straight line, when extended to the extremes of the percentage scale, lies within the specification limit the machine is considered to be capable (i.e. 99.994 per cent of the product will fall within specification). A typical plot for machine capability is shown in Figure 15.7.

If the machine is not capable, as indicated by the graph, an estimate of the percentage of product not meeting the specification can be read from the graph.

Non-linear plots indicate non-normality. In this case, various types of graph paper exist for other statistical distributions (for example, log normal and Weibull) which will enable an assessment of machine capability to be made. Other methods involve the transformation of the data in some way so that it appears as a normal distribution.

The following indices are used to quantify the variability of a machine relative to the specification:

A capability index (*Cm*) which is a measure of the spread of the machine

$$= \frac{\text{Total specified tolerance}}{6\hat{\sigma}}$$

A capability index (*Cmk*) which indicates both the spread and setting and is a minimum of:

$$\frac{\text{Upper specified limit} - \bar{\bar{X}}}{3\hat{\sigma}}$$

or

$$\frac{\bar{\bar{X}} - \text{Lower specified limit}}{3\hat{\sigma}}$$

where $\hat{\sigma}$ is an estimate of the standard deviation from the data.

A *Cmk* value of 1.33 is for ±4 standard deviations capability.

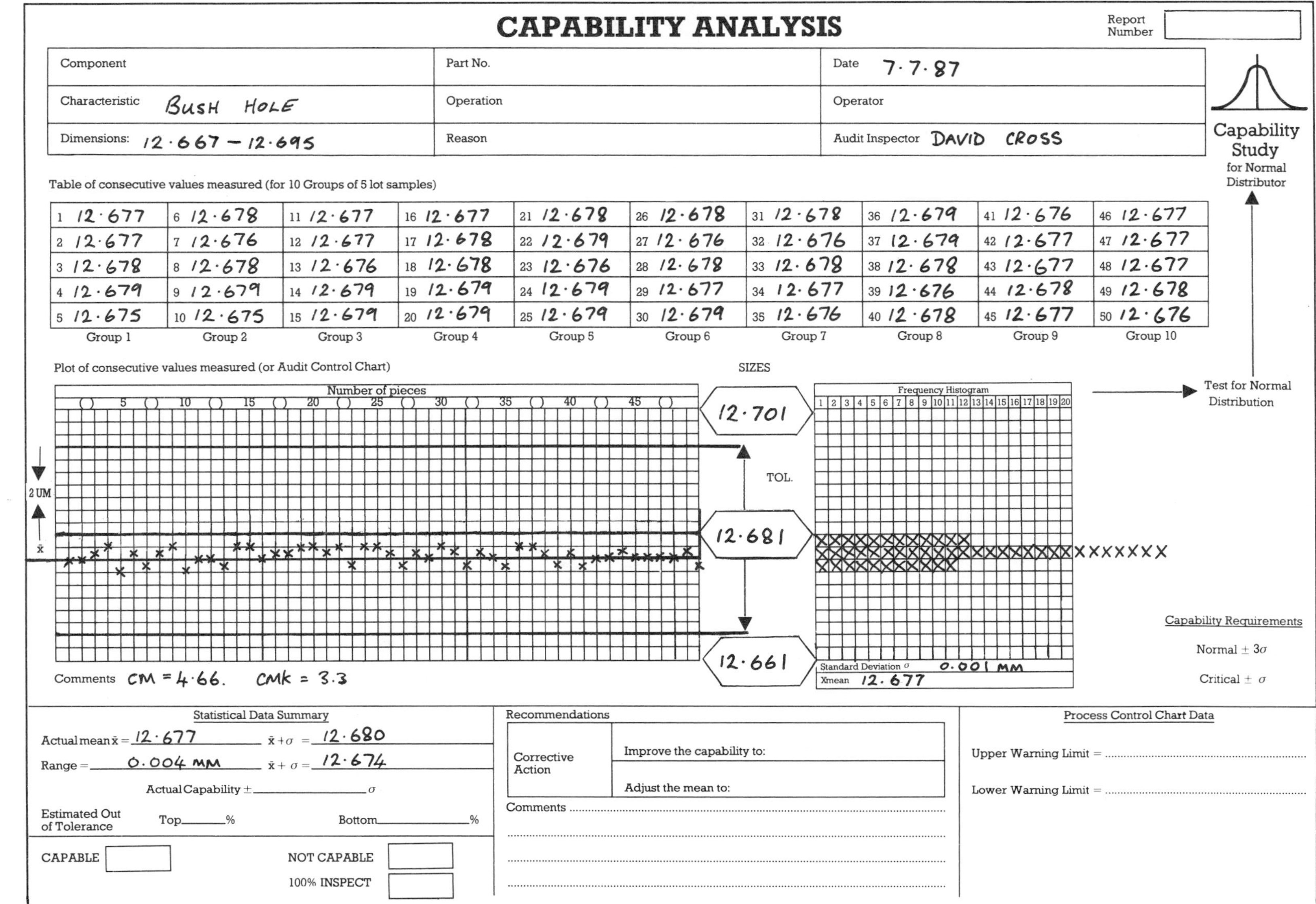

CAPABILITY ANALYSIS

Report Number

Component	Part No.	Date 7·7·87
Characteristic BUSH HOLE	Operation	Operator
Dimensions: 12·667 – 12·695	Reason	Audit Inspector DAVID CROSS

Table of consecutive values measured (for 10 Groups of 5 lot samples)

Group 1	Group 2	Group 3	Group 4	Group 5	Group 6	Group 7	Group 8	Group 9	Group 10
1 12·677	6 12·678	11 12·677	16 12·677	21 12·678	26 12·678	31 12·678	36 12·679	41 12·676	46 12·677
2 12·677	7 12·676	12 12·677	17 12·678	22 12·679	27 12·676	32 12·676	37 12·679	42 12·677	47 12·677
3 12·678	8 12·678	13 12·676	18 12·678	23 12·676	28 12·678	33 12·678	38 12·678	43 12·677	48 12·677
4 12·679	9 12·679	14 12·679	19 12·679	24 12·679	29 12·677	34 12·677	39 12·676	44 12·678	49 12·678
5 12·675	10 12·675	15 12·679	20 12·679	25 12·679	30 12·679	35 12·676	40 12·678	45 12·677	50 12·676

Plot of consecutive values measured (or Audit Control Chart)

Standard Deviation σ 0·001 MM

Xmean 12·677

Capability Requirements

Normal ± 3σ

Critical ± σ

Comments CM = 4·66. CMK = 3.3

Statistical Data Summary

Actual mean x̄ = 12·677 x̄ + σ = 12·680

Range = 0·004 MM x̄ + σ = 12·674

Actual Capability ± ______ σ

Estimated Out of Tolerance Top ______ % Bottom ______ %

CAPABLE ☐ NOT CAPABLE ☐ 100% INSPECT ☐

Recommendations

Corrective Action	Improve the capability to:
	Adjust the mean to:

Comments ....

Process Control Chart Data

Upper Warning Limit = ...

Lower Warning Limit = ...

Figure 15.7 A typical plot for machine capability

15.13 Preliminary process capability studies

It is of interest to note that the Ford Motor Company (1990) have replaced 'machine capability' studies with 'preliminary process capability' studies (PPCS). The argument was that 'machine capability studies disregards stability of the process and sequence of data from the process.' These are short-term studies which are carried out to determine early information on the performance of a new or revised process relative to customer requirements. The studies are based on at least twenty subgroups of typically three to five pieces. The minimum requirement laid down by Ford is a *Ppk* of 1.67. The calculations for *Pp* and *Ppk* are numerically the same as those for *Cp* and *Cpk*.

An initial study may be conducted at the equipment suppliers before taking delivery of new process tooling and/or equipment, providing an opportunity for convenient and timely resolution of any equipment concerns. Studies need to be conducted in-house at several stages in the evolution of the process whether or not new tooling and/or equipment is involved. A PPCS can only provide limited stability information but it is still of considerable diagnostic use and is a necessary prerequisite to credible capability analysis.

15.14 Constructing and interpreting a number defective (np) chart for non-conforming units (attributes)

In general, when the source of non-conformance has to be sought and removed, control charts based on attributes do not provide as much assistance as those for quantitative data. These charts depend on the presence of non-conforming units or non-conformities.

The objective of an attributes control chart is to detect an increase of the process proportion that are defective above some value. By the very simplicity of the assessment, for example, pass or fail, an attribute chart is not as sensitive as one based on variables. However, there are many occasions when control based on classification into 'good-bad' or 'pass-fail' must be used, or for when such a classification is more convenient than variables charts. A major advantage is that multi-attribute checking is possible whereas with variables a chart is required for each quality characteristic to be controlled.

In a number defective (np) chart the charted data are the observed number of defectives in a sample. However, because of the variation that is inherent in the sampling process, the number of defective items occurring in a sample will vary from sample to sample, even if the underlying process proportion defective is constant. The presence of this pattern of variation gives rise to two dangers when the number defective in a sample is used as a criterion for controlling the proportion defective in the underlying process. These dangers are expressed as the type 1 or type 2 risks mentioned earlier.

The collection of data and setting of control limits are similar to the method previously described for the $\overline{X}$ and R chart. The formulae commonly used for setting control limits are as follows:

Process average (np) $\pm$ 3 standard errors

Based on the binominal distribution,

$$\sigma = \sqrt{\left[n\bar{p}\left(1-\frac{n\bar{p}}{n}\right)\right]}$$

Upper action line (UAL) or control limit

$$\text{UAL} = (\text{UCL}_{np}) = n\bar{p} + 3\sqrt{\left[n\bar{p}\left(1-\frac{n\bar{p}}{n}\right)\right]}$$

Lower action line (LAL) or control limit

$$\text{LAL} = (\text{LCL}_{np}) = n\bar{p} - 3\sqrt{\left[n\bar{p}\left(1-\frac{n\bar{p}}{n}\right)\right]}$$

Upper and lower warning lines may be set at:

$$n\bar{p} \pm 2\sqrt{\left[n\bar{p}\left(1-\frac{n\bar{p}}{n}\right)\right]}$$

Since it is possible to observe only an integer

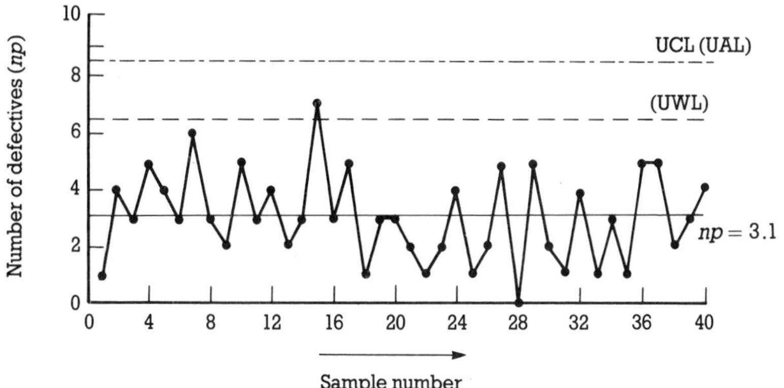

Figure 15.8 Number defective chart for pen cartridges – process in control **Source:** Oakland & Followell, 1990

number of non-conforming items in a sample, the control limit is usually positioned between integer values to avoid the ambiguity of a point being plotted on the control limit. An example of an *np* chart for an in-control pen cartridge manufacturing process is shown in Figure 15.8.

An alternative method for setting control limits for attribute charts is described in BS 5701 (1980). This method has not been observed in use by the authors and has been omitted to avoid confusion. Those readers who are interested in studying this approach are referred to BS 5701 (1980).

The interpretation of plotted data on control charts for attributes is similar to that for variable data. However, the following should be kept in mind:

- A run of plotted points above the process average indicates a deterioration in the process, whilst a run below it indicates improvement.
- Unless the sample size is very large, it is unlikely that there will be a lower control limit.

15.15 Setting control limits for other attribute control charts

The formulae for setting control limits for the *p* chart for proportion of non-conforming units are:

$$\text{UAL} = \text{UCL}_p = \bar{p} + 3\sqrt{\left[\frac{\bar{p}(1-\bar{p})}{\bar{n}}\right]}$$

$$\text{LAL} = \text{LCL}_p = \bar{p} - 3\sqrt{\left[\frac{\bar{p}(1-\bar{p})}{\bar{n}}\right]}$$

where $\bar{p}$ = average proportion non-conforming
$\bar{n}$ = average sample size. (Unlike the *np* chart the sample size in a *p* chart is not necessarily kept constant and $\bar{n}$ is used, in most cases, to allow constant control limits to be drawn. For very large or very small sample sizes, the control limits must be calculated individually using n, rather than $\bar{n}$. Again upper and lower warning lines may be set at $p \pm 2\sigma$.)

An out-of-control *p* chart for issued components is illustrated in Figure 15.9 overleaf.

The application of attributes charts discussed so far has been restricted to charting non-conforming units. There are cases when interest is centred on the non-conformities creating the non-conforming unit. In such situations the poisson probability distribution is used to model the sampling variability. This distribution describes the number of non-conformities in samples where each unit may have zero, one or more non-conformities, and the possible number of which may have no upper limit.

The formulae for setting control limits for the *c* chart for number of non-conformities are:

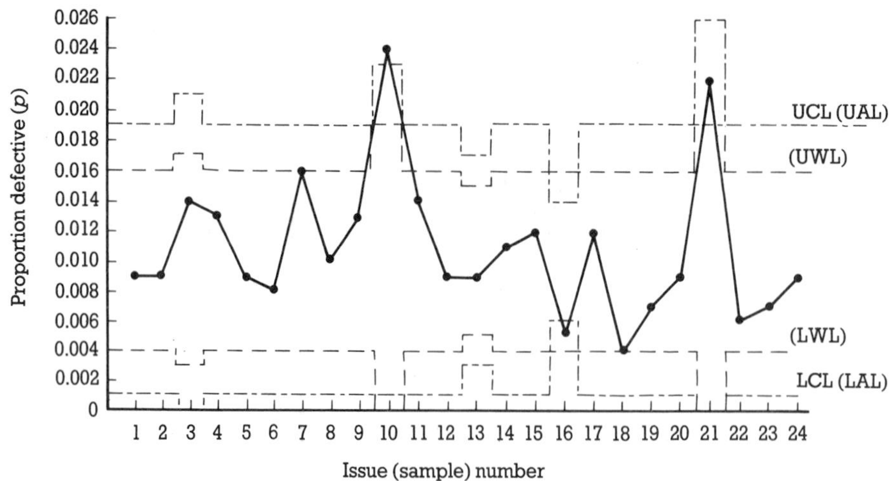

Figure 15.9 *p* chart – for issued components **Source:** Oakland & Followell, 1990

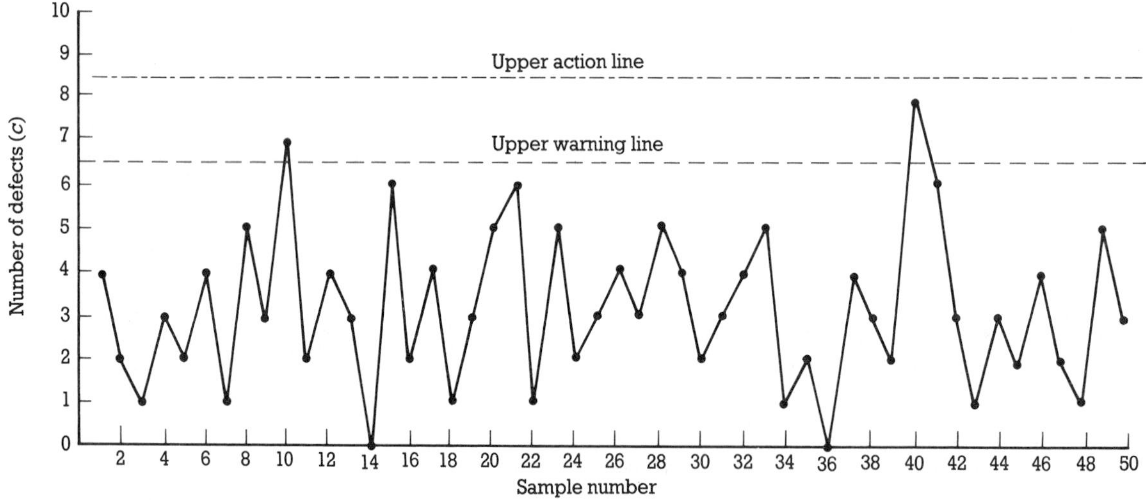

Figure 15.10 *c* chart – for polythene fish-eyes **Source:** Oakland & Followell, 1990

$$\text{UAL} = \text{UCL}_c = \bar{c} + 3\sqrt{\bar{c}}$$

$$\text{LAL} = \text{LCL}_c = \bar{c} - 3\sqrt{\bar{c}}$$

where $\bar{c}$ = the process average number of non-conformities (in the Poisson distribution, $\sigma = \sqrt{\bar{c}}$). Again upper and lower warning lines may be set at $\bar{c} \pm 2\sqrt{\bar{c}}$.

An illustration of an in-control *c* chart for polythene fish-eyes is given in Figure 15.10.

The formulae for setting control limits for the *u* chart for non-conformities per unit are:

$$\text{UAL} = \text{UCL}_u = \bar{u} + 3\sqrt{\frac{\bar{u}}{\bar{n}}}$$

$$\text{LAL} = \text{LCL}_u = \bar{u} - 3\sqrt{\frac{\bar{u}}{\bar{n}}}$$

where $\bar{u}$ = the process average non-conformities per unit and $\bar{n}$ = the average sample size. Once again, upper and lower warning limits may be set at

$$\bar{u} \pm 2\sqrt{\frac{\bar{u}}{\bar{n}}}$$

An out-of-control process for producing cooling blades is shown in the *u* chart of Figure 15.11.

If attribute control charts are in use it is obvious that zero defectives or defects are not being achieved. Process capability for attributes is generally expressed as the average proportion conforming to specification (i.e. a conformity rate), or defect rate $\bar{p}$ or $\bar{c}$.

15.16 Cumulative sum charts (cusum charts)

Basis of cusum charts

The cusum charts have the same objectives as the traditional control charts. The essential principle is that a target or reference value (T) is subtracted from each observation. This target value is generally a constant, corresponding to the target mean of the process or the expected number of non-conformances or non-conformities. The cumulative sum of the deviations from target is formed, and this cusum is plotted against the serial number of the observation. For example, in a cusum chart for controlling measured variables the procedure would be for each observed sample average ($\overline{X}$) to subtract the target value (T). The current ($\overline{X}$ – T) value is then added to the cumulative sum of all the previous ($\overline{X}$ – T) values, the resulting value is then plotted on a graph.

Bissell gives an interesting description of the cusum method when he compares it 'to cumulating a golf score against par for each hole, the resulting positive or negative total giving an indication of a player's progress, at any stage of a round, against a target (namely, par for the course)' (Bissell, 1984).

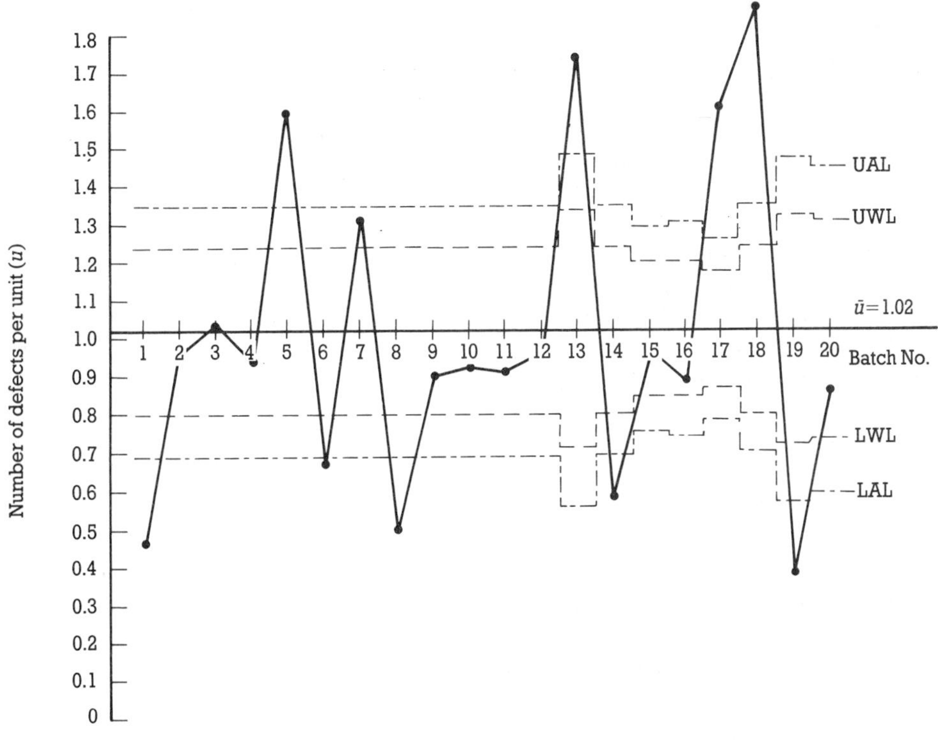

Figure 15.11 *u* chart – for cooling blades

Source: Oakland & Followell, 1990

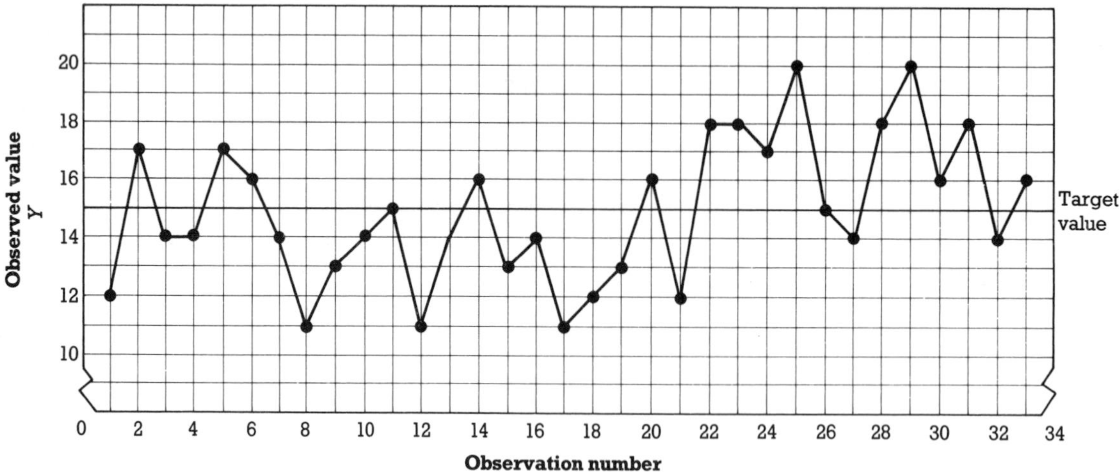

Figure 15.12 Run or individuals chart of data from Table 15.1

The cusum method of plotting data results in the representation of averages by the local slope of the chart. The key factor in the interpretation of a cusum plot is its slope. When the average corresponds to the target value, the path of the cusum lies roughly parallel to the axis. When the local average of the series is greater than the target value, the cusum slopes upwards (positive slope). Conversely, when the local average is less than the target value, the cusum slopes downwards (negative slope). The greater the discrepancy between the local average and the target value, the steeper the slope of the cusum path.

The result of plotting in the cusum mode is that changes in the average level (mean or variability) of the process over different subdivisions of the sequence of observations are clearly indicated by changes in the slope of the chart.

The above principles are best explained by a simple example. The data given in Table 15.1 have been obtained, over a time sequence, in the order shown and a target value of 15 has been set. It can be seen from Figures 15.12 and 15.13 that plotting the data in the cusum mode gives a much clearer display of the changes taking place than the simple run chart or individuals chart.

Once the data have been plotted on a cusum chart, as with conventional control charts, some decisions need to be made about it. The

Table 15.1 Data for cusum plotting

Observation number	Observed value	Deviation from target (15)	Cumulative deviations
1	12	−3	−3
2	17	+2	−1
3	14	−1	−2
4	14	−1	−3
5	17	+2	−1
6	16	+1	0
7	14	−1	−1
8	11	−4	−5
9	13	−2	−7
10	14	−1	−8
11	15	0	−8
12	11	−4	−12
13	14	−1	−13
14	16	+1	−12
15	13	−2	−14
16	14	−1	−15
17	11	−4	−19
18	12	−3	−22
19	13	−2	−24
20	16	+1	−23
21	12	−3	−26
22	18	+3	−23
23	18	+3	−20
24	17	+2	−18
25	20	+5	−13
26	15	0	−13
27	14	−1	−14
28	18	+3	−11
29	20	+5	−6
30	16	+1	−5
31	18	+3	−2
32	14	−1	−3
33	16	+1	−2

Source: BS 5703: Part 1, 1980

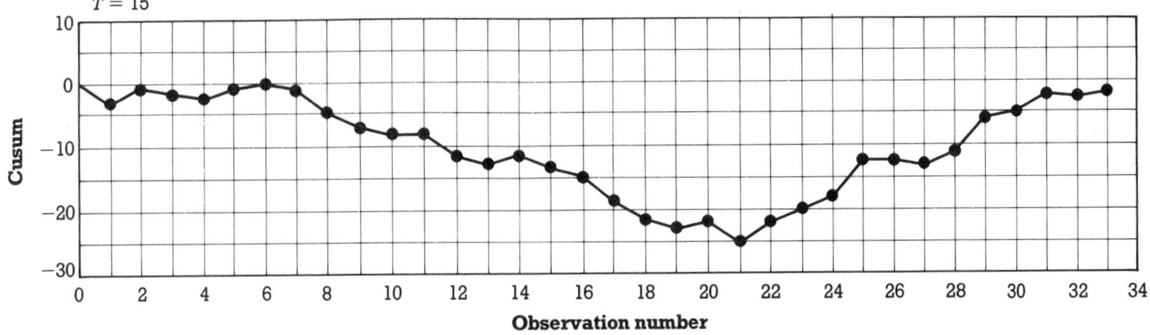

Figure 15.13 Cusum chart of data from table 15.1

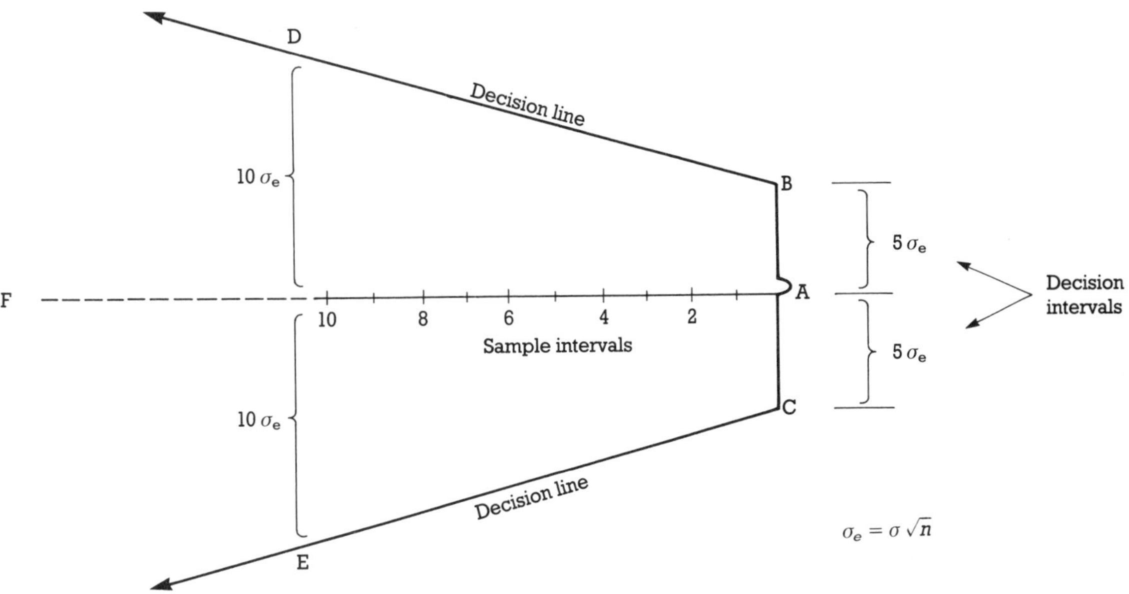

Figure 15.14 General-purpose truncated V-mask

decision procedure is analogous to the control lines used on a conventional chart for averages, but is used to assess the slope of the plot rather than the ordinate of a plotted point. The simplest cusum decision rules are embodied in a V-mask. Different configurations of V-masks are used, but the principle of application and effect are identical. The V-mask can be cut out of card or engraved on transparent plastic-type material.

The construction of the mask is based on the standard error of the plotted variable, its distribution and the average number of samples taken up to the point at which a signal occurs, i.e. the required average run length properties. The essential features of a mask are shown in Figure 15.14. They are:

- a datum point, *A*, which is placed over any point of intersect on the chart and is often the most recent point plotted;
- the vertical half distances, *AB* and *AC*, known as decision intervals;
- the sloping decision lines *BD* and *CE* – an out-of-control signal is indicated if the cusum path crosses or touches either of these lines;

- for ease of alignment on the chart, the horizontal line *AF* may be useful. This line, representing the zero slope of the cusum when the process is running at its target level, should be parallel to the sample axis of the chart.

The geometry of the truncated V-mask shown in Figure 15.14 is the version that is recommended for general use and has been chosen to give properties broadly similar to the traditional chart with action and warning lines at the 0.001 and 0.025 probability levels. If this particular configuration of V-mask is not judged to be suitable, BS 5703: Part 3 (1981) gives a total of six possible configurations of mask.

The relationship between the cusum and sample number scales will determine the appearance of the chart. Too large a cusum scale will produce a chart with a saw-tooth appearance on which small changes will be difficult to detect, while large shifts in average will quickly send the cusum off the top or bottom of the graph paper. Too small a scale will effectively dampen out minor variations but may also suppress real changes in the mean level of the data. A widely-accepted convention is that a distance on the vertical (cusum) scale equal to one sample interval should represent approximately two standard error units of the plotted variable.

Types of data amenable to cusum charting

The fundamental requirements for cusum charts are that the observations should be at least on an interval scale of measurement and there should be logical grounds for their being sorted into a sequence for plotting.

Sample means and ranges can be plotted in sequence to provide a continuous assessment of the state of a process. Cusums can be used for measured variables and counted attributes. Cusum charts are based on the same probability models as traditional control charts.

Traditional or cusum charts?

The advantages of cusum charts can be briefly summarised as follows:

- For the same sample size, a cusum chart will give more vivid illustration of any changes that are occurring (purely by visual examination of the plot, without recourse to decision rules).
- The cusum chart uses cumulated data more effectively, thereby giving cost savings.
- The cusum gives clear indication of the location and magnitude of change points in a process.

Possible disadvantages of cusum charts are as follows:

- The procedure is comparatively less well known, and there is a problem with re-educating those familiar with conventional control chart methods. In particular, it is sometimes difficult to establish the basic principle that the control parameter is the slope of a plot rather than its vertical ordinate.
- It is sometimes maintained that the calculations for the cusum plot are more complex than those for the conventional plot and the interpretation of the results is clearly more complex.
- There can be difficulties in constructing the V-mask.
- As the average value is indicated by slope, staff using the charts require training to achieve effective interpretation. The cusum charts are generally more difficult to interpret than traditional control charts.

  A comparison of a mean chart and a cusum chart for means of samples of steel rod lengths is given in Figure 15.15.

15.17 The implementation of SPC

A number of authors (for example, Oakland and Followell (1990), Dale et al (1989) and Owen (1989)) and companies such as the Ford Motor Company have given their guidelines for the implementation of SPC in an organisation. Several points about the implementation process are worthy of special mention.

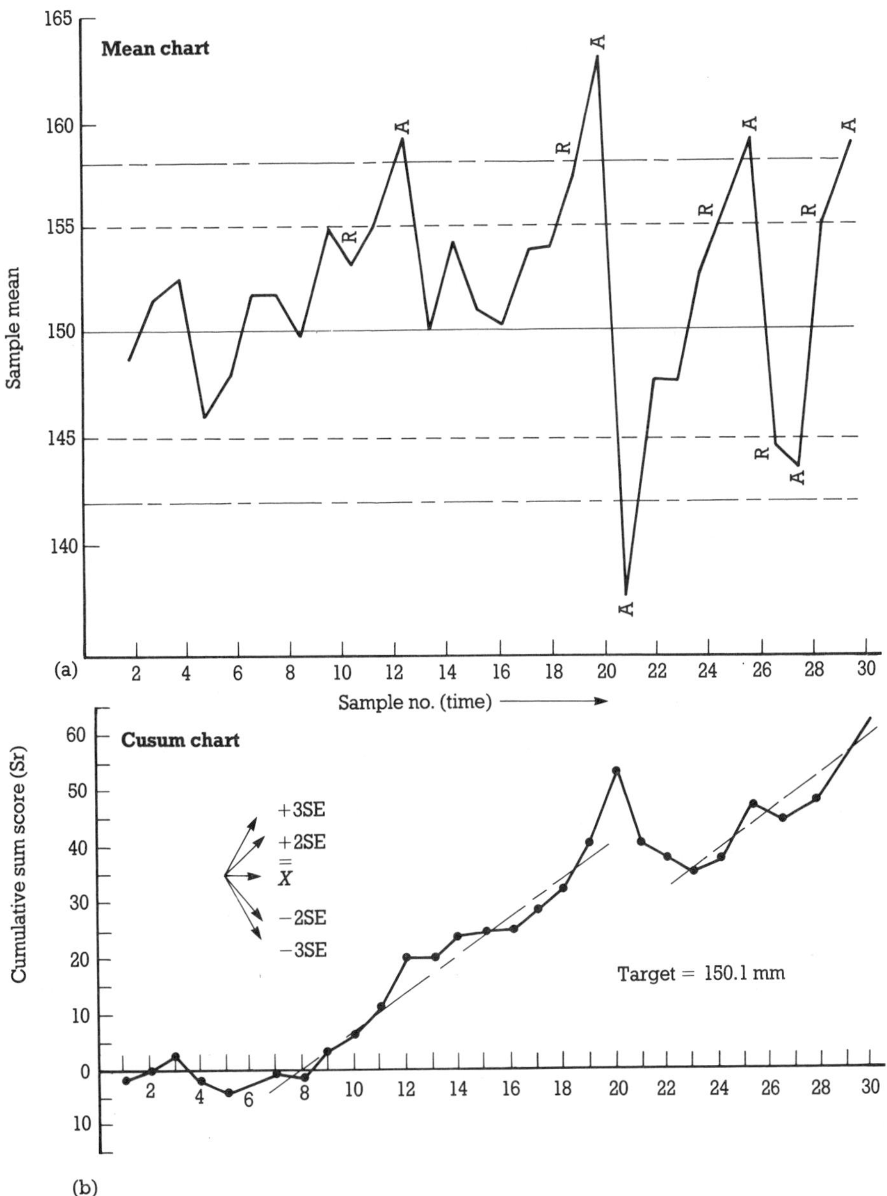

Figure 15.15 Shewhart and cusum charts for means of steel rods

Source: Oakland & Followell, 1990

Awareness

Everyone in the organisation should have some basic understanding of SPC and its use. People should not be frightened and intimidated by SPC; the tendency to over-complicate training should be avoided. It is vital that a training strategy for SPC is developed.

The training and education programme should start with the senior management team and then filter down, using different and appropriate modes of training, through the organisational hierarchy. The process must begin with senior management since, if SPC is to be successful over the longer term, they need to take their obligations seriously and provide the necessary visible leadership and resources. Training on SPC must not be seen as something solely for staff at lower levels in the organisation. The time between SPC training and the introduction of SPC should be kept to a minimum.

Selection of a SPC facilitator

The rôle of the facilitator is that of co-ordinator, providing a source of expertise on SPC and acting as the SPC 'champion'. The facilitator plays a vital rôle in the establishment and continued success of SPC. The typical responsibilities of a facilitator, include:

- ensuring that everyone in the organisation is kept informed of progress and developments;
- monitoring progress in individual areas and assisting staff as and when required;
- organising and monitoring training on SPC and related tools and techniques;
- initiating applications of SPC in areas or departments not currently using it and reacting positively to the initiative of others;
- providing advice on all aspects of statistical methods relating to process improvement;
- encouraging people to use SPC;
- assisting with all aspects relating to the charting and analysis of data;
- analysing available indicators and providing, at regular intervals, a state-of-the-art picture of the benefits and savings achieved through using SPC;
- assessing the company's commitment to continuous improvement.
- self-development in terms of statistical methods and applications.

In their SPC course notes, the Ford Motor Company recommended that the appointment of a facilitator should take place early in an organisation's SPC programme (Ford Motor Company, 1985). However, Dale *et al.* (1989) reporting on the findings of a questionnaire survey of 158 Ford Motor Company suppliers found that despite this guidance, 54 (34 per cent) of the 158 respondents had not appointed a facilitator. Dale and Shaw (1989) claim that companies who appoint a facilitator are less likely to experience difficulties with the introduction and application of SPC.

From the work of Dale and Shaw (1989) it is possible to get an outline profile of an SPC facilitator. The appointment is likely to be made from within the organisation, the job will be in addition to the individual's normal workload, the individual will be of middle or senior management status and their discipline will be either quality or technical.

Setting up a steering committee for SPC

It is useful to establish a steering committee or steering arm to oversee the SPC programme; its main function should be to guide, publicise and manage the progress of SPC. This body will give continuity and structure to the programme and will help to ensure that SPC does not become too dependent on a few individuals for its success. It also gives visibility to SPC and shows that management are serious about its use. To be effective the committee needs to be active and plan well ahead. If a steering committee is not established then the implementation and progress of SPC should be treated as a regular agenda item at management meetings.

Selection of a pilot programme area

A number of organisations fall into the trap of trying to apply SPC to all areas or departments at the same time (the big bang approach), it is not uncommon to find organisations setting weekly targets for the number of process parameters or product/service characteristics for which a control chart is required to be constructed or the number of control charts which will be in use. Consequently, too much data are collected and organisations find themselves not able to respond to the signals from the process. If the introduction of SPC is rushed then the implementation is not properly planned, resulting in key elements, which are necessary for success, not being considered in sufficient detail. A better approach is to apply SPC in one area where the chances of success are high. This will allow an organisation to check out its implementation planning thoroughly and enable feedback to be gathered, on all the likely pitfalls. Once SPC has been used successfully in one area, it is much easier to extend its use to other departments.

15.18 Difficulties experienced in implementing and using SPC

The aim of SPC is straightforward – to reduce variation in process output by; first establishing whether or not a process is in a state of statistical control; secondly, if it is not, getting it under control by eliminating special causes of variation and; finally, striving to reduce random or common causes of variation so that the output from the process is consistently around a nominal or target value.

A number of organisations do encounter problems in the implementation and application of SPC. In a recent study of the use of SPC by suppliers in the automotive-related industry, Dale *et al.* (1989) reported on the main stumbling blocks which are typically encountered and these are shown in Tables 15.2 and 15.3. One hundred and twenty two (77 per cent) of the 158 respondents indicated that they had experienced difficulties when implementing SPC, and 130 (82 per cent) encountered difficulties in its application. The top three difficulties in implementing SPC were: lack of knowledge or expertise on SPC, poor understanding and awareness within the company of the purpose of SPC, and lack of action from senior management. The three main difficulties in its application are: applying SPC to a particular process, resistance to change, and deciding which product characteristic and/or process parameter to chart. These confirmed Oakland's earlier findings in the Chemical Industry (Lockyer *et al*, 1981; Oakland and Duprey, 1983).

Looking at the difficulties outlined in Tables 15.2 and 15.3, it is clear that organisations do encounter a wide range of stumbling blocks in their endeavours to use SPC, indicating that there is no easy recipe for success.

It is also clear that the vast majority of

Table 15.2 Main difficulties experienced in the implementation of SPC

Difficulty	Survey 1 (*N* = 57)	Survey 2 (*N* = 63)	Total score (*N* = 120)
Lack of knowledge/ expertise on SPC	91	58	149
Poor understanding and awareness within the company of the purpose of SPC	63	73	136
Lack of action from senior management	73	45	118
Lack of SPC training for operators	50	56	106
Lack of knowledge of which parameters to measure and/or control	45	52	97
Difficulty in convincing people that SPC is beneficial	4	90	94
Negative reaction of operators	40	47	87
Negative reaction of senior management	44	41	85
Negative reaction of middle management	45	27	82
Negative reaction of line management	24	58	82
A general lack of encouragement	50	30	80
Lack of action from line management	37	41	78
Deciding which of the various charting techniques to use	43	31	74
Lack of SPC training for senior management	46	19	65
Lack of action from middle management	33	31	64
Lack of SPC training for line management	31	27	58
Poor communication between management and the shop floor	22	35	57
Lack of SPC training for middle management	33	14	47
Deciding whether to express data in an attribute or variables format	27	16	43
Literacy/numeracy of operators	13	29	42
Negative reaction of trades union	16	14	30
Literacy/numeracy of line supervision	5	6	11

(continued)

Table 15.2 *continued*

Difficulty	Survey 1 (N = 57)	Survey 2 (N = 63)	Total score (N = 120)
Feedback of data	6	3	9
Lack of resources devoted to SPC	5	4	9
Difficulty in measuring key product characteristics	–	7	7
Small batch production	–	6	6
An inadequate computer system	5	–	5
Organisational changes	5	–	5
Operators' workload	–	5	5
Deciding on manual or computer-aided charting	–	5	5
Lack of appropriate gauges	–	3	3
Replacement of machinery	2	–	2
The nature of product non-conformities	–	1	1

Note: Respondents were asked to select and rank the five main inhibitors to the introduction of SPC. The score was awarded by allocating points of 5, 4, 3, 2 and 1 respectively to the first, second, third, fourth and fifth inhibitor given.

difficulties are caused by a lack of commitment, awareness and vision of middle and senior managers. While SPC is a bottom-up activity, used by staff responsible for improving their work processes, senior management must take seriously their obligations for quality improvement, if SPC is to be effective over the longer term. SPC should not be treated as an easy let-out for management allowing them to present a picture to their customers that they are doing something positive about quality improvement, when in reality this is not the case. SPC, when properly applied, will reduce variation in processes, products and services, which in turn will lead to reductions in waste and costs, and increases in market share and competitiveness. It is worth doing properly.

Dale and Shaw (1991) writing on the common issues and queries which organisations raise in relation to SPC make the point that a number of people who are considering the use of SPC in their organisation and those concerned with its implementation do not understand the fundamentals underlying the concept. They go

Table 15.3 The difficulties encountered in applying SPC

Difficulty	Survey 1 (N = 60)	Survey 2 (N = 70)	Total score (N = 130)
Applying SPC to a particular process	96	43	139
Resistance to change	50	58	108
Deciding which characteristic and/or parameter to chart	50	43	93
Deciding which charting technique to use	54	41	85
Lack of management commitment	38	47	85
Lack of problem-solving skills	26	26	52
Time restraints	9	39	48
Poor understanding of the SPC techniques	20	21	41
Lack of a company-wide training programme on SPC	3	32	35
Attitudes of the workforce	1	32	33
Poor understanding of the SPC philosophy	–	31	31
An inadequate computer system	3	–	3
Unrealistic specifications	–	3	3
Difficulty in demonstrating the benefits of SPC	–	3	3
Small batch production situation	–	3	3
Attitudes of first-line supervision	–	3	3
Incapable processes	–	2	2
Difficulty experienced in measuring product characteristics	–	2	2
Lack of feedback to the workforce	–	1	1
Lack of equipment to measure specific characteristics	1	–	1
Lack of appreciation of the disciplines necessary to support SPC	1	–	1

Note: Respondents were asked to select and rank the three main difficulties encountered in applying SPC. The score was calculated by allocating points of 3, 2 and 1 respectively to the first, second and third difficulty indicated.

on to say that there is still a degree of resistance in some industries to its introduction and use. The following profile of an organisation which questions the use of SPC is presented:

- The Board of Directors and senior management team are not devoting sufficient time and resources to TQM, in general, and SPC, in particular.
- There is a lack of corporate vision, mission, policies and values.
- Meeting the production schedule is the number one priority.
- The emphasis is on firefighting and not on quality planning and prevention-type activities.
- A lack of attention is devoted to the production and preparation stage.
- Education and training is accorded a low priority and is not properly assessed and monitored.
- The organisation does not have an SPC facilitator.
- Emphasis is on the individual and not on teamwork.
- Engineers are divorced from the realities of the factory shop floor.
- The manufacturing function is not considered a top priority.

(Dale and Shaw, 1991)

15.19 Definitions and terminology

The following are some definitions and terms used in this chapter.

Assigned causes: factors (usually systematic) that can be detected and identified as contributing to a change in a quality, characteristic or process level.

Average run length (to detection) (ARL): the expected value of the number of samples plotted on the chart up to and including the point that gives rise to a signal that an assignable or special cause of variation is present.

Chance causes: the factors, generally many in number, but each of relatively small importance, contributing to variation, which have not necessarily been identified and are neglected.

Control chart: a chart on which limits are drawn and on which are plotted values of any statistic computed from successive samples of a production run. The control chart is used to investigate if a process may be considered to be under control. The statistics which are used (mean, range, per cent defective) define the different kind of control charts.

Control limits (upper and/or lower): in a control chart, the limit below which (upper limit) or above which (lower limit) or the limits between which the statistic under consideration lies within a very high probability when the process is under control.

Frequency distribution: an expression of the relationship which exists between the magnitude of an observable variable characteristic and the frequency of its occurrence.

Mean (often called average or arithmetic mean): the sum of the observations divided by their number.

Median: when sample measurements are arranged in order of magnitude, the median is the middle value.

Normal curve: a particular type of symmetrical distribution curve with a definite mathematical equation, found by experience to represent a great many frequency distributions in practice.

Range: the difference between the maximum and minimum, or the extreme observations.

Process capability: a statistical measure of inherent process variability for a given characteristic process quality control.

Process control: that part of quality that is concerned with maintaining the product, process, or service characteristic within specified limits.

Sample: one or more sampling units taken from a population (lot or process) and intended to provide information on the population (lot or process) and possibly to serve as a basis for a decision on the population (lot or process).

Standard deviation: the square root of the average of the sequences of the deviations (a deviation is the difference between an observation and the average of all the observations).

Systematic variations; systematic effects: the non-random patterns in an otherwise stable process (e.g. at regular intervals).

British Standards

BS 600: 1935 *The application of statistical methods to industrial standardization and quality control.*

BS 600R: 1942 *Quality control charts* (withdrawn and replaced by BS 2564).

BS 2564: 1955 *Control chart technique when manufacturing to a specification with special reference to articles machined to dimensional tolerance.*

BS 2846: *Statistical interpretation of data* Part 1: 1991 *Routine analysis of quantative data*; Part 7: 1984 *Test for departure from normality* (ISO/DIS 5479: 1984)

BS 4778: *Quality vocabulary* Part 2: 1991 *Quality concepts and related definitions.*

BS 5700: 1984 (1992) *Process control using quality control chart methods and cusum techniques.*

BS 5701: 1980 *Guide to number-defective charts for quality control.*

BS 5703: *Guide to data analysis and quality control using cusum techniques* Part 1: 1980 *Introduction to cusum charting;* Part 2: 1980 *Decision rules and statistical tests for cusum charts and tabulations;* Part 3: 1981 *Cusum methods for process/quality control by measurement;* Part 4: 1982 *Cusums for counted/attributes data.*

BSCECC 00016: 1991 *Basic specification: Basic requirements for the area of statistical process control (SPC) in the CECC System.*

References

Bissell A F. *An Introduction to Cusum Charts.* The Institute of Statisticians, Suffolk, UK, 1984.

Dale B G, Owen M and Shaw P. *SPC in the motor industry: what is the state-of-the-art?* Occasional Paper Number 8902, Manchester School of Management, UMIST, 1989.

Dale B G, Owen M and Shaw P. 'Supplier Quality: the Ford Motor Company Regional Training Initiative.' *International Journal of Vehicle Design*, 10(2), pp 125–35, 1989.

Dale B G and Shaw P. 'The application of statistical process control in UK automotive manufacture: some research findings.' *Quality and Reliability Engineering International*, 5(1), 5–15, 1989.

Dale B G and Shaw P. 'Statistical Process Control: an examination of some common queries', *International Journal of Production Economics*, 22(1), pp 33–41, 1991.

Deming W E. *Quality, Productivity and Competitive Position.* Massachusetts Institute of Technology, Centre for Advanced Engineering Study, Massachusetts, USA, 1982.

Deming W E. *Out of the Crisis*, Massachusetts Institute of Technology, Centre for Advanced Engineering Study, Massachusetts, USA, 1986.

Duncan A J. *Quality Control and Industrial Statistics.* Richard D Irwin, Illinois, USA, 1974.

Followell R F and Oakland J S. 'Research into methods of implementing statistical quality control.' *Quality Assurance*, 11, (2) pp 27–32, 1985.

Followell R F and Oakland J S. 'Research into the use of statistical quality control in British manufacturing industry – Part I.' *Quality and Reliability Engineering International*, 1 (2), pp 85–92, 1985 Part II, 3, 1, pp 33–9, 1987.

Ford Motor Company. *Worldwide Quality System Standard* Q–101, Michigan, USA, 1990.

Ford Motor Company. *Statistical Process Control Course Notes.* EAO Statistical Methods Council, Essex, UK, 1985.

Ford Motor Company. *Statistical Process Control Instruction Guide. Essex*, UK, 1986.

Lockyer K G, Oakland J S and Duprey C H. 'Quality control in the UK chemical manufacturing industry – a study,' Part I. *International Journal of Production Research*, 19 (3), pp 317–25, 1981.

Lockyer K G, Oakland J S, Followel R F and Duprey C H. 'The barriers to acceptance of statistical methods of quality control in UK manufacturing.' *International Journal of Production Research*, 1984, 22 (4), pp 647–60.

Montgomery D C. 'The economic design of control charts: a review and literature survey.' *Journal of Quality Technology*, 12(2), pp 75–87, 1980.

Murdoch J and Barnes J A. *Statistical Table for Science, Engineering, Management and Business*

Studies. Macmillan Education, Hamps, UK, 1986.

Oakland J S. 'The role of SPC in TQM' in *Manufacturing Technology International – Europe,* 1989.

Oakland J S and Duprey C H. 'Quality control in the UK chemical manufacturing industry – a study,' Part II. *International Journal of Production Research,* 21 (1), pp 31–9, 1983.

Oakland J S and Followell R F. *Statistical Process Control: a Practical Guide.* (2nd edition), Butterworth–Heinemann, Oxford, UK, 1990.

Oakland J S and Murrey I. 'Detecting lack of control in a new untried process', *Quality and Reliability Engineering International,* 5 (5), pp 331–8, 1988.

Oakland J S and Porter L J. 'Measuring process capability – some new considerations', *Quality and Reliability Engineering International,* 6 (1), pp 19–27, 1990.

Oakland J S and Porter L J. 'Process capability indices – an overview of theory and practice', *Quality and Reliability Engineering International,* 7, pp 437–448, 1991.

Owen M. *SPC and Continuous Improvement.* IFS Publications, Bedford, UK, 1989.

Porter L J and Caulcutt R. 'Control chart design – a review of standard practice', *Quality and Reliability Engineering International,* 8 (2), pp 113–122, 1992.

Shewhart W A. *Economic Control of Quality of a Manufactured Product.* Van Nostrand, New York, USA, 1931.

SMMT *Guidelines to Statistical Process Control.* The Society of Motor Manufacturers and Traders, London, UK, 1986.

CHAPTER 16

Teamwork for quality improvement

16.1 Introduction

The development of people and their involvement in a process of continuous quality improvement, both individually and through a variety of forms of teamwork, is a key feature of a company's approach to TQM, providing an opportunity for co-operative action.

The subject of teamwork is given scant coverage in the current British Standards. This chapter provides a brief overview of the issues involved in teamwork; for more detailed coverage the reader is referred to Oakland (1993), Dale and Cooper (1992), Adair (1987), Aubrey and Felkins (1988), Scholtes (1990) and Wellins *et al.* (1991).

16.2 The features of teamwork

The complexity of most of the processes which are operated in industry, commerce and the services places them beyond the control of any one individual. The only efficient way to tackle process improvement or problems is through the use of some form of teamwork. The use of the team approach to problem solving and improvement has many advantages over allowing individuals to work separately:

- a greater variety of complex problems may be tackled, which are beyond the capability of any one individual or even one department or function, by the pooling of expertise and resources;
- problems are exposed to a greater diversity of knowledge, skill, experience, and are solved more efficiently;
- the approach is more satisfying to team members and boosts morale and ownership through participation in problem solving, improvement and decision making; it also assists with personal development;
- problems which cross departmental or functional boundaries can be dealt with more easily, and the potential/actual conflicts are more likely to be identified and solved;
- the recommendations are more likely to be implemented than individual suggestions as the quality of decision making in good teams is high;
- the approach aids communication up, down and across the organisation and will encourage changes in behaviour and attitudes.

When properly managed and developed, teams improve the processes of problem solving and improvement, producing results quickly and economically. Much of what has been taught previously in management has led to a culture in the West of independence, with little sharing of ideas and information. Teamwork devoted to quality improvement changes the independence to interdependence through improved communications, trust, awareness and the free exchange of ideas, knowledge, data and information. The use of the face-to-face interaction method of communication, with a common goal, develops over time, the sense of dependence on each other. This forms a key part of any quality improvement process, and provides a methodology for employee recognition and involvement, through active encouragement in group activities.

Teamwork provides an environment in which people can grow and use all the resources effectively and efficiently to make continuous improvements. As individuals grow, so does the organisation. It is also worth pointing out, however, that employees will not be motivated towards continual improvement in the absence of:

- commitment to quality from top management;
- the organisational quality 'climate',
- a mechanism for enabling individual contributions to be effective;
- recognition of these efforts.

All these are focused essentially on enabling people to feel, accept and discharge responsibility. More than one organisation has made this part of their quality strategy – to 'empower people to act'. If one hears from employees comments such as, 'We know this is not the best way to do this job, but if that is the way management want us to do it, that is the way we will do it', then it is clear that the expertise which exists at the point of operation has not been harnessed and people do not feel responsible for the outcome of their actions. Responsibility and accountability foster pride, job satisfaction and better work.

Empowerment to act is very easy to express conceptually, but it requires real effort and commitment on the part of all managers and supervisors to put into practice. Encouragement of ideas and suggestions from the workforce, particularly through their involvement in team or group activities, requires investment. The rewards are total involvement, both inside the organisation and outside through the supplier and customer chains.

Teamwork for quality improvement has several components. It is driven by a strategy, needs a structure, and must be implemented thoughtfully and effectively. The strategy, which drives the quality improvement teams at the various levels, in essence comprises the mission of the organisation, its critical success factors and key processes. The structure of having the top management team in a quality council, the key processes being owned by process quality teams, which manage quality improvement projects through quality improvement teams, quality circles, quality forums and project action teams, should provide the organisational requirements for implementation of quality improvement.

16.3 Councils, committees and teams

There are a number of different types of teams with differing operating characteristics, which can act as the vehicle for people getting involved in quality improvement activities. Some teams have a narrow focus coming from one functional area, others are wider and tend to be cross-functional dealing with the deep-rooted problems between internal customers and suppliers. The name given by organisations to the teams are varied and include Quality Councils, Quality Circles, Process Quality Teams, Quality Improvement Teams, Problem Elimination Team, Process Improvement Groups, Task Groups, SPC Teams, Error Cause Removal Teams, Corrective Action Teams, Kaizen Teams and Cross Functional Teams. There are also natural working groups of people which may be hybrids between two or more types of teams.

To devise, introduce and develop Total Quality Management for an organisation takes considerable time and ability. It must be given the status of a senior executive project. The creation of cost-effective quality improvement is difficult because of the need for full integration with the organisation's strategy, operating philosophy and management systems. This may require an extensive review and substantial revision of existing systems of management and ways of operating.

Any review of existing management and operating systems will inevitably uncover problems that have been successfully buried and smoothed over, perhaps for years. Authority must be given to those charged with following through actions that they consider necessary to achieve the goals. Their commitment will be continually questioned and will be weakened, perhaps destroyed, by the failure to delegate authoritatively.

The following steps for the establishment of teams are suggested in general terms. Clearly, different types of organisations will need to make adjustments to the detail, but the component parts are the basic requirements.

Firstly, a disciplined and systematic approach to continuous improvement must be established in the form of a Quality Council. The Council should meet at least monthly to review strategy, plans, resources, implementation progress and improvement. It should be chaired by the Chief Executive who must attend every meeting. Clearly, postponement may be necessary occasionally but the Council should not carry on meetings without the Chief Executive present. The Council members should include the top management team and the chairmen of any 'site' TQM Steering Committees, or Process Quality Teams, depending on the size of the organisation. The objectives of the Council are to:

- provide overall strategic direction on TQM for the organisation;
- establish plans for TQM on each 'site';
- set up and review the Process Quality Teams who will own the key or critical business processes;
- review and revise quality plans for implementation.

The Process Quality Teams (PQTs) and any site steering committees should also meet monthly, prior to the Council meetings. Every senior manager should be a member of at least one PQT. This system provides the 'top-down' support for employee involvement in process management and development, through either a quality improvement team, a quality circle programme or similar team activity. It also ensures that the commitment to quality improvement at the top is communicated effectively through the organisation.

The three-tier approach of Quality Council, Process Quality Teams (PQTs) and Quality Improvement Teams (QITs) allows the former to concentrate on quality strategy, rather than become a senior problem-solving group. Progress is assured if the PQT chairman is required to present a status report at each meeting.

The Process Quality Teams or steering committees will control the QITs and have responsibility for:

- the selection of projects for the QITs;
- providing an outline and scope for each project to give to the QITs;
- the appointment of team members, facilitators, leaders and sponsors or mentors;
- monitoring and reviewing the progress and results from each QIT project;
- ensuring that the teams' findings are fully implemented.

As the focus of this work will be the selection of projects, some attention will need to be given to the sources of nominations. Projects may be suggested by:

a) council members, representing their own departments, process quality teams, their suppliers or their customers, internal and external;
b) quality improvement teams;
c) suppliers;
d) customers.

The PQT members must be given the responsibility and authority to represent their part of the organisation in the process. The members must also feel that they represent the team to the rest of the organisation. In this way the PQT will gain knowledge and respect and be seen to have the authority to act in the best interests of the organisation, with respect to their process.

Quality improvement teams

A quality improvement team (QIT) is a group of people with the appropriate knowledge, skills and experience who are brought together by management specifically to tackle and solve a particular problem, usually on a project basis. Quality improvement teams mean different things to different people but usually they are cross-functional and often multi-disciplinary.

The 'task force', a 'project team' has long been a part of the culture of many organisations at the 'technology' and management levels. But quality improvement teams go a step further; they expand the traditional definition of 'process' to include the entire production or operating system. This includes paperwork, communication with other units, operating procedures and the process equipment itself. By taking this broader view new problems can be addressed.

The actual running of quality improvement teams involves several factors:

- team selection and leadership;
- team objectives;
- team protocol;
- team meetings;
- team assignments;
- team dynamics;
- team results and reviews.

Team selection and leadership

The most important element of a QIT is its members. People with knowledge and experience relevant to solving the problem are clearly required, but there should be a limit of five to ten members to keep the team small enough to be manageable, yet allow a good exchange of ideas. Members should include appropriate people from groups outside the operational and technical areas directly 'responsible' for the problem, if their involvement is relevant or essential. In the selection of team members, it is often useful to start with just one or two people concerned directly with the problem. If they construct flow charts of the processes involved, the requirement to include other people, in order to understand the process, pinpoint process ownership and responsibilities and complete the charts, will aid the team selection. This method will also ensure that all those who can make a significant contribution to the improvement process are represented.

The team leader has a primary responsibility for team management and maintenance and his/her selection and training is crucial to success. The leader need not be the highest ranking person in the team, but must be concerned about accomplishing the team objectives (this is sometimes described as 'task concern') and about the needs of the members (often termed 'people concern'). Weakness in either of these areas will lessen the effectiveness of the team in solving problems. Team leadership training should be directed at correcting deficiencies in these crucial aspects.

Team Objectives

At the beginning of any QIT project and at the start of every meeting, the objectives should be stated as clearly as possible by the leader. This can take the simple form, 'This meeting is to continue the discussion from last Tuesday on the provision of current price data from salesmen to invoice preparation, and to generate suggestions for improvement in its quality'. Project and/or meeting objectives enable the team members to focus thoughts and efforts on the aims, which may need to be restated if the team becomes distracted by other issues.

Team meetings

An agenda should be prepared by the leader and distributed to each team member before every meeting. This should include the following information:

- meeting place, time and how long it will be;
- a list of members (and co-opted members) expected to attend;
- any preparatory assignments for individual members or groups;
- any supporting material to be discussed at the meeting.

Early in the life of a project the leader should

orient the team members in terms of the approach, methods and techniques they will use to solve the problem. This may require a review of the:

- systematic approach and any documentation to be used in managing the team process;
- team-building process;
- procedures and rules for using some of the basic problem analysis tools, e.g. brainstorming;
- rôle of the team in the overall continuous improvement process;
- authority of the team;
- measurement methods.

A team secretary should be appointed to take the minutes of meetings and distribute them to members, as soon as possible after each meeting; it is usual to rotate this role between the team members. The minutes should not be formal, but should reflect decisions and carry a clear statement of the action plans together with assignments of tasks. They may be handwritten initially, copied and given to team members at the end of the meeting, to be followed later by a more formal document which will be seen by any member of staff interested in knowing the outcome of the meeting. In this way the minutes form an important part of the communication system involving other teams or people involved in some way with the process.

Team assignments

It is never possible to solve problems by meetings alone; what must come out of the meetings is a series of action plans which assign specific tasks to team members. This is the responsibility of the team leader. Agreement must be reached regarding the responsibilities for individual assignments, together with the time scale, and this must be made clear in the minutes. Task assignments must be decided while the team is together and not by individuals in after-meeting discussions. Members must always leave a meeting clear on what actions they are responsible for before the next meeting of the team.

Team dynamics

In any team activity the interactions between the members is vital to success. If solutions to problems are to be found, the meeting and ensuing assignments should assist and harness the creative thinking process. This is easier said than done because many people have either not learned or been encouraged to be innovative. The team leader clearly has a rôle here to:

- create a 'climate' for creativity;
- encourage all team members to speak out and contribute their own ideas or build on others;
- allow differing points of view and ideas to emerge;
- remove barriers to idea generation – e.g., incorrect preconceptions which are usually destroyed by asking 'Why?' at least once;
- support all team members in their attempts to become creative;
- take a passive or interventionist rôle, depending on how the team is functioning.

In addition to the team leader's responsibilities, the members have responsibilities to:

- prepare themselves well for meetings, by collecting appropriate data or information (*facts*) pertaining to a particular problem;
- share ideas and opinions;
- encourage other points of view;
- listen 'openly' for alternative approaches to a problem or issue;
- help the team determine the best solutions;
- reserve judgement until all the arguments have been heard *and* fully understood;
- accept individual responsibility for assignments and group responsibility for the efforts of the team.

Techniques such as Belbin's (1991) team roles and the Myers-Briggs Type Indicator may be useful here.

Team results and reviews

A QIT approach to problem-solving functions most effectively when the results of the projects are communicated and acted upon. Regular feedback to the teams, via their leaders, will assist them to focus on project objectives and review progress, thereby improving effectiveness.

Reviews also help to deal with certain problems which may arise in teamwork. For example, certain members may be concerned more with their own personal objectives than those of the team. This may result in some manipulation of the problem-solving process to achieve different goals, resulting in the team splitting apart through self-interests. If recognised, the review can correct this effect and demand greater openness, honesty and sincerity.

A different type of problem is the failure of certain members to contribute evenly and take their share of individual and group responsibility. Allowing other people, in particular, the team leader, to do their work results in an uneven distribution of effort and in bitterness. The review should make sure that all members have assigned and specific tasks, and perhaps lead to the documentation of duties in the minutes. A team roster may prove helpful.

A third area of difficulty, which may be improved by reviewing progress, is the ready-fire-aim syndrome of action before analysis. This often results from team leaders being too anxious to deal with a problem and failing to follow the key steps in the systematic problem-solving approach. A review should allow the problem to be redefined adequately and expose the real cause(s). This will release the trap the team may be in of doing something before they really know what should be done. The review will provide the opportunity to rehearse the steps in the systematic approach outlined below:

Record data	all processes can and should be measured all measurements should be recorded
Use data	if data is recorded and not used it will be abused
Analyse data systematically	data analysis should be carried out using the seven basic quality control tools
Act on the results	recording and analysis of data without action leads to frustration

Another area of difficulty commonly encountered is that some team members are unable to identify with the project and cannot see how they or the function they represent will benefit from its resolution. A regular review will help to identify this difficulty.

Quality circles

Quality circles (QCs), when operated in the 'classical' manner, have characteristics which are different from other forms of teamwork. They have been the subject of many books, e.g. Hutchins (1985) and Robson (1984), and the focus of much research, e.g. Bradley and Hill (1983), Hayward *et al.* (1985) and Hill (1986).

A Quality Circle is a voluntary group of between six and eight employees from the same work area. They meet usually in company time, for one hour every week or fortnight, under the leadership of their work supervisor, to solve problems relating to improving their work activities and environment.

The characteristics of Quality Circles are:

- membership is voluntary and people can 'opt out' as and when they wish;
- members are usually drawn from a single department and are doing similar work;
- all members are of equal status;
- the QCs operate within the existing organisational structure;
- members are free to select, from their own work area, the problems and projects which they wish to tackle – these tend to be the ones they have to live with every day; there is little or no interference from management;
- the QC members are trained in the use of the seven basic quality control tools, meeting skills and presentation techniques;
- appropriate data collection, problem-solving skills and decision-making methods are employed by QC members for the project under consideration;

- a large number of short duration meetings are held;
- there is minimum pressure to solve the problem within a set time frame;
- a facilitator is available to assist the QC with the project;
- the solutions are evaluated in terms of their cost-effectiveness;
- the findings, solutions and recommendations of the QC are shown to management for comment and approval, usually in a formal presentation;
- the QC implements its recommendations, where practicable;
- once implemented, the QC monitors the effects of the solution and considers future improvements;
- the QC carries out a critical review of all its activities related to the completed project.

Fabi (1992) has carried out a wide-ranging analysis of the literature published between 1982 and 1989 on QCs and has analysed 40 empirical studies on QCs. From this work, using contingency factors, he has identified the following factors which are critical to QC success:

- management commitment and support;
- involvement and support of employees and unions;
- training of members and leaders;
- organisation and financial stability;
- personal characteristics of the facilitator;
- individual characteristics of members;
- external and organisational environments;
- organisation readiness and implementation.

Kaizen teams

Kaizen is a philosophy of continuous improvement involving all the employees in an organisation, so that they perform their tasks a little better each day (Imai, 1986). It is a never-ending journey which is centred on the concept of starting anew each day with the principle that methods can always be improved. Using this approach it is reported that Pratt and Whitney reduced reject rates on one process from 50% to 4%, and in 12 months eliminated overdue deliveries on a key sub-assembly.

Kaizen Teian is a Japanese system for generating and implementing employee ideas. Japanese suggestion schemes have helped companies to improve quality and productivity, and reduced prices to increase market share. They concentrate on participation and the rates of implementation, rather than on the 'quality' or value of the suggestions. The emphasis is on involving everyone in individually making improvements. Their objectives are typically:

- to improve the power to work and individual abilities;
- to promote friendly and healthy human relations amongst all employees;
- to vitalise company activities;
- to improve the company structure and its operations.

Kaizen Teian suggestions are usually small-scale ones, which involve the worker's own area and are easy and cheap to implement. It is not uncommon to find in Japanese organisations between 50 and 100 suggestions made annually by every employee. Key points are that the rewards given are small, and implementation is rapid, which results in many small improvements that accumulate to massive total overall savings and improvements.

16.4 A methodology for quality improvement through teamwork

Involve the whole organisation

When an organisation and its people are well motivated and managed for quality improvement, a number of quality improvement projects or activities of varied complexity will be continuously undertaken and implemented by teams, in a variety of forms, involving all members and levels of the organisation. Quality improvement projects and activities will vary from those necessitating cross-functional management or Process Quality Teams to those which will be selected and implemented by either individual members, Kaizen teams, Quality Circles, etc., and will be based on departmental and functional problems.

Benefits from quality improvement will accumulate steadily when an organisation pursues projects and activities through teamwork in a consistent, disciplined series of steps based on data collection and analysis. A quality improvement project or activity usually starts with the recognition of an improvement opportunity. This recognition can be based on measures of quality losses, failure, non-value-added activity and/or on comparisons (benchmarks) against organisations recognised as leaders in a particular field. Once defined, the quality improvement project or team activity should progress through a series of steps and is completed with the implementation of actions taken on the process to reach and maintain the new, improved level of performance. As quality improvement projects or activities are completed, new quality improvement projects and team activities should be selected and implemented.

Initiate quality improvement projects or team activities

The need, scope and importance of a quality improvement project or team activity should be clearly defined. The definition should include the relevant background and history, the associated quality losses, and the current status of the situation, if possible, expressed in specific, numerical terms. In some organisations, it is one of the first tasks of the team to establish measurement criteria in relation to the project they are pursuing. A team, including the team leader and an appropriate facilitator and mentor, should be assigned or volunteered to the project. It is necessary to establish a schedule and allocate adequate resources and training. Provision should be made for periodic reviews of project scope, schedule and resource allocation.

Investigate possible areas for improvement

The purpose of this step is to increase the understanding of the nature of the process to be improved by the collection and validation of data. It is important for the team to carry out this step with the utmost objectivity, without any preconceptions of what the causes or preventative measures might be.

Establish cause and effect relationships

The data are analysed to gain insight into the nature of the process to be improved and to formulate possible cause and effect relationships. The relationships that appear to have a high degree of consistency with the data need to be tested, based on further data collection. New data have to be collected according to a carefully constructed plan to confirm these relationships.

Take improvement action

After cause and effect relationships are established, alternative proposals for improvement action to address the causes should be developed and evaluated by the team. The advantages and disadvantages of each proposal should be examined by the team members who will be involved in implementing the improvement action. Successful implementation depends on the co-operation of all those involved, including members of the department(s) likely to be affected by the project.

Quality improvements are secured by improvement actions on the process so that more satisfactory outcomes occur and/or unsatisfactory outcomes no longer occur or their frequency is substantially reduced. Relying solely on corrective actions in relation to process outcomes such as repairing, reworking reblending or sorting perpetuates quality losses.

Confirm the improvement

After implementing improvement action, appropriate data should be collected and analysed by the team to confirm that an improvement has been made and is of the estimated scale. The data should be collected on the same basis as that prior to implementation. Investigations also need to be made for side-effects, either desirable or undesirable, that may have been introduced.

If after taking action undesirable results continue to occur, it will be necessary to redefine the quality improvement project and for the team to return to the initiation step.

Sustain the gains

After the quality improvement has been confirmed, it needs to be sustained. This may involve a change in specifications and/or operating or administrative procedures and practices, necessary education and training, and making sure that the changes become an integral part of the job content of everyone concerned, that is, they should be standardised. The improved process then needs to be controlled at the new level of performance.

Continue the improvement

If the desired improvement is obtained, new quality improvement projects and team activities are selected and implemented. Since additional quality improvements are always possible, a project may be repeated based on new objectives. It is advisable to set priorities and time limits for each quality improvement project or team activity.

Throughout a total quality organisation, each process-oriented team must develop its own conscience, and focus its efforts on quality improvement. Each needs to be given the encouragement, tools and responsibility to achieve the requirements at the next interface. Clearly, the organisational issues discussed in this chapter will have great impact on the ease with which that is brought about.

British Standards

BS 7850 *Total quality management* Part 1: 1992 *Guide to management principles;* Part 2: 1992 *Guide to quality improvement methods.*

References

Adair J *Effective Teambuilding*, 2nd Edition, Pan Books, London, UK, 1987.

Aubrey C A and Felkins P K. *Teamwork: Involving People in Quality and Productivity Improvement*, ASQC, Milwaukee, WI (USA), 1988.

Belbin R M. *Management Teams: Why they succeed or fail*, Heinemann Professional Publishing, Oxford, UK, 1981.

Bradley K and Hill S. 'After Japan: The Quality Circle Transplant and Production Efficiency', *British Journal of Industrial Relations* 21(3), pp 291–311, 1983.

Dale B G and Cooper C. *Total Quality and Human Resources – An Executive Guide*, Blackwell, Oxford, UK, 1992.

Fabi B. 'Contingency Factors in Quality Circles. A Review of Empirical Evidence', *International Journal of Quality and Reliability Management* 9(2), pp 18–33, 1992.

Hayward S G, Dale B G and Frazer V C M. 'Quality Circle Failure and How to Avoid it', *European Management Journal*, 3(2), pp 193–111, 1985.

Hill F M. 'Quality Circles in the UK; A Longitudinal Study', *Personnel Review*, 15(3), pp 25–34, 1986.

Hutchins D. *The Quality Circle Handbook*, Gower, Aldershot, UK, 1985.

Imai M. *Kaizen: The Key to Japanese Competitive Success*, McGraw-Hill, New York, USA, 1986.

Oakland J S. *Total Quality Management*, 2nd Edition, Butterworth-Heinemann, Oxford, UK, 1993.

Robson M, *Quality Circles: A Practical Guide*, 2nd Edition, Gower, Aldershot, UK, 1984.

Scholtes P R. *The Team Handbook*, Joiner Associates, Madison, NY, USA, 1990.

Wellins R S Byham W C. and Wilson J M. *Empowered Teams*, Jossey Bass, Oxford, UK, 1991.

CHAPTER 17

Managing quality improvement

17.1 Introduction

Quality management concepts are basically very simple and make good common sense, but putting them into practice is often fraught with difficulties. To bring about improvements in quality requires considerable organisational change, considerable attention to detail and changes in the way people behave, changes in internal and external relationships, changes in the management methods and systems, changes in the usage of tools and techniques, and the change from independence to interdependence. To make these changes stick not only involves tremendous hard work but total tenacity by a number of local champions.

The standards referred to throughout this book can facilitate the understanding of the basic concepts of quality management through definitions of terms and explanation of concepts, in a standard format usable throughout the English-speaking world. Many of the referenced standards have other national, European and international standard equivalents and are, therefore, universally acceptable.

The evolution from inspection, embedded in the principle of scientific management, through quality control (QC), quality assurance (QA), Juran's breakthrough, total quality control (TQC) and company-wide quality control (CWQC), to total quality management (TQM) has changed the face of many organisations throughout the various business sectors. It should be noted that the terms TQC, CWQC and TQM are now used interchangeably and mean essentially the same thing.) International competitiveness has driven companies and whole countries to search for better ways of managing quality, and the use of standards has been bound up with these changing processes.

Several gurus of quality management have greatly influenced the way managers behave towards product and service quality and this, together with various government-funded programmes, campaigns and award schemes, has caused the commercial world to become far more serious about the use of standards to assist them to develop good management systems and improve data handling, analysis and action.

17.2 Environment for quality improvement

The responsibility and leadership for creating the environment for continuous quality improvement belongs to senior management. Only by their actions, constancy, tenacity, hard work and dedication of resources do managers convey to all levels of the organisational hierarchy the leadership and commitment necessary for creating an environment which is conducive for quality improvement. Managers lead quality improvement by communicating purpose and goals, by continuously improving their own work processes, by behaving as rôle models and symbols in their day to day activities, by fostering an environment of open communication, teamwork, and respect for the individual, and by enabling and empowering everyone in the organisation to improve their work processes.

The environment for quality improvement often requires the development of a new set of shared values, attitudes, behaviours and setting ever more challenging goals for doing this as efficiently as possible. Values, attitudes, and behaviours that are essential for continuous quality improvement include the following:

- Attention is focused on satisfying the needs of both internal and external customers.
- The entire supply chain from suppliers to customers is involved in quality improvement activities.
- Management commitment, leadership and involvement are critical to continuously improve processes.
- Management listens to its employees.
- Continuous quality improvement is a part of everyone's job.
- All processes can be continuously improved.
- Failures and defects are addressed by improving the process and the systems within which it operates.
- An environment of open communication, teamwork, honesty, truth and respect for the individual is created and maintained.
- Ongoing education and training for everyone are essential.

Quality improvement goals need to be established and defined with care. They should be closely integrated with the overall business goals and strategy and provide a focus for increasing customer satisfaction and process efficiency. They should be clearly understandable, challenging, pertinent and agreed to by all who work together to achieve them.

Effective management requires sound communication. Open communication and teamwork remove organisational and personal barriers that interfere with effectiveness, efficiency and continuous improvement of work processes; this includes suppliers and customers. Team activities can be most effective for improving communication between personnel and can provide an opportunity for supportive participation and co-operation in solving problems. Trust is essential if communication and teamwork are to be effective. This is important if everyone is to be involved in identifying and following up opportunities for improvement.

Regular communication should be a feature at all levels of the organisation. The existence of an appropriate information system is an essential tool for communication. The methods of communication may include:

- management briefings;
- information exchange meetings;
- documented information;
- information technology facilities;
- 'our department' and 'our business' presentations;
- quality action days.

These last two initiatives are discussed in detail by Bunney *et al.* in Dale (ed) 1994.

The recognition process should be consistent with the values, attitudes and behaviours necessary for quality improvement. Successful recognition allows the development and growth of individuals, including the factors which influence the individual's work performance (e.g. opportunity, organisation, environment). Successful recognition processes also allow group performance and group recognition, and give rise to frequent and informal feedback.

17.3 Creating appropriate organisational structures

Quality management is achieved through the ongoing, incremental improvement of an organisation's processes. This invariably creates a need to continually review the appropriateness of the business organisational structures, and change them where necessary. Such changes may be necessary in the following areas:

- the management processes of the organisation such as reward, payment, recognition, training, strategic and business planning;
- the methods of resource allocation;
- the administrative support processes such as secretarial, clerical, human resources and purchasing;
- building and maintaining an environment that allows the members of the organisation to improve quality continually based on mutual trust and collaboration;
- planned training for all members of the organisation;
- the work processes and procedures of the organisation.

The administrative activities such as typing, finance, purchasing, stores, reproduction and servicing that may be apparently outside the main stream objectives or only peripheral to the objectives should be treated as processes by their owners and develop goals relating to the overall business objectives and their own customer requirements (see Chapter 7 on company-wide quality system registration).

17.4 Organising, planning and costing quality

Quality improvement has to be managed, and executives have to demonstrate leadership; it will not happen just by sheer strength of mind or willpower. The organisational aspects of quality are vital, and these must be set in the right framework of objectives and strategies. A quality improvement framework is outlined by Dale and Boaden (1993).

Long-term planning based on visions of the future and corporate mission statements have become a common part of total quality operations. Clearly, a vital part of this is the quality system which must be organised in such a way that rôles and responsibilities are properly defined. This will not create bureaucracy, but ownership of the processes which convert the inputs to the outputs, whether they be services, artefacts, information or paperwork.

A major point to be made about the organisational aspects of improvement is that quality must be managed in the line functions. It cannot be managed by a separate department or quality manager. There is a rôle for a quality management representative, at board or senior management level, but this is concerned with facilitation, support, planning, promotion and co-ordination.

Planning quality improvement, implementing the plan, analysing the results and replanning is a continuous cycle. It will be necessary to review the existing planning process to ensure that inter-related improvement plans are deployed at all levels of the organisation as follows:

- corporate
- operating site;
- department/unit;
- process;
- individual.

When initiating this process it is essential to ensure that goals for improvement are agreed with all concerned and implemented from the top down. Staff commitment to change is maximized when the individuals affected by, or operating, the process or any changes to it are closely involved in the generation and deployment of the improvement plans.

Management should set and agree with process owners quality improvement goals for reducing quality loss. Plans should be developed within the business planning cycle to provide strategic guidance and direction for meeting these goals and for implementing quality policy. These plans should address the most important quality losses and should be deployed throughout all functions and all levels of the organisation. The development of quality improvement plans should involve everyone in the organisation along with the supplier(s) and customer(s) of the organisation.

Quality improvement plans are often implemented through a set of specific quality improvement projects or activities. Management should take care to monitor and control such implementation activities to ensure their integration into the overall goals and business plans of the organisation. Plans for quality improvement should focus on newly identified opportunities and on areas where insufficient progress has been made. The planning process has inputs from all levels of the organisation, from reviews of achieved results, and from customers and suppliers.

Quality planning, review, and replanning are the foundations of quality improvement. Without this basis the development of product and service designs, specifications, operational specifications and instructions, quality manuals, reviews and evaluation procedures will be poorly structured and badly focused.

An important area in which standards have helped organisations to structure their approach is in the determination of the total costs of quality. In some organisations only the downside – the price of poor quality or nonconformance – is preferred, but this avoids the complex, but never the less quantitative links between the so called prevention, appraisal, internal failure and external failure cost categories. These costs must be budgeted and managed like any other measure of managerial performance and a thorough understanding of quality-related costing, based on sound principles, is an important part of any serious quality improvement activity (see Chapter 14). Again, real management commitment, training, teamwork and participation are essential for an effective system to retain credibility.

17.5 Implementing process management concepts

Whilst the organisational structure adopted will vary from company to company, there is a common need to ensure that management responsibilities for the processes, especially those that flow across organisational boundaries, are clearly defined and that these processes and their constituent parts contribute to the overall business objectives. Within each process the responsibilities of management and the process owner include the following:

- defining and agreeing the purpose of each process and its relationship with overall company business objectives;
- identifying both internal and external customers and determining their needs and expectations;
- identifying the needs and expectations of the process owner to his/her supplier(s);
- setting appropriate performance standards for the key activities of the process;
- initiating a systematic measurement of process performance coupled with the search for improvement opportunities.

Chapters 5 and 7 provide some useful insights into how to facilitate such responsibilities.

17.6 Understanding, designing and meeting market needs

Quality begins and ends with customers, both internal and external, and a critical component of improvement is a never-ending commitment to understanding and meeting their current and future requirements at the various interfaces. This means systematic and effective marketing. Quality management requires far more than aggressive selling and the marketing input is the key to creating and managing the right processes. The outputs from the marketing effort must also interface readily with the creative and design effort.

The simple two-by-two matrix, created by considering the things companies are required to do and the way they do them will help any organisation to examine its performance in terms of really understanding the requirements of customers and designing outputs to satisfy them (see Figure 17.1). The operational aspects which determine whether the execution is right or wrong will become irrelevant if the marketing and design effort is deficient. It is a salutary lesson for most organisations to find out what proportion of the time is spent in doing the right things right.

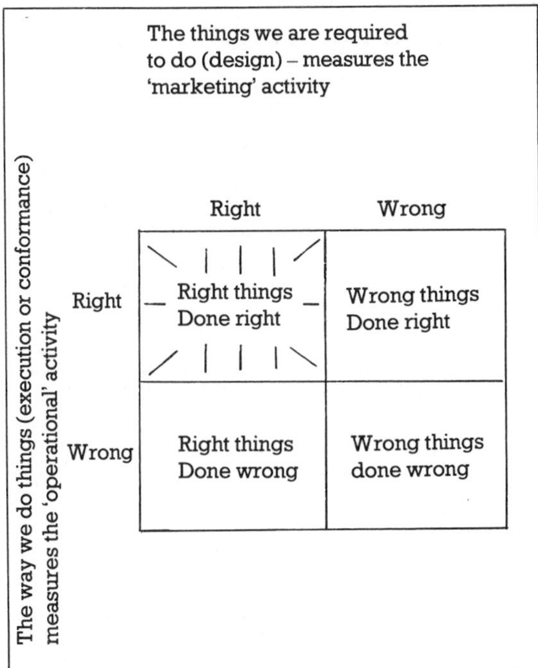

Figure 17.1 Requirements and actions matrix

It is no coincidence that successful and superior performing companies are those that understand and monitor the marketplace, build relationships with their customers and suppliers, and systematically manage the organisational and operational changes to improve their match of products and/or services with the true customer needs. The use of standards in this area is not widely understood or appreciated, but the efficiency and profitability of an organisation can be greatly affected by marketing's detailed knowledge of standardisation issues that affect the business, and can be used to help and influence customers.

17.7 Systems for managing improvements in quality and reliability

Quality systems, based on national and international standards, such as the BS 5750 (ISO 9000) series, are the key to successful process management and continuous improvements. Deming's (1982) simple cycle of plan, do, check, act (PDCA) is manifested in the various clauses of such standards (see Figure 17.2). The simple steps of justifying and writing down what is done, doing it that way, recording and analysing what was done through system audits and reviews, and revising what will be done through corrective action (Figure 17.2) ensures a continuous improvement process, provided that the audits and reviews are carried out in this manner.

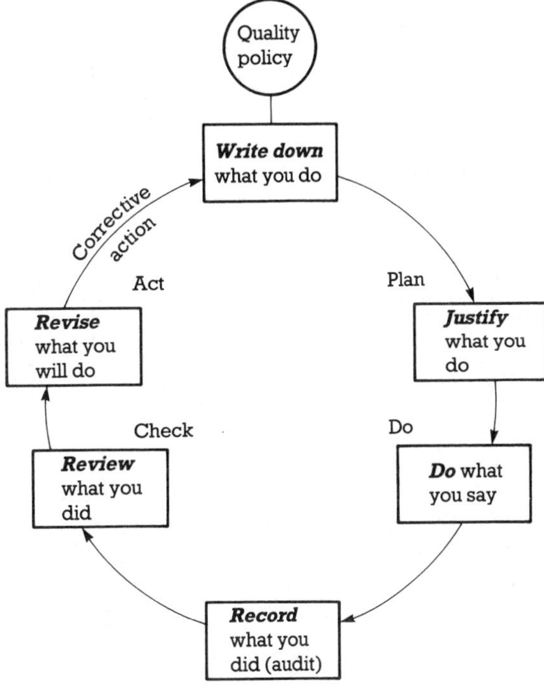

Figure 17.2 Deming's cycle present in the quality system standards

In some organisations, the independent third-party assessments of quality systems against standards, has tended to distort this approach and to focus on certification for its own sake. Organisations which use such standards and certification bodies in this way deserve the feeling of bureaucracy which this creates. They are missing a vital opportunity to use the system's internal audits and reviews, corrective actions and assessment schemes, in the way they were intended – as the road to quality improvement through continuous managerial monitoring and action. In our opinion it is the process of auditing which ensures that improvements and gains are made

Table 17.1 Selecting an appropriate tool or technique

Tool or technique	When to select
Data collection form	Gather a variety of data in a systematic fashion for a clear and objective picture of the facts
Tools for non-numerical data	
Affinity diagram	Organize into groupings a large number of ideas, opinions, issues, or other concerns
Benchmarking	Measure your process against those of recognized leaders
Brainstorming	Generate, clarify and evaluate a sizeable list of ideas, problems, or issues
Cause and effect diagram	Systematically analyse cause and effect relationship and identify potential root causes of a problem
Flow chart	Describe an existing process, develop modifications, or design an entirely new process
Tree diagram	Break down a subject into its basic elements
Tools for numerical data	
Control chart	Monitor the performance of a process with frequent outputs to determine if its performance reveals normal variations or out-of-control conditions
Histogram	Display the dispersion or spread of data
Pareto diagram	Identify major factors and distinguish the most important causes of quality losses from the less significant ones
Scatter diagrams	Discover, confirm or display relationships between two sets of data

Source: BS 7850: Part 1 (1991)

to stick. Having said that, companies must not see the BS 5750/ISO 9000 series as the panacea that will cure all quality problems or as the pinnacle of their quality achievements. It ensures that procedures, controls and disciplines are in place, and is an essential foundation on which to build a total approach to quality management, but it must be properly supported by commitment, measurement and teamwork.

The separation of reliability and quality is necessary only for detailed understanding and knowledge of some of the special techniques required. Many of the managerial activities required to bring about quality improvement will also affect reliability. The organisational, marketing, design and operational activities are common and the separate systems standards for quality (BS 5750/ISO 9000 series) and reliability (BS 5760 series) reinforce the points that the general management principles are common. The increased use of techniques such as failure mode and effects analysis (FMEA) by major motor manufacturers and the requirements on their suppliers to do the same, in the general context of quality improvement, have cemented this relationship.

17.8 Analysis and diagnosis tools

Decisions based on the analysis of situations and data play a leading role in quality improvement activity. Many tools are used in the identification, rating and solving of problems, the improvement of processes and the effective use of resources. Table 17.1 gives some guidance on the selection of an appropriate tool or technique. Success of quality improvement projects is usually enhanced by correct application of these tools and techniques.

Quality management tools and techniques can be used at various stages of a problem solving process and are useful for the following:

- identifying subjects for improvement;
- placing subjects in order of priority;
- identifying and analysing causes of problems;
- collecting data for analysis;

- assessing alternative solutions to problems;
- selecting the optimum solution for action.

Lascelles and Dale (1990) make the point that as organisations start to develop and advance their process of improvement they begin to use the more advanced tools and techniques.

Where possible, quality improvement decisions should be based on numerical data. Decisions regarding differences, trends and changes in numerical data should be based on proper statistical interpretation. Some quality improvement decisions may be based on non-numerical data. Such data play an important role in marketing and research and development and more generally in management decisions. Appropriate tools should be used to process this kind of data properly and to transform it into useful information for decision making. Examples of such tools are brainstorming, cause and effect diagrams and affinity diagrams.

All members of the organisation should receive appropriate training in applying quality management tools and techniques to improve their work processes. Appendix M provides an overview of some of the more commonly used tools and techniques. Although the application of any of the techniques described in Appendix M will give some incremental improvement, their full potential can only be realised if they are applied and co-ordinated within a structured framework. This requires organising, planning and measuring for quality improvement as outlined earlier.

17.9 Measurement of performance

A system of objective, data-based measurements should also be established for monitoring the results of quality improvement activities and for tracking the performance of all key functions and processes. A well-developed system includes measurements at corporate, operating unit, department and cross-functional levels. The measurements should relate to quality losses associated with customer satisfaction, process efficiencies, and losses sustained by society as follows:

- Measures of quality losses associated with customer satisfaction may be based on information from surveys of current, potential and lost customers, surveys of competing products and services, changes in revenues, routine inspections by service personnel, information from sales and service staff, and customer complaints and claims.
- Measures of quality losses associated with process efficiency may be based on labour, capital and material utilization, producing, sorting, correcting or scrapping unsatisfactory process output, process re-adjustments, waiting time, cycle times, delivery performance, unnecessarily redundant designs, size of inventories and statistical measures of process capability and process stability.
- Measures of quality losses sustained by society may be based on failure to realise human potential (e.g. as indicated by employee satisfaction surveys and exit interviews), damage caused by pollution and disposal of waste, and depletion of scarce resources.

In relation to the management of improvement, it is important that organisations have positive quantitative measures of quality as seen by their customers (i.e. measuring themselves from the customer's viewpoint). This enables them to keep focused on the market in terms of customer needs and future expectations. Customer satisfaction can only be achieved when an organisation has identified and understood what its customers want. Many organisations do not have such measures and rely on internally focused measures.

Measuring and tracking trends from a base line of past performance are important, in addition to establishing and meeting numerically given targets. The measurements should be reported and reviewed as an integral part of the management accounting and control practices of the organisation.

17.10 Training

Training programmes are important in creating and maintaining an environment for quality improvement. All members of an organisation, including the highest levels of management should be trained in quality principles and practices and in the application of appropriate methods for quality improvement. This enables them to perform their individual process, to be aware of its relationship to other processes and the part it plays in ensuring customer satisfaction and the objectives of the organisation, and to be able to contribute effectively to the process of continuous improvement. All training programmes should be reviewed, on a regular basis, for consistency with the quality principles and practices of the organisation. Subjects for training can include the following:

- management;
- technical;
- process;
- the use of quality management tools and techniques;
- communication;
- skills;
- organisation;
- awareness.

17.11 Operating for quality improvement

The general principles of good purchasing, supplier development, manufacturing or operational procedures, measurement and calibration systems, and sampling methods, whether for acceptance or process control, must be applied in any organisation which desires to improve quality. In these areas managers are well supported by standards. Detailed guidance on how to set up systems for specifications, selecting suppliers, assessing and rating vendors, material product and process control, process capability studies, controlling equipment and maintenance, work procedures, inspection, (including sampling, measurement and test equipment) can be found.

Standards are sometimes accused of being complex in structure and difficult to read. This is greatly exaggerated and some managers would derive great benefit from a proper study of what help is available from these sources. It is hoped that this book will act as an introduction to these valuable sources. The authors do acknowledge areas of quality management in which current standards are weak. In particular, marketing, servicing, teamwork and the service sector are poorly represented and served.

During recent years, the use of statistical process control (SPC) has literally exploded throughout the world, especially in manufacturing companies, but also in the service sector. The powerful tools of SPC aid the collection, handling and presentation of data and decision making for managers and operators at all levels. SPC is far more than a tool kit, it is a strategy for continuous improvement, based on the reduction of the variation inherent in all processes. The tools are less important than the philosophy behind their use and much damage can be done by the insensitive teaching of control chart methods, without sufficient time spent on their wider context.

Using standards written on SPC will be much strengthened by reference to recent writers on the subject, and, in particular, the approaches prescribed by Deming and his disciples. In Europe these writers include Dale, Followell, Oakland, Owen, Price and Shaw who have attempted to simplify the approaches and successfully eased the introduction of SPC into many European organisations. These authors have rightly promoted the use of SPC as part of the total quality framework.

Employing teamwork in moving an organisation from independence through to interdependence is clearly a component of quality improvement (Oakland, 1993). The role of quality improvement teams, corrective action teams, problem elimination teams, quality circles and the like is to use the tools to measure the effect of the management systems and then to use the collective brainpower and expertise of the team to make appropriate changes to the processes and systems. Continuous improvement relies upon people with their specialist skills, knowledge and experience working together, and recognition that standardisation will benefit the open approach which is required.

When an organisation is well motivated and managed for quality improvement, a number of quality improvement projects or activities of varied complexity will be continuously undertaken and implemented by all members and levels of the organisation. Quality improvement projects and activities will vary from those necessitating cross-functional or task teams to those which will be selected and implemented by either individual members or teams.

Quality improvement benefits will accumulate steadily when an organisation pursues quality improvement projects and activities in a consistent, disciplined series of steps based on data collection and analysis. A quality improvement project or activity usually starts with the recognition of an improvement opportunity. This recognition can be based on measures of quality losses and/or on comparison (benchmarks) against organisations recognised as leaders in a particular field. Once defined, the quality improvement project or activity progresses through a series of steps and is completed with the implementation of actions taken on the process to reach and maintain the new, improved level of performance. As quality improvement projects or activities are completed, new quality improvement projects or activities are selected and implemented.

Quality improvement action depends on the identification of one or more situations requiring improvement. Such situations may arise for example from quality cost studies, significant problems arising from customer complaints, manufacture or service processes or health and safety considerations. In these examples, it is usually management who make the identification and initiate action.

Individuals and groups should also be encouraged to use problem solving techniques to identify opportunities and actions for improvement in their own work areas on a voluntary basis. It is important to recognise that the techniques can be applied equally to all areas of the business. Often, these improvements will be small ones for which management would not normally fund the resources. In time though, their cumulative effect on the overall business can become very significant.

The need, scope and importance of a quality improvement project or activity should be clearly defined and demonstrated. The definition should include the relevant background and history, the associated quality losses, and the current status, if possible, expressed in specific, numerical terms. A person or a team, including a team leader, should be assigned to the work. It is necessary to establish a schedule, allocate adequate resources to set priorities, and to assign time limits for each quality improvement project or activity. Provision should be made for periodic reviews of scope, schedule and resource allocation.

To make the best use of resources, the priority of an improvement project should be reviewed before it is cleared for action. A logical and systematic process for achieving improvements is desirable for all processes and levels of an organisation from corporate to individual.

After implementing improvement action, appropriate data should be collected and analysed to confirm that an improvement has been made. The data should be collected on the same basis as that prior to implementation. Investigations also need to be made for side effects, either desirable or undesirable, that may have been introduced.

If after taking action undesirable results continue to occur, it will be necessary to redefine the quality improvement project or activity by returning to the initiation step.

After the quality improvement has been confirmed, it needs to be sustained. This usually involves a change of specifications and/or operating or administrative procedures and practices, necessary education and training, and making sure that these changes become an integral part of the job content of everyone concerned (i.e. the improvements have been standardised). The improved process then needs to be controlled at the new level of performance.

If the desired improvement is obtained, new quality improvement projects or activities are selected and implemented. Since additional quality improvements are always possible, a quality improvement project or activity may be repeated based on new objectives.

17.12 Difficulties and development

The authors have carried out a great deal of research, teaching and advisory work in the area of TQM. Inevitably they have encountered organisations which have experienced difficulties in starting the process of TQM. The three main difficulties they have found are:

- 'Flavour of the month' type attitude – for example, a lack of commitment to facilitate changes in behaviour, attitudes and values, not converting the cynics, indifference and not taking the concept seriously.
- Lack of structure for TQM and lack of real leadership – for example, no monitoring or reporting of results, no focus, a lack of people to make things happen, lack of improvement objectives and targets, lack of time and resources, inadequate infrastucture for improvement and inadequate communication.
- Lack of top management commitment and vision.

It is clear that in a large number of organisations the board of directors and members of the senior management team may be saying that they are committed to TQM but these words are not being translated into effective action and leadership.

Many organisations have experienced difficulties in *sustaining* the process of quality improvement. The three main difficulties encountered by the authors are:

- Time pressures, work loads and resources – for example, not releasing people for improvement activities, the lack of time which key decision makers spend on TQM activities, in particular on fostering improvements, the chief executive officer not being prepared to develop his or her understanding of the subject and a lack of understanding of teamworking.
- Complacency with the progress being made – this usually relates to those organisations which view TQM as a programme with a start and an end point. Consequently, after making some improvement, the management think they have done enough, progress then slows, some gains are even lost, and a plateau is reached. TQM is not a programme it is a continuous or never-ending process. The word 'programme' should not be used in conjunction with TQM and when it is it usually shows a lack of understanding of the subject. Customer requirements are increasingly rigorous and if an organisation's competitors are pursuing improvement, the organisation which thinks it has done enough is almost bound to lose market share.
- Conflicting strategies and business priorities. The world-class organisations ensure, through a system of quality policy deployment (see Dale, 1990 and Akao, 1991 for details), that their top level policies and targets are communicated and implemented through each level of the organisational hierarchy, with improvement objectives established at each level. This enables staff at all levels to carry out activities with the aim of achieving common goals and it ensures that every individual in the organisation is working in one direction.

Quality improvement is a labyrinth, a maze of interrelated activities, systems, procedures, people, techniques and commitment. The role of standards is to provide the framework on which we can build our visions for the future. Without that skeleton the future will collapse but the job of putting the flesh on the bones remains the art and science of management.

17.13 Definitions and terminology

The following are some useful definitions and terms used in this chapter.

Customer: any person(s) internal or external to the organisation, who receive(s) the output of the process.

Mission statement: broad statement of the main aims of an organisation.

Quality assurance: all those planned and systematic actions necessary to provide adequate confidence that a product or service will satisfy given requirements for quality.

Quality control: the operational techniques and activities that are used to fulfil requirements for quality.

Quality management: that aspect of the overall management function that determines and implements the quality policy.

Supplier: any person(s) internal or external to the organisation, who supplies (supply) an input to the process.

British Standards

BS 4778: *Quality vocabulary* Part 1: 1987 *International terms* (ISO 8402: 1986) (EN 28402: 1991).

BS 5750: 1987 *Quality Systems* (ISO 9000: 1987) (EN 29000: 1987); Part 8: 1991 *Guide to quality management and quality systems elements for services* (ISO 2004–2: 1991).

BS 5760: *Reliability of systems, equipment and components* Part 0: 1986 *Introductory Guide to Reliability*.

BS 7850: *Total quality management* Part 1: 1992 *Guide to management principles*; Part 2: 1992 *Guide to quality improvement methods*.

References

Akao Y. (Ed) *Hoshin Kanri: Policy Deployment for Success TQM*, Productivity Europe, Bucks, 1991.

Dale B G. 'Policy Deployment', *The TQM Magazine*, 2(6), p 321–4, 1990.

Dale B G. (Ed) *Managing Quality* (2nd Edition), 1994, Chapter 30 by Bunney H S, Birchall G and Dale B G, 'Quality improvement at Grace Dearborn'.

Dale B G and Boaden R J. 'A robust framework: applying the UMIST quality improvement framework to a multi-site manufacturer', *European Quality*, 11, pp 68–72, 1993.

Deming W E. *Quality, Productivity and Competitive Position*. Massachusetts Institute of Technology, Centre for Advanced Engineering Study, Massachusetts, USA, 1982.

Lascelles D M and Dale B G. 'The use of quality management techniques, *Qaulity Forum*, 16 (4), pp 188–192.

Oakland J S. *Total Quality Management*, 2nd edn, Butterworth–Heinemann Professional Publishing, Oxford, UK, 1993.

Appendices

Appendix A

List of national standards organisations

AENOR
Asociacion Espanola de Normalizacion y Certificacion (Spain)

AFNOR
Association francaise de normalisation (France)

BSI
British Standards Institution (UK)

DIN
Deutsches Institut fur Normung e.V (Germany)

DS
Dansk Standardiseringsrad (Denmark)

ELOT
Hellenic Organization for Standardisation (Greece)

IBN/BIN
Institut Belge de Normalisation (Belgium)

IPQ
Instituto Portugues da Qualidade (Portugal)

ITM
Inspection du Travail dt des Mines (Luxembourg)

NNI
Nederlands Normalisatie-instituut (The Netherlands)

NSAI
National Standards Authority of Ireland (Ireland)

NSF
Norges Standardiseingsforbund (Norway)

ON
Osterreichisches Normungsinstitut (Austria)

SFS
Suomen Standardisolmisliitto r.y. (Finland)

SIS
Standardisseringskommissioneni Sverige (Sweden)

SNV
Association Suisse de Normalisation (Switzerland)

STRI
Technological Institute of Iceland (Iceland)

UNI
Ente Nazionale Italiano di Unificazione (Italy)

Appendix B

An example of a quality plan

QUALITY PLAN

New grades of Hy-Vin Rigid PVC compounds for injection moulding by customer XYZ Ltd.

The plan covers the following phases:
Phase 1 – Definition of objectives
Phase 2 – Formulation
Phase 3 – First production
Phase 4 – Trial at customer
Phase 5 – Full production
Phase 6 – Modification and improvement

Authorised by .... Date ....

Phase 1 Definition of objectives

Activity	Performed by	Documents	Procedures
1. Identify customer products and components	Commercial		
2. Identify customer's measure of his products and components	Commercial	Customer specification for a) the products b) the raw materials	
3. Identify customer's measure of material – properties – processing	Development	Customer test methods for a) and b)	
4. Identify customer's data requirements	Development	Standards, specifications and other normative documents from down the customer chain. Design codes.	
5. Identify regulatory requirements (including product liability)	Regulatory affairs	Food contact, pharmacopaeia, fire regulations, consumer protection	
6. Identify customer QA requirements (validation, traceability, record storage)	Development		
7. Identify manufacturing plant, test equipment or services needed and new training	Development		
8. Draw up Project Proposal	Development	Project proposal	
REVIEW 1	Development commercial	Above documents	

DECISION TO PROCEED – NO – Archive review 1.
POSTPONE – Repeat review (as review 1.1) at later date with new data.
YES – Phase 2.

Phase 2 Formulation

Activity	Performed by	Documents	Procedures
1. Do exploratory laboratory work to refine recipes and formulation	Development	Test reports. Special project reports (SPR)	
2. Identify new Raw Material needs:	Development		
2.1 Supplier contact	Development	Visit report	
2.2 New raw material evaluation safety, COSHH	Development Regulatory affairs	Material safety data sheets	
Technical performance in laboratory	Development	Raw material report	
2.3 Accept new raw material Assign experimental part number (T 99999)	Development		HPL – TEC – 001
2.4 Provide provisional specification	Development	Suppliers' specification	HPL – TEC – 001
3. Decide foundation suitable for plant manufacture	Development		
4. Assign experimental part number XM 99999	Development		HPL – TEC – 001
5. Define required: Sampling Testing by QC Testing by development Testing by external facilities Colour standard		Request for colour matching (RCM)	
REVIEW 2	Development		

DECISION TO PROCEED – NO – Archive review 2.
POSTPONE – Repeat review (as review 2.1) if necessary.
YES – Phase 3.

Phase 3 First production

Activity	Performed by	Documents	Procedures
1. Raise experimental works trial documentation	Development of process quality	EWT forms	HPL – TEC – 003
2. Run production needs:	Production	Run sheets Process records	
3. Product test by QC	Process and quality	CTM (specified compound test methods)	
4. Special product testing	Development	DTM (development test methods) Test records	
5. Pass off material	Process and quality development		HPL – TEC – 003
REVIEW 3 – Evaluate production	Development process and quality production		

DECISION TO PROCEED – NO – Archive review 3.
Dispose of material.
YES – Phase 4.

Phase 4 Trial at customer

Activity	Performed by	Documents	Procedures
1. Witness customer evaluation	Development Commercial		
2. Report	Development	Technical visit report	
3. Refine customer requirements	Development Commercial		
4. If necessary, refine formulation, repeat phases 2, 3 and 4.	Development		
REVIEW 4 – Evaluate Customer appraisal	Development Commercial	Above documents Produce development status report (DSR)	

DECISION TO PROCEED – NO – Archive review 4.
YES – Phase 5.

Phase 5 Full production

Activity	Performed by	Documents	Procedures
1. Check formulation: documentation	Development	Special project report	
1.1 New raw material(s) transferred to full part number reference(s) B 99999	Process and quality		HPL – TEC – 001
1.2 Specification arranged with RM supplier	Process and quality		HPL – TEC – 001
1.3 Control plans for B 99999 defined	Process and quality	MTM (material test methods)	HPL – TEC – 001
1.4 If necessary, establish quality status of suppliers	Quality assurance		HPL – QA – 004
2. Transfer finished product grade reference from experimental (XM 99999) to full sales reference VM 999.	Development		HPL – TEC – 002
2.1 Amend entry on contract review check file	Development		HPL – COM – 001
3. Define sampling and test plan	Process and quality	CMP – 259	
4. Define audit test plan	Process and quality	CMP – 259	
5. Arrange for QC testing and training for new tests. Create test method, if necessary.	Development process and quality	CTM	HPL – ADM – 011
6. Run production	Production		
7. Assess results.	Development		
8. Repeat production(s)	Production		
9. Define product control limits.	Development		HPL – TEC – 005
10. Produce data sheet.	Development		HPL – TEC – 005
11. Produce sales specification	Process and quality	CMP – 159	
12. If required, produce customer specification (Issue 1)	Process and quality	Customer specification CCS – VM 999 – XYZ – 1	
13. Generate control data, capability indices, etc.	Process and quality		

(cont.)

Phase 5 Full production (*cont.*)

Activity	Performed by	Documents	Procedures
14. Review QC inspection plan 15. Generate test data in BS 7008 format	Process and quality Development		
16. Generate melt flow data: 16.1 Put data onto commercial melt flow data bases	Development Development		
17. Customer assessment	Commercial		
REVIEW 5	Commercial development process and quality		

DECIDE TO MAINTAIN – No further action
MODIFY – Phase 6

Phase 6 Modification and improvement

Activity	Performed by	Documents	Procedures
1. Identify new requirements documentation 2. Reformulate – if necessary, repeating phases 2, 3 and 4. 3. Fix new formulation as VM 999/1 and go to phase 5.	Commercial Development Development Development	Technical sales report Technical service report	 HPL – TEC – 002
REVIEW 6	Commercial Development	Above documents	

DECISION TO PROCEED – NO – File review 6.
Take no further action.
YES – Either install VM 999/1 at Customer XYZ.
or
New product required.
Start phase 1.

Source: Hydro Polymers Ltd, Vinyls Division

Appendix C

Guidance notes on cost elements of prevention appraisal and failure

Prevention costs

These costs are incurred to reduce failure and appraisal costs to a minimum. The usual categories include the following:

Quality planning. The activity of planning quality systems and translating product design and customer quality requirements into measures that will ensure the attainment of the requisite product quality. It includes that broad array of activities that collectively create the overall quality plan, the inspection plan, the reliability plan and other specialised plans as appropriate. It also includes the preparation and vetting of manuals and procedures needed to communicate these plans to all concerned. Such quality planning may involve departments other than the quality organisation.

Design and development of quality measurement and test equipment. Included are the costs of designing, developing and documenting any necessary inspection, testing or proving equipment (but not the capital cost of the equipment in question).

Quality review and verification of design. Quality organisation monitoring activity during the product's design and development phase to assure the required inherent design quality. Quality organisation involvement with design review activities and in verification activity during the various phases of the product development test programme including design approval tests and other tests to demonstrate reliability and maintainability.

This includes quality organisation effort associated with that part of process control which is conducted to achieve defined quality goals.

Calibration and maintenance of production equipment used to evaluate quality. The costs of calibration and maintenance of templates, jigs, fixtures and similar measurement and evaluating devices should be included: but not the cost of equipment used to manufacture the product.

Supplier assurance. The initial assessment, subsequent audit and surveillance of suppliers to ensure they are able to meet and maintain the requisite product quality. This also includes the quality organisation's review and control of technical data in relation to purchase orders.

Quality training. Includes attending, developing, implementing, operating and maintaining formal quality training programmes.

Quality auditing. The activity involving the appraisal of the entire system of quality control or specific elements of the system, used by an organisation.

Acquisition, analysis and reporting of quality data. The analysis and processing of data for the purpose of preventing future failure is a prevention cost.

Quality improvement programmes. Includes the activity of structuring and carrying out programmes aimed at new levels of performance, e.g. defect prevention programmes, quality motivation programmes.

Appraisal costs

These costs are incurred in initially ascertaining the conformance of the product to qualify requirements; they do not include costs from rework or re-inspection following failure. Appraisal costs normally include the following:

Pre-production verification. Cost associated with testing and measurement of pre-production for the purpose of verifying the conformance of the design to the quality requirements.

Receiving inspection. The inspection and testing of incoming parts, components and materials. Also included is inspection at supplier's premises by purchaser's staff.

Laboratory acceptance testing. Costs related to tests to evaluate the quality of purchased materials (raw, semi-finished or finished) which become part of the final product or that consumed during production operations.

Inspection and testing. The activity of inspecting and testing firstly during the process of manufacture, and then as a final check to establish the quality of the finished product and its packaging. Included are product quality audits, checking by production operators and supervision and clerical support for the function. It does not include inspection and testing made necessary by initial rejection because of inadequate quality.

Inspection and test equipment. The depreciation costs of equipment and associated facilities; the cost of setting up and providing for maintenance and calibration.

Materials consumed during inspection and testing. Materials consumed or destroyed during the course of destructive tests.

Analysis and reporting of tests and inspection results. The activity conducted prior to release of the product for transfer of ownership in order to establish whether quality requirements have been met.

Field performance testing. Testing is performed in the expected user environment, which may be the customer's site, prior to releasing the product for customer acceptance.

Approvals and endorsements. Mandatory approvals or endorsements by other authorities.

Stock evaluation. Inspecting and testing stocks of products and spares which may have limited shelf life.

Record storage. The storage of quality control results, approval and reference standards.

Failure costs

These are sub-divided into two; internal costs arising from inadequate quality discovered between the transfer of ownership from supplier to customer; and external costs arising from inadequate quality discovered after transfer of ownership from the supplier to the customer.

The *internal failure costs* include the following:

Scrap. Materials, parts, components, assemblies and product end items which fail to conform to quality requirements and which cannot be economically reworked. Included is the labour and labour overhead content of the scrapped items.

Replacement, rework and repair. The activity of replacing or correcting defectives to make them fit for use including requisite planning including the cost of the associated activities by material procurement personnel.

Troubleshooting or defect/failure analysis. The costs incurred in analysing non-conforming materials, components or products to determine causes and remedial action, whether non-conforming products are usable and to decide on their final disposition.

Reinspection and retesting. Applied to previously failing material that has subsequently been reworked.

Fault of supplier. The losses incurred due to failure of purchased material to meet quality requirements, and payroll costs incurred. Credits received from the supplier should be deducted, but costs of idle facilities and labour resulting from product defects should not be overlooked.

Modification permits and concessions. The costs of the time spent in reviewing products, designs and specifications.

Downgrading. Losses resulting from a price differential between normal selling price and reduced price due to non-conformance for quality reasons.

Downtime. The cost of idle facilities and personnel resulting from product defects and disrupted production schedules.

The *external failure costs* include the following:

Complaints. The investigation of complaints and provision of compensation where the latter is attributable to defective products or installation.

Warranty claims. Work to repair or replace items found to be defective by the customer and accepted as the supplier's liability under the terms of the warranty.

Products rejected and returned. Here are included the costs of dealing with returned defective components. This may involve action to either repair, replace or otherwise account for the items in question. Handling charges should be included.

Note. While loss of customer goodwill and confidence is normally associated with external failure costs, it is difficult to quantify.

Concessions. Cost of concessions, e.g. discounts made to customers due to non-conforming products being accepted by the customer.

Loss of sales. Loss of profit due to cessation of existing markets as a consequence of poor quality.

Recall costs. Cost associated with recall of defective or suspect product from the field including the cost of preparing plans for product recall.

Product liability. Cost incurred as a result of a liability claim and the cost of premiums paid for insurance to minimise liability litigation damages.

Source: BS 6143: Part 2, 1990

Appendix D

Example of a quality cost report

Group:				Division:		
Unit:				Period: Year:		
Current period				Year to date		
Budget £	Actual costs £	Difference £		Budget £	Actual costs £	Difference £
			Prevention costs Quality planning. Design and development of quality measurement, test and control equipment. Quality review and verification of design. Calibration and maintenance of quality measurement, test and control equipment. Supplier assurance. Quality training. Quality auditing. Acquisition, analysis and reporting of quality data. Quality improvement programme.			
			Total prevention costs			
			% of total quality costs			
			Appraisal costs Pre-production verification. Receiving inspection. Laboratory acceptance testing. Inspection and testing. Inspection and test equipment. Materials consumed during inspection and testing. Analysis and reporting of test and inspection results. Field performance testing. Approvals and endorsements. Stock evaluation. Record storage.			
			Total appraisal costs			
			% of total quality costs			
			Internal failure Scrap. Replacement, rework and repair. Troubleshooting or defect/failure analysis. Reinspection and retesting. Fault of supplier. Modification permits and concessions. Downgrading. Downtime.			
			Total internal failure costs			
			% of total quality costs			

(*cont.*)

Group:			Division:			
Unit:			Period: Year:			
Current period				Year to date		
Budget £	Actual costs £	Differ-ence £		Budget £	Actual costs £	Differ-ence £
			External failure Complaints. Warranty claims. Products rejected and returned. Concessions (deviations) Loss of sales. Recall costs. Product liability.			
			Total external failure costs			
			% of total quality costs			
			Total quality costs (TQC)			
			Typical ratios TQC as a percentage of:			
TQC x 100 / Sales revenue %			Sales revenue	TQC x 100 / Sales revenue %		
TQC x 100 / Value added %			Value added	TQC x 100 / Value added %		
TQC x 100 / Direct labour costs %			Direct labour costs	TQC x 100 / Direct labour costs %		
Distribution:						
Issued by:				Date:		

Source: BS 6143: Part 2, 1990.

Appendix E

Process cost model and report for a personnel department

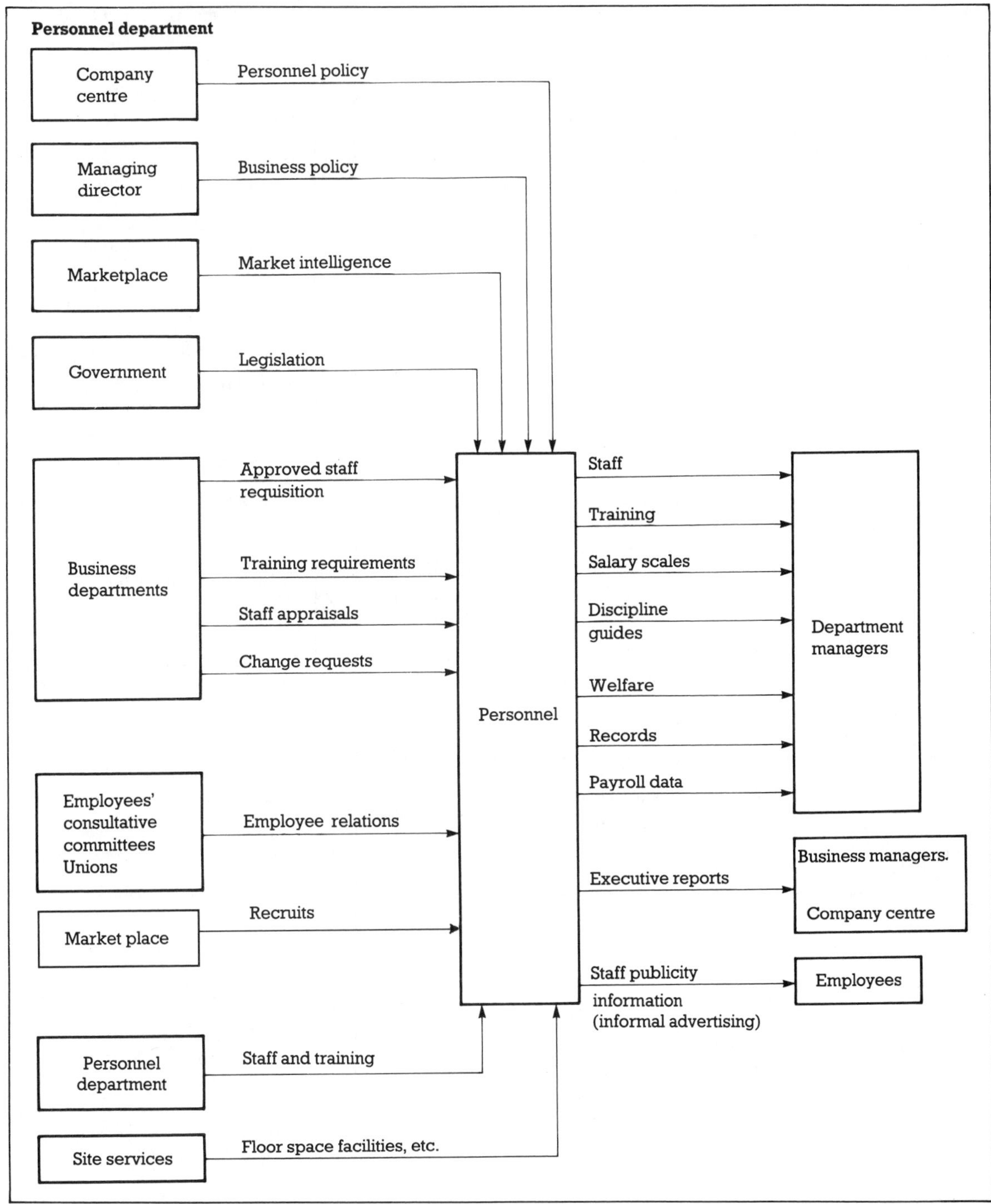

Source: BS 6143: Part 1, 1992

PROCESS COST REPORT

PROCESS Personnel department | **PROCESS OWNER** Personnel manager | DATE

PROCESS CONFORMANCE	COST			PROCESS NON-CONFORMANCE	COST			COST DATA SOURCE
	Act.	Syn.	£		Act.	Syn.	£	
People Attitude surveys Salary audits Publicity Appraisals		✓ ✓ ✓ ✓ ✓						Hours taken to complete the task x hourly rate
				Progressing non-returns (appraisals, etc) Industrial action Staff turnover		✓ ✓ ✓		Hours taken to complete task x hourly rate Hours taken during negotiation x hourly rate (Total hours for all staff) Termination interviews, hours x hourly rate. Payment in lieu of notice.
Recruitment costs to satisfy requirements								Interview expenses, relocation expenses, advertising, labour costs for recruitment staff
				Inadequate recruitment	✓			Special training needs
				Sponsored students not joining company	✓			Cost of sponsorships
Training	✓			Cancellations or non-attendance at training courses		✓		Accounts package Cost of training course
Consultative committees, health and safety, grading, union/manager		✓						Total hours spent x hourly rate
				Appeals/failures to agree		✓		Total hours spent x hourly rate
Executive reports (routine)		✓						Hours taken to prepare report x hourly rate
				Special reports – statistical, accident, etc		✓		Hours taken to prepare report x hourly rate
Environment Floor space, site changes	✓							Accounts package – floorspace, site services, telephones, site administration
Materials and Methods Training material, site publications								Invoiced cost
Personnel manual, directives, health and safety guidance		✓						Hours taken to prepare information x hourly rate
Total process conformance cost Prepared by				Total process non-conformance cost				

Source: BS 6143: Part 1, 1992

Appendix F

Example of a failure modes, effects and criticality analysis (FMECA) applied to a sub-system of a motor-generator set

This example illustrates the application of the FMECA technique to a motor-generator (M-G) system. The objective of the study was confined to that system only and was not concerned with the effects of failure on any loads supplied with electrical power from the M-G set or any other external effects of failures. This therefore defines the boundaries of the analysis. The example, shown in part only, illustrates how the system was represented in a hierarchical block diagram form. Initial sub-division identified five sub-systems (Figure F1) and one of these, the enclosure heating, ventilation and cooling system, is developed through lower levels of the hierarchical structure to the component level at which it was decided to start the FMEA (Figure F2). The block diagrams also show the numbering system adopted that was used as a cross reference with the FMEA worksheets.

One example of a worksheet is shown for one of the sub-systems of the M-G set (Figure F3). It also includes a particular method of using this same document to present a quantitative assessment of failure rates for the individual failure modes of each item. An FMEA worksheet was then used to combine all sub-subsystem FMEAs to present the FMEA for each sub-system and finally a third level worksheet presented the complete system.

An essential prerequisite for such an FMECA is the definition and classification of the severity of the effects of failures on the complete M-G system. For the particular application of the example system these were defined as follows (based on general definitions in DEF STAN 00–41):

(a) *Catastrophic*: failure to generate power for remainder of mission.

(b) *Critical*: system degradation for remainder of mission.

(c) *Major*: loss of power generation due to forced outrage until repaired.

(d) *Minor*: temporary system degradation until convenient to repair.

(e) *Negligible effect*: no loss or significant degradation of generating capability.

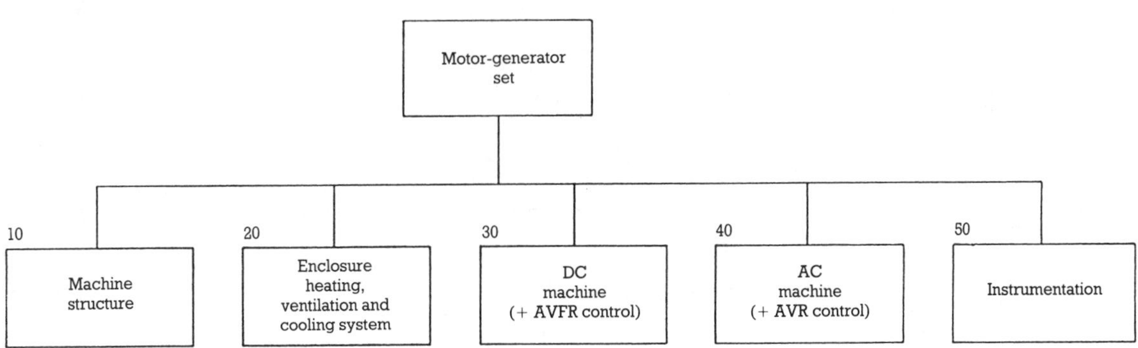

Source: BS 5760: Part 5, 1991

Figure F1 Block diagram of subsystems of a motor-generator set

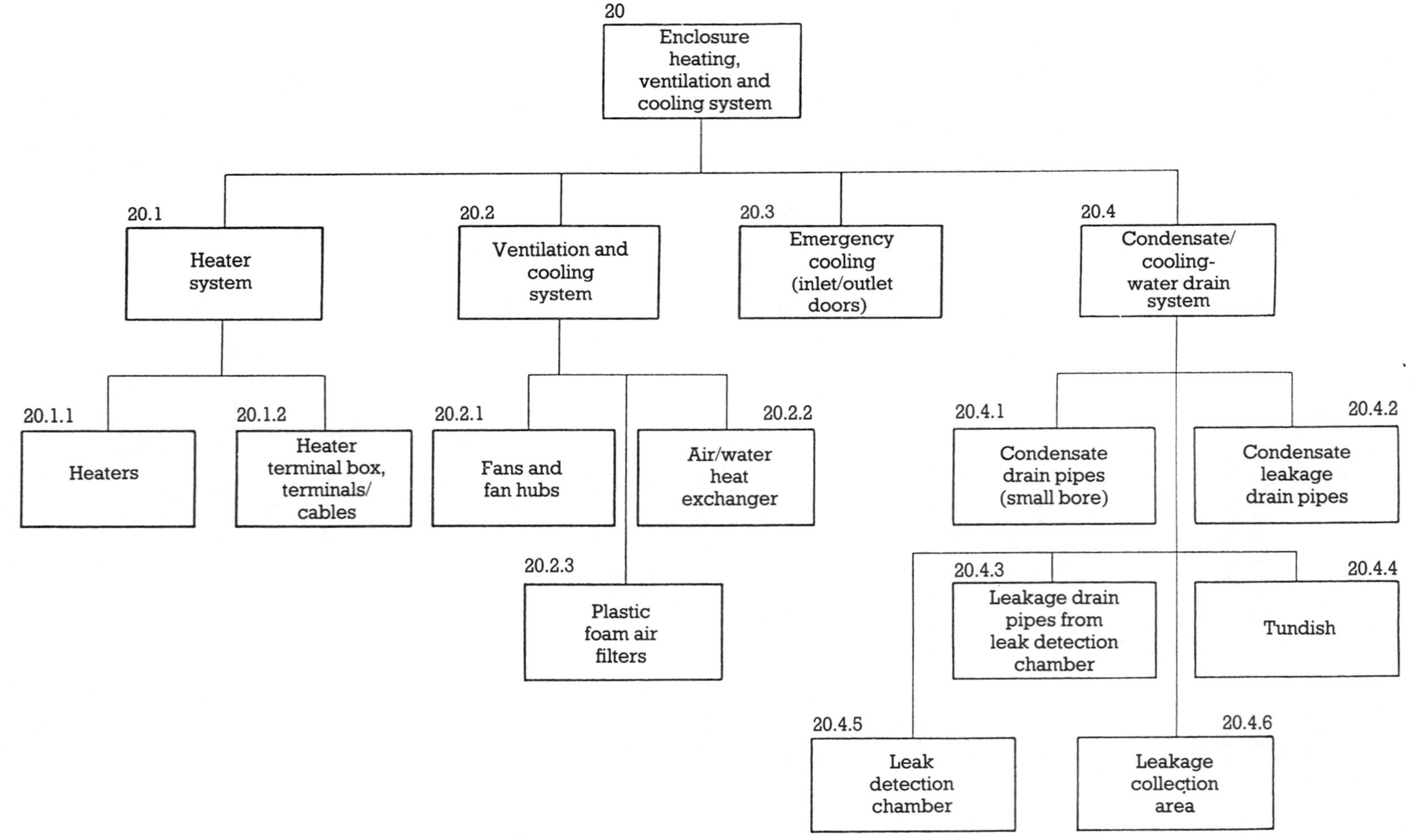

Source: BS 5760: Part 5, 1991

Figure F2 Block diagram of enclosure heating, ventilation and cooling system

Subsystem – 20 Enclosure heating, ventilation and cooling system												
Ref.	Component	Function	Failure mode	Failure effect	Detection method of symptom	Redundancy provided	Mode failure rate severity level f/10^6 h					Remarks
							1	2	3	4	5	
20.1	Heater system (12 off – 6 off at each end) (Only in use when machine non-operational)	To keep machine at temperature >5°C above ambient to prevent condensation on machine internals when not in use	All									NOTE. The machine may overheat if the heaters do not turn off automatically when running
20.1.1	Heaters	To heat up enclosure	a) o/c, burnt out heater	Reduced heating	a) Temperature indication <5°C above ambient						1.2	
			b) s/c or earth fault due to insulation breakdown	Loss of all heating – possible condensation	b) Supply, fuse, or circuit breaker monitored	All in parallel, no supply redundancy				0.3		One earth fault should not fail system
20.1.2	Heater terminal box, terminals, cables	Connect supply to heaters	a) o/c terminal or cable can fail one, three, six or all heaters	Loss or reduction of heating – condensation	Temperature <5°C above ambient					0.5		
			b) s/c terminals (tracking)	Loss of all heating – condensation	Supply monitored					neglig.		
						Totals				2.0		

Figure F3 FMEA of subsystem including failure rate assessment

Source: BS 5760: Part 5, 1991

Appendix G

Example of fault tree analysis for a hypothetical chemical reactor

Introduction. Fault tree analysis can be used to calculate the frequency of an undesired event which may typically cause danger, expense and/or downtime if it occurs. The event of interest is known as the top event. Below the top event, a fault tree is constructed to show the sub-events and states that can combine to produce the event in question. Alternative routes are combined through 'OR' gates while events and states that have to be coincident are combined through 'AND' gates. The tree is continued downwards to the level where reliability data are available for the individual items being considered.

Typical installation. A simple diagrammatic representation of a hypothetical reactor is shown in Figure G1 below. The oxidation process normally operates outside the flammability limits of the fuel/oxidant system, but a change in the ratio of the feeds (which increases the fuel/oxidant ratio) could lead to an explosion in the reactor. The fault tree for this top event is shown in Figure G2.

An explosive mixture can be formed by operating with too high a fuel feed or too low an oxidant feed. These conditions are normally prevented by the operation of emergency flow switches which will isolate the stream in question by closing an emergency isolation valve. These trips will not have 100% availability and the proportion of time that a trip will not be available to operate when required is called the fractional dead time (FDT). The method of determining the explosion rate is as follows.

The frequency of the event associated with an OR gate is given by the sum of the individual frequencies of the different causes of that event, while the frequency of the event associated with an AND gate is the product of the frequency and FDT leading to it. For example, the event rate for actually operating with a low flow of oxidant is given by the total rate of the faults which could lead to low flow multiplied by the total FDT of the trip system FE4.

This technique, and others related to it, are widely used in the chemical industry. However, as with any reliability technique, the underlying assumptions should be carefully examined when considering the use of the method.

Comments. This example is typical of many assessments made in the chemical industry where the frequency of an event, in this case an explosion, needs to be assessed.

This type of fault tree analysis, although relatively simple to understand, has many pitfalls. Particular care is needed in distinguishing between those events (demands) that could *initiate* the final event (explosion) and that are characterised by a frequency, and failures of the protective systems that will not directly initiate the final event and that will only matter if an initiating event (demand) occurs; these systems are characterised by a probability of being in a failed state (fractional dead time) or, in cases such as an operator response, by the probability of his or her failing to respond.

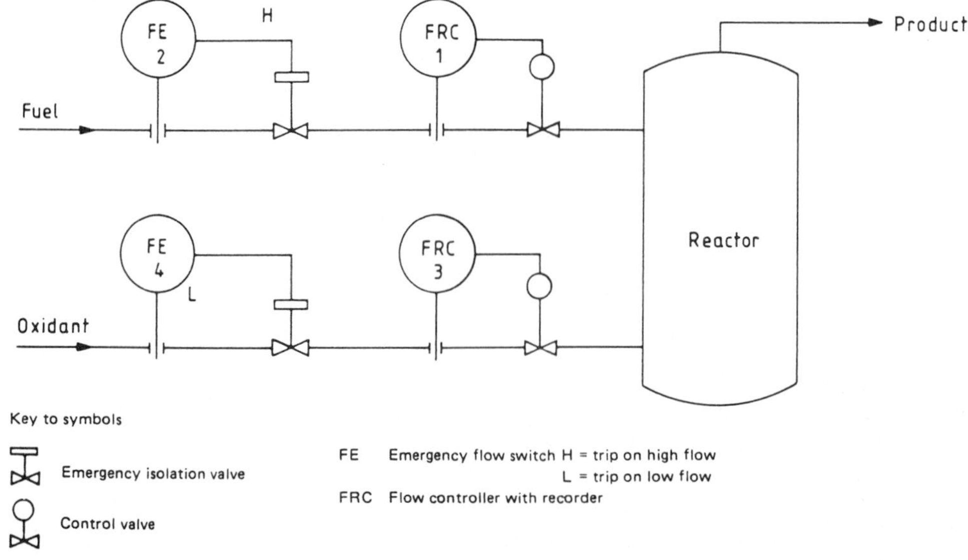

Figure G1 Diagrammatic representation of hypothetical reactor **Source:** BS 5760: Part 3, 1985

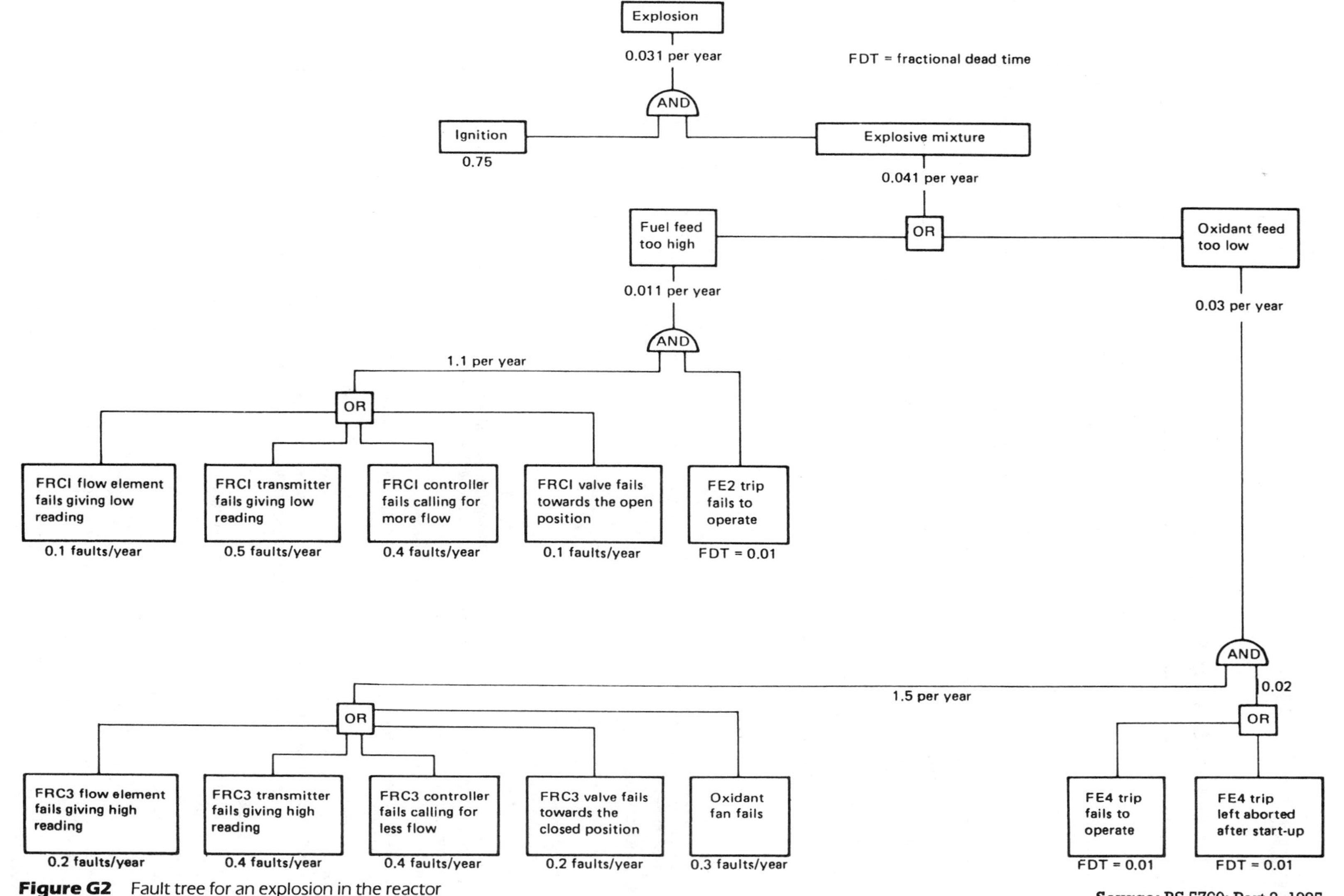

Figure G2 Fault tree for an explosion in the reactor

Source: BS 5760: Part 3, 1985

Appendix H

 **Quality System Survey Report**

Division/Operations Group		System Survey Rating =	Survey No.	Date
To		Producer personnel contacted		
Producer name	Producer code			
Plant	Phone			
Address		Description of products		
City and state				
Producer in conformance with Ford Q–101	Yes ☐ No ☐	Survey representative signature(s)		
Corrective action required	Yes ☐ No ☐			
Purchasing assistance required	Yes ☐ No ☐			
Producer acknowledgement signature				
Copies to Purchasing Product Engineering Customer Plants				

For each question, provide complete descriptive comments. Then assign a rating using the System Survey Scoring Guidelines.	Rating
PLANNING FOR QUALITY	
1. Is the responsibility for quality planning on new products clearly defined? Does the definition of responsibility make sense for the processes involved? • Describe the responsible organization. • Indicate reporting relationships. • Indicate the key contact personnel/department for quality planning and quality concern resolution.	______
2. Are Control Plans, Process Failure Mode and Effects Analyses, and other documented methods used as a basis for establishing quality programs for new (and specifically-identified existing) products? • Does the producer perform feasibility analysis on potential new products? • Assess the adequacy of the producer's quality planning effort.	______
3. Does the producer have available and use a procedure for reviewing design and process changes prior to implementation? • Are FMEAs and Control Plans reviewed and updated as part of this procedure? • Is customer approval obtained prior to implementing change? • Is there a procedure for updating operator instructions and visual aids for process and product changes?	______
TOTAL PLANNING FOR QUALITY (Total points available = 30) =	______
STATISTICAL METHODS	
4. Is Statistical Process Control (SPC) utilized for significant and Critical ( ) product characteristics and process parameters? • How are the significant characteristics chosen? • Describe the SPC methods used? Are they appropriate to the processes being controlled? • Evaluate the producer's reaction to out-of-control conditions. Is the reaction as specified in the Control Plan? What is the role of the operators? Of the supervisors? • Evaluate the producer's application of SPC, based on the evidence of the control charts, process logs, and other appropriate documentation.	______

Quality Dec 89 2955

Quality System Survey Report

Sheet 2 of ________

Producer	Date

STATISTICAL METHODS (Continued) — Rating

5. Are preliminary statistical studies conducted on new product characteristics and process parameters? ________

6. Are control charts being used effectively to monitor the processes? Do the charts indicate that statistical control has been achieved and that process capability has been demonstrated?
   - In all cases where process capability has not yet been demonstrated, is there a plan to improve the process? Is appropriate interim action (i.e., 100% inspection) being taken to prevent shipment of nonconforming parts. ________

7. Does the producer have a definite program to bring about continual improvement in quality and productivity?
   - Describe the program. Indicate the statistical methods and other tools used to promote continual improvement.
   - Are there improvement priorities identified and project teams established? ________

8. Does the producer have an effective system for assuring the quality of incoming products and services (e.g. plating, heat treating).
   - Are suppliers encouraged to meet Q-101 requirements?
   - Are suppliers encouraged to use SPC? Is evidence of statistical control and capability required from producers?
   - Assess the adequacy of the incoming material quality system? ________

TOTAL STATISTICAL METHODS (Total points available = 50) = ________

GENERAL

9. Are process/product auditing functions and responsibilities clearly defined?
   - Indicate which plant activities conduct process/product auditing (e.g., quality inspectors, production operators, laboratory technicians).

   Assess the adequacy of the producer's auditing program. ________

10. Are written procedures defining the significant quality-related functions available (i.e. a quality manual)?
    - Are these procedures appropriate to and adequate for the producer's operations? (e.g., is there an adequate procedure for reacting to ES test failures?)
    - Are the procedures implemented as written?
    - Is there a formal review system to verify implementation? ________

11. Are written process monitoring and control instructions available for incoming, in-process, laboratory, layout inspection and outgoing auditing?
    - Are all Critical and Significant characteristics included, specifically those affecting function, durability and appearance?
    - Are Control Items, their Critical Characteristics and related operations identified with the inverted delta symbol?
    - Are sample sizes and frequencies adequate?
    - Is appropriate statistical analysis specified? ________

12. Are appropriate gages, measuring facilities, laboratory equipment, and test equipment available to facilitate process control?
    - Is the selection of significant characteristics effectively incorporated in gage planning and design?
    - Are gages and test equipment and personnel appropriately located throughout the producer's operations?
    - Are adequate, well-lighted areas available for gaging, measuring, and testing the product? Evaluate the producer's gage planning and execution. ________

Quality System Survey Report

Sheet 3 of______

Producer	Date

GENERAL (Continued)	Rating
13. Does the producer have an effective gage and test equipment maintenance program? • Are new gages/test equipment inspected to design specifications, calibrated and approved before being used? • Do records indicate that gages and test equipment are periodically inspected and calibrated? • Does the producer use statistical methods to determine the stability and capability of gages, measuring, and test equipment? Assess the adequacy of the producer's gage and test equipment maintenance program.	______
14. What controls does the producer use to indicate the processing and inspection status of products throughout the producer's system? • Are effective controls in place to provide accurate part number identification throughout processing, storage, packaging and shipping? • Are controls adequate to prevent movement of rejected incoming materials into the production system? • Are nonconforming products separated from the stream of production? Are there effective controls to prevent their movement?	______
15. Does the producer have complete records supporting initial sample certifications?	______
16. Does the producer react appropriately to customer concerns? • Are in-plant and customer quality concerns effectively communicated to all members of the organization? • Are nonconforming parts returned by customers analyzed? Is the root cause of failure determined, verified, and corrective action taken? • Is a disciplined method of problem solving (the Eight Discipline Method) utilized?	______
TOTAL GENERAL (Total points available = 90) =	______
IN-PROCESS AND OUTGOING	
17. Are inspections, measurements, and tests being performed according to the instructions? • Are there adequate records of inspections, measurements, and tests?	______
18. Are documented rework and/or scrap procedures and standards available? Are reworked or sorted products audited for conformance to <u>all</u> customer requirements? Assess the adequacy of rework and sorting operations.	______
19. Are the handling, storage and packing adequate to preserve product quality? • For production and service parts, does the producer meet applicable packaging specifications? • Are effective controls in place to assure correct service part identification?	______
20. Are plant cleanliness, housekeeping, environmental, and working conditions conducive to quality improvement? • Are there working conditions that could be detrimental to quality improvement? • What actions have been taken to mitigate these factors?	______
TOTAL INCOMING, IN-PROCESS and OUTGOING (Total points available = 40) =	______
TOTAL RATING POINTS FROM QUESTIONS 1–20 (Maximum = 200 points) =	______

Quality Dec 89 2955–3 (Use Form No. 2955–2 for Continuation)

Source: Ford Motor Company, 1990

Appendix I

Part of a process or manufacturing FMECA for machined aluminium castings

								Existing conditions					Resulting conditions				
Ref.	Process	Failure mode	Effect on	Potential effect	V	Potential cause	Existing controls	Occ	Sev	Det	APN	Recommended action	Action taken	Occ	Sev	Det	APN
01-01-01	Inserts	Incorrect size or shoulder bend angle	i)a	Inserts without load onto the die Reduced productivity		Poor manufacture or quality control	Producer and acceptance sampling plans	1	9	1	9	Review of sampling plans. Segregation of defective stock from good stock. Training assemblers					
02			i)b	Insert malaligned. Scrap													
03			i)a	Incorrect thickness of skirt surrounding insert. Scrap													
04			iv)b	Reduced performance													
05			iv)c	Reduced life													
01-02-01	Inserts	Poor flash nickel plating	ii)a	Corrosion. Rejected at finishing stage			Visual inspection during acceptance sampling plan	5	6	1	30	Include instructions in sampling inspection to carry out visual check for correct plating					
01-03-01	Inserts	Inadequate face scoring	i)a	Poor metal flow. Incorrect wall thickness. Scrap		Poor manufacture or quality control	Visual inspection during acceptance sampling plan	2	8	6	96	Include instructions in sampling inspection to carry out visual check for correct plating					

(Cont.)

								Existing conditions					Resulting conditions				
Ref.	Process	Failure mode	Effect on	Potential effect	V	Potential cause	Existing controls	Occ	Sev	Det	APN	Recommended action	Action taken	Occ	Sev	Det	APN
02			ii)a	Thin walls found during final machining. Scrap													
03			iv)a	Reduced life													
01-01-01	Inserts	Contaminated (dust or grease)	i)a	Blow holes, thin walls. Scrap		Contaminated during storage handling or casting process	Sampling inspection on receipt from supplier. Arbitrary per use inspection of suspect contaminated struts after prolonged storage	.5	5	5	12.5	Issue formal instructions for pre-use inspection following prolonged storage					
02			ii)a	Blow holes found during final machining			Use of spatula by caster for transfer					Rotation of inserts stored for long periods					

Effect code:
i Effect on the casting process
ii Effect on the finishing process
iii Effect on the assembler
iv Effect on the end user

Criticality code:
Occ = Prob. of occurrence × 10
Sev = Severity of effect on 1–10 scale
Det = Prob. not detected before reaching customer × 10
APN = Occ. × Sev × Det (Action Priority Number)

Source: BS 5760: Part 5, 1991

Appendix J

Typical questions used in the evaluation or review of a measurement and calibration system

The following series of questions may be found useful as a guide when carrying out a review and/or evaluation of a measurement and calibration system. The questions essentially invite a YES or NO answer. It is emphasised that, obtaining answers to these questions only, may not provide a thorough and complete review and/or evaluation of a system. The questions are intended only to serve as indicators and reminders of important points to pursue in the objective review and/or evaluation of the system. It is further emphasised that an affirmative for all questions may not be necessary. These questions were from the now withdrawn BS 5781: Part 2 (1988) which has been repalced by BS 5781: Part 1 (1992).

Calibration system

(a) Are there prescribed procedures for the control and calibration of all measurement standards and measuring equipment?

(b) Is it effective and complied with?

(c) Are the appropriate management responsibilities documented?

(d) Does the system provide for the prompt detection of deficiencies to prevent subsequent inaccuracies?

(e) Is there a procedure to ensure corrective action?

(f) Does the supplier have properly defined and appropriate limits of calibration uncertainty.

Periodic review of the calibration system

(a) Is the procedure for review of the measurement and calibration system documented?

(b) Does it cover all facets of the system and is it effective and complied with?

(c) Are the reviews conducted systematically and is the periodicity satisfactory?

(d) Are records of the reviews maintained and do they provide objective evidence of the effectiveness of the system?

(e) Is senior management informed of the results of the review and is corrective action taken?

Planning

(a) Are the needs of calibration and measurement properly planned before starting new work?

(b) Are the necessary measurement standards and measuring equipment determined?

(c) Has the availability of all required equipment been determined?

(d) Are the calibration and measurement requirements reviewed to determine special, unusual or 'state of art' needs?

(e) Is there an appropriate area allocated for carrying out all in-house calibration work?

(f) Has the level of skill and training required by the calibration and measurement personnel been determined?

(g) Are controlled environments provided where necessary?

(h) Are there any measurement requirements that cannot be satisfied that are relevant to the products?

(i) Are reports of corrective action used to update planning schedules?

(j) Have the particular needs of automatic test equipment (ATE) been allowed for, and what plans exist for the verification of software?

Measurement limits

(a) Does the calibration system identify the source and magnitude of uncertainties associated with calibration and product characteristic measurements?

(b) In specifying product characteristic limits, are errors of practical significance taken into account as appropriate?

(c) Does the system identify the particular techniques used for the determination of errors and uncertainties of measurement?

Documented calibration procedures

(a) Are there prescribed procedures for controlling the calibration of measurement standards and is measuring equipment available and used for product verification?

(b) Where there are no in-house procedures, are appropriate and identifiable published standard practices or manufacturers' written instructions prescribed?

(c) Is there a clearly identified procedure for each item of measuring equipment?

(d) Is the latest issue of procedures identified and available?

(e) Is a check carried out to ensure that written procedures are adhered to?

(f) Where a sub-contractor is used in the measurement chain and special measurement procedures are required of him, are they adequately prescribed?

(g) Are procedures prescribed for the control and/or measurement of special environmental requirements, if appropriate?

Records

(a) Is there a system of record keeping that is appropriate to the calibration and measurement system in use?

(b) Are all the records required by BS 5781: Part 1 maintained?

(c) Do the records, as necessary, include details of calibration controls, environmental data, designated error limits and information necessary to establish traceability?

(d) Is simple and rugged measuring equipment included in the records?

(e) Do the records indicate that the equipment is capable of performing measurements within the designated limits?

(f) Does the record system allow for calling forward, at the appropriate interval, equipment requiring calibration?

(g) Does the record system indicate those equipments that are calibrated only in part?

(h) Does the system include the retention of calibration certificates or data used in support of all calibration of measuring equipment?

(i) Do the records document the software used for automatic calibration and test equipment procedure?

(j) Is the change procedure, relating to calibration and measurement, documented?

Calibration labelling

(a) Is there a prescribed system of labelling or coding that identifies the calibration status of measurement standards and measuring equipment?

(b) Is equipment that is not fully calibrated or has limited use fully identified?

(c) Is there a prescribed system to ensure compliance with requirements where labelling is not practicable?

Sealing for integrity

(a) Are there adequate procedures for sealing against misuse or accidental shift of present controls?

(b) Have any adjustable devices on measurement standards and measuring equipment that are not necessary to the normal operation of the equipment been fully sealed or safeguarded at the time of calibration?

(c) Are the methods and materials used for sealing such that any tampering will be noticeable?

(d) Is the sealing such as to prevent access into the equipment?

Intervals of calibration

(a) Have calibration intervals been established for all measurement standards and measuring equipment?

(b) Have the calibration intervals been established from the equipment manufacturer's recommendations or knowledge of equipment stability, purpose, degree of usage, calibration records and experience?

(c) Are calibration intervals adjusted on the basis of trend data obtained from previous calibration records?

(d) Are calibration intervals adjusted on the basis of the usage of the equipment?

Invalidation of calibration

(a) Do the prescribed procedures ensure the immediate removal from use, or conspicuous identification of any measurement standard or measuring equipment that

(1) has not been calibrated in accordance with the established time scale?

(2) has failed in operation in any measurement parameter?

(3) shows evidence of physical damage?

(4) is suspect for any reason?

(b) Are the procedures effective and complied with?

(c) Do the procedures provide for immediate notification of equipment failures or damage likely to have compromised product quality?

(d) What procedures or embargoes are in operation to prevent the unofficial use of privately owned equipment that is not covered by the calibration system?

(e) What safeguards are prescribed to ensure that equipment is not brought into use without adequate checking and calibration?

Sub-contractors

(a) Do procedures ensure that a sub-contractor employs a measurement and calibration system that complies with the requirements of BS 5781 : Part 1?

(b) Is the responsibility accepted by the supplier for ensuring that the procedures employed by a sub-contractor for calibration and measurement work are suitable and are properly documented?

(c) Is there a system for continuously evaluating sub-contractors?

Storage and handling

(a) Is there an adequate system for the handling, transporting and storing of measurement standards and measuring equipment?

(b) Is the system under the control of the calibration department?

(c) Do the procedures include a requirement for reporting damage, abuse or deterioration?

(d) Are storage and handling arrangements reviewed, particularly in respect of increased equipment sophistication?

Traceability

(a) Can all calibrations performed in-house or by subcontractors be traced through an unbroken chain of properly conducted calibrations to a national or international measurement standard?

(b) Are calibrations involving the use of natural physical constants or ratio type self-calibration techniques adequately controlled?

Cumulative effect of errors

(a) Do the procedures take into account the cumulative effect of errors and uncertainties in carrying out calibrations?

(b) Is suitable corrective action taken when the total uncertainty could compromise calibration or measurement capability?

(c) Is defined method used in respect of the manner in which the various errors and uncertainties of equipment or a system are determined?

(d) Is the total calibration or measurement uncertainty given on all certificates of calibration?

Environmental control

(a) Is environmental control provided where necessary?

(b) Are the environmental conditions provided appropriate to the uncertainty level of the calibration and measurement work undertaken?

(c) Are controlled environment areas properly laid out, monitored and controlled?

(d) Are environmental monitoring devices properly maintained and calibrated?

(e) Are environmental compensating corrections applied to calibration and measurement data when necessary?

(f) Do the procedures for calibration and measurement of the equipment indicate the required environment?

Evaluation of calibration system

(a) Is reasonable access made available for the evaluation of the system?

(b) Are adequate facilities provided?

Training

(a) Have all personnel performing calibration functions the appropriate experience or training?

(b) Is the experience or training applicable to the type of calibration work undertaken?

(c) Are calibration personnel sent on training courses?

(d) Is the competence of staff reviewed at the planning stage?

Source: BS 5781: Part 2, 1981 (1988) (now withdrawn)

Appendix K

Constants for use in design of mean ($\overline{X}$) and range ($\overline{R}$)

Control chart limits for sample average ($\overline{X}$)
To obtain limits multiply $\overline{R}$ by the appropriate value of $A'_{0.025}$ and $A'_{0.001}$ then add to and subtract from the gross average value or agreed objective ($\overline{X}$).

Sample size	For inner limits	For outer limits
n	$A'_{0.025}$	$A'_{0.001}$
2	1.23	1.94
3	0.67	1.05
4	0.48	0.75
5	0.38	0.59
6	0.32	0.50

Control chart limits for range ($\overline{R}$)
To obtain limits multiply $\overline{R}$ by the appropriate value of D'. To estimate standard deviation, σ, divide $\overline{R}$ by the appropriate value of d_n.

Sample size	For lower limits*		For upper limits		For standard deviation
n	$D'_{0.001}$	$D'_{0.025}$	$D'_{0.975}$	$D'_{0.999}$	d_n
2	0.00	0.04	2.81	4.12	1.13
3	0.04	0.18	2.17	2.99	1.69
4	0.10	0.29	1.93	2.58	2.06
5	0.16	0.37	1.81	2.36	2.33
6	0.21	0.42	1.72	2.22	2.53

*The lower limits are not generally used.

Classification of process variability relative to specification tolerance
Relative precision index (RPI = specification tolerance/average range).
Note. This table should not be used if the range is out of control.

Class	Low relative precision	Medium relative precision	High relative precision
Sample size n	RPI	RPI	RPI
2	< 6.0	6.0–7.0	> 7.0
3	< 4.0	4.0–5.0	> 5.0
4	< 3.0	3.0–4.0	> 4.0
5 and 6	< 2.5	2.5–3.5	> 3.5
State of production	Unsatisfactory*; rejections inevitable	Satisfactory, if averages are within control limits	Satisfactory if averages are within modified control limits

*Not necessarily, if the specification permits a small proportion of the product to be outside the limit. In such cases the limiting values for low relative precision can be 0.8 of those given above.

Source: BS 2564: 1955

The relationship between C_p and RPI is as follows:

$$C_p = \frac{\text{RPI} \times d_n}{6}$$

Appendix L

Constants for use in design of US style mean ($\bar{X}$) and range (R) charts

Control chart limits for sample average ($\bar{X}$)
To obtain limits multiply $\bar{R}$ by the appropriate value of A_2, then add to and subtract from the process average ($\bar{\bar{X}}$)

Sample size n	For control limits A_2
2	1.88
3	1.02
4	0.73
5	0.58
6	0.48
7	0.42
8	0.37

Control chart limits for sample range ($\bar{R}$)
To obtain limits multiply $\bar{R}$ by the appropriate value of D_3 or D_4.

Sample size n	For control limits UCL (D_4)	LCL (D_3)
2	3.27	0
3	2.57	0
4	2.28	0
5	2.11	0
6	2.00	0
7	1.92	0.08
8	1.86	0.14

Note: US tend to use d_2 rather than d_n for Hartley's constant.

Appendix M

Supporting tools and techniques for quality improvement

Introduction

This appendix describes some of the most common tools and techniques for supporting quality improvement. The following are presented for analysing both non-numerical and numerical data. Data collection forms are presented first since they apply to both types of data. Tools for non-numerical data are presented, followed by tools for numerical data.

Data collection form

Application

Systematically gather data to obtain a clear picture of the facts.

Description

The date collection form (see Figure M1 for an example) is a template for collecting and recording data. It promotes consistency of data and facilitates comparisons.

Procedure

a) Establish the specific purpose of collecting the data and the questions to be addressed by the data it is planned to collect.
b) Identify categories of information (for example, consequences of the problem) required to address these questions.
c) Brainstorm factors that affect these categories by asking fact-finding questions about, for example, frequency, timing, location.
d) Determine how data will be analysed.
e) Multivote to reduce both lists to an appropriate and practical number. Gathering some data may help to determine appropriate categories.
f) Construct a tabular form, using the categories in (b) for the column headings and factors in step (c) for the row labels. Provide a place to record information about the following:

- who collected the data;
- where, when, and how they were collected;
- the total population if data are from a sample.

Non-conforming copies					
	Missing pages	Muddy copies	Showthrough	Pages out of sequence	Totals
Machine jams					
Paper weight					
Humidity					
Toner					
Condition of originals					
Other (specify)					
					Total
Collection by:					
Date:					
Place:					
Formula:					

Figure M1 Example of a data collection form

Affinity diagram

Application

Organize a large number of options, ideas, or concerns.

Description

When large numbers of ideas, opinions, issues and other concerns are being collected, this tool organizes the information into groupings based on the natural relationships that exist among them. The process is designed to stimulate creativity and full participation. This tool is often used to organize ideas generated by brainstorming.

Procedure

a) State the issue in broad terms (details may prejudice the response).

b) Record individual response on small cards.

c) Mix the cards and spread them randomly on a large table or board.

d) Group related cards together:

- sort cards that seem to be related into groups;
- limit number of groupings to ten without force-fitting single cards into groups;
- locate or create a header card that captures the meaning of the group;
- place this header card on top;

e) Transfer the information from card onto paper, outlined by groupings.

Figure M2 illustrates an affinity diagram for a telephone answering machine.

Benchmarking

Application

Identify opportunities for quality improvement.

Description

Benchmarking measures products, processes or services against those of recognized leaders. This helps to establish priorities and targets that will lead to competitive advantage in the marketplace.

Procedure

a) Determine what items to benchmark. The items should be key characteristics of the output related to the needs of the customer(s).

b) Determine who to benchmark: companies, organizations, or groups who are direct competitors and or non-competitors with a 'best in class' reputation and key similarities such as:

- type of process, for example, billing and shipping;
- characteristic nature of work, for example, type of customers, size, outputs, performance.

c) Determine benchmarks:

- collect data by means of appropriate testing, surveys, interviews, personal and professional contacts, technical journals and advertisements;
- analyse data.

d) For each benchmark item identified determine the 'best in class' target.

Requirements are based on both the needs of the customer and on benchmarking targets.

If the results of benchmarking determine that the performance of the direct competitor(s) exceeds the needs of the customer(s) then the requirements should be at least as good as the targets of the direct competitor(s).

If the results of benchmarking determine that no direct competitor(s) achieves the needs of the customer(s) and if the non-competitor(s) also does not achieve the needs of the customer(s), then the needs of the customer(s) should be re-evaluated; if the non-competitor(s) achieves the needs of the customer(s), then the requirements should be as good as the customer needs.

Brainstorming

Application

Identify possible causes of quality losses. Identify opportunities for quality improvement.

Description

Brainstorming is an excellent technique for tapping the creative thinking of a team to quickly generate, clarify, and evaluate a sizeable list of ideas, problems and issues as follows.

a) *Generation phase*. The team leader reviews

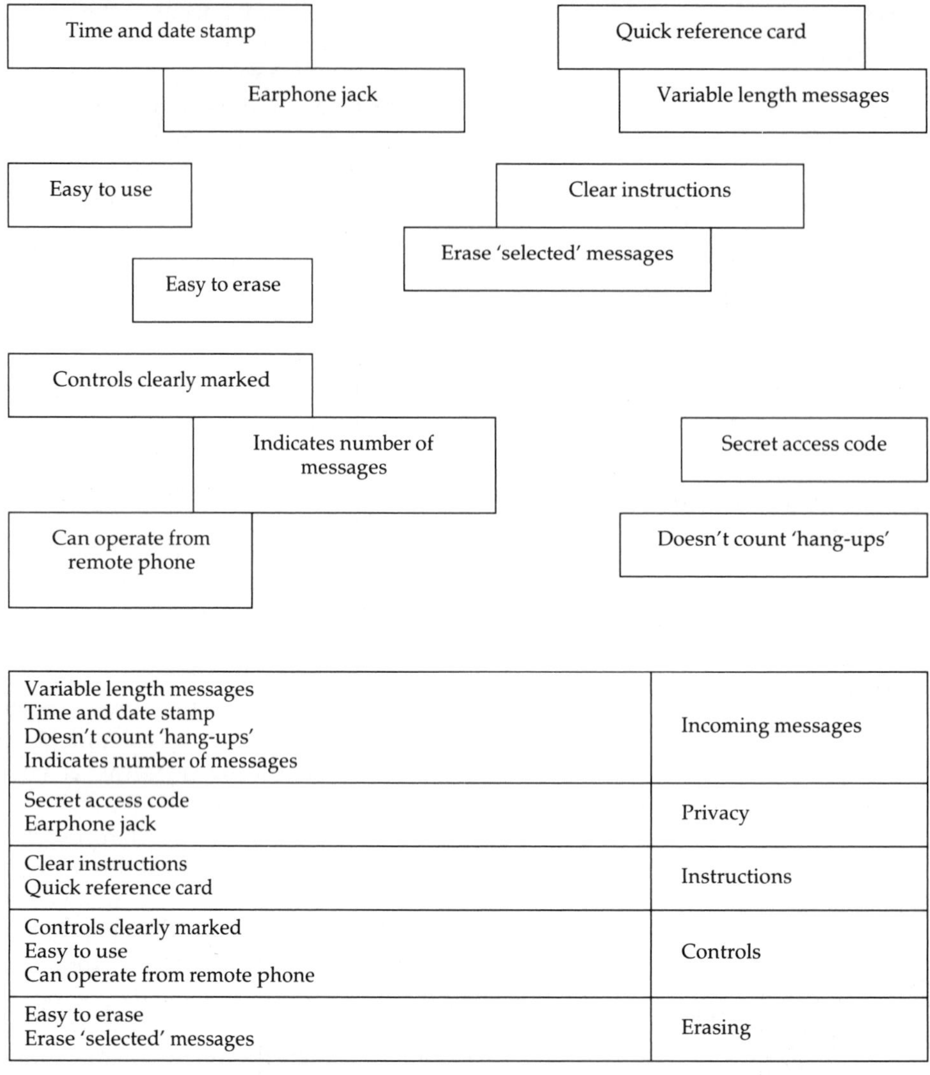

Variable length messages Time and date stamp Doesn't count 'hang-ups' Indicates number of messages	Incoming messages
Secret access code Earphone jack	Privacy
Clear instructions Quick reference card	Instructions
Controls clearly marked Easy to use Can operate from remote phone	Controls
Easy to erase Erase 'selected' messages	Erasing

Figure M2 Affinity diagram for a telephone answering machine

the rules for brainstorming and the team members generate a list of items. The objective is both quantity and quality of ideas.
b) *Clarification phase.* The team goes over the list to make sure that everyone understands all the items. Discussion will take place later.
c) *Evaluation phase.* The team reviews the list to eliminate duplications, irrelevancies, or issues that are off limits.

Rules for brainstorming

The typical rules for brainstorming are as follows:

a) State the purpose clearly.

b) Each person may take a turn in sequence, or ideas may be expressed spontaneously.

c) Offer one thought at a time.

d) Don't criticize ideas.

e) Don't discuss ideas.

f) Build on other's ideas.

g) Record all ideas where they are visible to team members.

Cause and effect (fishbone) diagram

Application

Analyse cause and effect relationships. Identify potential root causes of a problem.

Description

A cause and effect, or fishbone, diagram represents the relationships between a given effect and its potential causes (cause and effect analysis). Cause and effect diagrams are drawn to sort out and relate the interactions among the factors affecting a process. A well-detailed cause and effect diagram will take the shape of a fishbone hence its alias.

Procedure

a) Define the problem (effect) clearly and objectively.

b) Define the major categories of possible causes. Use generic branches.

Factors to consider include the following:

1) data and information systems;
2) monetary;
3) environment;
4) hardware;
5) materials;
6) measurements;
7) methods;
8) people;
9) training;
10) maintenance.

c) Begin to construct the diagram (see Figure M3), defining the effect in a box and positioning major categories as feeders to the effect box.

d) Brainstorm possible causes within major categories and position these to feed into related categories (see Figure M4).

Figure M5 illustrates a typical cause and effect diagram for poor photocopy quality.

e) Analyse each cause to focus on more specific causes.

f) Identify and circle the likely and actionable root causes.

g) Gather data to verify the most likely root cause(s). A Pareto diagram is a good way to display this data.

Flowchart

Application

Describe an existing process. Design a new process.

Description

A flowchart is a pictorial representation of the steps in a process. It is useful for investigating opportunities for improvement by gaining a detailed understanding of how the process actually works. Examination of how various steps in a process relate to each other can often uncover potential sources of troubles. Flowcharts can be applied to any aspect of the process from the flow of materials to the steps in making a sale or servicing a product. Flowcharts are constructed with a set of conventional, easily recognized symbols. These symbols are illustrated in Figure M6.

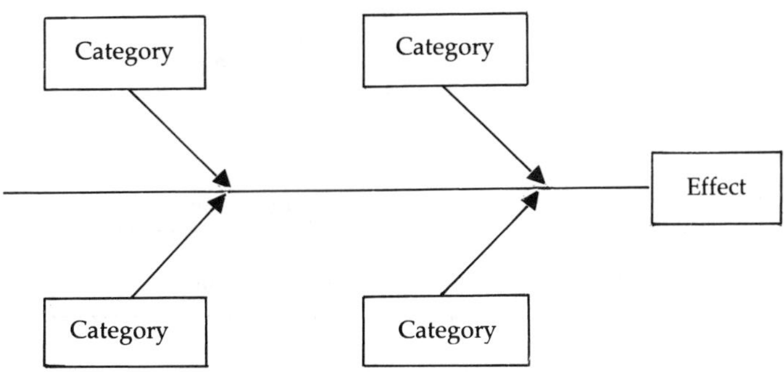

Figure M3 Basic cause and effect diagram 1st stage

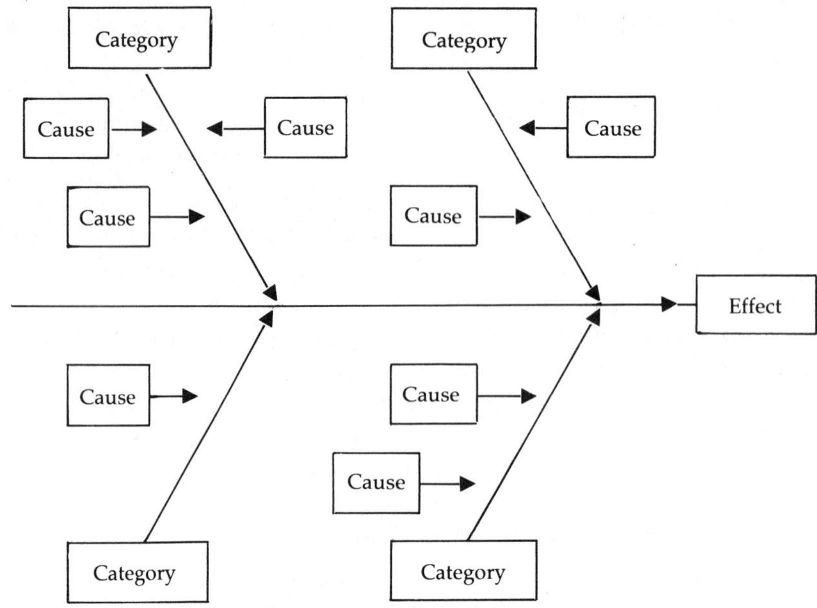

Figure M4 Basic cause and effect diagram with causes entered

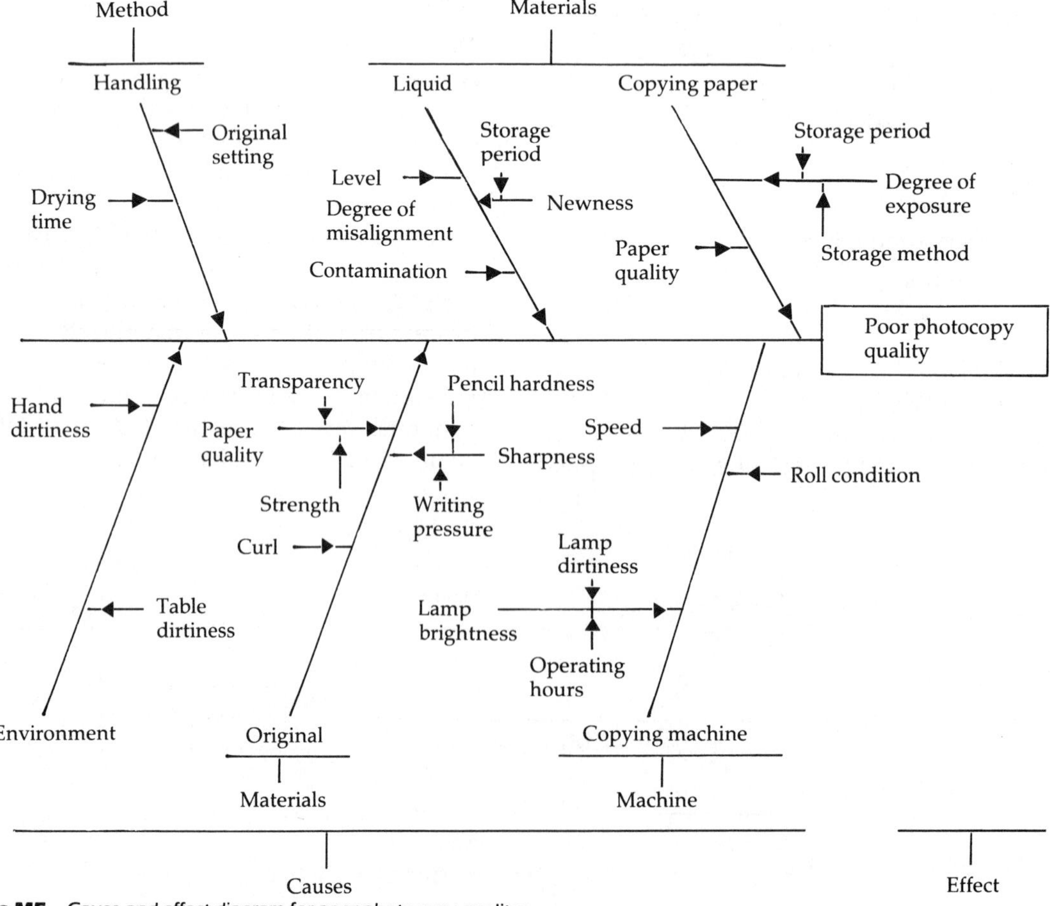

Figure M5 Cause and effect diagram for poor photocopy quality

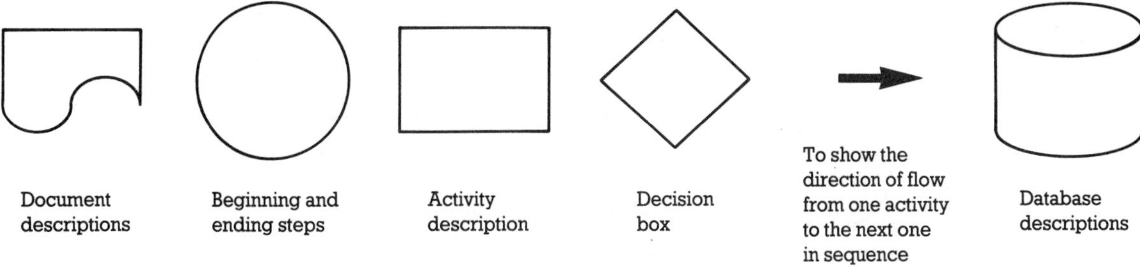

Figure M6 Flow diagram symbols

Procedure

a) List the inputs to the process or activity.

b) For each input, the following questions should be asked.

1) Who supplies the input?
2) Who receives the input?
3) What is the first thing that is done with the input?

c) List the outputs from the process or activity.

d) For each output, the following questions should be asked.

1) Who receives this output?
2) What happens next?

e) The appropriate flowchart symbols show activities and decisions involved in converting the inputs to outputs.

f) The chart continues to be built until connection is made into all outputs originally defined.

g) Review the chart and establish the following:

1) check all work information flows properly and maps into process inputs and outputs;
2) the chart shows the serial and parallel nature of the activities;
3) the chart shows all the potential paths work information can take, and questions special cases such as rework loops and ad-hoc procedures;
4) the chart accurately reflects all major decisions that are made;
5) the chart accurately captures what really happens, as distinct from how things should happen or how they were originally designed.

h) date the chart for future reference and use. It should serve as a record of how the current process actually operates.

Figure M7 illustrates a typical flowchart for the reproduction of a document.

Tree diagram

Application

a) Show relationship between a subject and its component elements;

b) Show means and procedures for achieving a goal;

c) Identify potential root causes of a problem.

Description

The tree diagram is used for systematically breaking down a subject into its basic elements. It shows the logical and sequential links between the subject and the component elements. This tool can be used in planning and problem solving. Its form is that of an organization chart laid horizontally. Ideas generated by brainstorming and ordered with an affinity diagram, can be converted into a tree diagram to show logical and sequential links. The tree diagram can be used in the preparation of matrix diagrams.

Procedure

a) Clearly and simply state the core issue, problem or goal.

b) Define major subcategories for the core issue, problem or goal. Brainstorm or use the header cards from the affinity diagram.

c) Begin to construct the diagram by placing the core issue in a box at the left. Branch the subcategories laterally to the right.

d) For each subcategory define the component elements (and if necessary subelements). Brainstorm or use the cards from the affinity diagram.

e) Laterally branch to the right elements and subelements for each subcategory.

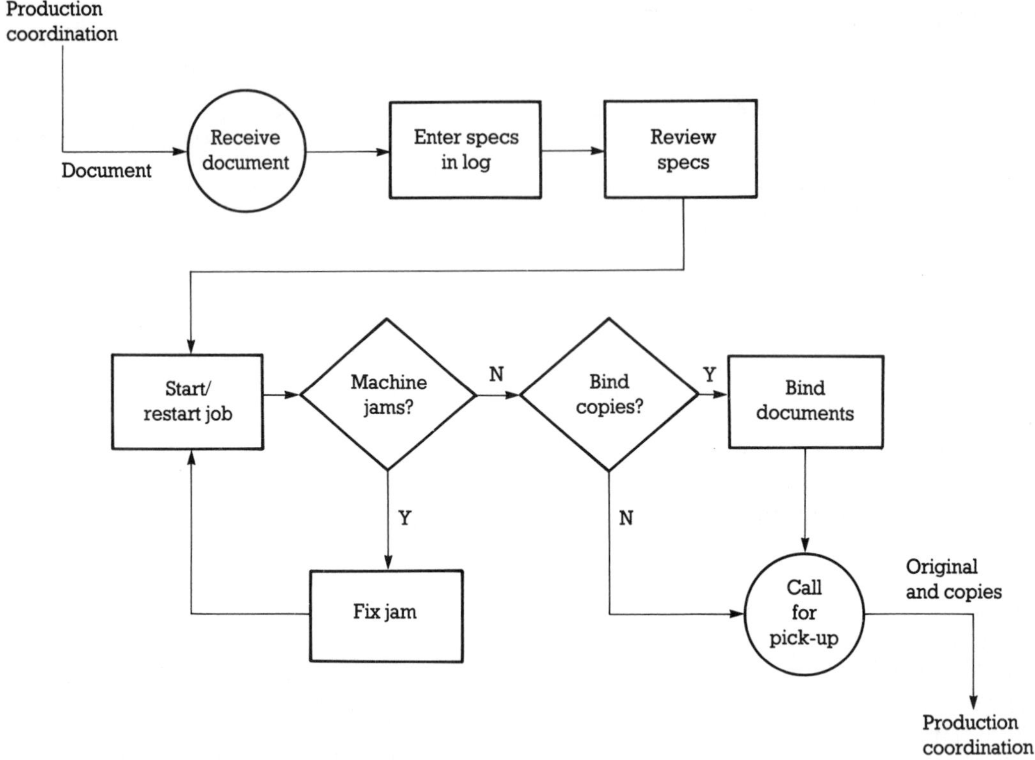

Figure M7 Flowchart for the reproduction of a document

f) Review the diagram to ensure that there are no obvious gasps in sequence or logic.

Figure M8 illustrates a tree diagram for a telephone answering machine.

Histogram

Application

Display the dispersion or spread of data.

Description

A histogram is a visual representation of the distribution of variable data. It is useful for visually communicating information about a process and for helping to make decisions about where to focus improvement efforts.

This information is represented by a series of equal-width columns of varying heights. Because column width represents an interval within the range of observations, columns are of equal width. Column height represents the number of observations within a given interval. Height, therefore, varies proportionately from column to column. With natural data there is a tendency for many observations to fall towards the centre of the distribution (central tendency), with progressively fewer towards the extremes.

Measures of central tendency include the following:

a) *Mean*. The sum of all the measured or counted data divided by the total number of data points.

b) *Mode*. The most common value or class interval grouping.

c) *Median*. The value of the data point that has an equal number of points above and below it when all the data points are arranged in ascending order of magnitude. If two values fall in the middle (even number of data points), the median is the average of the two.

Procedure

a) Collect data, count the total number of data points.

b) Arrange the data points in ascending order.

c) Determine the range of the data, subtract

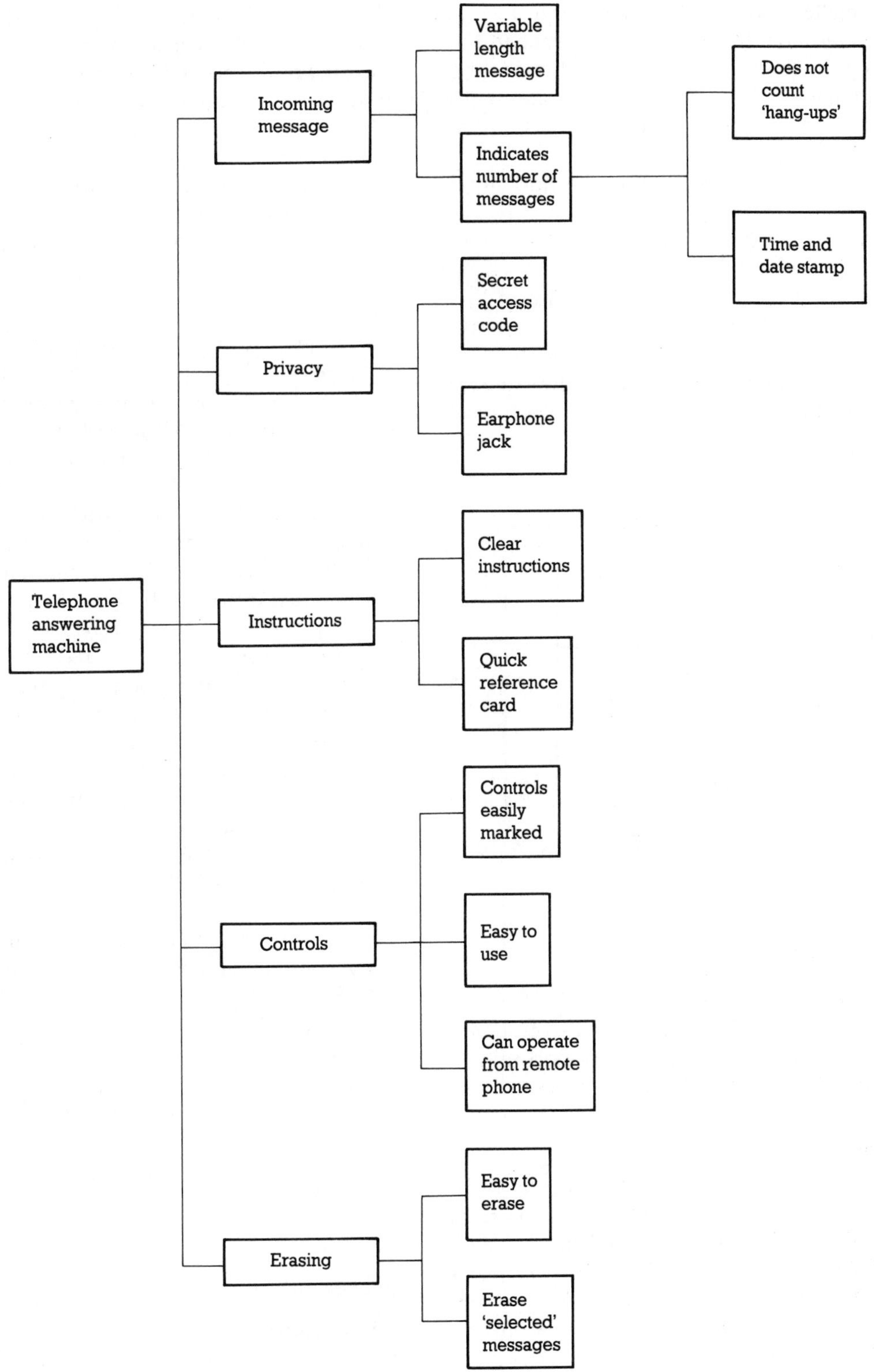

Figure M8 Tree diagram for a telephone answering machine

the smallest data point from the largest.

d) Determine the number of columns in the histogram (between 6 and 12) and divide the range (step c) by the number of columns to determine the width of each class interval (column).

e) Put class interval scale on the horizontal axis.

f) Put frequency scale (number or percent of observations) on the vertical axis.

g) Draw the height of each column in line with the point on the vertical axis that represents the number of data points that fall within that interval. The width is the same for each column. Figure M9 illustrates a typical histogram.

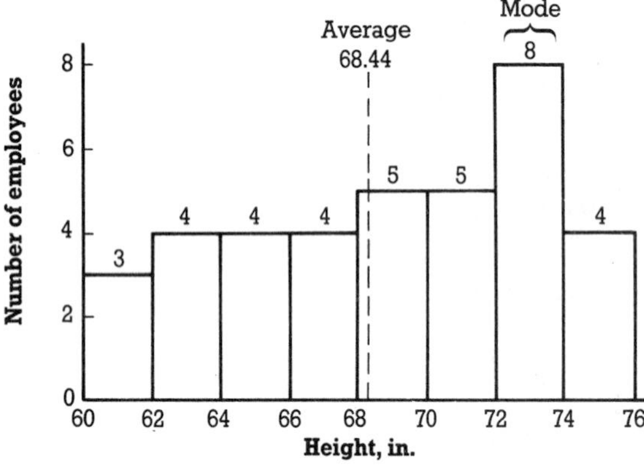

Figure M9 Histogram

Pareto diagram

Application

Identify the most important causes of quality losses. Identify improvement opportunities, rank improvement opportunities and set objectives.

Description

A Pareto diagram is a simple graphical technique for rank ordering causes from most to least significant. The Pareto diagram is based on the Pareto principle, which states that just a few of the causes often account for most of the effect. By distinguishing the most important causes from the less significant ones, the greatest improvement will be obtained with the least effort.

The Pareto diagram displays, in decreasing order, the relative contribution of each cause to the total problem. Relative contribution may be based on the number of occurrences, the cost associated with each cause, or another measure of impact on the problem:

a) blocks are used to show the relative contribution of each cause;

b) a cumulation line is used to show the cumulative contribution of causes.

Procedure

a) Select the items to be analysed.

b) Select the unit of measurement for analysis, such as number of occurrences, costs, or another measure of impact.

c) Select the time period to be analysed.

d) List the items from left to right on the horizontal axis in the order of decreasing magnitude of the unit of measurement. Categories containing the least items can be combined into an 'other' category. Place this category at the extreme right.

e) Construct two vertical axes, one at each end of the horizontal axis. The left scale should be calibrated in the unit of measurement, and its height is equal to the sum of the magnitudes of all items. The right scale has the same height and is calibrated from 0% to 100%.

f) Above each item, draw a rectangle whose height represents the magnitude of the unit of measurement for that item.

g) Construct the cumulative frequency line by summing the magnitudes of each item from left to right.

h) Use the Pareto diagram to identify the most important items for quality improvement.

Figure M10 illustrates a typical Pareto diagram for telephone faults.

Scatter diagram

Application

Display the relationships of two associated sets of data. Discover such relationships. Confirm such suspected relationships.

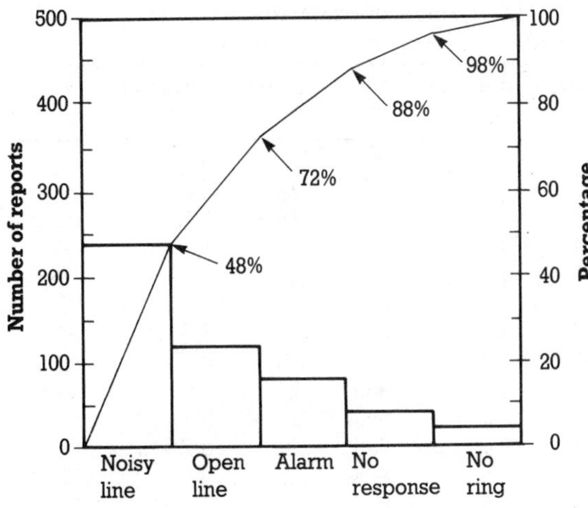

Figure M10 Pareto diagram for telephone faults

Description

A scatter diagram is a simple graphical technique for studying relationships between two sets of associated data. Data displayed by a scatter diagram form a cloud of dots. Relationships are inferred based on the shape of the cloud as depicted in Figure M11.

A scatter diagram is useful in any situation when a discovery or a confirmation of relationships is important in carrying out quality improvement projects or activities.

Figure M11 illustrates typical scatter diagrams.

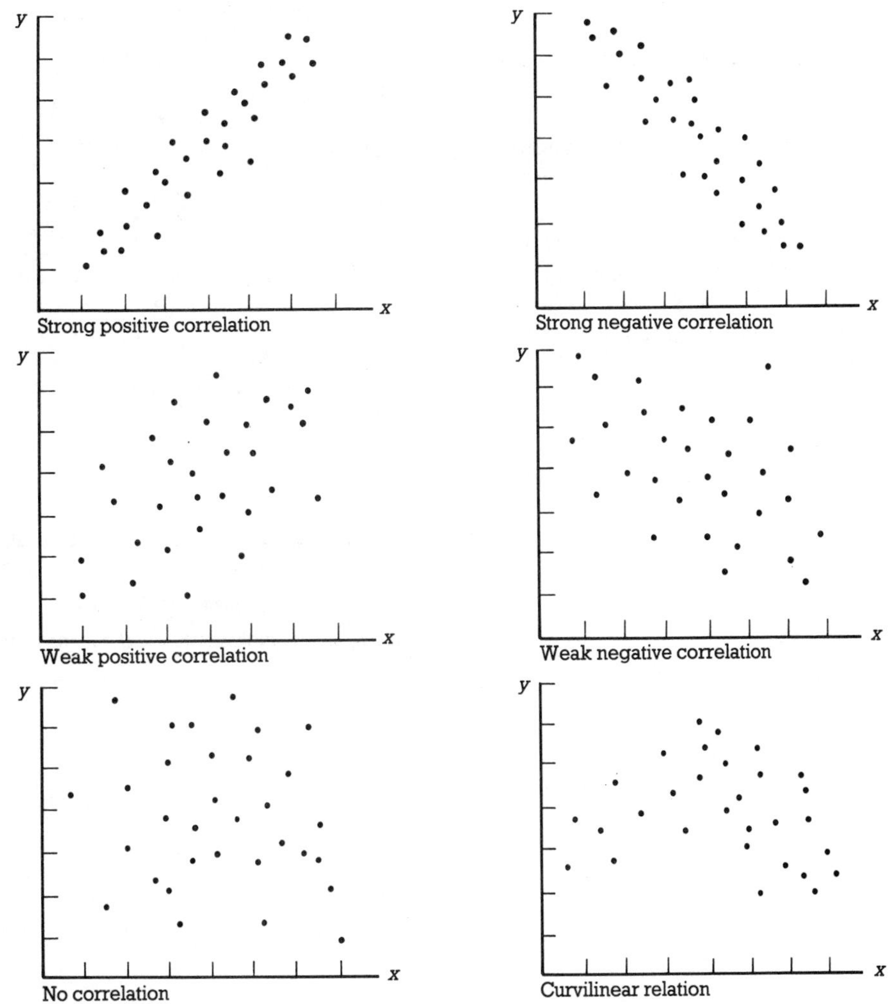

Figure M11 Scatter diagrams

Procedure

a) Collect paired data (x, y) between which the relationship is of interest. It is desirable to have about 30 pairs of data.

b) Find the minimum and maximum values of both x and y and graduate the horizontal (x) and vertical (y) axes. Use graph paper. Both axes should be about equal length. The number of graduations should be between 3 and 10 per axis. In case there is a reason to believe in the cause or a predictor of the other variable, use the horizontal (x) axis for the cause or predictor variable.

c) Plot the data on the graph paper. When the same data is obtained from different pairs, draw concentric circles, or plot the second point in the immediate vicinity of the first.

d) Label the axes with characteristics they represent.

e) Examine the pattern (cloud) of dots to discover the type and the degree of relationship. Refer to Figure M11 for interpretation of the patterns.

An example of the construction of a scatter diagram is given in Table M1 and Figure M12.

The scatter diagram shows a weak-to-moderate positive correlation between the weight of the additive 'A' and yield percentage.

Table M1 Example of scatter data
Data of additive 'A' and percent yield

Batch No.	Additive 'A' (g)	Yield (%)	Batch No.	Additive 'A' (g)	Yield (%)
1	8.7	88.7	16	8.4	89.4
2	9.2	91.1	17	8.2	86.4
3	8.6	91.2	18	9.2	92.2
4	9.2	89.5	19	8.7	90.9
5	8.7	89.6	20	9.4	90.5
6	8.7	89.2	21	8.7	89.6
7	8.5	87.7	22	8.3	88.1
8	9.2	88.5	23	8.9	90.8
9	8.5	86.6	24	8.9	88.6
10	8.3	89.6	25	9.3	92.8
11	8.6	88.9	26	8.7	87.2
12	8.9	88.4	27	9.1	92.5
13	8.8	87.4	28	8.7	91.2
14	8.4	89.4	29	8.7	88.2
15	8.8	89.1	30	8.9	90.4

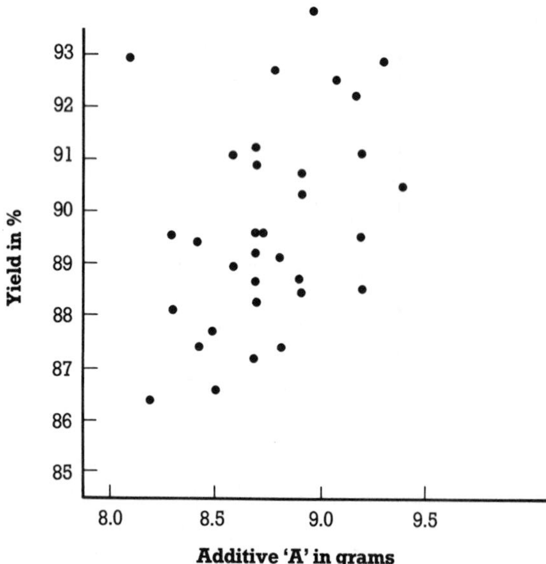

Figure M12 Sample scatter diagram application

Glossary

ACB	Association of Certification Bodies
AOQ	Average outgoing quality
AOQL	Average outgoing quality limit
AQAP	Allied Quality Assurance Publications
AQL	Acceptable quality level
ARL	Average run length
ASQC	American Society for Quality Control
ATE	Automatic test equipment
BASEC	British Approval Service for Electrical Cables
BATNEEC	Best available techniques not entailing excessive cost
BCS	British Calibration Service
BS	British Standard
BSI	The British Standards Institution
BSIQA	British Standards Institution Quality Assurance
CASCO	ISO Committee on Conformity Assessment
CCT	Compulsory competitive tendering
CEC	Commission of the European Communities
CECC	CENELEC Electronic Components Committee
CEN	European Committee for Standardisation
CENELEC	European Committee for Electrotechnical Standardisation
CGPM	General Conference on Weights and Measures
CIM	Computer integrated manufacturing
COC	Cost of conformance
CONC	Cost of non-conformance
COSHH	Control of substances hazardous to health
Cp and *Cpk*	Process capability indices
CR	CEN Report
DD	Drafts for Development
DEF	Defence
DoT	Department of Trade (see DTI)
DIR	Departmental improvement review
DPA	Department purpose analysis
DTI	Department for Trade and Industry (formerly DoT)
EAC	European Accreditation of Certification
EC	European Community
ECSC	European Coal and Steel Community
EDC	Economic Development Committee
EDI	Electronic data interchange
EFTA	European Free Trade Association
EN	European Standard
ENV	European Pre-standard
EOQ	European Organisation for Quality
EOTC	European Organisation for Testing and Certification
EQS	European Committee for Quality System Assessment and Certification
ETSI	European Telecommunications Standards Institute
FMEA	Failure modes and effects analysis
FMECA	Failure modes and effects criticality analysis
FTA	Fault tree analysis
HD	Harmonization document
IDEF	Computer-aided integrated program definition method
IEC	International Electrotechnical Commission
IEV	International Electrotechnical Vocabulary
IFAN	International Federation for the Application of Standards
IPC	Integrated Pollution Control
ISO	International Organisation for

	Standardisation
ISIR	Initial Sample Inspection Reporting
JIT	Just-in-time
KJ	Kawakita Jiro
LAL	Lower action line
LQ	Limiting quality
LTPD	Lot tolerance per cent defective
LWL	Lower warning line
MOD	Ministry of Defence
MoU	Memorandum of Understanding
MSB	Member Standard Bodies
MTBF	Mean time between failures
MTPM	Mean time for preventive maintenance
MTTF	Mean time to failure
MTTR	Mean time to repair
NACCB	National Accreditation Council for Certification Bodies
NAMAS	National Measurement Accreditation Service
NATLAS	National Testing Laboratory Accreditation Scheme
NATO	North Atlantic Treaty Organisation
NEDC	National Economic Development Council
NEDO	National Economic Development Office
NMM(UK)	Nissan Motor Manufacturing (UK)
NPL	National Physical Laboratory
NSB	National Standards Body
OC	Operating characteristics
PAF	Prevention-appraisal-failure
PAPD	Process average per cent defective
PD	Published documents
PDCA	Plan, do, check, action
PDPC	Process decision programme chart
POC	Price of conformance
PONC	Price of non-conformance
PPCS	Preliminary process capability studies
PPM	Parts per million
QFD	Quality function deployment
R & D	Research and development
RPI	Relative precision index
SDT	Supplier development team
SIRIM	Standards and Industrial Research Institute of Malaysia
SISIR	Singapore Institute of Standards and Industrial Research
SPC	Statistical process control
SQA	Supplier quality assurance
SQC	Statistical quality control
THE	Technical Help to Exporters
TPM	Total productive maintenance
TQC	Total quality control
TQM	Total quality management
UAL	Upper action line
UWL	Upper warning line

Index